QD
15
J7.5

# Selected Readings in the
# HISTORY OF CHEMISTRY

Compiled by

**Aaron J. Ihde**

*and*

**William F. Kieffer**

Reprinted from

## Journal of CHEMICAL EDUCATION

1965

0

# _____contents_____

## Organic Chemistry

## Industrial Chemistry

## Indexes

# Selected Readings in the History of Chemistry

**D**uring its first forty years of publication the Journal of Chemical Education has carried many papers dealing with various facets of the history of chemistry. This volume makes available a collection of some of the more significant of these papers.

Users of early volumes of the Journal will recall that prior to 1933 (volumes 1–9) the page size was smaller than at present. Despite the fact that a number of worthy papers appeared in the first nine volumes, their inclusion in this volume of reprints would have necessitated much waste of page space or expensive resetting. Hence, we reluctantly decided to exclude them from consideration.

It was also decided that papers which have had subsequent publication in book form after appearing in the Journal would not be included here. This excluded all of the papers which form chapters in Mary Elvira Weeks' *Discovery of the Elements*, Martin Levey's *Chemistry and Chemical Technology in Ancient Mesopotamia*, and Alfred B. Garrett's *Flash of Genius*. Papers dealing with alchemy and archeological chemistry were omitted, thus keeping the time span covered largely within the past two centuries.

Within the above limitations, we have sought to include a selection of papers which reveals the development of chemical concepts and indicates the flow of those developments. Although the list of selections appears to be heavily biographical, these selections have been determined on the basis of historical value rather than purely biographical content. Biographical selections generally exclude the better known chemists who are adequately treated in such books as Edward Farber's *Great Chemists* and Gunther Bugge's *Das Buch der grossen Chemiker*, except when the paper has unique content not customarily found elsewhere. In a few instances, selections were made on the basis of richness of illustrative material.

In most cases the papers are reprinted as they originally appeared. In a few instances there have been deletions; usually these were illustrations which added little to the value of the paper. Occasionally text of highly specific nature (which did not significantly enlighten the reader) was deleted.

We wish to acknowledge with gratitude the assistance and advice of O. Theodor Benfey, Albert Costa, Erwin Hiebert, Louis Kuslan, Leonard K. Nash, and Derek de Solla Price. Each of these men took valuable time to examine our preliminary selections and make suggestions regarding suitability for inclusion as well as calling attention to certain worthy papers not on the original list. We also thank the many authors who supplied us with copies of reprints, the personnel of the business and publications office at Easton, Pennsylvania, and especially Mr. B. F. Gould of the New York City office of this Journal.

AARON J. IHDE
University of Wisconsin
Madison, Wisconsin

WILLIAM F. KIEFFER, *Editor*
Journal of Chemical Education
College of Wooster
Wooster, Ohio

**J. R. Partington**
University of London
England

# The Discovery of Oxygen

Many careful chemical authors[1] say that oxygen was "discovered by Priestley on 1st August, 1774." At least as early as 1846[2] the opinion was expressed that, although he had obtained oxygen on August 1, 1774, Priestley did not then know that he had prepared a new gas and that his "effective discovery" of oxygen should be dated in March, 1775. It is the object of the first part of this paper to give reasons for accepting the earlier date.

The meaning of "discovery" is well known in chemistry. When a substance is prepared for the first time by a clearly described method, and sufficient details are given which distinguish it from other substances, it is said to be "discovered." Glycerol was discovered by Scheele and not by Chevreul or Berthelot, ethylene by the Dutch chemists and not by Dalton. In a modern laboratory a student would be credited with an identification of oxygen if he had shown that: (1) a taper burnt in the gas with a very vigorous flame, (2) a glowing chip inflamed in the gas, and (3) the gas was practically insoluble in water. Such a gas could not be nitrous oxide; the taper flames are quite different (as anyone who has seen them knows) and nitrous oxide is appreciably soluble in water. If the student were sent back to try the action of nitric oxide he might think this was a little unfair, although useful.

## Priestley's Discovery of Oxygen

Priestley wrote up his discovery of oxygen early in 1775 and it was published in that year.[3] As usual, he told the story fully, clearly, and accurately, but it is important to appreciate that he had then formed a theory of the "true nature" of oxygen; it was a compound of nitric acid and an earth. We know from his own statement that Priestley's discovery was made in Calne, in Wiltshire, where he was staying (in his own house) in attendance on his patron, Lord Shelburne, and (as he repeatedly said) that it was accidental. He had been given a large burning glass by Parker, in London, and was trying the effect of heating with it a number of substances given him by Warltire, among which was red oxide of mercury made by heating the metal for a long time in air, and hence called red precipitate, or mercury calcined, per se. Priestley put some of the substance into a small bulb filled with mercury, inverted the bulb in mercury, and heated the substance at the top with the burning glass.[4]

With this apparatus, after a variety of other experiments, . . . on the 1st of August, 1774, I endeavoured to extract air from *mercurius calcinatus* per se [mercuric oxide]; and I presently found that, by means of this lens, air was expelled from it very readily. Having got about three or four times as much as the bulk of my materials, I admitted water to it, and found that it was not imbibed by it. But what surprized me more than I can well express, was, that a candle burned in this air with a remarkably vigorous flame, very much like that enlarged flame with which a candle burns in nitrous air, exposed to iron or liver of sulphur [i.e. in nitrous oxide]; but . . . as I knew that no nitrous acid was used in the preparation of *mercurius calcinatus*, I was utterly at a loss how to account for it.

In this case, also, though I did not give sufficient attention to the circumstance at that time, the flame of the candle, besides being larger, burned with more splendor and heat than in that species of nitrous air; and a piece of red-hot wood sparkled in it, exactly like paper dipped in a solution of nitre . . . ; an experiment which I had never thought of trying with nitrous air.

Priestley had previously[5] described the flame in the gas made by the action of iron on nitrous air (his name for nitric oxide); this

. . . makes it not only to admit a candle to burn in it, but enables it to burn with an enlarged flame, by another flame (extending every where to an equal distance from that of the candle, and often plainly distinguishable from it) adhering to it.

[1] DAVY, SIR H., "Elements of Chemical Philosophy," **1812**, p. 227; BRANDE, W. T., "A Manual of Chemistry," Vol. 1, **1848**, p. *lxiv;* ROSCOE, SIR H. E., AND SCHORLEMMER, C., "A Treatise on Chemistry," Vol. 1, **1920**, p. 240.

[2] HARCOURT, REV. W. VERNON, *Phil. Mag.*, **28**, 498 (1846); RODWELL, G. F., *Nature*, **27**, 8 (1882)—full of errors; HARTOG, SIR P. G., *Annals of Science*, **5**, 31 (1941); and others.

[3] PRIESTLEY, J., "Experiments and Observations on Different Kinds of Air," London, Vol. 2, **1775**, pp. 29f; *Alembic Club Reprint*, No. 7 (**1901**).

[4] The illustration of the apparatus given in CONANT, J. B., "On Understanding Science," Yale University Press, New Haven, Conn., **1947**, p. 79, Fig. 10; "Harvard Case Histories in Experimental Science," Cambridge, Mass., **1**, **1957**, p. 95, Fig. 2, does not agree with Priestley's description.

[5] PRIESTLEY, J., "Experiments and Observations on Different Kinds of Air," London, **1774**, p. 216 (this volume, the first in the series, is not numbered and the size is smaller than that of the remaining volumes).

Chemists everywhere applauded the designation in November, 1961, of Professor J. R. Partington as the Dexter Award Winner. His books on the history of chemistry stand along with his writings on inorganic chemistry as the work of a true scholar and teacher. He is now professor emeritus of Queen Mary College, University of London, having held the chair of chemistry there since 1919. His early work with Nernst set his pattern of investigating reactions with the utmost precision by physical methods. The same sense of integrity and precision is the outstanding quality in his language for communication. The literature of chemistry is richer because he continues to make his encyclopedic knowledge available in presentations of meticulous clarity.

In November, 1774, Priestley found the same results with a specimen of red precipitate per se obtained from Cadet in Paris, which he was sure had not been made by heating mercuric nitrate, and at the same time he found that the gas after repeated agitation with water still supported the combustion of a candle with a strong flame, and hence was not nitrous oxide. He also obtained oxygen by heating red lead, which is not made with nitric acid. When he wrote up the results in 1775 Priestley was convinced that oxygen was a compound of nitric acid and earth, and he thought that red precipitate per se, made by heating mercury in air, and red lead, made by heating litharge in air, had both imbibed nitric acid from the atmosphere; in April, 1775, he wrote that he had obtained oxygen:

... first from *mercurius calcinatus* per se, red lead, &c.; and now, from many other substances, as quick-lime (and others that contain little phlogiston,) and spirit of nitre [nitric acid], and by a train of experiments demonstrated that the basis of our atmosphere is spirit of nitre. Nothing I ever did has surprized me more, or is more satisfactory.

When we are told that Priestley had not recognized the "true nature" of oxygen until early in 1775 we should remember that by this he meant its composition from nitric acid and earth, not that it was a gas different from nitrous oxide, which he knew in the autumn of 1774. What he did in 1775 was to show by his nitric oxide test that the new gas was "between four and five times as good as common air" (we should say that air contains a quarter or a fifth of its volume of oxygen), and that it supported the respiration of a mouse longer than common air. These were observations with a gas already known. For Priestley, the new gas was atmospheric air deprived of phlogiston, dephlogisticated air, its degree of phlogistication being one-fourth or one-fifth that of common air. When Cavendish discovered hydrogen in 1766, describing its preparation and its characteristic properties, he thought it was pure phlogiston, but this misconception of its "true nature" does not deprive him of the discovery of hydrogen.

My argument is, therefore, that Priestley on August 1, 1774, had found properties which distinguished oxygen from the only other gas it could be (nitrous oxide), and that he had described these properties. Even if he misunderstood the results, this does not deprive him of the discovery of oxygen on that date.

When he discovered oxygen in August, 1774, Priestley had not formed his theory of its "true Nature," that it was a compound of nitric acid and earth, for he says:

I will frankly acknowledge, that, at the commencement of the experiments recited in this section [the one with mercuric oxide being the first he describes], I was so far from having formed any hypothesis that led to the discoveries I made in pursuing them, that they would have appeared very improbable to me had I been told of them.

Although not directly connected with the discovery of oxygen, I would like to mention another experiment by Priestley which does not seem to have attracted much attention. Boyle had made experiments on the calcination of tin in sealed retorts, but owing to his manner of working he thought the increase in weight when he weighed the retort after it had been opened, when he heard air rush into it, was due to the fixation of ponderable particles of fire. Lomonosov pointed out that the *sealed* retort should have been weighed after the calcination, and some work which he did not publish showed that there was no change in total weight.

In describing some experiments "made in the Year 1773, and the Beginning of 1774," Priestley says:[6]

That the calces of metals contain air, of some kind or other, and that this air contributes to the additional weight of the calces, above that of the metals from which they are made, had been observed by Dr. Hales; ... I had likewise found, that no weight is either gained or lost by the calcination of tin in a close glass vessel; but I purposely deferred making any more experiments on the subject, till we should have some weather in which I could make use of a large burning lens, which I had provided for that and other purposes; but in the meantime I was led to the discovery in a different manner ....

I immediately filled a small phial with the red-lead, and heating it with a candle, I presently expelled from it a quantity of air about four or five times the bulk of the lead, the air being received in a vessel of quicksilver.

Priestley had obtained oxygen here, but he had not discovered it, since he gives none of its properties.

### Scheele's Discovery of Oxygen

The only independent discoverer of oxygen, apart from Priestley, was Scheele. His discovery was made before Priestley's, probably in 1771-72,[7] as is known from his laboratory notes, i.e. at least two years before Priestley's. Scheele's book, "On Air and Fire," describing his discovery, was not published until 1777, but the manuscript was completed at the end of 1775 and Bergman, in an introduction to the book, says that the work described in it was finished in 1775. Early in 1776 the printer sent the manuscript to Bergman, and the latter in his introduction says that he had repeated, with some modifications, the experiments described in it, and had confirmed them. One reason for the delay in publication was thus the time taken by Bergman in repeating the experiments. Bergman says:

Chemistry teaches that the elastic fluid which surrounds the earth at all times and in all places has a unique composition, comprising three different materials, viz. good air [oxygen], vitiated air [nitrogen] and aerial acid [carbon dioxide]. The first Priestley called, not incorrectly but in a very forced way, dephlogisticated air, Scheele on many grounds fire air, since it alone supports fire, whilst the other two extinguish it ... I have also repeated, with different modifications, the principal experiments on which he [Scheele] based his conclusions, and found them completely correct. If in consequence, in small subsidiary considerations, some slight rectification might be necessary, this is no way invalidates the main conclusions, based on many confirmatory researches. Heat, fire, and light have fundamentally the same components, good air and phlogiston ... Of the kinds of matter now known, good air is the most effective in removing phlogiston, which appears to be a true elementary matter which enters into most materials. For this reason I have placed good air at the top of the phlogiston column in my new table of attractions .... In conclusion I must mention that this masterly work has been complete for two years [i.e. in 1775], although for various reasons, which it is superfluous to name here, it is only now published. In consequence, it has happened that Priestley, without knowledge of Scheele's work, has previously described various new properties belonging to the air. They are seen, however, to be of a different kind and presented in a different connexion.

We know that Bergman corresponded with Priestley in the period when Scheele was doing his work, and it

---

[6] *Ibid.*, p. 192.
[7] I have discussed the matter of date in the forthcoming volume of my "History of Chemistry," Vol. 3, pp. 219f.

was suggested that he may have informed Priestley of some of the latter. Priestley, in his account of his discovery of oxygen says:

I am not conscious to myself of having concealed the least hint that was suggested to me by any person whatever, any kind of assistance that has been given me, or any views or hypotheses by which the experiments were directed, whether they were verified by the results or not.

No one who appreciates Priestley's absolute truthfulness can doubt his word, and I think it is certain that neither Priestley nor Scheele knew anything of the work of the other.

The way in which Scheele was led to his discovery, the manner in which he made it, and the hypothesis which he proposed to explain his results, are well known[8] and need not be repeated here. It will be sufficient to say that he obtained oxygen in a variety of ways: the decomposition of nitric acid vapor by heat, heating mercuric oxide and silver carbonate, heating manganese dioxide with sulphuric or arsenic acid, etc., and that he explained his results by the assumption that heat is a compound of fire air [oxygen] and phlogiston. He also, like Cavendish, identified phlogiston with hydrogen, so that in burning hydrogen in air he thought the product of the union of hydrogen and fire air was heat; he missed the formation of water since he worked over hot water.

## Bergman's Memoir, 1775

Less well known is the fact that Bergman had published in 1775 a summary of Scheele's experiments, of his discovery of oxygen, and of his theory.[9] This occurs in a section of Bergman's memoir on affinity. In the part on phlogiston he says:

We have previously noted the great force with which air removes phlogiston from iron and copper. Nitric acid has also a great affinity for this principle . . . Nitrous air [nitric oxide] over water in an inverted bottle is an elastic, pellucid, colorless gas. When mixed with pure air [oxygen] the mass instantly reddens and, as if with effervescence, heat is produced and the whole volume disappears. With common air more than a quarter disappears, corresponding with an equal goodness.

These phenomena are ascribed to the migration of phlogiston from the acid to the air, and are easily explained by what has been so well demonstrated by the experiments of Mr. Scheele, that the matter of heat is nothing else than phlogiston intimately united with pure air, in which combination originate the heat produced and the diminution of the volume previously occupied.

Nitric acid destroys platinum in the dry way [by fused nitre]. Then follow the calces of noble metals, which form the metals solely by the action of heat and without addition of phlogiston. Here the matter of heat is resolved into its principles, which Mr. Scheele has so ably demonstrated are pure air and phlogiston intimately united. Following him, I carried out an experiment in a somewhat modified form.

Half an ounce of mercuric nitrate was previously calcined by heat to red precipitate. This was introduced into a small retort to which was adapted a long tube with the curved end

passing into a jar of water.[10] Then the bottom of the bulb was moderately heated and more than half the jar was filled with air, which did not render lime water at all turbid, but powerfully supported combustion and respiration. The calx at the same time was reduced to running mercury. Whence came this air? I reply, from the decomposition of the heat passing through the pores of the vessel, giving up phlogiston to the metal calx, which done, the air loses its faculty of penetrating the glass. The air was not contained in the calx, since the calces of both noble and common metals require phlogiston for reduction, not that this occurs differently but the former can attract it with such a greater force that they can decompose heat in an experiment like this.

The calces of silver and gold can similarly recover the metallic form and provide pure air. The calces made, not by heating but by precipitation with alkali [alkali carbonate], do not give pure air but this contaminated with aerial acid [carbon dioxide], which can easily be separated by lime water from the mixed air liberated by heat. With well washed gold calx this does not happen, since it rejects aerial acid.

Scheele's theory was that a calx could be reduced to a metal in two ways. With calces of common metals, phlogiston had to be supplied by a substance rich in it, such as charcoal. With calces of noble metals, which can be reduced by heating alone, the phlogiston was supplied by the decomposition of heat, which was a compound of fire air [oxygen] and phlogiston. The phlogiston reduced the calx to metal and the fire air was set free.

Bergman's memoir, giving a summary of Scheele's work, was almost certainly published in 1775. Professor Gunnar Malmquist, Secretary of the Royal Society of Sciences of Uppsala, very kindly informs me that the date on which the memoir was communicated, and the date when this volume of the "Nova Acta" was published, are not available in the Archives of the Society. At a meeting on February 10th, 1774, the vignette for the titlepage of Vol. 2 was discussed and at a meeting on February 23rd the titlepage was approved. At a meeting on June 16th the bill for the printing of Vol. 2 was approved. It seems to follow that the volume was actually in print on that date, and hence Bergman's communication of Scheele's discovery of oxygen was at least three months prior to Priestley's discovery, and the publication was in all probability before that of Priestley. Although it is commonly said that Scheele had lost priority of publication by some two years as compared with Priestley, Bergman's publication restores to him a date of announcement of his discovery at least not later than Priestley's.

The subject of the discovery of oxygen is one which has, perhaps, occupied historians of chemistry more than any other. There are very many publications on it and it might have seemed that nothing more of any significance could possibly remain. It is hoped, however, that the present short communication will not be without interest in the matter.

[8] Ibid., pp. 219–229.
[9] BERGMAN, T., "Nova Acta Regiae Societatis Scientiarum Upsaliensis," Vol. 2, Uppsala, 1775, pp. 232–4.

[10] Bergman refers to a figure in a paper on the Aerial Acid in the same volume, reproduced in my "History of Chemistry," Vol. 3, p. 126.

✦   ✦   ✦

# THE CHEMICAL REVOLUTION—THE SECOND PHASE

**SIDNEY J. FRENCH**
Colgate University, Hamilton, New York

THE Eighteenth Century revolution in science falls quite naturally into five rather distinct phases, the entire period encompassing less than two decades.

The first phase begins with the questioning of the phlogiston theory by Lavoisier late in 1772, and his subsequent attempt to develop a new conceptual scheme to explain combustion and calcination. While he made considerable progress, he was unable to complete the new concept, and in the summer of 1774 he had reached the tentative conclusion that fixed air (carbon dioxide) was the gas which combined with metals to increase their weight when they were calcined.

The second phase begins with Priestley's work on the calx of mercury in August, 1774, and is concluded with the publication, respectively, of Priestley's letters to the Royal Society in March, 1775, announcing his new discovery, and Lavoisier's now famous Easter Memoir to the French Academy of Science in April of the same year on "The nature of the principle that combines with metals in calcination and that increases their weight."

The third phase stems directly from the second. It involves Lavoisier's refinement of his conceptual scheme and his subsequent discovery, based on Priestley's careful work, that the atmosphere is composed of two gases, only one of which supports combustion. It was in this period that Lavoisier's celebrated experiments with mercuric oxide were performed which demonstrate the composition of the atmosphere.

The fourth phase completes the conceptual scheme by explaining the composition of water and the nature of oxidation and reduction. It is, of course, based upon Cavendish's important discovery that water is produced in the combustion of inflammable air (hydrogen).

The fifth phase which overlaps the fourth completes the establishment of a new nomenclature in chemistry by the well-known group of French chemists including Lavoisier and is climaxed by the publication of Lavoisier's book in which the new terminology was first used. It marks, as well, growing support for the new theory and Lavoisier's final and victorious attack on the phlogistonist creed.

This paper is particularly concerned with the second phase which is without doubt the most striking and certainly the most controversial. Reference to other phases is made as it becomes necessary to throw further light upon the controversy which still exists over the relative contributions of Priestley and Lavoisier to the solution of the combustion problem, the controversy which was set off by Priestley's statements that he told Lavoisier in October, 1774, about the gas he had recently obtained by heating a supposed calx of mercury.

In the course of nearly a century and three quarters many points concerning the great controversy have been settled. But others still remain unsettled and need further consideration. It is clear, for example, from the careful and painstaking work of Meldrum (1) that Lavoisier's conceptual scheme—the first phase—involving a revolution in science was the *product* of his own mind, and his only. Priestley had no part in it; the whole scheme was thought out and well advanced before Lavoisier ever met Priestley. It is not necessary to review this evidence and no one any longer believes the loose statements of some earlier historians to the effect that Lavoisier hurried to his laboratory following his talk with Priestley, repeated Priestley's experiment and came out with his new theory based on what Priestley had told him. This interpretation has long since joined the egregious myths of history and is deeply buried.

But the elimination of this myth has by no means lifted the shroud of suspicion from Lavoisier's decapitated and unidentified corpse. There still remains the possibility and, from circumstantial evidence at least, the probability, that Lavoisier made good and effective use of what Priestley *told* him in carrying forward the *second* phase of the revolution.

Did he? That is the question which needs more careful examination and to which this paper is primarily addressed.

By the time Lavoisier met Priestley in Paris in October, 1774, he had made considerable progress in developing his new conceptual scheme, but he had arrived at a practical *impasse*. From his own experiments, from careful study of the work of others, from his preparation and publication of a book on gases he had learned many things. He was more than ever satisfied that metals increased in weight when they were calcined and in so doing absorbed something from the air. His memoir on this subject had been prepared the preceding spring but was not read to the Academy until November, 1774. The one thing which puzzled him was the *nature* of the substance absorbed by the metal from the air. For a variety of reasons, including careful study of Black's work on the relationships between lime, chalk, and fixed air, his own studies of heating diamonds, and his knowledge of the gas produced when the calx

4

of a metal was heated with charcoal, he had been forced to the tentative conclusion that the substance absorbed was fixed air (carbon dioxide). Yet this did not seem to square with other facts. He had tried, for instance, adding fixed air to the residual air in which a metal had been calcined, but found that this did not restore the combustible properties of the air.

Lavoisier's interest in gases was specific; he wanted to know their relationship to combustion. Likewise, his interest in metals was specifically related to problems of calcination. He was considerable of a novice in experimenting with gases, quite unlike Priestley who was the expert in this field, but whose experiments "roamed all over the map." It was also true that no consistent theory of gases had been developed. Some regarded all gases merely as variants of the atmosphere due to the presence of certain impurities. Others recognized distinct differences and regarded some of the better known gases as distinct entities.

During this period, and just preceding it, several important incidents took place which have a seemingly important bearing on the eventual solution of Lavoisier's problem. One was, of course, the meeting of Priestley and Lavoisier; another had to do with the significant contemporary work of a little known Parisian scientist.

Early in the year 1774, Bayen, a Parisian scientist, produced several interesting papers bearing closely upon Lavoisier's problem. All were published in *Observations*. In the first of these papers published in February, 1774, Bayen stated that the calx of mercury could be converted into the metal merely by heat and without the use of charcoal to provide the necessary phlogiston. Furthermore, the calx lost weight in the process. This result seemed, according to Bayen, to have some bearing on the work recently reported by Lavoisier in his *Opuscules* on the gain in weight of metals on calcination. The second paper, which also appeared before Lavoisier *read* his memoir on calcination in November, reported that the elastic fluid obtained by heating the calx of mercury with charcoal was soluble in water and had the properties of fixed air. It also reported, surprisingly enough, that when the calx was heated *without* charcoal a gas was evolved which had the same properties; it was also soluble in water.

There are several surprising and interesting things about these papers. In the first place, if the calx of mercury (and Bayen also felt that the red oxide should be regarded as a true calx) could be converted to the metal without the use of charcoal, it was the first instance of its kind known. What, then, provided the necessary phlogiston for the operation? In the second place, the gas produced was, according to Bayen's hasty conclusions, fixed air.

On September 3, 1774, Cadet reported to the Academy of Science that *red precipitate of mercury per se could be reduced to mercury without the addition of charcoal*. While it had *not* been clearly established that red precipitate (prepared by dissolving mercury in nitric acid, then adding alkali to precipitate the oxide, which was then filtered out and dried) was identical with the red calx prepared by heating mercury moderately in air, there was a growing tendency to regard them as the same substance. Bayen's work, in fact, indicated that mercury calx might be prepared in a number of different ways.

So important did Cadet's report seem to the Academy (and it seems likely that Cadet's report was based on Bayen's work) that a special committee was appointed to verify the experiment. *Lavoisier was a member of that committee*, which reported *November 19, 1774*, that Cadet's contention was correct. Thus, Lavoisier must have known this fact before or, at latest, shortly after he talked with Priestley.

It is too bad that Bayen blundered in one of his results, otherwise he might at least have shared the credit as a discoverer of oxygen. But the error is easily understandable; he had been reading Lavoisier's *Opuscules* carefully. He therefore would probably assume that the gas obtained in heating the calx of mercury *ought* to be fixed air. Perhaps he made only a perfunctory test; perhaps his apparatus contained some fixed air because he had not swept it clean after a prior experiment. In any event he missed his chance, probably because he had a preconceived idea of what he should get; probably also because he had had very little experience in working with gases—a new subject to most French scientists, including Lavoisier. It must be realized, too, that Bayen's interest in the gas produced was quite secondary to his interest in the fact that mercury could be produced from the calx without the use of charcoal.

Thus, at the time Lavoisier met Priestley in October, 1774, he had already prepared his memoir on the increase of weight in metals upon calcination; he still felt that the principle absorbed from the atmosphere was fixed air; he must have suspected, at least, that the calx of mercury could be reduced to mercury by mere heating and without the aid of charcoal; and because of Bayen's error—and his own convictions—he would regard the gas produced in this process as fixed air.

With this in mind the possible impact of Priestley's statements can be judged, but since we are attempting to follow the sequence of events only as they impinged upon Lavoisier's thinking, much of the very brilliant work of Priestley on gases must be omitted and only that portion which might have affected Lavoisier's actions can or need be included. Priestley is rightly credited with many important discoveries, among them, oxygen.

On August 1, 1774, Priestley heated what he thought was red calx of mercury. He was interested in seeing what kind of a gas might be produced from such action; he had a new powerful lens with which he might thus examine a variety of substances. Unlike Bayen (about whose work with mercury calx he probably did not know), he had no preconceived ideas about the nature of the gas. Furthermore, since he heated the calx over a mercury trap he would not note that *mercury was produced* in the process. His prime interest was in the kind of gas he might get; Bayen's was in the production of the metal.

Priestley got his gas, and looking upon it as an unknown, proceded to apply several tests. It was not fixed air; it supported the burning of a candle vigorously. "But what surprised me more than I can well express," wrote Priestly, "was that a candle burned in this air with a remarkably vigorous flame, very much like that enlarged flame with which a candle burns in nitrous air, exposed to iron or liver of sulfur (nitrous oxide); but as I had got nothing like this remarkable appearance from any kind of air besides this particular modification of nitrous air, and I knew no nitrous acid was used in the preparation of *mercurious calcinatus*, I was utterly at a loss to account for it" (2).

In Priestley's case, too much knowledge proved a dangerous thing. He had previously prepared the gas, nitrous oxide, which he called modified nitrous air and had seen a candle burn in it with a very vigorous flame, more vigorous than in atmospheric air. He knew furthermore that substances containing niter could burn "*en vacuo*, in fixed air, and even under water, as is evident in some rockets, which are made for the purpose." His superior knowledge of nitrous oxide and niter blinded him to the right answer. He believed the gas produced must be akin to nitrous oxide, not to the atmosphere, yet he knew full well that neither niter nor nitric acid had anything to do with the preparation of the calx of mercury. From whence, then, came the nitrous oxide—as he supposed the gas to be—in which the candle burned?

In casting about for a possible answer he came to a tentative conclusion that the material he thought to be red calx of mercury might instead be red precipitate of mercury, prepared by first treating mercury with nitric acid. This treatment might account for the modified *nitrous* air. He therefore tried some red precipitate of mercury and got the same result. He secured another sample which he felt was an authentic sample of the *calx*—and got the same result. Perhaps the calx, prepared by heating mercury in air, had received "something of nitre" from the atmosphere, he reasoned. It is obvious that Priestley regarded the calx and the red precipitate as different substances at the time when the dilemma was being resolved in France largely through Bayen's work. Finally, Priestley got the same kind of air by heating red lead.

At this point, in October, 1774, he was forced to drop his interesting work and accompany his patron, Lord Shelburne, on a trip to Paris. It was in Paris at a dinner given by Lavoisier (the two scientists had not previously met nor is there any indication that they had ever exchanged correspondence) that Priestley says he described his recent work to the assembled company.

"And Mr. and Mrs. Lavoisier, as much as any, expressed great surprise," wrote Priestley later. He wanted to be certain the world of science knew that he had talked about his experiments in Lavoisier's presence. He, with others, felt later that Lavoisier had appropriated his ideas.

Just what did Priestley tell the assembled company; what did Lavoisier get from it? Why did Priestley say, "And Mr. and Mrs. Lavoisier, *as much as any—*"?

A dinner party is probably not the most appropriate place to communicate ideas of a precise or technical nature requiring careful attention to details. Certainly if Priestley's reactions to the French people were correct, it would be hard to communicate precise ideas to them at any time. "In general," he wrote, "the French are too much taken up with themselves to admit of that minute and benevolent attention to others which is essential to politeness. This appears in nothing more than their continually interrupting one another in discourse, which they do without the least apology so that one half of the persons in company are heard talking at the same time."

Not only did Priestley stutter, he also spoke poor French—this in spite of his great linguistic ability. Lavoisier understood—and spoke—English poorly. Was what Priestley told the "assembled company" *understood* by Lavoisier as Priestley, himself, *understood* it, or even as he *told* it? One can well doubt it, considering the normal difficulties of communication, even in a common language, on a technical subject.

Even if it were understood by Lavoisier as Priestley understood it, what did Lavoisier learn? He learned that a substance which might or might not be the red calx of mercury yielded a gas on heating which appeared to be modified nitrous air in which a candle burned vigorously. This was certainly interesting and would call perhaps for something more than *polite* surprise. There is the implication in Priestley's statement, however, that Lavoisier's surprise was somehow connected with a secret knowledge of what this discovery would mean to his own work. That, certainly, was the interpretation given by earlier historians who claimed that Lavoisier then rushed to his laboratory, repeated Priestley's work and came out with his new theory of combustion based upon Priestley's discovery. The implication is that Priestley by some divine-like coincidence in timing had provided the missing clue Lavoisier was groping for, and Lavoisier recognized it instantly. Scientific discoveries seldom proceed that way! And Lavoisier was by no means ready to recognize such a clue—if it were one.

Priestley comes back time and again to his complaint that he told Lavoisier about his work. "I frequently expressed my surprise at the kind of air which I had got from this preparation to Mr. Lavoisier, Mr. Le Roy, and several other philosophers, who honored me with their notice in that City; and who, I daresay, cannot fail to recollect the circumstances." Again, "It appears by Mr. Lavoisier's paper, that, after I left Paris, where I procured the *mercurious calcinatus* above mentioned and had spoken of the experiments that I had made and that I had intended to make with it, he began his experiments upon the same substance, and presently found what I have called dephlogisticated air." Priestley refers here to Lavoisier's memoir published in the spring of 1775. To Thomas Henry, publisher of the English translation of Lavoisier's book he wrote, "He ought to have acknowledged that my giving him an account of the air I had got from *mercurious calcinatus* and buying a quantity of M. Cadet while I was in Paris, led him to try what air it yielded, which he did presently after I left."

Priestley's persistent, if plaintive, cry comes from his desire to protect his right to the discovery of oxygen (dephlogisticated air). He had every right to complain as far as the discovery of oxygen was concerned—*he was shortly to make that discovery*—but in so complaining he confused the historians who attached the complaint not only to the discovery of oxygen but to the discovery of the principle of combustion (which was clearly Lavoisier's) as well. They seized upon Priestley's words to condemn Lavoisier without careful study of what had gone before or what was to follow. Priestley's complaint was specific. History broadened it to throw suspicion on the whole of Lavoisier's work.

No one today questions Priestley's right as an independent discoverer of oxygen. By similar token, the careful work of Meldrum, McKie, and others (*3, 4, 5*) has shown that Lavoisier had his conceptual scheme well developed before he talked with Priestley—some six months before Priestley discovered that his new gas, far from being modified nitrous air, was indeed a pure form of atmospheric air.

What happened after Priestley left Paris? Lavoisier tells us that he experimented with *mercury precipitate per se* in November. But his wording leaves one in doubt concerning the results he obtained. The following statement appears as a footnote to his now famous Easter Memoir of 1775: "Les premières expériences relatives à ce Mémoir, ont été faites il y a plus d'un an; cellessur le *mercure précipité per se*, ont d'abord été tentées au verre ardent, dans le mois de Novembre 1774, et faites ensuite avec toutes les précautions et les soins nécessaires dans le Laboratoire de Montigney, conjointement avec M. Trudaine, les 28 Février, 1er et 2 Mars de cette année; enfin elles ont été répéttés de nouveau le 31 Mars dernier, en présence de M. le Duc de la Rochefoucault, de M.rs Trudaine, de Montigny, Macquer & Cadet" (*6*).

The statement deserves more careful attention than it has generally been accorded. It has usually been interpreted to imply that Lavoisier *performed* the experiment in November. He is careful to say, however, that the experiments "were attempted" (été tentées). He then goes on to say that they were completed or accomplished (faites ensuite) with all necessary precautions. There is a definite implication that the *November* experiments were incomplete, inconclusive, or unsuccessful. As a matter of interest I asked five of my colleagues who teach French to translate the passage independently. None knew the background of the particular controversy or what parts of the passage might be in question. Three stated that the "experiments with *mercury precipitate per se* were 'tried' ....'"; two that they were "attempted." In translating "faite ensuite" in the context of the whole

statement each used a different term as follows: "performed, made, done, accomplished, completed." In another writing this term is translated as "continued."

There is definite reservation, therefore, about the completeness or success of the November experiments. But, were this the only evidence suggesting failure the matter could be passed over lightly as a mere case of inadequate statement. It is not the only evidence!

Lavoisier was a man of action. In fact he sometimes made haste too rapidly and came out with statements which were not adequately verified by experiment. He was a man of means, supported by his investments, who could—and did—devote long and strenuous hours to his scientific work. He had a vision of a revolution in science and was doing everything possible to push matters along. He had already made notable progress but had reached an *impasse*. If Priestley had given him a clue which he recognized he certainly would have let no grass grow under his scientific feet. Yet, following the November attempt he seems to have done nothing further with the calx of mercury *for nearly four months*. He did, however, work on other experiments including the calcination of lead, and was conjecturing in his notebook on the nature of charcoal. It were as though the Priestley episode had dropped completely from his conscious mind. Lavoisier's previous work had been with such metals and calces as iron, lead, and tin. The evidence makes it all too clear that he did not regard mercury calx or *mercury precipitate per se* in the same category with these other calces. In fact, Priestley's statements could well have confused him even more concerning the nature of this substance.

We will probably never know just why Lavoisier's attention became fixed upon the calx of mercury again in late February, 1775. He gives no particular explanation. Perhaps the unconscious merged at this point with the conscious. He might have been giving further thought to Bayen's work or Cadet's report. Or he may have just happened to pick up a container of mercury calx in the laboratory and decided to work with it. The one thing he did *not* seem to do at this time, however, was to recall what Priestley had told him—unless one were to accept the unlikely view that he was deliberately trying to throw historians off the track. An entry in his private journal—not written for public view—seemingly made on February 28, 1775, provides the rather surprising evidence. It reads as follows:

Air from *mercury precipitate per se*. It was fully believed that this air liberated from a sort of metallic calx was fixed air and the air was submitted to the test with lime water. It made it slightly opaline without any precipitation. Trial was made by introducing a light into it; but far from being extinguished, the flame on the contrary was greatly enhanced (*7*).

This is a significant passage as it relates to Lavoisier's thinking. It would appear to provide irrefutable evidence that the November experiment had not been carried to a successful conclusion. If it had been, why would Lavoisier now be expecting to get fixed air? Either he did not understand what Priestley had told him or else he did not connect Priestley's work with what he was now doing.

The key to the confusion, however, probably lies in the phrase "a *sort* of metallic calx." He was not certain that this substance belonged in the same category with the calces of iron, lead, and tin, with which he had formerly worked. In the first place, there seemed to be two substances, prepared in different ways, but with very similar properties. Priestley was not sure which one he had worked with and apparently mentioned his own confusion—and got a fresh sample of the *calx* from Cadet. It is not surprising therefore that Lavoisier did not seem to connect Priestley's work with what he was now attempting.

Furthermore, Lavoisier was not now attempting to *repeat* Priestley's experiment. He was using quite a different method. Priestley used a burning glass, as did Lavoisier in November. Lavoisier was now using a small retort the neck of which was placed under an inverted bell jar filled with *water*. He wanted to see what was left after the calx was heated; this was impossible by Priestley's method in which the calx was heated directly in an inverted container of *mercury*.

That, until he tried this experiment, he was still confused concerning the real nature of *mercury precipitate per se* is further evidenced by his statements in his Easter Memoir, "*Mercury precipitate per se*, which is nothing else than a calx of mercury, as several authors [Bayen?] have already maintained and as the reader of this Memoir will be even convinced.... In order to be sure that *mercury precipitate per se* was a true metallic calx, whether it would give the same results and the same kind of air on reduction, I tried at first to reduce it by the ordinary method that is to say to use the accepted expression, by the addition of phlogiston [charcoal]." He had at last convinced himself that this substance was a true calx, it would seem.

While Lavoisier's Easter Memoir gives an orderly statement of his procedures in which he speaks first of reducing the calx with charcoal and getting fixed air, and then reducing it without charcoal and getting pure common air, there is every reason to believe from his journal entry that he actually proceeded in an opposite manner. In fact, he says in the Memoir that the observations made during a number of experiments have been "combined into one account."

Priestley had said in October that the gas obtained from heating the calx of mercury seemed to be nitrous oxide. He continued to believe this for several months and in fact did not finally discover his error—and apply the common test for atmospheric air until early March, 1775—just at the time Lavoisier was also discovering that this gas had the properties of common air. This was an interesting coincidence in timing, but nothing more. There was a great difference in the way the two went at the problem. Lavoisier never stumbled at this point. When he discovered that a candle burned in the gas *he went right on to apply the nitric oxide test*, the commonly accepted test of that day, which Priestley was very familiar with, to test the goodness of common

air. Lavoisier, it would seem, had no mental hurdle to leap. If he had been following Priestley's lead he should have regarded this gas as nitrous oxide, not pure common air. There is no shred of evidence that he ever so regarded it! What it took Priestley six painful months to discover from the time of his first experiment in August, 1774, Lavoisier discovered in the course of a day or two. Why did it take Priestley so long to come to this inescapable conclusion while Lavoisier arrived there immediately? Probably because Priestley had one sort of preconceived notion and Lavoisier another.

When Lavoisier saw that a candle burned in the gas his agile mind must have leapt ahead many strides. Things began to fall in place in an orderly manner. The gas was pure common air—nothing else would fit his theory and this discovery clinched the theory. When the calx was heated with charcoal he got fixed air; when heated alone, pure common air. The relation of fixed air to combustion was explained; he wrote, "From the fact that common air changes to fixed air when combined with charcoal it would seem natural to conclude that fixed air is nothing but a combination of common air and phlogiston [carbon]."

It must have been a thrilling moment in Lavoisier's career when the solution to his problem dawned on him during the course of these few days in late February and early March. Yet, in his rather cryptic and precise writings he seldom expresses such feelings, as Priestley so delightfully and frequently does.

There is further evidence that Lavoisier was completely satisfied with the answer he had obtained. He seems not even to have bothered to test the gas with a live animal—which Priestley was doing continuously, to discover that the animal lived far longer in this gas than in common air. Finally, on March 31 after he had prepared his memoir, and seemingly as an afterthought or as a more convincing test, Lavoisier did place a bird in the gas, but apparently was satisfied when the bird lived and went no further to find out how *long* it would live.

The question arises, at what point did Lavoisier finally recognize the similarity of Priestley's earlier experiments, described in Paris, to his? The evidence seems quite clear on this matter. He did not recognize any similarity at least until he had performed the experiment on February 28 and had obtained a gas in which a candle burned. Up to that point he had expected to get fixed air; he was relying on Bayen and his own preconceived notion. If he recognized the similarity when he found that a candle burned in the gas he apparently devoted little time or thought to Priestley's conclusions, because he immediately applied the test for common air. *The evidence supports the conclusion that the similarity struck him only after he had found his own answer to his own problems.* When it did strike him, and if he were fully aware of what Priestley had said about the nature of the gas, then he must have realized that he had corrected Priestley's error. He had also corrected Bayen's error. He was not responsible to anybody for his results. The fact that he had come to use the calx of mercury for his work was important—very important—for this was the one substance with which he could—and did—prove his point. But he owed no particular credit to Priestley for this. Many people had worked with this substance. He had used it in an experiment quite different from Priestley's and had certainly come to different conclusions. There is no reason to suppose that Lavoisier felt indebted to Priestley. There is no reason to assume that Priestley had any influence on Lavoisier's work in the second phase of the revolution. The controversy appears to be one of those surprising, yet frequent, coincidences in timing.

Perhaps Lavoisier could have avoided criticism from Priestley and others by failing to mention the fact that he had attempted to repeat Priestley's experiment in November. This was the statement which Priestley seized upon in his complaints. If it had no bearing on his later work and was, indeed, a failure, mention of it could well have been omitted. On the other hand, Lavoisier was anxious to link his new work back to his old and probably threw this mention in as such a link. He did not know, of course, that Priestley would have corrected his own error in the meantime. Had he known the storm he would create, he certainly would have handled the matter otherwise. Certainly it was no attempt to cover up or play a clever game.

Yet, Lavoisier never attempted to answer Priestley's charges. Actually there was nothing tangible to answer. Priestley had talked about his work in Paris, there was no denying that. But what Priestley had said and what Lavoisier found out were two different things. Furthermore, the one did not lead to the other, as Priestley imagined, but there was no way of making this clear except as the evidence spoke for itself. Lavoisier must have had a clear conscience and the feeling that little weight could be attached to the complaint. It is, of course, also true that the matter of giving credit in scientific work had not at that time become established as it is today.

Lavoisier even made claim in a mild way as a co-discoverer of oxygen. "This gas which Mr. Priestley, Mr. Scheele, and I discovered at about the same time." This claim, rightly denied by history, is sometimes used as a further instance of Lavoisier's avaricious nature. It has another, more valid, interpretation. If Lavoisier arrived at his conclusions of March, 1775, independently of Priestley's help as he seems to have done, he had every right to press a claim as co-discoverer with a clear conscience. The very fact that he asserted it is further evidence of no conscious reliance on Priestley.

However, his claim has been denied because, unlike Priestley, he did not make a careful and exhaustive study of this gas to discover that it was "far better" than common air. He was satisfied to regard it as "pure" atmospheric air. By this he obviously meant that the various impurities and contaminants of common air had been removed. He fell into the trap of assuming that the principle which combines with metals on calcination and increases their weight was the *whole* of the atmospheric air. Yet, earlier he talked about the "acid part" which combines with metals.

To understand Lavoisier's failure here it is necessary to try to look at the matter as he must have then seen it. In the first place, he must have been so delighted to discover that mercury precipitate released a gas which supported combustion, and that he therefore had found the substantial answer to his complex problem, that he was eager to publish the results at once. As far as he was concerned his conceptual scheme was now complete. As a matter of fact, it was! The modern principle of combustion could stand alone on this discovery.

Lavoisier's preconceived ideas prevented him from going further. In a sense, his mind was on one track and could not make the necessary switch. With Priestley, it was a different matter. He was working with gases and, as he so often tells us, had no preconceived ideas and no particular motives. He was exploring all possible areas and depths. Looking backward, it is easy to be critical of Lavoisier's failure here; it is equally easy to understand from his point of view, looking forward, why he failed.

When Lavoisier read of what Priestley had actually discovered, he shortly came to the realization that his own work was incomplete. He then began a series of careful experiments on the gas to discover, as Priestley had, that the gas was "far better" than common air. In this, the third phase, he privately gives Priestley credit for assistance in a number of places. However, Lavoisier's interpretations of Priestley's work led him shortly to the discovery of the true composition of the atmosphere, which Priestley never recognized or accepted. In President Conant's recent book, "The Growth of the Experimental Sciences (8)," appears a most interesting comparison of Lavoisier's memoir of 1775 as first published and as later altered and published in 1778, in the light of Priestley's discoveries and Lavoisier's further advances. Both interesting and significant is the fact that Lavoisier could, with so few changes in the original Memoir, bring it up to date to include his later findings based on Priestley's discovery and his own further work.

But the very fact that this Memoir was published twice has, until recently, been a source of great confusion to historians. As is often the case, the publication schedule of the Academy was far behind the actual presentation of papers, so much so that the Academy's Memoires for 1774 and 1775 were actually not published until 1778. Thus, Lavoisier had nearly three years in which to study the problem further, conduct additional experiments, and revise both his thinking and his writing. He made use of the time by repeating much of Priestley's work and frequently mentions this in his journal in such passages as "l'air dephlogistique de M. Prisley." As McKie says, "Lavoisier's debt to Priestley is very evident here; for it was undoubtedly through these repetitions that he was led to revise his memoirs of 1774–75...."

Earlier historians, however, who seemed to be not aware of this lag in publication assumed that the final memoir was the one read at Easter time in 1775 and published shortly thereafter in Rozier's journal, *Observations*. On this assumption the case might look quite different to an historian. It might in effect greatly strengthen Priestley's claim of virtual piracy by Lavoisier. Here were two men seemingly coming out with conclusions remarkably alike at about the same time, and it was known that the one had told the other about the early progress of his work. Just how Lavoisier could have found out what Priestley's *final* results were and have acted upon this information so promptly is not, of course, explained; but the circumstantial evidence pointed strongly toward the appropriation of Priestley's results by Lavoisier. Incidentally, Priestley, himself, did not seem to realize that Lavoisier's first findings were more limited than his own for he wrote, "... and [he] presently found what I have called dephlogisticated air." Actually, Lavoisier had not "found" dephlogisticated air but, rather, what he then regarded as pure common air.

However, when both the original and the revised memoirs are spaced in their now known sequence the case assumes a new significance, and it becomes clear that Lavoisier had gained nothing from *conversation* with Priestley but that he later gained a great deal from reading about Priestley's final results. It is here, in the third phase, that Lavoisier should have acknowledged publicly (as he did in private) his debt to Priestley. That he did not see fit to do so is unfortunate. It would probably have eliminated Priestley's complaints; at least it would have limited them to that area of the controversy where they belong. It is not easy to forgive Lavoisier for this oversight. One can choose to believe that he felt that he was dealing mainly with the principle which combines with metals and not with the discovery of a new gas, that Priestley's findings were already public property by publication and were therefore known to his scientific contemporaries anyway. This but strengthens the case for some public acknowledgment. The fact remains that this principle which combined with metals was identical with Priestley's new gas. We can but suppose that having gone as far as he did alone, having established the essential facts of his new conceptual scheme, he was determined to carry it to completion alone and thus bring to full fruition the revolution in science which he, alone, actually foresaw in 1773 when he wrote: "The importance of the end in view prompted me to undertake all this work, which seemed to me destined to bring about a revolution in physics and chemistry."

Nevertheless, Lavoisier's failure, in the third phase, to recognize his indebtedness to Priestley does not alter the case for the second phase and in view of the evidence it seems right to conclude that Lavoisier carried through the second phase of the revolution without reliance on Priestley. The October conversations between the two scientists in Paris form an interesting historical episode, but little more. They certainly do not have the significance so often attached to them. Lavoisier got no usable clue from Priestley, made no use of Priestley's work in bolstering his own. The most that can be said is that Lavoisier's attention was directed toward the calx of mercury as an interesting substance to experiment with. Eventually this substance proved more than interesting; it was vital—the material *par-excellence* with which Lavoisier could, and did, prove his point. But it was not Priestley who pointed this out.

Although there is a tendency to side-step the issue, most writers are still inclined to feel, in the absence of careful step-wise analysis, that what Priestley told Lavoisier in Paris in October, 1774, became a significant factor in guiding Lavoisier to his subsequent discovery. The confusion is understandable but the evidence lends no support to such a view. Lavoisier must not be forever damned because of some pleasant and stimulating conversations with Priestley in Paris. If Priestley had never visited Paris, or had never talked about his unfinished business in science—a highly unlikely thing for Priestley incidentally—the outcome of Lavoisier's work in the spring of 1775 would in all probability have been the same, with some possible variation in timing. Both men were great scientists, but just as Lavoisier deserves no claim to the discovery of oxygen, so, Priestley deserves no share in the second phase of the revolution which resulted in the substantial establishment of Lavoisier's conceptual scheme. This phase as well as the firstf was Lavoisier's, and his only.

## LITERATURE CITED

(1) MELDRUM, A. N., "The Eighteenth Century Revolution in Science—The First Phase," Longmans, Green and Company, Ltd., London, **1930**.
(2) PRIESTLEY, JOSEPH, "Experiments and Observations on Different Kinds of Air," London, **1775**. (Reprinted in *Alembic Club Reprints*, No. 7, William F. Clay, London, **1894**).
(3) McKIE, DOUGLAS, "Antoine Lavoisier, The Father of Modern Chemistry," J. B. Lippincott, Philadelphia, **1935**.
(4) FRENCH, SIDNEY J., "Torch and Crucible—The Life and Death of Antoine Lavoisier," Princeton Press, Princeton, New Jersey, **1941**.
(5) HARTOG, SIR PHILIP, "The Newer Views of Priestley and Lavoisier," *Annals of Science*, 5, No. 1, August (1941) (Reprinted).
(6) LAVOISIER, ANTOINE, "Memoir on the Nature of the Principle Which Combines with Metals During Calcination and Increases Their Weight," Memoires de l'Academie des Sciences, **1775**, p. 520. (Also published in Rozier's *Observations* for May, **1775**. English translation of both versions published in "The Growth of the Experimental Sciences," **1949**).
(7) *Loc. cit.*, MELDRUM, p. 58.
(8) CONANT, JAMES BRYANT, "The Growth of the Experimental Sciences," Harvard University Press, Cambridge, Massachusetts, **1949**.

# THE GMELIN CHEMICAL DYNASTY

**PAUL WALDEN**
Tübingen-Gammertingen, Germany
*(Translated by Ralph E. Oesper)*

Heidelberg and Tübingen—two old German university towns on the Neckar—are both well known in America and are often mentioned in chemical circles. Ira Remsen (1846–1927) was at Tübingen during his five-year period of study in Germany (1867–72),[1] and while there as assistant to Rudolf Fittig became the friend and tutor of William Ramsay (the future discoverer of the noble gases). The memory of Remsen's stay remains alive in the University of Tübingen, since the Remsen-Reihlen "Einleitung in das Studium der Chemie" (15th ed., 1950) is still used in the beginning course. Is it necessary to do more than mention Heidelberg and its great chemists Bunsen and Victor Meyer? Göttingen, the third university town of interest here, was graced for many years by the teaching of Friedrich Wöhler (1800–82). Americans trained under him returned to organize the laboratory instruction at Harvard, Yale, and Johns Hopkins.[1]

During the period approximately 1700–1860, these three university cities were the academic sites of the labors of numerous members of the Gmelin family, namely, about a dozen professors of jurisprudence and the sciences, of medicine and chemistry. As in the former ruling houses, or dynasties, it was customary here likewise to distinguish between an older and a younger Tübingen line, and one spoke of three kinds of Gmelin professors: those who had passed away, those who were on the lecture platform, and those who were still in the cradle.

For the chemical historian this dynasty of professors presents the following seven representatives. In genealogical-chronological order they were:[2]

[1] Getman, F. H., "The Life of Ira Remsen," Chemical Education Publ. Co., Easton, Pa., **1940**, pp. 31–5. See also van Klooster, H. S., *Chymia*, **2**, 10, 13–15 (1949).

[2] Compare "Stammbaum der Familie Gmelin," lxviii + 133 pages and genealogical tables, Karlsruhe, **1877**.

(1) Johann Georg Gmelin (1674–1728), the progenitor of both Tübingen lines. His sons:

(2) Johann Georg Gmelin, Jr. (1709–55) and

(3) Philipp Friedrich Gmelin (1721–68). Their oldest brother Johann Konrad (1707–59) took over the patrimonial pharmacy. His ninth child (among 15) was

(4) Samuel Gottlieb Gmelin (1744–74), scientist. His brother was the apothecary Christian Gottlob Gmelin (1749–1809). One of the latter's seven children was

(5) Christian Gottlob Gmelin (1792–1860), chemist. On the other hand, the five children of P. F. Gmelin (see 3) included

(6) Johann Friedrich Gmelin (1748–1804), scientist, whose youngest son was

(7) Leopold Gmelin (1788–1853), chemist.

A study of this rare continuity in the choice and creative prosecution of a specific area of knowledge is of significance to the history of chemistry and culture, and likewise to the workings of tradition. This examination also yields valuable insights into the academic surroundings, the course of education, the accomplishments, and personal fortunes of these scientists.

(1) In 1674 a son, Johann Georg, was born to Samuel Gmelin, schoolmaster in Münchingen, a little town in the Duchy of Württemberg, which had suffered greatly from the Thirty Years' War. At the age of 13, the boy began his apprenticeship at Stuttgart, and at 19 as "journeyman" he began his *Wanderschaft* in Ulm, Dresden, Leipzig, Delft (1697) and finally in the Royal "Laboratori chymici" in Stockholm (1699). After seven years he returned home (1706) and through marriage with the daughter of a druggist became the proprietor of an apothecary's shop in Tübingen.

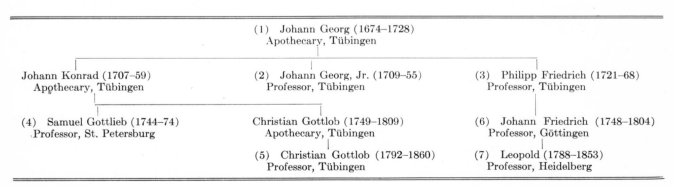

(1) Johann Georg (1674–1728)
Apothecary, Tübingen

Johann Konrad (1707–59)
Apothecary, Tübingen

(2) Johann Georg, Jr. (1709–55)
Professor, Tübingen

(3) Philipp Friedrich (1721–68)
Professor, Tübingen

(4) Samuel Gottlieb (1744–74)
Professor, St. Petersburg

Christian Gottlob (1749–1809)
Apothecary, Tübingen

(6) Johann Friedrich (1748–1804)
Professor, Göttingen

(5) Christian Gottlob (1792–1860)
Professor, Tübingen

(7) Leopold (1788–1853)
Professor, Heidelberg

(The building still houses a drug store!) He also held lectures on chemistry from time to time, and enjoyed quite a reputation in the academic circles. His health began to deteriorate in his early fifties; in 1726 he had fainting spells, and a stroke, and after a "burning fever" he died prematurely in 1728.

(2) Johann Georg Gmelin, Jr.,[3] was born at Tübingen in 1709 and died there in 1755. He was the second of the twelve children of J. G. Gmelin, Sr., just discussed. A precocious boy, he was not subjected to the usual apothecary apprenticeship, but instead—at the age of 14—he was enrolled at the local university. He studied the sciences (particularly botany) and medicine, and held his first disputation in 1725. He graduated in 1727, at 18, as licentiate in medicine; his dissertation dealt with the Teinacher mineral spring. He then started on an "educational tour," whose goal was the distant and strange city of St. Petersburg. Peter the Great had founded an Academy of Sciences there in 1725, and two of Gmelin's teachers had been called from Tübingen, namely, Duvernoy, the zoologist, and Bilfinger, the philosopher and physicist. The latter had urged Gmelin to follow him to St. Petersburg. After the University of Tübingen conferred the M.D. degree on Gmelin in 1728, the Academy granted him a salary, and in 1730 he was given a teaching post. The next year, only 22, he was made professor in ordinary of chemistry and science. He delivered lectures (in Latin) and published several short papers on geology, chemistry, etc. It was scarcely possible for him to carry out a genuine chemical research in his own laboratory. Instead, another vast and novel task was offered to him: the leadership of the geographical expedition (together with the historian Gerhardt Fr. Müller and the astronomer L. de l'Isle de la Croyère) within the "second Kamchatka Expedition" planned by the Empress Anna. This expedition through Siberia extended from July, 1733, to the return to St. Petersburg in February, 1743. It showed off Gmelin's competence as a botanist. Its literary product was the monumental "Flora Sibirica" in four volumes (Volumes 3 and 4 edited by Samuel Gmelin) published at St. Petersburg 1747–69, and also his "Reise durch Sibirien," Parts 1–4 published at Göttingen 1751, 1752. On his return to St. Petersburg Gmelin resumed his former offices. After completing the arrangement of his collections for his book, he, the *first* occidental chemist of the Russian Academy, requested (1747) permission to return to Tübingen.[4] Here he became ordinary professor of medicine, botany, and chemistry, whereby he also turned his attention to laboratory instruction in chemistry. A new laboratory (costing 653 florins) was built in 1753, and courses were given there *every three years*. Naturally, these consisted only of demonstrations and qualitative

Johann Georg Gmelin, Sr. (1674–1728)

examination of drugs and so forth, and did not comprise a series of chemical exercises such as those Liebig created at Giessen in 1825. Like his father, he died too soon; his death in 1755 likewise prematurely closed his chemical career.

It should be noted that the scientific education of those days ordinarily took the following course: An early doctorate was not followed by intensification in a specialty through personal experimental researches and an assistantship; rather, the "promotion" was followed by a "scientific tour" of two to three years' duration; its objective was to gain a knowledge of the outside world and to acquire general culture, combined with the inspection of scientific institutes and technical installations (factories, mines, etc.) in foreign lands.

(3) Philipp Friedrich Gmelin (b. 1721, d. 1768 in Tübingen) was the ninth of 12 children (and the sixth of seven sons) of the apothecary Johann Georg Gmelin (compare (1)). Like his brother (compare (2)) he was sent to the University of Tübingen at an early age (15). In 1742 he defended his medical doctoral thesis, and started a two-year "scientific tour" to Holland, England, and the rest of Germany. After his return (1744) he practiced medicine in Tübingen, but maintained contact with the University by lectures. He obtained an extraordinary professorship of medicine (1750), of anatomy (1751), and following his brother's death (1755) succeeded to the ordinary professorship of botany and chemistry. Each three years he conducted practical courses in the laboratory, as dis-

---

[3] Compare "Johann Georg Gmelin 1709–1755, der Erforscher Sibiriens," Munich, 1911.

[4] By a strange twist of fate, exactly 200 years later, the writer of this paper (Paul Walden) the *last* west-European chemist of the Imperial Academy, also finally landed in Tübingen.

cussed in (2). He also published a number of short papers, program essays, etc. He too died early, at the age of 47.

(4) Samuel Gottlieb Gmelin (1744–74) also began his medical studies at Tübingen when quite young and received the doctor's diploma at 19. The obligatory "scientific tours" took him through France and Holland. In 1768, though only 24, he received a call as

Johann Georg Gmelin, Jr. (1709–55)

professor of natural history to the Imperial Academy at St. Petersburg. Like his famous uncle, the "Siberian traveler" (compare (2)), he was commanded (1768) by Catherine II (the Great) to make a scientific expedition in the Don region and the Caspian provinces. After five successful years, he was recalled in 1773, but on his way back was captured by the Khan of the Chaitakens. The negotiations concerning his release for a ransom of 30,000 rubles were protracted for months, and in July, 1774, the captive succumbed to dysentery. Against his return to Tübingen, he had been named professor of botany in 1768 and also professor of chemistry in 1772. He published the third and fourth volumes of his uncle's "Flora Sibirica," and his own four-volume work, "Reise durch Russland," appeared at St. Petersburg, 1771–86.

An aura of romanticism and the Viking spirit surrounds these youthful German scientists, botanists, and chemists. They had a longing for the faraway and the unknown. They all moved into a cultural

vacuum, and as members of the Academy these "academicians" had no real corresponding possibilities of doing scientific work and no intellectual sounding board. In a historical study of the first chemical academicians in Russia, the writer (1909) referred to them as the "traveler academicians,"[5] since they, as courageous explorers, had first of all to learn at first hand the peoples, customs, natural and mineral treasures of the far-flung Russian provinces.

(5) Christian Gottlob Gmelin (1792–1860) followed the family tradition. After obtaining his M.D. degree at Tübingen (1814) he, together with his cousin Leopold (compare (7)), went to Paris. His desire (like that of Liebig in 1822) was to work in Vauquelin's laboratory, to attend the lectures of Gay-Lussac and Thenard, and also to listen occasionally to the great crystallographer Haüy. (The chemical instruction imparted at Tübingen by Kielmeyer could hardly be called satisfactory; in addition to chemistry, he also lectured on botany, materia medica, anatomy, physi-

[5] Compare the article, "Über die Pflege der Chemie in Russland bis zum Ausgang des XVIII Jahrhunderts," by the author in P. Diergart's "Beiträge aus der Geschichte der Chemie," Leipzig, 1909, pp. 369–77. See also his article (ibid., pp. 533–44) on the eminent physico-chemist Tobias Lowitz (b. 1757, Göttingen; d. 1804, St. Petersburg) as Imperial Court Apothecary and Academician. His assistant was C. G. S. Kirchhoff (b. 1764 at Teterow-Mecklenburg; d. 1833 at St. Petersburg). He discovered (1811) the saccharification of starch, and (1814) the action of diastase. Concerning Lowitz, compare LEICESTER, H. M., J. CHEM. EDUC., 22, 149 (1945), and Chymia, 1, 47 (1949).

Christian Gottlob Gmelin (1792–1860)

ology, and comparative zoology. There was no provision for laboratory work in chemistry.) However, Gmelin was in Paris only a few months. When Napoleon appeared in the Tuileries in 1815, Gmelin hastily left Paris and went to Berlin in order to work with the great analytical chemist M. H. Klaproth (1743–1817). The venerable master had not done experimental work for a long time, nor had he had any students, and his laboratory had fallen into neglect. Consequently, by the end of 1815, Gmelin was again on the move, this time to Stockholm and Berzelius. Gmelin worked there seven months and learned particularly the analysis of minerals. Also, he and Berzelius made excursions together and gathered rocks. The winter of 1816–17 was spent in England, where Gmelin made the acquaintance of Davy (then busy with the construction of his safety lamp), Wollaston, and others. Here again, visits to English and Scotch industrial and mining districts were a source of much information. On the homeward journey he received the pleasant news of his appointment as ordinary professor of chemistry and pharmacy at Tübingen. Therefore, the 25-year-old M.D. and apothecary-chemist sprang, as it were, from the stagecoach into the professorial chair without any previous accomplishments in chemistry and with no teaching experience. He held this post from December, 1817,[6] until May, 1860. He died suddenly, just a few days after turning over the Chemisches Institut to his successor, Adolf Strecker (1822–71).

As teacher and researcher Gmelin did not have an easy row to hoe. His laboratory in the nonheatable rooms of the old palace kitchen (together with the tiny laboratory budget) exerted no attractions. None the less, he carried out mineral analyses and found new facts. Thus in 1818, when analyzing lithia mica, he discovered the red flame reaction of lithium. Likewise, mineral analysis led him to the discovery of ultramarine or artificial lapis lazuli. From 1822 he had been studying the mineral ittnerite, which occurs at Kaiserstuhl (Baden). The ash-gray to bluish-gray mineral turned a beautiful blue when heated; the search for a tinctorial metal oxide was fruitless, and the analysis revealed the presence only of silica, alumina, soda, and sulfate or sulfur. Here was a chemical mystery, and its significance was increased when it was remembered that the costly lapis lazuli, which once was worth its weight in gold, had a similar chemical composition and likewise evolved hydrogen sulfide when treated with sulfuric acid. Could this local mineral be a chemical brother of the precious azure

stone imported from China and Hindukush, and might it be made artificially from cheap raw materials? The attempts with insufficient means and the lack of genuine comparison material were greatly handicapped. When Gmelin made his second visit to Paris (1827) he discussed the matter with his former teacher, Gay-Lussac. The result, however, was surprising: in February, 1828, Gay-Lussac reported to the Académie des Sciences that the chemist Guimet had succeeded in preparing artificial ultramarine by a secret process (from the year 1826). Germany at that time had no patent protection for discoveries and inventions, and so in 1828 C. G. Gmelin had to content himself with announcing his findings and to being a sorrowful witness of the speedy installation of the manufacture of ultramarine. His services gained the praise of Liebig, who in his "Chemische Briefe" (1844) stated: "The crown of all discoveries of mineral chemistry with respect to the production of minerals was indubitably the artificial manufacture of lapis lazuli."[7]

Gmelin studied several other minerals, and later investigated some organic natural materials, e. g., the bark of the mezereon (Daphne mezereum). He also made physiological studies on the action of rare elements on the animal organism.

In 1837, he wrote a two-volume introduction to chemistry which had original features. Worthy of special note are his services as a pupil of Berzelius, since he translated the first three years (1822–24) of the Swedish master's Jahresberichte into German and arranged for their publication in Tübingen. The university there owes to him the erection of a separate, modern chemical building (1846), in which his successors, A. Strecker (to 1869), R. Fittig (to 1876) and then Lothar Meyer[8] carried on. Gmelin's lectures on chemistry were clear and original. He was a friend of the poets Gustav Schwab and Ludwig Uhland.

Even though Gmelin did not found a school, he had one pupil who took the place of an entire school. This was no other than the renowned Julius Robert Mayer

---

[6] His inaugural lecture was entitled "Historia theoriae combustionis." Moreover, his ancestor Johann Georg Gmelin had published in 1730 a paper with the title, "De augmento ponderis quod capiunt quaedam corpora, cum igne calcinantur." Contemporaneously with Christ. Gottlob Gmelin, there taught at Tübingen his older brother Ferdinand (1782–1848) as professor of medicine and sciences, and Christian Gmelin (1750–1823), son of the above-mentioned Joh. Georg, as professor of law. Regarding the biography of C. G. Gmelin, compare also A. WANK-MÜLLER, Pharm. Zentralbl., **89**, 8–12 (1950).

[7] From the standpoint of the history of civilization, the synthesis of ultramarine represents a striking dramatic action, namely, the chemical dethronement or "democratization" of a natural material that at one time was far beyond the reach of the common people. It has been found in the archeological discoveries coming from the royal palace of the Sumerian capital Ur (fourth millenium B.C.), where the excavations have yielded consummately artistic gold jewelry along with mosaic ornaments consisting of mother-of-pearl figures on lapis lazuli backgrounds. Egyptian hieroglyphics reveal that in the second millenium B.C. the nobles of Assu brought the Pharaohs lapis lazuli as tributary offerings. Moreover, as should be noted, a so-called "Babel lazulite" was offered as tribute in addition to the genuine lapis lazuli or bluestone, and the Egyptians themselves manufactured this artificial lazulite. Several Munich chemists (Prandtl, Büchner, and Bertram) analyzed (1926) a specimen of this highly prized bluestone from Babel and found it to be a soda-potash-lime-lead glass colored blue with cobalt and copper. Today the modern ultramarine serves as a cheap oil and water color, used by the laundress and youngest water color artist; it serves to whiten (or blue) paper, linen, starch, sugar, etc. In reviewing the history of this "king of the mineral substances" one may fittingly write: Sic transit gloria mundi.

[8] WINDERLICH, R., J. CHEM. EDUC., **27**, 365–8 (1950).

(1814–78), the discoverer (1842) of the "law of conservation of energy."[9]   He was a medical student under Gmelin and took his M.D. in 1838 with a dissertation, "Das Santonin."   When Berzelius spent a week in the midsummer of 1819 as guest of Gmelin, he was especially struck by the "studied barbaric appearance" of the Tübingen students, who sought to recall the spirit of the days of yore.[10]   This somewhat crude custom may perhaps also have been extended to our subject, at least so far as can be deduced from his nicknames: "schwefelsaurer Christian, Schmiedsknecht, Holzspälter."

Of Gmelin's nine children, including three sons, none took over the paternal family apothecary's shop. It was sold in 1844.   This step marked the farewell from the good genius of the original firm in Tübingen, a renunciation of pharmacy as a stepping stone to academic posts, a breach in the family tradition. There still remains the venerable original firm, which as formerly is even now known as the "Gmelin Apotheke"; a tablet placed on the house by the University of Tübingen in 1927, on the occasion of the 450th anniversary of its founding, states:

Stammhaus der Tübinger Familie *Gmelin,* zum Gedächtnis ihres Begründers, des Apothekers Johann Georg Gmelin 1674–1728 und der vielen hervorragenden Glieder dieser schwäbischen Familie, insbesondere ihrer zahlreichen Tübinger Hochschullehrer.

This memory is also kept alive by the existence of the Gmelinstrasse in the Tübingen university quarter.

(6)   Johann Friedrich Gmelin (b. 1748 at Tübingen, d. 1804 at Göttingen) was the oldest child of Philipp Friedrich (compare (3)).   He obtained his medical education at Tübingen and was awarded the M.D. degree at 21 (1769).   His "scientific tour" took him to Holland, England, and then Vienna.   Returning home (1771) he lectured at the University on natural history and botany; he became (1772) extraordinary professor of medicine at Tübingen.   The next year, though only 25, he was called to Göttingen as ordinary professor of philosophy and extraordinary professor of medicine.   In 1778 he became ordinary professor of chemistry and botany, and also mineralogy.   He was responsible for the erection (1783) of a student chemical laboratory in Göttingen, though it remained for his successor, Fr. Stromeyer (1775–1835)[11] (1805–35) to fit up this building and to initiate a corresponding course of instruction.   Gmelin's chemical studies were confined entirely to the qualitative observations usual at that period.

His literary output was important.   It included the following books: "Allgemeine Geschichte der Pflanzengifte" (1777); "Einleitung in die Chemie" (1780); "Einleitung in die Pharmazie" (1781); "Chemische Grundzüge der Gewerbkunde" (1795); and particularly the three-volume "Geschichte der Chemie" (1797–99).   This latter work was the first attempt to present an extended discussion of the history of the development of chemistry.   Of permanent value are the careful compilations of the contents of the writings of earlier authors, but in contrast are the incorrect evaluations of the work of the "ancients," *e. g.,* the dubbing of Paracelsus as a "gold cook," "quack," "charlatan," etc., and Glauber as the "Paracelsus of the seventeenth century."

(7)   Leopold Gmelin[12] (b. 1788 at Göttingen, d. 1853 at Heidelberg) was the youngest son of J. F. Gmelin (compare (6)).   After finishing the course at the lyceum at Göttingen, he, at 16, attended his father's lectures on mineralogy.   In 1804 he was sent to Tübingen to work in the family apothecary's shop, and (also traditionally) to study at the university there. He pursued the courses in medicine and mathematics; from 1805 to 1809 he was at Göttingen for medicine and chemistry (under Stromeyer).   He took his medical degree at Göttingen in 1812;   the dissertation was

[9] OESPER, R., J. CHEM. EDUC., 19, 134 (1942).
[10] BERZELIUS, J. J., "Reiseerinnerungen aus Deutschland," Verlag Chemie, 1948, p. 2 ff.   See also OESPER, R., J. CHEM. EDUC., 26, 202 (1949).

[11] Stromeyer discovered cadmium in 1817.   His most distinguished student was Robert Bunsen (1828–31) and his eminent successor (1836) in the chair at Göttingen was Friedrich Wöhler (1800–82).   Compare J. CHEM. EDUC., 30, 202 (1953).
[12] Compare PIETSCH, E., *Ber.,* 72A, 5 (1939), and also the papers issued by Pietsch in 1938 to commemorate the 150th anniversary of Gmelin's birth.

Gmelin Apotheke in Tübingen: Corner House on Left

based on an experimental study he had made in Vienna on "The black pigment of steers' and calves' eyes." After a stay in Italy (1812–13) he carried out an analytical investigation under Stromeyer's guidance on the mineral haüynite (1813) and habilitated with this study at Heidelberg in the fall of 1813. The very next year he was advanced to extraordinary professor. In 1814–15 he and his cousin Christian Gottlob (compare (5)) made a study trip to Paris. In 1817, he was promoted to ordinary professor of chemistry (and medicine, as he signed himself) in the medical faculty at Heidelberg. His three-volume "Handbuch der theoretischen Chemie" appeared in 1817–19. Altogether, very busy and fruitful years. The family motto, *Festina lente*, would have seemed to advocate a less hectic pace.

Gmelin turned gray early; by his fifth decade he was snow-white "like a blooming cherry tree."

He lectured on inorganic and organic chemistry, analytical chemistry, metallurgy (with excursions), and materia medica. His delivery was often hesitant and punctuated with sudden interruptions. The first stroke in the spring of 1848 was followed by others, and in 1851 he asked for retirement. This success-filled life came to an end on April 4, 1853.

Gmelin's experimental activities fell principally in the years (1815) 1820–47.[13] He put out about 28 papers on mineralogical-inorganic topics, and 20 of physiological-organic nature. Of greater scientific interest are the later (after 1820) papers, in which he had the collaboration of Friedrich Tiedemann (1781–1861), professor of anatomy and physiology at Heidelberg. They made a physiological-chemical study of digestion (1820–26), the gall and blood; and in the course of their work they isolated, for the first time, taurin (in ox-gall, 1824), cholic acid, hematin (in blood), pancreatin (1826), and they discovered that saliva contains potassium thiocyanate. In the mineralogical-inorganic field, the important points were: the study of lapis lazuli (1815, compare (5)); the conversion of yellow prussiate of potash into the red salt (1822) (the latter compound is his discovery); the discovery of the mysterious croconic acid on the reduction of $K_2CO_3$ by carbon (1825).

Leopold Gmelin's fame rests primarily on his great literary feat, his "Handbuch der theoretischen Chemie." It appeared first (1817) in three thin volumes, and in successive editions, issued to the year of his death, grew into a multi-volume reference work. It is the product of an exemplary concentration of effort on this simple problem: To arrange systematically all the precisely determined facts concerning every element and compound, to state these facts succinctly and accurately, and also to give the pertinent references to the literature. In this task he proceeded logically in a calm and critically inquiring manner, regarding every

Johann Friedrich Gmelin (1748–1804)

speculation as hazardous. "Nothing was in keeping with the times except the temperate consideration of observations, and Gmelin was the right man to represent a tendency of this kind. He united boundless industry with wide knowledge and he understood how to turn both of these qualities to account in his *Handbook*. In adducing facts, completeness and conscientiousness were his watchwords, and these were adhered to."[14] From the first edition on, and for the first time in German textbooks, he employed the conceptual formulation "organic chemistry"; he speaks of the "imponderable elements" (heat, light, electricity) and devotes considerable space to them along with the "ponderable elements." He also coined new terms, *e. g.*, "Traubensäure" in place of "Vogesensäure," "Ester" instead of "Saureäther," "ketones" as a class name. He used the Laurent "Nucleus Theory" as the basis for the systematization of the organic compounds, and gives names to the "nuclei" (*radicaux*). His "Handbuch der Chemie" was *the* book of chemistry for more than a generation, and it exerted a fundamental influence on the development of the science, not only through its character as a canon of facts, but also because of the theoretical views presented in it. However, the latter proved to be a disturbing and retarding influence on the development of the atomic views, particularly of the Berzelian system of atomic weights. Contrary to

---

[13] The period 1816–19 shows a definite pause in his experimental studies. He was occupied with preparations for his lectures and the composition of the first edition of his "Handbuch" (1817–19).

[14] LADENBURG, A., "History of Chemistry," translated by L. DOBBIN, Edinburgh, 1900, p. 174.

the latter, Gmelin and his school advocated the theory of the stoichiometrically determinable combining weights or equivalents[15] such as $H = 1$, $O = 8$, $C = 6$, $S = 16$, water $= HO$, etc. The chemical valence of the elements did not enter as the prime factor, and the atomic and molecular theories were regarded as incidental. The confusion in the chemical literature with respect to the ideas of atom-equivalent and molecule increased to such an extent that the editor of the *Journal für praktische Chemie* (Erdmann in Leipzig) wrote: "Every paper must be preceded by a key as in music." The resolution of this critical state was the objective of the famous convention (the first international chemical congress) which met at Karlsruhe (Baden) in September, 1860, at the invitation of Kekulé, Wurtz, and Weltzien.[16] All this might be set down as a black mark against Gmelin when one is considering the lasting values of his career.[17]

One of Gmelin's great services was his persuading the young Wöhler to turn to chemistry. He induced the 23-year-old medical doctor to study chemistry with Berzelius at Stockholm (compare (5)) and thus nipped in the bud Wöhler's intention to become a practicing obstetrician.[18]

In 1922 the Deutsche Chemische Gesellschaft assumed the continuation of the monumental "Handbuch der anorganischen Chemie" (eighth edition). The work (which from the fifth edition on had not been supervised by Gmelin himself) had to be fundamentally revamped both internally and externally. The name "Gmelin" was retained as a symbol of the scientific purpose of the new work. Since 1935 the editorial board has been under the direction of Erich Pietsch.[19] The activities are now centered at Clausthal, the Gmelin Institut, which was created by Pietsch, whose energy and initiative successfully made possible the move from Berlin after the Hofmann Haus was destroyed. He mobilized the material assistance of the ERP, which is thus furnishing another instance of the cooperation of the U. S. A. for the rebuilding of Germany, and under the sign of the old "Gmelin" there has emerged a new spiritual bond between our two cultures.

These "brief biographies" have presented data of interest not only regarding the history of chemistry and chemical personalities but also applying to general and university history. The first point of interest is the fact that all of these chemists went through the medical course of study and came to chemistry with the M.D. degree and uniformly at a young age (18–21 years). Secondly, to us moderns it seems strange that these doctors immediately went on "tours" instead of going into the laboratory to deepen their chemical knowledge by research. Thirdly, these journeys, usually of about two years' duration, seemed to be adequate qualifications for appointment for a chemical chair. It is a fair question: when and where was the chemical education obtained? Or, in those days was there really a chemical curriculum and was laboratory instruction actually available?

The science which Paracelsus[20] had once established through a revolutionary overturning of academic tradition had persisted as iatrochemistry through three centuries, and as late as 1840 Liebig[21] wrote concerning the recent past: "Chemistry was the handmaiden of the physician, for whom she prepared purgatives and emetics; ingrafted in the medical faculties she could not attain independence. Only the medical student learned to know her of necessity; except for him and the pharmacy student she did not exist."

Consequently, at the beginning of the nineteenth century there still persisted this spiritual and practical dependence of chemistry on medicine in the Paracelsian sense. This fact refutes[22] the view that Robert Boyle endowed chemistry with new goals and fundamentals, and that he was the "founder of modern chemistry."[23] The crucial point was the separation of chemistry from medicine—in spirit and doctrine—by the removal of chemistry from the medical faculty and its inclusion in the philosophical faculty as an independent discipline. The first to take this anti-Paracelsian step was the Weimarian minister, poet, and scientist J. W. Goethe[24] who, in 1789, without the consent of the University of Jena, appointed the apothecary J. F. Göttling (1753–1809) as professor of chemistry in the philosophical faculty and designated as his successor (from 1810) the gifted J. W. Döbereiner (1780–1849).[25] And did not the 21-year old Liebig go (1824) from Gay-Lussac's private laboratory in Paris directly to a professorship in the philosophical faculty at Giessen, by appointment and not by election?[26] Only then was the way indicated and made free for chemistry to live a scientific life of its own, and also for the second cardinal question: instruction in a chemistry laboratory. Gradually the viewpoint prevailed that old, poorly heated "palace kitchens" (as in Tübingen and Jena) were *not* still good enough for chemistry, and that secularized monastic buildings with scanty facilities and maintenance funds—despite the monkish admonition: *ora et labora*—were not fit places for chemical instruction and research (as had been the case in Heidelberg and Breslau, for instance).

Hence, in spite of the limitations imposed on them, the Gmelins, as teachers and augmenters of chemical

[15] VON MEYER, E., "History of Chemistry," translated by G. McGowan, New York, **1906**, pp. 237, 302, 306.

[16] DEMILT, C., *Chymia*, **1**, 153–69 (1948).

[17] It must, however, be pointed out that according to the preface in the 4th edition of the "Handbuch" (since 1843) Gmelin "definitely has gone over to the atomic hypothesis."

[18] In a sense, Wöhler did realize his youthful intentions, since as the great synthesist he officiated at the "birth" of many new chemical "individuals."

[19] OESPER, R., J. CHEM. EDUC., **26**, 251 (1949).

[20] PARACELSUS, "Paragranum," **1530**.

[21] LIEBIG, J., *Ann.*, **34**, 102 (1840).

[22] WALDEN, P., *Naturwissenschaften*, **37**, 169–72 (1950); compare also SARTON, G., *Chymia*, **3**, 163, 189 (1950).

[23] PARTINGTON, J., "A Short History of Chemistry," London, **1937**, p. 67.

[24] WALDEN, P., *Naturw. Rundschau*, **2**, 536–43 (1949).

[25] PRANDTL, W., J. CHEM. EDUC., **27**, 175 (1950).

[26] OESPER, R., J. CHEM. EDUC., **4**, 1461 (1927).

facts, worked unswervingly as pioneers in the movement for the establishment of an independent science of chemistry, actuated directly by the impressions they had gained on their educational journeys. From first to last, they were conscious of the honorable and responsible tradition of the name *Gmelin*.

# ● LIEBIG AND HIS AMERICAN PUPILS

### H. S. VAN KLOOSTER
Rensselaer Polytechnic Institute, Troy, New York

IN AN article published in THIS JOURNAL in 1932 (*1*), Browne gave some brief biographical sketches of eight of Wöhler's most outstanding American pupils. One of them was H. B. Nason, for 30 years teacher at Rensselaer Polytechnic Institute. The fact that Wöhler's earliest American pupil, James C. Booth of Philadelphia (1810–88), who came to him in Cassel in 1833, was a student of Amos Eaton, the founder and first professor of the Institute, led to a search for other American students of chemistry who went to Göttingen during Wöhler's professorship (1836–80) at that famous center of chemical research. The results of this study were published in 1944 (*2*). Dr. Browne also mentions seven outstanding American pupils of Liebig and notes that they "are only a few of the leading American teachers of chemistry who were schooled under Liebig. The list could be greatly extended."

In view of the fact that one of the seven men mentioned was Eben N. Horsford, a pupil of Amos Eaton, the writer recently made a search for other noted pupils of Liebig in this country. Although the results were disappointing, some interesting data concerning Horsford have recently become available which induced the writer to present the results of his exploration into this corner of the past history of American chemists. To this end the first edition of "American Men of Science," published in 1906, was carefully examined. Only three more names turned up in addition to those mentioned in Browne's article. A search through Liebig's *Annalen* from 1834 to 1873, the year Liebig died, was also made. Only one new name was found, that of Ogden R. Rood of New Haven.

The question may be raised why there are so few American pupils of Liebig compared with the very large number of Wöhler's pupils in this country. The obvious explanation is as follows. Liebig started his laboratory in 1824 and left Giessen in 1852 to go to Munich. He was then at the height of his career, 50 years old, but exhausted and tired of his daily contact with students. Before coming to Munich he had stipulated that he was to be relieved entirely from laboratory work, and would confine himself exclusively to lecturing. He was free, however, to continue his own research in a small private laboratory, with post-doctorate assistants. More and more, and particularly after 1860, he worked at his desk, revising his texts and his "chemical letters" and replying to his many opponents in various countries.

## JOHN LAWRENCE SMITH

John Lawrence Smith (1818–83), Liebig's first pupil from this side of the Atlantic, was a Southerner. He entered the University of Virginia in 1835, studying chemistry and civil engineering for two years. In 1838 he enrolled in the Medical College of his home state of South Carolina and became an M.D. in 1840. He then went abroad for further study, first in Paris, with Orfila, Dumas, and Elie de Beaumont, and then in Giessen. Here he decided to make chemistry his life's work. He undertook at Liebig's suggestion the study of spermaceti. The results were published in the *Annalen* (**42**, 241 (1842)) under the heading "On the composition of spermaceti and its oxidation by nitric acid." He returned to Charleston in 1843. Some research that he had done on certain soils of his native state led to his selection by James Buchanan, then Secretary of State and later President (1857–61), to go to Turkey to advise the government of that country on the feasibility of cotton culture there. On his arrival in 1847 he was diverted to study the mineral resources of the Turkish Empire. A brief communication on two new minerals, one of which he named Liebigit, was published in the *Annalen* (**66**, 253 (1848)). Smith came back to America in 1850, became professor of chemistry at the University of Virginia in 1852 and in 1854 professor of medical chemistry and toxicology at the University of Louisville, which chair he held until 1866. He was a prolific writer; a total of 145 papers is listed in his bibliography. He was highly regarded professionally, being president of the American Association for the Advancement of Science in 1874, and president of the American Chemical Society in 1877. A more detailed account of his life and work may be found in E. F. Smith's article on mineral chemistry (*3*) and in an illustrated article by Sampey (*4*).

## EBEN NORTON HORSFORD

Liebig's second pupil from America was Eben Norton Horsford (1818–93), who started out in life as a civil engineer, became a chemist later on, then professor, inventor, and manufacturer, and finally, on retiring from business, a hobbyist and philanthropist. He was born in Moskow, Livingston County, New York, on July 27, 1818, and attended Temple Hill High School in Genesee, New York. He entered the Rensselaer Institute in September, 1837, finished a two-year course within one year, and graduated with the class of 1838 as a civil engineer. After graduation, Horsford went for six weeks to the Adirondack iron mines to survey the mines and to fix sites for dams. On reporting his findings in Albany he was engaged by Hall for a survey of New York State on the division west of Albany, which kept him occupied for two years. At the same time he assisted Dr. Simmons with his chemical lectures at the

Eben Norton Horsford

Albany Female Academy during the winter. This led to his appointment there as a science teacher in 1840. He kept this position until some time in 1844. An essay on mechanical powers which he had prepared, earned him a gold medal from the Young Men's Association in Albany. He did some work in cooperation with Samuel Morse, the well-known inventor of the first practical telegraph; he established the first daguerreotype gallery in Albany in partnership with Thomas Cushman; he also found time to give some lectures on chemistry at Newark College in Delaware in 1843 and 1844. Horsford's growing reputation brought him in contact with John W. Webster, professor of chemistry at Harvard University. Webster, being familiar with Liebig's "Organic Chemistry in Its Application to Agriculture and Physiology," first published in 1841, urged him to go to Giessen. This involved considerable expense and would have consumed more than his savings. He was helped by friends in Albany, who were willing to pay for part of the cost of the trip and to lend him funds to go abroad. One of them was Luther Tucker (1802–73), a highly influential member of the New York State Agricultural Society, and the owner and publisher of *The Cultivator*,[1] a monthly farm paper.

Horsford's first interview with the great man "whose genius has given such impulse to chemical and agricul-

[1] *The Cultivator* carried on its masthead the motto: "To improve the soil and the mind."

tural science" was in Liebig's private laboratory and the reception seemed "rather that of a military officer than of a scientific man." Horsford, while being conducted through the various rooms of the laboratory, felt that working and thinking were the characteristic attributes of the place. Even conversation was carried on in an undertone as if it were contraband. The visitor was told, "You may converse in English two or three days, but not more." This was said without a smile and impressed upon the listener the necessity of study.

The first lecture that Horsford attended was in a room with about a hundred students (including a number of the medical class) and dealt with organic chemistry. When the lecture was about to begin, the murmur of conversation subsided to a whisper, the whole audience rose and Liebig, acknowledging the greeting, entered. Horsford describes the lecture as follows:

What it was about, I was able to see from the formula on the blackboard and from a word now and then which I understood, but I was too much absorbed with the manner, to give much attention to what he said. He is perhaps two or three inches less than six feet, and stands quite erect, though a little rounding of the shoulders from much writing, labor, and study, might be seen if made the special object of search. His figure is slender rather than stout, which makes him appear taller than he really is. All his movements, and particularly those connected with demonstration, experiment, or illustration, are graceful to a degree which I have not seen equaled in any lecturer. To see him hold in the same hand three glass test tubes and an equal number of stoppers, while with the other he pours from vessels containing reagents, at first a little excited my surprise. . . . There is an expression of thought in all his attitudes and movements, which I could have scarcely believed upon the mere relation, and which the crayon cannot commit to paper; whether with the chalk and sponge, or with the index finger along the chin and nose, presenting that most singular of all German attitudes, or in gesticulation, or with apparatus, it is all the same. He is all mind—and it beams as distinctly through its corporeal tenement, as his chemical compounds are seen through the vessels that contain them. His detail of chemical decompositions and recompositions is clear and expressed without any circumlocution in terms, comprehended by everyone. Occasionally these details bring him to review some investigations and theories of his own, and then a new animation is superadded to his ordinary bearing, and the illustrations are dramatic. His large eyes expand, and his features seem to glow. The gesticulations are sometimes so happy and so numerous, that I have fancied one might understand some of his themes even if he were unable to hear.

His notes consist of a few formulas, written out upon two or three little strips of paper; and yet his lectures are as systematic as if elaborated with the greatest care. I have heard the remark made that Liebig is not an expounder of chemistry or an operator in chemistry but chemistry itself. It is not difficult to see some of the probable data upon which this notion is founded. For example, he enters the laboratory, where he is surrounded by gentlemen engaged in a great variety of investigations. Here is one upon benzoic acid, there one upon hippuric acid, there one upon allantoin, there one upon the cyanogen compounds, here one upon a new gas, here one upon cheese, there others upon bread, and so on, all of them engaged in original investigation. He is ready to tell them the results for which they may look. Such is his familiarity with every fact in known chemistry, that its analogies are perpetually present, and enable him to premise almost anything with regard to problematical investigations. This vigilant surveillance, this powerful local memory, this readiness in affording explanation in all difficult matters connected with chemistry have induced the expression of the above opinion. However, Liebig has quite deprived the opinion of its poetry, for he has said, for the encouragement of all his pupils, that every fact in the science cost him labor to acquire and labor to retain; and though now ready to pronounce upon the history and properties of every known organic and inorganic compound, he has acquired this prodigious mass of scientific information, only with prodigious labor.

It is interesting to compare Horsford's account of a lecture by Liebig with that of an earlier student, Carl Vogt (1817–95) who attended Liebig's lectures regularly in the summer semester of 1834. A verbatim report of part of a lecture, translated into English, appeared in THIS JOURNAL in 1936 (5). Of Liebig's lectures in Munich, Volhard (6), who was his *fidus Achates* in those years, said that they were neither very fluent nor perfect, frequently even halting with unmotivated pauses. His mind seemed to be wandering. After a while his consciousness returned and he resumed the thread of his interrupted story.

Horsford's day in Giessen began at 5:30 A.M. After consuming a biscuit and a cup of milk (his regular breakfast) he attended a lecture by Fresenius on sugar at 6:15; at 7:00, another lecture by Ropp on crystallography. He started working in the laboratory at 8:15. At 11:05, Horsford listened, with about 90 others, to Liebig's lecture (given every weekday) till about 12:30. Notes were taken in ink to recall to mind the mass of facts and theories given. The midday meal, at his lodgings, consisted of a kind of bread and milk soup, a bit of wild swine flesh, potatoes, and a dessert. Relaxation after dinner was furnished by perusing the *Cultivator*, *Argus*, and *Journal* sent by obliging friends in Albany. The rest of the afternoon was again spent in the laboratory till 6:30. A walk for a mile and a swim in the Lahn followed and then back to his room at 8:00 for a luxurious (?) supper of biscuit and milk. The rest of the evening was spent calculating analyses, reading the chemical journals, and closing the affairs of the day. Presumably not every day was as strenuous as this particular day, an account of which Horsford gave in a letter to Tucker.

The work Horsford performed at Liebig's suggestion dealt with the value of different vegetable nutrients, as deduced from their nitrogen content. It involved the analysis of wheat, rye, oats, corn, and the ash of clover. He also worked on the ammonia content of glaciers, and finally on glycocoll and some of its decomposition products. All of this was published in the *Annalen* and read before the members of the Albany Institute on Horsford's return to Albany in the spring of 1846. He did not stay long enough in Giessen to obtain a Ph.D. in spite of the fact that all further tuition fees were to be waived in case he should decide to remain. He had two good reasons: he did not want to incur more debts, and he needed a job badly in order to marry the girl he had left behind. He did not have to wait very long. Thanks to the excellent recommendations of Liebig and Webster he was appointed in 1847 to the Rumford professorship of science as applied to the arts, at Harvard University. On August 4, 1847, he married Mary L. Gardiner, who died in 1856, leaving him four daughters. Two years later he married his sister-in-law Phoebe Gardiner by whom he had one daughter. Horsford was fortunate in being able to interest Abbot Lawrence (1792–1855), a successful businessman and manufacturer, in the promotion of education in science. With a donation of $50,000 for the establishment of a scientific school, to be named after the donor, Horsford organized its studies on the example of Liebig's laboratory and started lecturing and teaching analytical chemistry to individual students. He was a good lecturer with a sanguine, enthusiastic temperament, and directed the new school for 16 years. Being of a practical turn of mind, he became absorbed in the study of foods, as is shown by many of his articles published in Silliman's *American Journal of Science*, in the *Memoirs of the American Academy of Arts and Sciences* and in the *Proceedings of the American Association for the Advancement of Science*. In 1861 he published a book on "Theory and Art of Breadmaking." He took out numerous patents on his inventions, some of which dealt with a new baking powder in which acid phosphate was used. This led to the establishment (in 1856) of the Rumford Chemical Works in Providence, Rhode Island, which is still in operation.

These outside activities took up a good deal of Horsford's time so that in his later years at the school most of the teaching was done by his assistant C. W. Eliot (1834–1926). Horsford resigned in 1863 to devote all his time to his business. He was succeeded by Wolcott Gibbs, much to the regret of Eliot, who had hoped to succeed Horsford. Six years later, however, Eliot became president of Harvard University. Horsford prospered to such an extent that he could afford to indulge in a number of hobbies and, being blessed with five daughters, spent part of his acquired wealth in supplying Wellesley College with books and scientific apparatus. He continued to live in Cambridge until his death on January 1, 1893. The accompanying picture of Horsford represents him in middle age. Another one taken when he was well over 60 appeared in THIS JOURNAL in 1940 (7).

## OLIVER WOLCOTT GIBBS

When Horsford, a rural up-state New Yorker, left, a city-bred New Yorker appeared in Liebig's laboratory. This was Oliver Wolcott Gibbs (1822–1908), the gifted son of well-to-do parents, who enjoyed all the advantages that wealth and standing can confer. He graduated from Columbia (at that time still a college) in 1841, and spent some time as assistant to Robert Hare in Philadelphia. In 1845 the College of Physicians and Surgeons in New York awarded him an M.D. degree. Instead of starting a practice, Gibbs went abroad (1845–48) to study chemistry, first in Germany, under K. F. Rammelsberg (1813–99), then under Heinrich Rose (1795–1864) for a whole year, and finally under Liebig. Gibbs arrived in Giessen at the time Horsford left. Apart from the daily contact with Liebig and his students, he undertook no doctoral work at Giessen, and his publications in the *Annalen* of 1853 and later refer to research carried out in America. On leaving Giessen, Gibbs spent a year in Paris, attending the lectures of Laurent, Dumas, and Regnault. Returning home in 1848, he became professor of chemistry at the College of the City of New York, remaining there for 14 years. In 1863 he succeeded Horsford as Rumford professor, and took charge of the laboratory of the Lawrence Scientific School. When the school was consolidated with the chemistry department of Harvard in 1871, Gibbs confined himself to lecturing in spectroscopy and thermodynamics, while maintaining a private laboratory. Retiring at 65, he continued research for ten more years. He died at his estate in Newport, Rhode Island, in 1908. He was a founder and at one time president of the National Academy of Sciences and was chosen an honorary member of the German, the English, and the American Chemical Societies. His many chemical achievements were recorded in 1909 by Th. W. Richards in a lengthy obituary (8). An excellent picture of Gibbs was published in THIS JOURNAL in 1929 (9).

## CHARLES MAYER WETHERILL

The next American pupil of Liebig was Charles Mayer Wetherill (1825–71), on whose life and work a lengthy illustrated biography was published in 1929 (10). A few brief data will therefore suffice here. Wetherill was born and educated in Philadelphia, where he graduated from the University in 1845. He then spent one year at the analytical laboratory of Booth and Boyé and continued his studies abroad, first in Paris and then in Giessen. He matriculated there on November 6, 1847, and obtained his Ph.D. on May 30, 1848, with a thesis "Über Schwefelsaures Aethyloxyd und dessen Zersetsungsproducte mit Wasser" which was published in the *Annalen* (**66**, 117 (1848)). Wetherill opened a laboratory of his own, which he conducted till 1853. After his marriage in 1856 he moved to Lafayette, Indiana, where he published a treatise on the manufacture of vinegar in 1860. In 1862 he became the first chemist connected with the newly created Department of Agriculture. In 1864 he was appointed professor of chemistry at the newly founded Lehigh University, in Bethlehem, Pennsylvania. He died there of heart failure in 1871.

## JOHN ADDISON PORTER

The last American to study under Liebig in Giessen was John Addison Porter (1822–66), a native New Yorker, born in Catskill on May 15, 1822. He entered Yale College in 1838 and graduated in 1842. In May 1844 he was appointed tutor in Delaware College in Newark, New Jersey, which position he resigned in 1847 to go to Germany, where he studied agricultural chemistry under Liebig. Porter's researches dealing with ash analyses of human excrements, of oats, and of hay were published in the *Annalen* in three brief communications in 1849 and 1850. On his return to America Porter was for a few months assistant to Horsford. From Cambridge he went to Brown

University and from there to Yale where he succeeded Norton as professor of analytical and agricultural chemistry in 1852. Yale University conferred an honorary M.D. on Porter in 1854. Porter succeeded in interesting his father-in-law, Joseph E. Sheffield, in the Yale Scientific School and because of his many donations it was named the Sheffield Scientific School in 1861. Porter was its first dean of the faculty, and in 1862 also became professor of organic chemistry. He resigned in 1864 because of poor health and died on August 25, 1866.

## FREDERIC AUGUSTUS GENTH

One more name can be added to those given above, that of Frederic Augustus Genth (1820–93), a countryman of Liebig. Born at Wächtersbach in Hessen Kassel on May 17, 1820, he studied (as was frequently the custom in Germany) at several different universities: first at Heidelberg, then at Giessen (around 1843), and finally at Marburg, where he obtained his Ph.D. under Bunsen in 1845. He established himself as Privat-dozent in mineralogy and chemistry at Marburg but then abandoned his plans for a university career and emigrated to America in 1848, where he opened a laboratory for analytical chemistry, first in Baltimore and later in Philadelphia. When the chair of chemistry and mineralogy at the University of Pennsylvania became vacant in 1871 it was offered to Weatherill, and on his sudden death, to Genth, who taught there from 1872 to 1888. He resigned in 1888 to resume his private practice. He died on February 2, 1893. Genth's first work, on masopin, a new kind of resin, was undertaken at Liebig's request. It was published in the *Annalen* in 1843 (**46**, 124 (1843)). Three more papers appeared in the *Annalen* for 1845 and 1846. These were sent to Liebig from Marburg. Some more research, carried out in Philadelphia, was published in the *Annalen* in 1851 and 1852. Genth's later work was exclusively on mineral chemistry in which field he was pre-eminent. He is credited with the discovery of 20 new minerals. Dr. Edgar Fahs Smith, who knew Genth well, wrote a commemorative article in 1926 (3).

## SAMUEL WILLIAM JOHNSON

Of the few Americans who went to Liebig in the final 20 years of his life, the best known is Samuel William Johnson (1830–1909). Born on July 3, 1830, at Kingsboro, New York, he spent his boyhood on his father's farm at Deer River, New York, and then attended Lowville Academy where he received his first instruction in chemistry. While still of precollege age he wrote an essay, "On fixing ammonia," which was published in the August, 1847, issue of Luther Tucker's *Cultivator*. In 1848 he accepted an instructorship at Flushing Institute on Long Island. The following year he entered Yale University where he studied chemistry under Norton, after which he taught chemistry, physics, and human physiology at the State Normal School in Albany for one year (1851–52). On the advice of Norton he went abroad for two years (1853–55), first to Leipzig where he took up analytical chemistry under O. L. Erdmann (1804–69) and then to Munich where he obtained permission to work in Liebig's private laboratory. Here he investigated the ashes of various plants and the contents of soils and streams, and also made a study of the alkali salts of mucic acid. The results were published in two articles in the *Annalen* of 1855. Liebig was so well pleased with his pupil that he asked Johnson to translate a polemical paper against J. B. Lawes into English. It was published the same year in Tucker's *Country Gentleman*. On his return to America Johnson was appointed professor of analytical chemistry at the Yale Scientific School in 1856. The next year, when Yale conferred an honorary M.A. on Johnson, he also taught agricultural chemistry which he kept up for 40 years (until 1896). Although he had little time for research in his later years, he acquired an encyclopedic knowledge of agriculture and agricultural chemistry. His two books, "How Crops Grow" and "How Crops Feed," published in 1868 and 1870, became standard texts and gained wide circulation both here and abroad (in translation into six other languages). To chemists in this country Johnson is known through his translation of Fresenius' manuals. As early as 1856 Johnson started to examine commercial fertilizers and thus became responsible for the introduction of regulatory measures. He was also an early advocate of state agricultural experiment stations, and for 23 years (1877–1900) was director of the Connecticut Agricultural Experiment Station. In 1888 he induced Osborne to undertake a study of the vegetable proteins, a step which Vickery (*11*) considers one of the greatest of Johnson's contributions to science in view of the many outstanding accomplishments of Osborne and his co-workers. Johnson was professionally connected with the activities of the American Chemical Society and was its president in 1878. He died on July 21, 1909.

Only brief mention is made here of three other American chemists who were students in Munich in Liebig's time. They attended Liebig's lectures but received laboratory instruction from his able assistant Volhard, and might better be classified as pupils of Volhard. William H. Brewer (1828–1910) studied in Munich in 1858 and was professor of agriculture at Yale from 1864 to 1903 (*12*). Henry Adam Weber (1845–1912), who taught agricultural chemistry at Ohio State University from 1884 to 1897, studied in Munich around 1868 (*13*). Edward Renouf (1848–1934) spent two semesters in Munich (1867–68) and taught at Johns Hopkins from 1888 to 1911 (*14*).

Two items may finally be added here to support the writer's ideas regarding the apparently small number of American pupils of Liebig. As Volhard (*6*) has pointed out, there were at the beginning only pharmacists in Liebig's laboratory, and it took some time before chemistry students also went to Giessen. When

James C. Booth, having worked a year with Wöhler in Cassel (1833–34), wanted to go elsewhere for further study, his choice was not Liebig, but Berzelius. The latter considered himself too old to be of further help to Booth, who then went to Vienna and later to Berlin, to study under Gustav Magnus (1802–70),

Samuel William Johnson

a pupil of Berzelius. The movement of foreign students to Giessen, which did not start in earnest until around 1842, when Liebig's famous book made its triumphant march around the world, lost its momentum abruptly with Liebig's departure for Munich in 1852.

## LITERATURE CITED

(1) BROWNE, C. A., J. CHEM. EDUC., 9, 696 (1932).
(2) VAN KLOOSTER, H. S., J. CHEM. EDUC., 21, 158 (1944).
(3) SMITH, E. F., *J. Am. Chem. Soc.*, Golden Jubilee Number, 48, 71 (1926).
(4) SAMPEY, J. R., J. CHEM. EDUC., 5, 123 (1928).
(5) GOOD, H. G., J. CHEM. EDUC., 13, 557 (1936).
(6) VOLHARD, J., *Ann.*, 328, 1–40 (1903).
(7) BLISS, A. D., J. CHEM. EDUC., 17, 353 (1940).
(8) RICHARDS, Th. W., *Ber.*, 42, 5037 (1909).
(9) SMITH, E. F., J. CHEM. EDUC., 6, 1219 (1929).
(10) *Ibid.*, 1076, 1215, 1461, 1668, 1916, 2160.
(11) VICKERY, H. B., J. CHEM. EDUC., 19, 73 (1942).
(12) JOHNSON, A., *Editor*, "Dictionary of American Biography," Vol. III, C. Scribner's Sons, New York, 1929, p. 25.
(13) MALONE, DUMAS, *Editor*, "Dictionary of American Biography," Vol. XIX, 1936, p. 582.
(14) CATTELL, J. McK., AND JAQUES CATTELL, *Editors*, "American Men of Science," 4th ed., The Science Press, Lancaster, Pennsylvania, 1927, p. 809.

# Friedrich Wöhler and His American Pupils

## H. S. VAN KLOOSTER

*Rensselaer Polytechnic Institute, Troy, New York*

AMONG the 19th century masters of chemistry whose fame as investigators and teachers has spread to all corners of the globe, Friedrich Wöhler occupies a unique position. Of the hundreds of Americans who went abroad for postgraduate training a considerable number spent one or more semesters at the Hanoverian city of Göttingen where Wöhler taught for nearly half a century. Göttingen, the third in the list of four German universities most favored by Americans (the other three being Berlin, Leipzig, and Heidelberg), had close to 1200 American students in the period from 1810 to 1910 and of this number about 200 studied chemistry (1). Numerous colleges and universities had or still have on their staff one or more professors who at one time were students at the George Augustus University, founded in 1735 under the auspices of George II of England (1683–1760) who was also Elector of Hanover. Taking as an example the institution with which the writer has been connected for 25 years, we find no fewer than eight men on the Institute faculty who received their training, wholly or partly, at Göttingen and of these, four came under the influence of Wöhler. As a matter of fact, the first alumnus of the Rensselaer Institute to cross the Atlantic (in 1833) for further study, *viz.*, James Curtis Booth (1810–88) was the first American pupil of Wöhler (2). Booth, who taught at the Institute in 1831, was no doubt attracted by Wöhler's early successes in synthesizing urea (1828) and in isolating beryllium and aluminum (1827). At that time Wöhler was not yet a university professor, but taught at a newly founded industrial school (Gewerbe Schule) in Cassel. His fame did not spread so rapidly as that of his noted contemporary, friend, and co-worker, Liebig. It was only in the early fifties, when Wöhler had practically completed his lifework as a creative chemist, though he was to continue his teaching career for another 30 years, that American students of chemistry went to Göttingen to study under Wöhler.

The earliest of these American chemists were Newton Spaulding Manrosz (1828–62) and William Smith Clark (1826–86). On March 18, 1852, Wöhler wrote to Liebig: "I am sending an article by Manrosz on the 'artificial production of crystallized minerals.'" This was Manrosz' doctoral thesis which was published in the *Annalen* (**82**, 348). Manrosz, a graduate of Yale (1850), taught later at Amherst (1861–62) and found an untimely death at the battle of Antietam (1862). In the same year (1852) Clark obtained his degree with a thesis on "metallic meteorites" which was, likewise, published in the *Annalen* (**82, 367**). A graduate of Amherst (1848), Clark, on his return to America became professor of chemistry at his Alma Mater. He fought in the Union Army (1861–64) and in 1868 entered upon his duties as president of the newly established Massachusetts College of Agriculture. In 1877 he took a year's leave of absence to promote the founding of the Imperial College of Agriculture in Sappora (Japan).

Another pupil of Wöhler who finished his training in 1852 was John William Mallet (1832–1910) who presented a thesis on "the chemical examination of Celtic antiquities." Mallet, an Irishman, returned to his native city of Dublin in 1853 but came to Amherst the same year at the urgent request of his friend Clark. He did not stay long but went South and finished his distinguished career in 1908 at the University of Virginia (3).

From the titles of the three theses just mentioned, it is evident that Wöhler left his pupils considerable latitude in the choice of topics, since they deal with materials found in their native country. These investigations were published under single and not joint authorship. It is noteworthy that during Wöhler's half century of active work most of his contributions appear under his own name. Apart from some 15 articles published with Liebig there are barely half a dozen in the *Annalen* that indicate close cooperation between master and pupil. Obviously, Wöhler, in his later years was more active as a teacher than as a researcher. The direction of the many "practica" was left to his assistants, Fittig, Limprecht, von Uslar, and others whose names are most frequently associated with the published work of his students. This is forcefully brought out in a letter to Liebig of December 29, 1871, in which he writes: "After every lecture it bothers me to realize that formerly I did not present matters the way I do now. That is why I enjoy lecturing and abhor the laboratory periods. One might like the contact with a few intelligent people but not the company of 75, most of them incompetent" (4).

Owing to his linguistic abilities and long-continued correspondence with his former teacher Berzelius whose works he had translated into German, Wöhler's literary talents were developed to such an extent that he easily became one of the foremost epistolary writers of his time. As such he endeared himself to several of his American students by furnishing them with letters of introduction to his bosom friend Liebig. Some of these are published in the "Liebig-Wöhler Briefwechsel," sometimes without mentioning the go-between. In a copy of this correspondence the writer found a letter written by Dr. Samuel P. Sadtler in which he says: "You will find on p. 310 of Vol. II the letter under date of April 20, 1871. I had just obtained my degree and was starting for a six weeks' trip to southern Germany, Switzerland, and northern Italy before returning to America. So he (W.) said, he had just written to Liebig and I should deliver it and have an opportunity of meeting Liebig which I of course appreciated very much."

CHARLES A. GOESSMANN
ABOUT 1875

In 1853 the first native Yorker to take his degree under Wöhler, Charles Aram Joy (1823–91), finished his studies at Göttingen, after a two years' stay, the customary period required to take the coveted Ph.D. degree in Germany. During the last year of his stay at the university Joy was also quite active in the affairs of the American Colony at Göttingen, of which he was the first recorded "Patriarch." His five immediate successors were also chemistry students. In fact, during the fifties the chemists formed the majority of American students (12 out of a total of 15 in the summer of 1855). On his return to America, Joy went back to his Alma Mater, Union College, as professor of chemistry. In 1857 he left for New York where he taught at Columbia University and later also at the School of Mines (1865–77) until ill health forced him to resign. Frequent mention is made in the Liebig-Wöhler correspondence of the Joys, particularly of Mrs. Joy, a native of Minden (Hanover) whom Joy had married on his second trip to Germany in 1855. Wöhler, a homely individual, whose features remind us somewhat of Lincoln, was intensely human and greatly impressed by the "eternally feminine that attracts all of us" (Goethe). The charm of the "pretty" and "witty"

Mrs. Joy was "unforgettable" and Wöhler notifies Liebig that he keeps up a lively correspondence with Mrs. Joy which he (L.) would love to read if it appeared in print.

Another pupil of Wöhler who took his doctor's degree in 1853 was Charles Anthony Goessmann (1827–1910), born in Naumburg (Hessen-Kassel), for 53 years a resident and for 42 years a citizen of the United States. His life and work have been fully described in a memorial volume issued by the Massachusetts Agricultural College in 1917 (5). After serving as an assistant to Wöhler for five years, Goessmann left for Philadelphia to become chemist and superintendent of the sugar refinery conducted by two of his Göttingen students, the brothers E. P. and J. H. Eastwick. Resigning this position in the fall of 1860, he spent the next eight years as chemist to the Onondaga Salt Company in Syracuse (New York). A few months after his appointment in Syracuse, Professor C. F. Chandler of Union College in Schenectady (New York) urged him to accept the professorship of chemistry at the Rensselaer Polytechnic Institute in nearby Troy, which had become vacant through the death of the incumbent William Elderhorst (1828–61).

WILLIAM ELDERHORST

A compatriot of Goessmann and a native of Celle (Hanover) Elderhorst as a youth had first joined the cadet corps of the Hanoverian army in which his father held the rank of lieutenant colonel. On account of his weak eyes he was discharged in 1845. He then matriculated at the University of Göttingen where he studied chemistry, mineralogy, and botany till 1850 without, however, completing the requirements for a doctor's degree. Coming to America in the fall of 1853 he spent some time in Charleston (South Carolina) and New York before he was called to Rensselaer in 1855. Here he served for six years as professor of theoretical and practical chemistry. On a trip to Venezuela in the summer of 1861 he was taken sick with yellow fever and died in Maracaibo on July 28th. (Prof. Chandler's recommendation was largely responsible for Goessmann's appointment, in the fall of 1861, as professor of chemistry and physics at Rensselaer.) This position, which gave Goessmann his first chance to teach in America and to build up a thorough course of instruction in chemistry, was on a part-time basis, occupying only the winter season when there was little activity in the salt works. Unable to discharge the duties of both positions satisfactorily, Goessmann in 1866 relinquished Troy for Syracuse. In 1868 he reëntered the teaching profession at the urgent solicitation of his former classmate Clark who had just then been made president of the Massachusetts Agricultural College at Amherst. Here Goessmann stayed for the rest of his days and accomplished his lifework as chief chemist and director of the Massachusetts Agricultural Experiment Station. In 1854 only one American student, Samuel S. Garrigues, obtained his degree in Göttingen. On his return to America, Garrigues settled in his home town, Philadelphia, as manufacturing chemist. Later on he went to Ann Arbor as state inspector of salt, in which capacity he framed, with the help and advice of Goessmann, the salt laws of Michigan.

In 1855 and 1856 there was a sizable group of a dozen American chemistry students of which no fewer than five took their doctor's degree under Wöhler. These men were the last to profit from the laboratory instruction of Goessmann. On December 20, 1855, they presented their "honored teacher" a beautiful balance with a plate bearing the names of John Dean, Chas. F. Chandler, Evan Pugh, George C. Caldwell, Edward P. Eastwick, Joseph H. Eastwick, James F. Magee, David K. Tuttle, James D. Hague, and Henry B. Nason. This was a remarkable group of men, several of whom occupied in later life prominent positions in their respective fields of activity. Two of them, Chandler and E. P. Eastwick, were among the founders and charter members of the American Chemical Society, organized in April, 1876, and three of them, Chandler, Nason, and Caldwell became president of the Society. The outstanding chemist of this team was Charles Frederick Chandler (1836–1925), one of the founders of the Columbia School of Mines and a pioneer of chemical industry in America (6). After graduation from the Lawrence Scientific School of Harvard University, Chandler in 1855, on the advice of Prof. Joy of Union College, went to Göttingen to work under Wöhler, and graduated in 1857 on a thesis dealing with the analysis of minerals. Armed with his doctor's diploma Chandler rushed back to Schenectady and found that there was no job open except that of janitor at $500 a year, which he promptly accepted. Two years later Prof. Joy was called to Columbia University, and Chandler at the age of 21 was promoted from janitor to adjunct- and shortly afterwards to full professor. In 1864 Chandler left for New York where he remained till his death in 1925.

Evan Pugh (1828–64) obtained his degree in 1856 with a thesis on "Miscellaneous chemical analyses." After some further study in Germany, he went to England where he worked for two years at the Rothhamsted Experiment Station. Having established a well-deserved reputation in agricultural chemistry he became, on his return to America, the first president and professor of chemistry at Pennsylvania State College. He has left a diary, some parts of which have been published in THIS JOURNAL (7). Pugh was an excellent scholar and a keen observer. In one of his letters he makes the remark: "Go to Wöhler and get excellent lectures embracing principles easily understood and good process instruction in the laboratory .... As a teacher he (Wöhler) is unsurpassed; his only fault (if any he has) is that he teaches too much." This agrees with what William Dittmar wrote: "As a teacher Wöhler ranks with Liebig and Berzelius. In a sense he was the greatest of the three. Berzelius never had the opportunity to teach large numbers of students in his laboratory and Liebig lacked the many-sidedness so characteristic of the Göttingen laboratory as long as it was really under Wöhler's personal direction" (8).

Another noted agricultural chemist who obtained his doctor's degree in 1856, with a thesis on the fatty acids contained in the oil of arachis hypogaea, was George C. Caldwell (1834–1907). Graduating from Harvard University in 1854, he attended the College of Agriculture at Cirencester (England) and finished his training under Wöhler and Goessmann. Upon returning to America he first taught at Pennsylvania State College and from 1867 until his retirement, at Cornell University where he became the head of the Chemical Department. In 1869 he published "Agricultural Chemical Analysis," for a good many years the standard treatise upon this subject.

Of the two Americans who finished their studies in Göttingen in 1857, viz., Nason and Tuttle, the former was, without doubt, better known among contemporary chemists.

Henry Bradford Nason (1831–96), a native of Foxborough, Massachusetts, and a graduate of Amherst (1855), entered the University of Göttingen in the fall of 1855. He studied chemistry, mineralogy, and geology and obtained his Ph.D. with a thesis on the formation of ether. Appointed professor of natural history at the Rensselaer Institute in 1858 and at the same time at Beloit College in Wisconsin, he divided his time between Troy and Beloit until 1866 when he became the successor of his former teacher Goessmann and resigned the position at Beloit. He traveled widely both here and in Europe to broaden his knowledge of mineralogy, metallurgy, and geology, which subjects he also taught in his later years at the Institute. A versatile and scholarly writer, he published a number of textbooks on qualitative analysis and determinative mineralogy, translated Wöhler's "Handbook of Mineral Analysis," and edited a revised version of Elderhorst's "Manual of Blowpipe Analysis," a popular text first published in 1856 and subsequently reissued in four editions, the last one in 1878. He was the recipient of several honorary degrees and became president of the American Chemical Society in 1890.

David K. Tuttle (1835–1915) was graduated from Harvard in 1855 and spent two years at Göttingen, obtaining his degree in 1857. The next four years he was assistant professor of chemistry at the University of Virginia. From 1861 to 1886 he was connected with various industrial works and from 1886 to his death he was assayer, melter, and refiner at the Mint in Philadelphia, a position which Booth had held before him. A patriarch of the American Colony in his student days, he was in his mature years the president of the Göttingen Verein in Philadelphia. Next to New York and Massachusetts no state has sent more students to Wöhler than Pennsylvania, and of this number a large percentage came from Philadelphia where Booth had established a training school for budding chemists in his analytical laboratory.

Elijah P. Harris (1831–1920) was the third Amherst graduate (1855) to receive his Ph.D. under Wöhler, in 1859. After six years of teaching in Victoria (British Columbia) and two in Beloit, he returned to Amherst in 1868 where he taught chemistry till his retirement in 1907. Modest and unassuming, yet forceful and a strict disciplinarian, Harris was a sturdy pioneer of science, who taught two generations of students, the best of whom (28 in all) he "sent" to the University of Göttingen. Most of these returned with a Ph.D. degree and secured prominent positions in the educational field. To them, the "Old Man," as they called him with affection, was the "Father of American chemistry teachers."

The ten Americans mentioned above, who obtained their Ph.D.'s in chemistry in the decade from 1850 to 1860 comprise over 45 per cent of a total of 22 who can be classed as pupils of Wöhler. The remaining 12 (C. Gillingham, E. Hungerford, J. Dean, E. P. Eastwick, J. H. Eastwick, J. F. Magee, J. D. Hague, E. Marsh, A. Muckle, A. P. S. Stewart, T. E. Hart, and T. Parkman) with two exceptions, stayed only one year. Most of these men went into business as consulting or manufacturing chemists with the exception of Dean, who became a practicing physician in Waltham (Massachusetts), Stewart, who taught chemistry at Lincoln (Nebraska), and Hague, who became a consulting mining engineer and manager of various mining companies. The Eastwicks ran a sugar refinery in Philadelphia which existed only a few years, whereupon the two brothers went into business independently, the older in New York as a member of the firm of Havemeyer and Eastwick and the younger in Philadelphia. Both had received their preliminary training in Booth's laboratory as had also their mutual friend, Magee.

HENRY B. NASON

From the diary and the letters of Magee, published in 1932 under the title "An American Student Abroad" (9), one gains a lively picture of the studies and wanderings of a young American chemist in Europe nearly a hundred years ago.

James Francis Magee (1834–1903), a native Philadelphian, on the completion of his high-school training, attended the Mount Airy Agricultural Institute in Germantown in 1850 and 1851. He then entered the

ELIJAH P. HARRIS

26

service of the Pennsylvania Railroad as a rodman. In the latter part of 1853 he gave up surveying and began the study of chemistry in Booth's laboratory. Here he stayed a year and a half. Provided with a recommendation from Booth he left, in the company of his friends, the Eastwicks, for Europe in the spring of 1855. After two semesters in Göttingen, he spent one term with Bunsen in Heidelberg and returned home in November, 1856, when he established himself as a manufacturing chemist, first alone and later in partnership with his friend and colleague, Garrigues. The partnership was dissolved in 1861, whereupon Magee organized with his brother Michael the firm of James F. Magee and Company. This firm, which dealt mainly in photographic chemicals, existed till 1877 when Magee retired from active business at the age of 43.

GEO. W. MAYNARD

The following extracts from Magee's letters may be of interest to present-day readers. On May 18, 1855, he wrote: "I get up every morning at five, study German to seven, when I take breakfast, go to the laboratory, remaining there till one. We hear from nine to ten a lecture on chemistry by Professor Wöhler. From one to two is dinner, then we return to the laboratory again till six, when I generally walk till seven, at which time I take supper. In the evening I read chemistry till ten, then I retire." Speaking of his fellow compatriots he says: "America has a delegation here of which she need not be ashamed. All study hard and late and make good use of their time. We associate but very little with the German students whose only pleasure seems to be in drinking beer, smoking pipes, and fighting duels, none of which are pleasant amusements for the Americans." Comparing the facilities at Göttingen with those of Heidelberg where he went

in the spring of 1856, Magee makes the statement: "I only wish the laboratory was as good as the one in Heidelberg. There you have everything you want, all the newest arrangements, and although I should prefer to remain in Göttingen, the advantages there (in H.) are not to be overlooked. I may find a better laboratory, but I can't find a better chemist, a pleasanter man, and one who is more attentive to his students than Wöhler."

As might be expected, the War between the States in the early sixties cut down the enrollment of American students to a minimum. From the spring of 1860 to that of 1865 only five: M. Perkins, G. W. Maynard, S. W. Tyler, P. N. Welch, W. H. Lee, and Wm. H. Bruckner enrolled in chemistry. With the exception of Bruckner who stayed three years, they remained one year or less and did not complete their studies.

Maurice Perkins (1835–1901), a native of New London (Connecticut) studied at the College of Physicians and Surgeons in New York and obtained an M.D. degree in 1859. After an extensive tour abroad where he studied at Göttingen, Tübingen, and Heidelberg, he returned to this country and became professor of analytical chemistry at Union College and later also part-time professor at Albany Medical College, holding both positions until his death.

George William Maynard (1839–1910), a noted mining engineer, at one time referred to as "dean of American mining engineers," received his early education in Brooklyn. After graduating from Columbia University in 1859, he went abroad the next year and spent one semester in Göttingen and one term in Clausthal (1862–63) to specialize in mining and metallurgy. His many diversified interests took him to Ireland, Colorado, and later also to Russia. From 1868 to 1872 he was consulting engineer for the Steel Works in Troy, New York, and during that period he taught metallurgy at the Rensselaer Polytechnic Institute. Since the Institute at that time was without means to establish an adequate School of Mines, Maynard returned to New York, where he conducted a highly successful consulting practice.

From 1865 to 1870 the number of American chemists in Göttingen again increased, and reached a maximum in 1869 when no fewer than 11 worked in Wöhler's laboratory. Out of a total of 27, only eight (R. Marx, J. H. Eaton, H. Carmichael, M. S. Southworth, H. E. Storrs, Ch. K. Jewett, D. E. Mellis, and R. D. Williams) stayed two years or longer and the records show that five (H. C. Bolton, H. Carmichael, H. E. Storrs, I. Remsen, and D. E. Melliss) obtained their Ph.D.'s during that period. Henry Carrington Bolton (1843–1903), a New Yorker by birth, studied at Columbia University under Joy, graduated in 1862, and spent the summer of 1865 with Wöhler, under whom he started his work on fluorine compounds of uranium. He continued this research in Hofmann's laboratory and took his degree in 1866. He taught for a number of years at Trinity College in Hartford (Connecticut) (1877–87) and resigned to devote his remaining years to special studies. His role as "historian and bibliographer of chemistry" has been described in THIS JOURNAL (10).

Henry Carmichael (1846–1924), born in Brooklyn, New York, studied at Amherst, graduating in 1867. He then spent four years in Göttingen, obtaining his Ph.D. in 1871. On his return he taught one year at Grinnell College, next at Bowdoin College and the Maine Medical School (1872–86) while at the same time acting as state assayer. He finally settled in Boston as assayist and inventor.

Probably the best known of all Wöhler's pupils is Ira Remsen (1846–1927), a native New Yorker, who after obtaining an M.D. degree at Columbia University in 1867, switched to chemistry, spending three semesters at Göttingen, where he obtained his doctor's degree in 1870 on a subject suggested and directed by Wöhler's assistant, Fittig. For the next two years Remsen acted as assistant to Fittig in Tübingen. Returning to America in 1872, Remsen taught chemistry for four years at Williams College and came to Johns Hopkins University in 1876, where he wound up his brilliant career as president of the university. His life and work have been fully recorded in THIS JOURNAL and in a recent monograph by his pupil Getman (11).

Only brief mention can be made of some other old Göttingen students who pursued academic careers in later life. Mase Shepard Southworth was Remsen's successor at Williams College where he taught from 1876 to 1881. J. H. Eaton taught at Beloit College, and Chas. A. Schaeffer at Cornell University. Eugene A. Smith, who obtained his Ph.D. degree at Heidelberg in 1880, specialized in mineralogy and geology, subjects which he taught from 1871 to 1911 at the University of Alabama.

With the exception of J. P. Battershall who held a government position in New York City, the majority of this large group, which includes A. Dung, R. Marx, D. Whitney, S. A. Murphy, C. A. Duval, F. Crook, L. H. Bullard, R. Emory, G. H. Gray, J. J. Kunkel, W. H. Frueauff, J. Barringer, and J. C. F. Randolph, entered the business world.

During the final decade of Wöhler's teaching career from 1870 to 1880, the number of American chemists dropped to 25, but more than 50 per cent of them stayed long enough in Göttingen to obtain a Ph.D. degree. The complete list, in chronological order, contains the names of N. M. Terry, T. R. Baker, S. P. Sadtler, L. B. Hall, H. N. Morse, A. D. Lawrie, L. Mears, E. F. Smith, W. F. Smith, J. T. Stoddard, S. M. Babcock, S. W. Dabney, and L. W. Andrews. Most of these men, as the following brief sketches indicate, have achieved prominence in their chosen specialities.

Nathaniel M. Terry (1844–1922), an Amherst graduate in the class of 1867, got his Ph.D. in 1871, and the next year became professor of physics at the U. S. Naval Academy. From 1886 to 1913 he also taught chemistry at the Academy.

Thomas R. Baker (1837–1930), a B.S. of Pennsylvania State Normal School, taught mathematics at Pennsylvania State College from 1861 to 1867. In 1869 he went to Göttingen where he obtained his degree in 1871. He then taught at his Alma Mater from 1871 to 1886. In 1887 he moved to Florida where he established a private laboratory in Orlando. From 1892 to 1912 he was connected with Rollins College.

Samuel P. Sadtler (1847–1923) studied at Pennsylvania (now Gettysburg) College where he obtained the degrees of A.B. and A.M. in 1867 and 1870. After spending one year at Göttingen he obtained his Ph.D. (in 1871) and returned to Pennsylvania College as professor of chemistry, remaining there till 1877 when he was appointed professor of general and organic chemistry at the University of Pennsylvania. He held this position until 1891. He then established with his

FROM LEFT TO RIGHT: DR. LEVERETT MEARS, DR. EDGAR F. SMITH, AND DR. W. F. SMITH, ON GRADUATION DAY

son a consulting and analytical concern under the name of Samuel P. Sadtler and Son. Meanwhile he continued teaching at the Philadelphia College of Pharmacy till 1916. He was the author of several popular texts and was the founder and first president of the American Institute of Chemical Engineers.

Lyman Beecher Hall (1852–1935), a native of New Bedford (Massachusetts) and a graduate of Amherst College (1873), obtained his Ph.D. under Wöhler in 1875. The next four years he spent at Johns Hopkins. In 1880 he became professor of chemistry at Haverford College, where he remained till his retirement in 1917.

Harmon Northrop Morse (1848–1920), born at Cambridge (Vermont), a classmate of Hall, stayed two years in Göttingen, and also finished in 1875. After one year of teaching at Amherst he served at Johns Hopkins, first as assistant professor and later as full professor and director of the chemical laboratory. He is best known for his painstaking and accurate measurements of osmotic pressures.

Leverett Mears (1850–1917) of Essex (Massachusetts), also an Amherst man (class of 1874), on completing the requirements for his doctor's degree under Wöhler (some years later he named one of his sons after his revered teacher) went back to Amherst as instructor from 1876 to 1881, when he was appointed professor of chemistry and physics at Williams College. In 1888 he became professor of chemistry there and continued in that position till his death in 1917.

Edgar Fahs Smith (1856–1928) of York (Pennsylvania), a pupil and later colleague of Sadtler, graduated from Pennsylvania College in 1874, whereupon he went abroad to study under Wöhler, probably at Sadtler's suggestion. He finished his studies at the same time as his friends, W. F. Smith and Mears. His outstanding record as a teacher, administrator, investigator, and, last but not least, as a historian of chemistry in America has already been given in THIS JOURNAL (12) and need not be repeated here. Some of his early student experiences have also been recorded (13). Dr. Smith has left a manuscript of 55 pages on "German university life," from which, by courtesy of Miss Eva V. Armstrong, curator of the Smith Memorial Collection, a number of excerpts are quoted.

Speaking of the professors with whom he came in contact, Smith says:

. . . "These men were usually reticent and extremely modest, and of my own professors I know none of whom this could be more truly said than of the renowned Wöhler, whose labors not only overthrew the erroneous and prevalent views upon organic chemistry, but also gave us the elements silicon, boron, cerium, and last but not least in importance, aluminum. It was his custom in his chemical lectures invariably to preface the description of the compound of a metal with a brief history of the isolation of the metal itself. But when describing the above elements he omitted their history. On such occasions, or when it was known that he was likely to speak of them, his large lecture room would be crowded to overflowing and at the mere mention of the name of one of the elements loud cheers were sent forth. Often the applause was so loud and continued that he was compelled to retire. The official title of this dear old gentleman was Herr Geheimer Obermedicinalrath Professor Doctor F. Wöhler. Every student was acquainted with this fact and invariably tried to use it when addressing him but the recipient would dismiss it with a wave of the hand. He suffered no one to call him more than Herr Hofrath (Mr. Court Councillor). A more deeply interested painstaking instructor never lived. His great desire was that every student should thoroughly understand every step in his study of the elements. To us Americans he was especially gracious. Of all the eminent European scientists he was pre-eminently the favorite with our countrymen. On one occasion, during Christmas holidays, several of us called upon him as Director of the University Laboratory, begging permission to prosecute our work during the vacation. It was granted. Some German acquaintances hearing of what we were doing, took it for granted that they had the same privilege. When the Hofrath heard of their action he visited us and ordered them out. His excuse for permitting us to work and refusing them was 'The Americans are our most diligent students: they have come thousands of miles for this special work; they are separated from those dear to them and for these reasons I favor them.' That ended all controversy. . . ." . . . "I devoted on an average eighteen hours per week in attendance upon lectures. The remainder of my time was occupied with practical work in the different laboratories. . . . For more than two years I was in the laboratory at work by 6:30 A.M., taking dinner at one o'clock and continuing with practical work until 6:30 and 7 P.M. . . ."

. . . "After I had completed my course of lectures and worked out an original investigation or 'Arbeit' I made application to present myself for examination. The first thing I did was to write my thesis . . . in the German language. The next thing was to write my autobiography or 'Vita' in Latin. . . . The request for an examination, the thesis, and the Vita were sent to the Dean of the Philosophical Faculty. . . . They were returned to me with a document announcing that I would be permitted to present myself for examination upon a certain day. The next thing was to procure a black full dress suit, swallowtail coat, and silk hat. Clothed in these, wearing white kids and white necktie, I stepped forth to call upon the 26 members of my faculty and extend each a cordial invitation to be present at my examination. . . . Two days subsequently at 6 P.M., I repaired to the house of the Dean, was ushered into a cosy waiting room and left to my own thoughts. Such an experience I never again desire. I only then realized into what a predicament I'd suffered myself to be led. I couldn't recall anything of the subjects upon which I expected to be quizzed. At length a beadle announced the faculty assembled and ready to receive me. I was arrayed in my dress of two days before. The beadle ushered me into the other room and announced: Herr Candidat Smith. While I stood, the Dean read me something to the effect that the examination of my thesis, etc., had been satisfactory and that they were pleased . . . to proceed with the examination. I was told to be seated. . . . I sat at one end of a long table. Arrayed on either side was the august Faculty—at the opposite end of the table the Dean, and upon the table, wines of various kinds and cakes. The gentleman to my immediate right began. Question followed question for three long hours. With eyes firmly riveted on the dial of an old-fashioned clock at the opposite end of the room I answered to the best of my ability 'in der deutschen Sprache.' Once a kindly faced, aged professor moved a glass of wine and cakes towards me. I uttered thanks and continued answering. Finally, the several inquisitors declared themselves satisfied. I felt better, when up rose the Professor of Latin and observed that he had noted in the 'Vita' of the candidate frequent use of the accusative with the infinitive—'Why,' he asked, 'was this?' For a moment I hesitated, then an early lesson suggested the reply. . . . No further interrogations were put. That ended the first act. Monday morning at nine the play resumed. The examiners were other men. They found questions enough to hold me until one o'clock. Then I was permitted to retire for about a quarter of an hour. At the expiration of that time I was summoned before the entire august body and made happy by being told that I had been granted *philosophische doctorwürde*. Congratulations followed. On my return to my room I discovered in my study a large fruit cake, iced over in colors—*Vivat, crescat, floreat, Dr. E. F. S.* This cake is something every doctor receives. . . . Next day I again donned the swallow tail and tie to pay my final respects to my faculty. All of them saw me and gave me Godspeed and good wishes. It was over. The ceaseless daily toil and nightly application were finished. . . ."

John T. Stoddard (1852–1919) was another of the numerous Amherst delegation that was attracted to Göttingen by the fame of Wöhler. Graduating from Amherst in 1874, Stoddard obtained his Ph.D. in 1877. He then returned to his native city of Northampton where he taught physics and mathematics at Smith College from 1878 to 1881, chemistry and physics from 1881 to 1897, and chemistry from 1897 to 1919.

Two noted agricultural chemists, *viz.*, Babcock and Dabney, conclude the list of those who finished their degree work before Wöhler's retirement in 1880. Andrews, although a contemporary of both, did not make his Ph.D. until 1882.

Stephen Moulton Babcock (1843–1931), a native Yorker, graduated from Tufts College in 1866. After serving for two years (1875–77) as instructor at Cornell under professor Caldwell he studied two years under Wöhler, obtaining his degree in 1879. Appointed chemist at the Agricultural Experiment Station at Geneva (New York) in 1882, he remained there six years. In 1888 he became professor of agricultural chemistry at the University of Wisconsin, combining this position with that of chief chemist and later director (in 1899) of the Agricultural Experiment Station until his retirement in 1913.

Charles W. Dabney (1855–1945), now living in Cincinnati, is probably the last surviving American pupil of Wöhler. A graduate of the University of Virginia of the class of 1877, he went to Göttingen in the following year with a letter of introduction from his professor of chemistry, John W. Mallet. Here he worked for some months under Wöhler's direction, on the separation of the rare earths in gadolinite, gaining valuable experience which filled him with gratitude for the never-tiring efforts of the kind old hofrath to help his students. After some further study under Hofmann in Berlin, Dabney returned to Göttingen where he took up his thesis work under Hübner, Wöhler's immediate successor, and obtained his degree a few weeks after Wöhler's retirement, in August, 1880. On his return he became State chemist of the North Carolina Experiment Station. In 1887 followed his appointment as professor of agricultural chemistry and director of the Experiment Station of Tennessee. At the same time he occupied the presidency of the University of Tennessee but relinquished these posts in 1904 for the even more important administrative position as president of the University of Cincinnati, which he filled till his retirement in 1920.

Launcelot W. Andrews (1856–1938), a graduate of Yale in the class of 1875, matriculated at the University of Göttingen in the fall of 1878, remained there for three consecutive terms, and obtained his Ph.D. in 1882. He became professor of chemistry in the College of Pharmacy at the University of Iowa in 1885. He left this position in 1904 to become research chemist for the Mallinckrodt Chemical Works in St. Louis. In 1910 he resigned and founded the Andrews Chemical Works in Davenport (Iowa).

Of the nongraduates of the 1870–80 period (F. Blackington, A. Nette, H. M. Johnson, W. A. Talbot, W. Wheatley, F. F. Jewett, A. F. Taylor, T. Goff, H. Voorhes, J. A. Myers, L. Norton, and J. Marshall) only one stayed over three years while the others enrolled for one or two semesters. Two of these, Jewett and Marshall, were active in the field of education.

Frank Fanning Jewett (1844–1924), born in Newton Corner (Massachusetts), studied at Yale where he obtained his A.B. degree in 1870 and the degree of A.M. in 1873. He spent one year in Göttingen (1874–75), taught for three years in Japan (1877–80), and returned to America in 1880, when he became professor of chemistry at Oberlin College. He retired in 1914 at the age of 70. It was Jewett who urged his student Hall "to go after aluminum" which, as every high-school boy knows, turned out to be a successful venture.

John Marshall (1855–1925), a native of Philadelphia, obtained his M.D. degree at the University of Pennsylvania in 1878 and spent the summer semester of the following year in Göttingen. He specialized later in toxicology and taught chemistry in the Medical School of his Alma Mater from 1897 to 1925.

Wöhler's retirement on his 80th birthday (July 31, 1880) was made the occasion for a magnificent tribute from his friends, colleagues, and pupils. A large gold medal was presented to the old master. The necessary funds were secured from more than 300 subscribers in Europe and from 75 in America. It is interesting to note that among the American contributors there were a number of German Ph.D's who had followed the example of Goessmann and established themselves on this side of the Atlantic (M. Alsberg, F. Engelhardt, A. Koegler, A. Springer, E. Waller, and A. Wendell).

Dr. James Lewis Howe (Amherst 1880, Ph.D. Göttingen 1882) recently informed the writer that Wöhler used to make occasional visits to the laboratory in the two years following his retirement, stopping at each desk to inquire what the student was doing.

By the time Wöhler retired, the reputation of Göttingen as a center of chemical research was so well founded that the flow of chemistry students from America continued in full swing for 30 years. The records (1) show that in these three decades 40, 36, and 32 students, respectively, registered in chemistry and among these were two future Nobel prize winners: T. W. Richards (1888–89) and Irving Langmuir (1903–06), besides several others whose names are familiar to American chemists.

Wöhler was always greatly interested in his American students, as can be seen from the letters which he wrote, over a period of 18 years (from 1858 to 1876) to his former pupil Goessmann. These letters have been translated into English and were first published in 1917 (5).

EDITORS' NOTE: The letters are omitted in this reprint volume. *Cf.* J. CHEM. EDUC., **21,** 165–70 (1944).

## LITERATURE CITED

(1) SHUMWAY, *German-American Annals*, **8,** 171 (1910).
(2) SMITH, J. CHEM. EDUC., **20,** 315 (1943).
(3) DUNNINGTON, *ibid.*, **5,** 183 (1928).
(4) "Liebig-Wöhler Briefwechsel," F. Vieweg, Braunschweig, **1888,** Vol. II, p. 323.
(5) "Goessmann Memorial Volume," Mass. Agric. Coll., Amherst, **1917.**
(6) *Columbia Alumni News*, **17,** 301 (1926).
(7) BROWNE, J. CHEM. EDUC., **7,** 499 (1930).
(8) Ref. (5), p. 173.
(9) MAGEE, "An American Student Abroad," The Magee Press, Philadelphia, **1932.**
(10) BROWNE, J. CHEM. EDUC., **17,** 457 (1940).
(11) GETMAN, *ibid.*, **16,** 353 (1939).
(12) BROWNE, *ibid.*, **5,** 656 (1928).
(13) McPHERSON, *ibid.*, **5,** 1554 (1928).

# THE STORY OF LIEBIG'S ANNALEN DER CHEMIE

## H. S. VAN KLOOSTER

Rensselaer Polytechnic Institute, Troy, New York

Few people know that Liebig's *Annalen der Chemie* which have been in continuous existence since 1832 were originally designated as *Annalen der Pharmazie*. This is not so strange as it may appear at first sight. Practical chemistry had its origin in the mines (assaying) and in the drug store (pharmacy), and its emergence as a separate science was gradual. There was, to be sure, in Liebig's youth, a periodical which was, in a small way, a forerunner of Ostwald and van't Hoff's *Zeitschrift für physikalische Chemie*, started in 1887. This was Gilbert's *Annalen der Physik und physikalischen Chemie* (the successor of Gilbert's *Annalen der Physik* (1799–1819)), which became Poggendorff's *Annalen der Physik und Chemie* in 1824 and later, from 1877 to 1899 Wiedemann's *Annalen der Physik und Chemie* until finally it emerged as *Annalen der Physik*, under Drude as editor.

Liebig who had started on his first job as a druggist's apprentice in Heppenheim, near his home town of Darmstadt, in the Grand Duchy of Hesse, had no qualms of conscience in publishing the results of his work and that of his friends and pupils in a periodical with an established clientele of subscribers. As a matter of fact the *Annalen der Pharmazie* started out as a combination of two pharmaceutical periodicals, viz., the *Magazin für Pharmazie und Experimentalkritik* (Vol. 37, 1832) and the *Archiv des Apothekervereins im nördlichen Deutschland* (Vol. 40, 1832). The title of the combined publications, viz., *Annalen der Pharmazie* was given on the left side of the front page, while on the right the original journals were mentioned separately with their respective editors. The *Annalen* appeared monthly, three numbers forming one volume. The custom of publishing four volumes a year persisted until 1873. In 1861, 1863, 1865, 1866, 1867, 1868, 1870, and 1872 supplementary volumes, distinguished by Roman numerals I to VIII, were issued. Beginning with 1873, the number of volumes per year varied, all the way from one (in 1916) to nine (in 1929). The publishing was, at first, done in two places, in Lemgo (near Bielefeld) and in Heidelberg, but later, starting with Volume 11, for a long time exclusively in Heidelberg.

Liebig's connection with the *Annalen* began as follows. His colleague Philipp Lorenz Geiger (1785–1836), a pharmacist, since 1824 professor of pharmacy at Heidelberg and editor of the *Magazin für Pharmazie und die dahin einschlagenden Wissenschaften*, was anxious to be relieved of the daily management of his journal and asked Liebig to join him as co-editor. Liebig who had to support a wife and three children on only 800 florins a year accepted this new position reluctantly. On March 8, 1831, he wrote to Berzelius:

I have, recently, been burdened with a heavy load, by joining Geiger as co-editor of his journal, all for the sake of the damned money involved. At the small university where I live, I am almost on the verge of starvation.

Once embarked on this literary activity Liebig went at it with his usual energy. The final three volumes of 1831 (34, 35, and 36) carry the new title *Magazin für Pharmazie in Verbindung mit einer Experimentalkritik*, to express Liebig's intention to criticize the material published in the journal and to check, in so far as possible, the recorded data by new experiments. The following year (1832) a second pharmaceutical journal was merged with Geiger's journal. This was the *Archiv des Apothekervereins im nördlichen Deutschland*, mentioned before, edited by Rudolph Brandes (1795–1842), pharmacist at Salzuffeln (Westphalia) and "Oberdirector" of the pharmacists of northern Germany. Liebig considered it the main duty of an editor to criticize, and his drastic innovations soon met with disapproval on the part of Brandes who withdrew from the management of the combined periodicals in 1836 and thereupon re-established his own journal under the shorter title of *Archiv der Pharmazie*.

For a brief period (1834–36, Volumes 11 to 17) there were four editors. This was the result of the merger of a third journal viz., the *Neues Journal der Pharmazie für Ärzte, Apotheker und Chemiker* with the other two. The editor of this third periodical was Johann Bartholomä Trommsdorff (1770–1837). Trommsdorff, like Geiger and Brandes, was a pharmacist and for many years professor of chemistry and physics, and director of the Royal Academy of Useful Sciences at Erfurt. Geiger died in 1836 and Trommsdorff in 1837. The former was succeeded as editor by Emanuel Merck (1794–1855), pharmacist at Darmstadt and founder of the well-known pharmaceutical concern. Trommsdorff was replaced by Friedrich Mohr (1816–79), pharmacist at Coblentz and later professor of pharmacy at Bonn. Mohr had been a frequent contributor to the *Annalen* and was held in high esteem by Liebig.

Having been invited to attend the Liverpool meeting of the British Association for the Advancement of Science, Liebig, in the summer of 1837, undertook a trip to England, Scotland, and Ireland and thus got acquainted with the elderly Thomas Thomson (1773–1852) and his pupil Thomas Graham (1805–69). The latter, Liebig judged to be a modest and unpretentious chemist of great accomplishments. On his return to Germany Liebig stopped over in Paris where he settled his controversies with Dumas and converted him to his own viewpoint so completely that a cooperative program for common action was agreed upon. Back in Giessen, Liebig expressed his dissatisfaction with the way Mohr had managed the affairs of the *Annalen* in his absence. Both co-editors resigned, presumably at Liebig's request. This left Liebig in complete control of the *Annalen* which were then, starting with Volume 25 (1838), edited "with the cooperation of Messrs. Dumas in Paris and Graham in London."

In a four-page announcement of the new arrangement Liebig stated that the journal, in order to become truly international, was to be issued simultaneously in England, France, and Germany. He also indicated his intention to devote the *Annalen* chiefly to the new, viz., the organic chemistry, without however neglecting discoveries in related fields of research. What Wöhler thought of this new arrangement we learn from a letter which he wrote to Berzelius on July 28 (1838):

I was greatly annoyed to see that Liebig since the beginning of this year published his Annalen with the co-operation of Dumas and Graham. Although I know for sure that this title is merely a trick in favor of the publisher and the sale of the journal, this alliance seems to me not only ridiculous, but fatal, because apart from everything else, it ignores shamefully all nationality and it humiliates us in the eyes of these Frenchmen. I told Liebig what I thought of it and in order to re-establish to some extent a kind of equilibrium, and also to show that he is not going to change his scientific partners every minute, I proposed to have my name also placed on the title page. Of course, I promised him not only my name like the other two, but also my real co-operation, and this, naturally, without any remuneration.

This suggestion was readily accepted by Liebig and starting with Volume 26 (1838) the *Annalen* were published under joint editorship of Friedrich Wöhler and Justus Liebig. As one of his first contributions, Wöhler, who had quite a sense of humor, sent in an unsigned article under the title: "The solved mystery of spirituous fermentation."[1] This persiflage of the microscopic observations of Cagniard-Latour (1777–1859) and Schwann (1810–82) pleased Liebig so well that he added a few more bad jokes (schlechte Späsze) of his own and published this combined concoction in Volume 29, 100 (1839). Much to Wöhler's surprise the sketch was taken seriously by a reviewer in the *Pharmaceutisches Centralblatt* of 1839.

Wöhler also made another, very sensible, suggestion to Liebig which is contained in a letter, dated October 18 (1838), in which he says:

For the Annalen der Pharmazie you must, in future, introduce the title "Annalen der Chemie und Pharmazie." The present title does not at all cover, for instance, our uric acid investigation. The publisher will certainly not object and the number of subscribers will only increase thereby. Bunsen in Cassel does not know the Annalen at all, because he figures that they deal only with pharmacy.

This suggestion was acted upon with Volume 33 (1840), and the new title was retained up to the time of Liebig's death in 1873. Volume 33 is particularly noteworthy for another humorous contribution of Wöhler entitled: "On the substitution law and the theory of types" (pp. 308–10), written under the pseudonym of S. C. H. Windler.[2] Wöhler was quite surprised to find that Liebig actually published the letter as written. In a letter to Liebig, dated Osnabrück, March 29 (1840), he stated that the letter was really meant for the amusement of Berzelius. If he had known that it was to be published he would have signed the letter (which was written in French) Professor Ch. Arlatan.

---

[1] For a literal translation of the original see J. Chem. Educ. **10**, 543 (1933).

[2] For a literal translation of the original see J. Chem. Educ. **7**, 635 (1930).

The same volume (33) contains a long article by Liebig (pp. 97–136) on "Chemistry in Prussia," in which he makes the bold statement: "There are no chemical laboratories in Prussia." For readers of today, it should be recalled, in this connection, that Göttingen where Wöhler taught for over forty years, is located in Hanover which was an independent kingdom until 1866, when it was annexed by Prussia.

Beginning with the final volume of 1839 Liebig included in the *Annalen* a progress report on the advances in chemistry of that year (Jahresbericht über die Fortschritte der Chemie in 1839). This first report was prepared by his colleague Buff. In succeeding years various authors, including Will and Kopp, cooperated in this work. The practice was discontinued in 1855 in order to save space for original contributions.

In 1842, beginning with Volume 41, the names of Dumas and Graham were omitted from the title page. The custom of printing articles by French authors in translation, frequently as abstracts, continued till the end of Liebig's editorship. Liebig who had been a pupil of Gay Lussac (who later sent his own son Jules to Giessen to study with Liebig) knew all the leading French chemists personally and was anxious to bring their work to the attention of his countrymen. He was so well known in France that on one occasion during his last visit to Paris, as an official delegate of Bavaria to the Paris World's Fair of 1867, he was the only dinner guest of the emperor and was interrogated in German for over an hour on such subjects as meat extracts, agriculture, and sewage disposal.

With Liebig's death in 1873, following the war of 1870–71 and the annexation of Alsace-Lorraine by Germany, many changes in the editorial policies of the *Annalen* were in evidence. In 1851, a year before he left Giessen, Liebig had invited his colleague Hermann Kopp (1817–92), the well-known historian of chemistry, who had helped him with the yearly progress reports for several years, to take over the management of the *Annalen*. Kopp's name as editor appeared for the first time on the title page of Volume 77 and was kept there until Volume 269 (in 1892).

Volume 170, the first one issued after Liebig's death, mentions Emil Erlenmeyer (1825–1909) and Jacob Volhard (1834–1910) as junior editors. The title was changed to *Justus Liebig's Annalen der Chemie und Pharmazie*. Two new editors, August Wilhelm Hofmann (1818–92) and Friedrich August Kekulé (1829–96), were added to the editorial board in 1874. Beginning with Volume 173, the journal became *Justus Liebig's Annalen der Chemie*, under which title it is still known today.

Volhard, who had obtained his Ph.D. in Marburg, had been Liebig's assistant for a while in Munich, had moved from there to London, then back to Marburg and finally back to Munich in 1863, where he died in 1910. He and Erlenmeyer, who was a pupil of Liebig and from 1868 to his retirement in 1880 professor of organic chemistry at the Technische Hochschule in Munich, took over the office work connected with the *Annalen* in 1871 at Liebig's request. From 1878 on, it was Volhard alone who was in charge of the *Annalen* with the other editors acting as editorial advisers and contributors. It was Volhard's policy to take only finished research papers from the whole field of chemistry and to exclude articles of a polemical nature. The development of science and industry in Germany in the forty years following Liebig's death, was astonishing. In addition to Göttingen and Heidelberg a number of prominent centers of chemical research had developed (e.g., in Munich under the leadership of Baeyer). A great many foreigners were trained who, in later years, sent their contributions from their home countries to the *Annalen*.

Volhard insisted on good, grammatically correct German and spent much of his time correcting manuscripts. Only original contributions, that had not appeared in print elsewhere, were taken. Occasional exceptions were made for articles previously published in Russia or Italy. Among the Russians who published their work in the *Annalen* we find Mendeléeff, Menschutkin, Butlerow, Zinin, Beilstein, Markownikov, Borodin, and Sabanéeff. Noted English contributors were Stenhouse, Thorpe, Crum Brown, and Roscoe. Americans who published their work regularly in the *Annalen* were Nef, Freer, Gomberg, and Mallet. Occasional contributions were also sent from Geneva (where Graebe taught from 1878 to 1906), Basel and Zürich in Switzerland, from Pisa and Florence in Italy, from Delft in Holland, from Graz in Austria, from Helsingfors (now Helsinki) in Finland, and from other countries in western Europe.

Wöhler's name disappeared from the list of editors with Volume 215 (1882) and the names of Kopp and Hofmann, who both died in 1892, with Volume 270. In 1896 Kekulé died and his place on the board of editors was filled by Rudolf Fittig (1835–1910), a pupil of Wöhler. The next year (Vol. 297) two famous organic chemists joined the board of editors, viz., Otto Wallach (1847–1931) and Adolf Baeyer (1835–1917), both regular contributors to the *Annalen*. Wallach, who had obtained his Ph.D. under Wöhler in 1869, had started his life work on terpenes and camphors in Bonn in 1884 when he was an assistant of Kekulé and continued in Göttingen where he succeeded Victor Meyer in 1889. He went on with his research until 1924 when his 129th paper appeared in the *Annalen*. The writer, who attended Wallach's lectures on elementary organic chemistry in the spring of 1909, was present when his advanced students celebrated the publication of Wallach's 100th paper on ethereal oils. Wallach was not only a great chemist, he was also an accomplished lecturer who always illustrated his lectures, without the aid of a single assistant, with a few simple but well-chosen experiments. The writer remembers vividly the roaring applause that followed when Wallach separated the alcohol in beer by boiling the beer in a flask provided with a meter-long tube and igniting the alcohol with a burning match as it issued from the tube. Wallach received the Nobel prize in 1910, five years after it had been awarded to Baeyer.

In 1903, on the occasion of the centenary of the birth of Liebig, Volhard added a forty-page commemorative article with a picture of Liebig to Volume 328 of the *Annalen*. In 1907, Emil Fischer who had received the second Nobel prize in chemistry, joined the board of editors. Volhard, who died in 1910, was succeeded by Johannes Thiele (1855–1918) as managing editor. In 1909 Erlenmeyer died and in the next year Fittig.

Their places on the board of editors were filled in 1911, beginning with Volume 379, by Carl Graebe (1841–1927) and Theodor Zincke (1843–1928), both frequent contributors to the *Annalen*. Graebe, best known for the synthesis of alizarin which he carried out in cooperation with Liebermann, had just retired from his professorship at Geneva. Zincke, the son of a druggist and a former pupil of Wöhler, had done his best work in organic chemistry at Marburg where he had been professor since 1875. Although close to retirement in 1911, he continued his publications in the *Annalen* until he was well over eighty, with more than 300 articles in the *Annalen* and the *Berichte* to his credit.

The first world war (1914–18), had a pronounced effect on the publication of scientific papers. From a high-water mark of 9 volumes in 1912, the number went down to 7 in 1913, 5 in 1914, 4 in 1915, and to only 1 in 1916. In the next ten years the numbers were 2, 4, 2, 2, 4, 4, 6, 5, 5, and 9. Due to the paper shortage in the postwar years, a poor grade of paper had to be used in several volumes. Baeyer died in 1917 and Thiele the next year. Their places were filled by Richard Willstätter (1872–1942) and Wilhelm Wislicenus (1861–1922). The latter, at that time professor in Tübingen, took over the duties of managing editor in the fall of 1918.

On the death of Emil Fischer in 1919 no one took his place on the editorial staff. In 1922 Wislicenus died, whereupon his place was filled by Heinrich Wieland (1877– ), a pupil of Thiele and successor of Willstätter at the university of Munich on the latter's retirement in 1925. Graebe and Zincke passed away in 1927 and 1928 and were replaced by Adolf Windaus (1876– ), Wallach's successor in Göttingen since 1915, and Hans Fischer (1881–1945), Wieland's successor at the Technische Hochschule in Munich since 1921. Windaus, Wieland, and Fischer all received the Nobel prize for chemistry in 1928, 1927, and 1930, respectively, and formed with Willstätter, the 1915 Nobel prize winner, and Wallach the most distinguished group of editors that ever presided over the destinies of a scientific journal. Of these five men, Wallach died in 1931 and Willstätter went to Switzerland in 1938 so that at the outbreak of the second world war only Wieland, Windaus, and Fischer were left on the editorial board.

During the period from 1923 to 1939 the main burden of editing the *Annalen* fell on Wieland. He succeeded in maintaining the high standing of the journal in the field of organic chemistry which occupied probably more than 90% of the contents of the *Annalen*. Only a few inorganic papers occasionally appeared. Contributions from neutral and from former enemy countries and also from the successor states of the dual monarchy of Austria-Hungary found their way into the *Annalen*.

At the outbreak of the second world war (1939–45) Wieland took complete charge of the *Annalen* and continued to publish articles emanating from countries under German domination. One short paper in Volume 556 (1944) was sent in by an Asiatic chemist from the École Polytechnique in Paris (!). Very few copies of the *Annalen* reached America during the war years. For the benefit of American libraries and research workers the office of the Alien Property Custodian authorized Edwards Brothers in Ann Arbor, Michigan, to make photostatic reproductions of these war issues and to distribute them in this country. The number of volumes published in the war years dropped to one (No. 556) in 1944. The next year only number one of Volume 557, published in Berlin, appeared; the second and third number did not get published until May 1 and May 15 of 1947 and were printed on poor, yellow, postwar paper. From then on the *Annalen* were published in Weinheim (north of Heidelberg) in issues of 3500 copies at first, under the editorship of Windaus, Wieland, and Richard Kuhn (1900– ) who had won the Nobel prize in 1938.

Thanks to the financial and technical help extended to the countries of western Europe by the United States, rapid progress has been made in the field of chemistry, and at present the *Annalen* are back at their prewar average of five to six volumes a year, the latest volume published being 595. The contents of the *Annalen* are now exclusively organic. Due to the revival of nationalism throughout the world, a number of new chemical periodicals have appeared, and so far no communications by non-Germans have been published in the *Annalen* since 1945. Of the four men who edited the *Annalen* prior to the war, Willstätter went in exile in 1938 and died in Switzerland in 1942; Hans Fischer, like Goebbels, Göhring, and Hitler, committed suicide when the Third Reich collapsed; Windaus and Wieland are no longer active because of age and sickness. The equivocal role of the present managing editor, Kuhn, in the war years has been well told by Dr. Goudsmit of Brookhaven Laboratories in his report on the work of the Alsos mission in 1944 and 1945.[3]

[3] GOUDSMIT, S. A., "Alsos," Henry Schuman, Inc., New York, 1947, pp. 80–83.

◄ ►

# CHEMICAL GENEALOGY

## VIRGINIA BARTOW

University of Illinois, Urbana, Illinois

SINCE a study of the history of chemistry is included in the chemistry curriculum at the University of Illinois, it has been found worth-while to use various devices to interest the seniors who take the work. Many students see little relationship between what has happened in the past and their present-day needs. Accordingly, as the lectures near their close, a presentation is made of a chemical genealogical tree as illustrated by the accompanying charts. The students are very much interested in seeing the inheritance which they have through their instructors from the great teachers of the past. The charts serve to emphasize once more the dependence of today's events on those of yesterday.

The diagrams include most of the senior staff of the chemistry department of the University of Illinois. Their names are connected to that of the men who directed their doctors' dissertations. In turn, these men were taught by others. The chemists listed fall rather naturally into three classes. There are the contemporary or nearly contemporary chemists whom the staff know. There are those who are not yet included in the histories of chemistry and whose academic records must be determined by theses, obituaries, and other biographical accounts. Finally, there are those men of the nineteenth century or earlier whose story is found in any history of chemistry. The information has been secured from these sources, the staff, and the biographical literature.

A very few points might be made clear. It is impossible to indicate all the chemists with whom every man has come in contact so that the doctor's degree in so far as it is possible has been used as the most significant study. The entire list is given, except in the case of Professor Dennis, who had no earned doctor's degree but who studied widely in Germany. Professor Dennis wrote a letter to give the information which illustrates so well what might be done for each of the men if space permitted.

For other chemists who had no formal degree, the person who seemed to have exerted the greatest influence was chosen as the "forebear." As so often happened in the nineteenth century, students traveled from one university to another, finally presenting their theses at one, so that it is difficult to ascertain to which they feel most indebted. On that account, some of the chemists are linked to more than one person. Perhaps Dumas should have been connected to both Thenard and Gay-Lussac.

Although the universities where the men studied are known, the major professor is not always expressly stated. This has led to one or two assumptions as in the case of Professor Sedgwick. He received his degree from the Johns Hopkins University. As Remsen was there at the time, Sedgwick must have had some contact with that eminent teacher. Both Professor Gomberg and Professor Chittenden obtained their degrees in this country but are known to feel very strongly that their European training meant a great deal. Therefore, they are shown as the students of Victor Meyer, Baeyer, and Kühne.

It is noteworthy that the lines from the men in this department converge to three chemists, Berzelius of Sweden, Berthelot and Fourcroy of France. The diagrams show the chemical center traveling from France to Germany as the nineteenth century progressed. As might be anticipated, Liebig and Wöhler play a prominent part in the instruction of the chemists of note in the German universities, at the time our American chemists started to cross the Atlantic for advanced work.

This brief presentation is made to introduce this

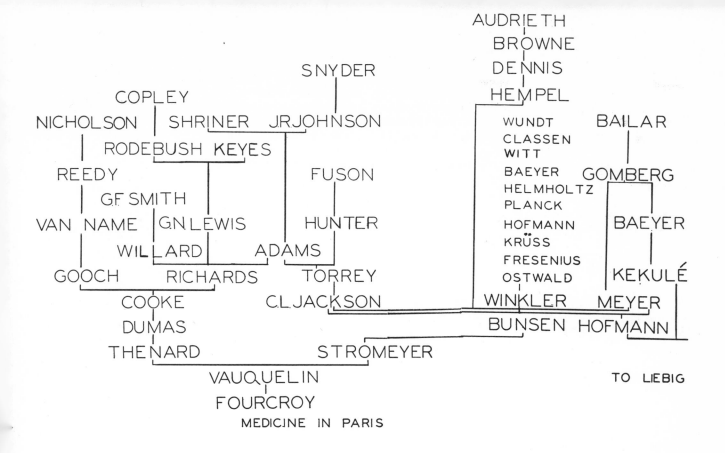

MEDICINE IN PARIS

TO LIEBIG

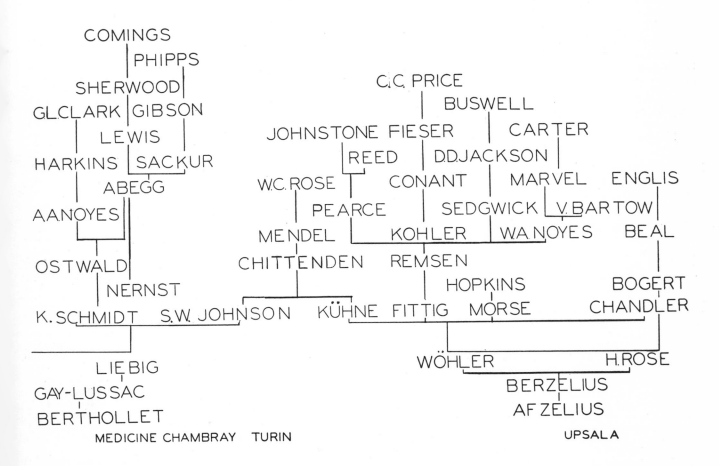

MEDICINE CHAMBRAY TURIN

UPSALA

device, which can be applied to any group with a little effort. The bibliography is listed for those men for whom the literature sources were used. Perhaps some reader will know of readjustments which should be made. In conclusion, the writer wishes to express her appreciation to those members of the department at the University of Illinois who contributed a considerable amount of the information.

LITERATURE CITED—SUBJECT AND REFERENCE

(1) BOGERT, M. T., *Ind. Eng. Chem.*, **12**, 189 (1920).
(2) CHANDLER, C. F., *ibid.*, **12**, 190 (1920).
(3) FITTIG, R., *Ber.*, **44**, 1339–83 (1911).
(4) GOMBERG, M., *Ind. Eng. Chem.*, **23**, 116 (1931).
(5) GOOCH, F. A., *ibid.*, **15**, 1088 (1923).
(6) HEMPEL, W., *Ber.*, **49**, 2839–41 (1916).
(7) JACKSON, C. L., *Ind. Eng. Chem.*, **18**, 872 (1926).
(8) JOHNSON, S. W., *Cf.* OSBORNE, ELIZABETH A., *editor* "From the letter files of S. W. Johnson," Yale University Press, New Haven, Conn., **1913**.
(9) KUHNE, W., *Ber.*, **33**, 3875–80 (1900).
(10) LEWIS, W. K., "Who's Who in America" Don Marquis Co., Chicago, Ill., Vol. 16, p. 1367.
(11) MORSE, H. N., *Science* [N. S.] **52**, 497–500 (1900).
(12) NOYES, A. A., *Ind. Eng. Chem.*, **23**, 443–5 (1931).
(13) OSTWALD, W., *Oesterr. Chem. Ztg.*, **35** [N. S.], 68 (1932).
(14) SACKUR, O., *Ber.*, **48**, 1–4 (1915).
(15) SCHMIDT, K., *ibid.*, **27**, 747 (1894).
(16) SEDGWICK, W. T., *Science* [N. S.], **53**, 171–8 (1921).
(17) TORREY, H. A., *Am. Chem. J.*, **20**, 395 (1898).
(18) WINKLER, C., *Ber.*, **39**, 4491–543 (1906).
(19) BERZELIUS, J. J., BUNSEN, R. W., GAY-LUSSAC, J. L., VAUQUELIN, L. N., THENARD, L. J., STROMEYER, F., WOHLER, F., *Cf.* WEEKS, M. E., "Discovery of the elements," Mack Printing Co., Easton, Pa., **1933**.
(20) BAEYER, A. VON, COOKE, J. P., KEKULE, A., LIEBIG, J., MEYER, V., REMSEN, I., RICHARDS, T. W., *Cf.* MOORE, F. J., "A history of chemistry" rev. by W. T. HALL, 2nd ed., McGraw-Hill Book Co., Inc., New York City, **1931**.
(21) BERTHELOT, C. L., DUMAS, J. B., ROSE, H., *Cf.* BROWN, J. C., "A history of chemistry," 2nd ed., P. Blakiston's Son and Co., Philadelphia, Pa., **1920**.

———————————•———————————

# Who Discovered Galvanism?

Luigi Galvani, after whom galvanism is named, was an Italian biologist who was studying the effect of an electric current on the nerves of skinned frog legs. The electricity caused the muscles to undergo convulsions and the leg to twitch. According to encyclopedias, legend has it that Galvani's wife, nee Lucia Galeazzi, daughter of a teacher of anatomy under whom Galvani studied, was a woman of superior intelligence. One day as she was preparing frog legs for her husband's experiments she noticed that when her scalpel touched the metal of the machine on the table and was simultaneously in contact with the nerve of the frog leg, the leg twitched just as when an electric current was imposed. Galvani, in his writings, states that one of his assistants made this observation; and most encyclopedias seem to assume that Galvani's wife was that assistant.

Over the years as I encountered many interesting aspects of galvanism relating to the corrosion inside food cans, I developed a real admiration for Galvani's wife as a result of her observation, and felt that she should be given credit for the discovery of galvanism rather than her husband. But this admiration received a severe shock from a lecture entitled "The Guide of Life" by C. J. Ducasse, professor of philosophy at Brown University, as published in the January 1958 issue of Phi Beta Kappa's *Key Reporter*. According to Ducasse's version, Galvani's wife was a consumptive, and her physician prescribed broth from frog legs to strengthen her. One day as Galvani stood on his balcony which had an iron railing to prepare frog legs for his wife's broth, he hung the prepared legs on the railing with copper hooks. He observed the same muscular contraction and twitching that an electric current caused. This version of the discovery, I find, has received ridicule in the literature as being an old wives' tale: If Galvani were cooking for his wife, he would more likely be doing it in the kitchen rather than in his laboratory or on his balcony. Moreover, why should he use copper hooks to hang the legs? To me, it seems strange that a physician, whom one would assume to be of a high order, would believe that the tremendous strength of frog legs would be an inherent property of the broth made from them. After all, Galvani was a biologist, and as such it is doubtful that he would harbor such a notion.

Neither Professor Ducasse nor I have been able to find conclusive evidence for the correctness of either of these stories. Recently I have checked through translations of Galvani's original publications dealing with this theme.

There is no doubt that Galvani studied the bimetallic effect on the nerves of many dead animals. He noted the effect of electricity produced by friction and electricity from a Leyden jar. He studied the effect of electricity from lightning at various distances and correlated this effect with the peals of thunder at great distances. Of most significance was his study of what has been termed a "marine torpedo," an electric animal, perhaps what we know as an electric eel. After finding that many sources of electricity applied to the nerves of dead animals caused muscular contraction, he found that the electricity from the marine torpedo had the same effect. As a biologist, he was not diverted from his contention that he was observing animal electricity, "De Viribus Electricitatis." When there was no lightning and he hung frog legs with copper hooks on his iron railings, he felt that he had discovered atmospheric electricity.

Probably his greatest achievement, as far as galvanism is concerned, was the arousal of interest in Alessandro Volta. When Galvani's work first came to Volta's attention, the latter was inclined to accept Galvani's idea that the electricity involved was animal electricity. He interpreted it as an upset in the amount of electricity in the muscle and in the nerve; the two metals served to complete the circuit and restore the balance. But as Volta experimented himself, he soon changed his mind. He first observed that when he placed a piece of tinfoil on his tongue in contact with a silver coin, there developed what he called a sourness. When he made his eye a part of the circuit between two metals, it created a sensation of light just as a blow on the eye does. Volta was soon convinced that the two metals were responsible for the electricity.

Then began the heated argument that is said to have led to the discovery of useful electricity. But the controversy was not between Galvani and Volta as is usually stated. Rather it was between Volta and Galvani's nephew, Giovanni Aldini, professor of physics at Bologna University. Galvani is reported to have tried to answer Volta in only one publication. He seems never to have realized that the electricity involving two metals results from a change in one or both to produce electric energy. Galvani reported that an assistant first noted the bimetallic effect on frog legs, though there seems to be no record of the identity of the assistant. I am quite willing to assume that the assistant was his wife.

Edward F. Kohman
385 Kings Highway
Cherry Hill, New Jersey

# THE CONGRESS AT KARLSRUHE

## CLARA deMILT

Newcomb College, Tulane University, New Orleans, Louisiana

THE Congress at Karlsruhe, which met September 3, 4, and 5 in 1860, was the first international congress in science and as such set the pattern for the congresses that have been held since this time.[1] August Kekulé has been rightly considered as the originator of the idea and Anschütz[2] believes that in the calling of this meeting Kekulé rendered an especially great service to the advancement of chemistry. A case might certainly be made for the opinion that this was Kekulé's greatest contribution to the development of chemistry. Without the help of Adolphe Wurtz and Carl Weltzien, however, the Congress would have been just another of Kekulé's dreams. In a letter to Weltzien, written from Ghent, March 14, 1860, Kekulé says of Wurtz, "Wurtz is, according to my opinion, the most important personality (in the organization of this meeting) and if he will join with us on this point the thing is half accomplished."[3] In the fall of 1859 Weltzien had agreed to have the meeting at the Technische Hochschule in Karlsruhe and to function as business manager, and during the winter of 1859 he sounded out the leading chemists of Europe on the proposed meeting. At the end of March, 1860, Kekulé and Weltzien met with Wurtz in Paris, and definite plans were then made for the conference. A circular was sent to the most outstanding chemists of Europe asking for their cooperation. As this first appeal was favorably received the time of the meeting was set and the announcements were sent out by Weltzien. They were written in English, French, and German. It is interesting to note that although the German version was dated July 10 the English one was dated July 1.[4] A translation of the German one follows.

Karlsruhe, July 10, 1860

Gentlemen:

Chemistry has reached a state of development when to the undersigned, it seems necessary that a meeting of a great number of chemists, active in this science, who are called upon to do research and teach, be held so that a unification of a few important points shall be approached.

The undersigned, therefore, invite to an international congress all those colleagues who on the basis of their attitude and work have a right to voice an opinion in this science.

Such a congress in the opinion of the undersigned, however, would not be in the position to make definite binding conclusions, but through a thorough discussion many misunderstandings might be removed; especially an agreement in regard to the following main points might be made easier:

More precise definitions of the concepts of atom, molecule, equivalent, atomicity, alkalinity, etc.; discussion on the true equivalents of bodies and their formulas; initiation of a plan for a rational nomenclature.

Although it is not expected that the meeting that is being called will succeed completely in harmonizing the divergent opinions, nevertheless, the undersigned are of the conviction that it should be possible by this means at least to prepare the way for a desirable agreement on these important questions.

Furthermore, a commission might be appointed whose task it would be to pursue further these questions. This commission might suggest that academies and other learned societies, which have the necessary facilities, take part in the solution of the questions stated above.

The meeting is to convene on September 3, 1860, at Karlsruhe. Our colleague, Weltzien, has taken over the function of business manager until the definite constitution of the congress has been drawn up and will open the latter on the designated day in the morning at nine o'clock.

It is urgently requested that those gentlemen who intend to attend the congress notify our colleague as soon as possible, so that the choice of the place of the meeting may be arranged according to the size of the congress.

Furthermore, the undersigned request that those receiving circulars take part in their distribution among scientific circles, so that those whose names have been inadvertently omitted may receive the announcement.

By Babo, Balard, Beketoff, Boussingault, Brodie, R. Bunsen, Bussy, Cahours, Cannizzaro, H. Deville, Dumas, Englehardt, O. L. Erdmann, v. Fehling, Frankland, Frémy, Fritzsche, Hlasiwetz, A. W. Hofmann, Kekulé, H. Kopp, J. v. Liebig, Malaguti, Marignac, E. Mitscherlich, Odling, Pasteur, Payen, Pebal, Peligot, Pelouze, Piria, Regnault, Roscoe, A. Schötter, Socoloff, Staedeler, Stas, Ad. Strecker, C. Weltzien, H. Will, W. Williamson, F. Wöhler, Ad. Wurtz, Zinin.

Of the above forty-five who signed the summons, twenty came: Babo, Boussingault, R. Bunsen, Cannizzaro, Dumas, O. L. Erdmann, v. Fehling, Hlasiwetz, Kekulé, H. Kopp, Marignac, Odling, Pebal, Roscoe, Stas, Ad. Strecker, Weltzien, H. Will, Wurtz, Zinin.

So far as I know none of the announcements reached the United States.[5] If some of them did, the date of arrival would hardly have given the chemists of this country time enough to make plans to attend the meeting. It is my opinion that Wolcott Gibbs and T. Sterry Hunt would have made the effort to attend the Congress had they received the announcement, as both of them had followed with interest the development of the unitary system and the new type theory.[6]

The official report of the Congress was written by Wurtz, one of the five secretaries elected on the first day of the meeting, and was deposited in the Archives

[1] BOGERT, M., *Chem. Eng. News*, **27**, 1992 (July 11, 1949).
[2] ANSCHÜTZ, RICHARD, "August Kekulé," 1929, Vol. I, p. 201.
[3] ANSCHÜTZ, R., *ibid.*, p. 183.
[4] ANSCHÜTZ, R., *ibid.*, p. 671.
[5] Louis Posselt, registered from Mexico, had worked in Mexico from 1849 when he left Heidelberg, but he had returned to Germany early in 1860.
[6] HUNT, T. S., *Am. J. Sci.* [2], **4**, 93–100; 171–85 (1847); [2], **6**, 170–8, (1848); [2], **31**, 256–263, (1861). GIBBS, W., *ibid.* [2], **31**, 246–51 (1861).

of the Technical College at Karlsruhe. It has been published in the account of the development of chemistry in Karlsruhe by Karl Engler, who wrote this portion of "The Presentation Volume for the Celebration of the Fortieth Anniversary of the Rule of his Royal Highness the Grand Duke Friedrich of Baden," Karlsruhe, 1892.[7] Richard Anschütz published the report of Wurtz in the original French as an appendix to Volume One of his life and work of Kekulé.[8] *Le Moniteur Scientifique* for October 15, 1860 (t. II, 984–6), contains a short account of the meeting which differs in minor details from the official report. From the context one would assume that the information must have been obtained not directly from Wurtz but from l'abbé Moigno and Louis Grandeau. *Chemical News* for October 6, 1860, (Vol. 2, 203) contains a very brief report. Another report was published in the same volume, pages 226, 227. This was placed under the heading, "Chemical Notices from Foreign Sources" and must have been sent to the editor by the journal's foreign correspondent in Paris, l'abbé Moigno[9] as in the details given it is like the report in *Le Moniteur Scientifique*. According to both accounts, after the sitting of the first meeting, September 3, closed, "the members fraternized together at a banquet laid for 120 persons in the large hall of the Museum. This supplementary meeting, which was not mentioned in the programme, was by no means the least scientific, the least relished, nor, above all, the least substantial, as we learn from the Abbé Moigno."

There must have been reports like these in a German weekly, but no reference has been made to a report in published comments on the Congress. In the St. Petersburg *Gazette* No. 280, 1860, appeared a letter from Mendeleev to his former teacher, A. A. Voskresenskiĭ, Professor of Chemistry in the University of St. Petersburg.[10] Mendeleev was twenty-six in 1860. In 1859 he had gone to Paris to study under Victor Regnault, probably the ablest and most experienced physical chemist at the Sorbonne. From Paris he had gone to Heidelberg and from this University he journeyed to Karlsruhe. His appreciation of the issues involved in the discussions at the meeting, of the importance of the debates, and of the value of this Congress in the future development of chemistry is amazing, and show the outstanding genius of this scientist.

The chemical Congress just ended in Karlsruhe produced such a remarkable effect on the history of our science that I consider it a duty, even in a few words, to describe all the sittings of the Congress and the results which it reached.

The essential reason for calling an international chemical congress was the wish to clarify and, if possible, agree on the basic differences which exist between the followers of different chemical schools. At first, Kekulé proposed to settle many questions: the question of the difference of molecules, atoms, and equivalents; the question of the size of the atomic weights, *i. e.*, whether the "particle" of Gerhardt or the particle of Berzelius as changed by Liebig and Poggendorf, and now used by most men, should be accepted; further, the question of formulas, and finally, even about the case where, in the present state of science, we should consider the reasons for chemical effects. But at the first sitting, September 3, the meeting found it impossible in such a short time to clarify such a great number of questions, and so resolved to settle only on the first two.

There was chosen a commission of thirty members for preliminary treatment of these two questions. S. Cannizzaro was finally also on it, whose animated speech, in justice, was met by general approval. In the second session of the Congress, September 4, the commission reported the resolution it had worked out, of this content: It is decided to take a different understanding of molecules and atoms, considering as a molecule the amount of a substance entering a reaction and determining physical properties, and considering as an atom the smallest amount of a substance included in a molecule. Further it reached an understanding about equivalents, considered as empirical, not depending on the understanding about atoms and molecules. On a vote on this resolution, most raised their hands. Who was against it? Timidly one hand was raised and then lowered. The result was unexpectedly unanimous and important. Understanding the difference between atoms and molecules, chemists of all countries understood the principle of the unitary system. Now when the principle is understood, the consequences will not admit of the great inconsistencies.

The third session, September 5, was devoted to the question of atomic weights, chiefly carbon: whether to accept the new weight of 12 or remain with the former one of 6, until then used by almost everyone. After a long debate, at its last session, September 6, J. Dumas made a brilliant speech proposing to use the new atomic weight only in organic chemistry leaving the old for inorganic. Against this Cannizzaro spoke heatedly, showing that all should use the same new atomic weight. There was no vote on this question, but the great majority took the side of Cannizzaro.

To this I add the remark that in all the debates there was not one unfriendly word between both parties. All this, it seems to me is full guarantee of the rapid success of the new ideas in the future. Half the chemists have already resolved not to vote against the ideas.

D. Mendeleev, Heidelberg, September 7, 1860.

Weltzien opened the meeting on the morning of September 3 with a short address of welcome.[11] He then asked Bunsen to take the chair. Bunsen declined and the assembly elected Weltzien the presiding officer for the first session. Kekulé, Roscoe (replaced by Odling in the third session), Strecker, Wurtz, and Shishkov were selected secretaries. A motion was made by

[7] ENGLER, KARL, "Vier Jahrzehnte chemischer Forschung unter besonderer Rücksicht auf Baden als Heimstätte der Chemie," pp. 346–55, in "Festgabe zum Jubiläum der vierzigjahrigen Regierung Seiner Königlichen Hoheit des Grossherzogs Friedrich von Baden," Karlsruhe, 1892.

[8] ANSCHÜTZ, R., *op. cit.*, Anlage 8, 671–88.

[9] Moigno is not listed by Wurtz as registered at the meeting. François Napoleon Marie Moigno (1804–84), Jesuit, mathematician, friend of Boussingault and Dumas, was one of the foreign correspondents of *Chemical News* from its beginning to about 1870. Grimaux describes Moigno as an intelligent commentator, capable of appreciating the great value of the work of Laurent and Gerhardt in opposing the dualistic theory held by the majority of the French school in the period 1846–56. See ÉDOUARD GRIMAUX, "Charles Gerhardt, sa vie, son oeuvre, sa correspondance," 1900, p. 190.

[10] For information about this letter and for its translation from the Russian I am indebted to Professor Henry M. Leicester of the College of Physicians and Surgeons, San Francisco, California. The letter was published by B. M. Menshutkin in "Chemistry and the Way of its Development," Academic Science Press, Moscow and Leningrad, 1937, p. 192.

[11] A translation of this address is given in *Chymia*, I, 163–4 (1948). For an account of the confusion in the writing of formulas, etc., that led Kekulé, Weltzien, and Wurtz to call this meeting, the reader is referred to the article in *Chymia*, "Carl Weltzien and the Congress at Karlsruhe," pp. 153–69.

Kekulé that a committee be appointed to prepare the questions to be discussed. Kekulé then spoke on the topics to be considered by the committee. Erdmann insisted that the questions presented to the assembly for deliberation be concerned not with points of doctrine, but with form. After remarks by Fresenius, Kekulé, Wurtz, Boussingault, and Kopp the first session of the Congress ended.

The committee met at eleven o'clock the same morning. Among those taking part in this first meeting of the committee Wurtz mentioned H. Kopp (chairman), Cannizzaro, Kekulé, Strecker, Wurtz, Fresenius, Erdmann, Béchamp, and Shishkov. Kopp summarized the discussion and formulated the first question:

(1) Shall a difference be made between the expressions "molecule" and "atom," such that a molecule be named the smallest particle of bodies which can enter into chemical reactions and which may be compared to each other in regard to physical properties, atoms being the smallest particles of those bodies which are contained in molecules?

Fresenius now called attention to the expression "compound atom," which, he said, implied a contradiction. His remarks led to the second question:

(2) Can, perhaps, the expression "compound atom" be suppressed and replaced by the expression "radical"?

Kopp then introduced the discussion of the term equivalent and the third question to be presented for deliberation by the Congress was stated:

(3) The concept of equivalent is empirical and independent of the concept of molecule and atom.

Erdmann followed Kopp as chairman of the committee. There was some discussion on notation but no agreement on a question was reached. The committee adjourned.

At the beginning of the session of September 4 Boussingault was elected the presiding officer. After thanking the Congress for the honor that had been shown him, he made a few remarks on the questions to be submitted pointing out that they united the old chemistry with the new, but adding: "There is no chemistry which is old, there are only old chemists." Strecker read the questions for the committee, and Kekulé spoke at length on Question 1, and was followed by Cannizzaro, and by Wurtz who thought that this question might be reserved for further deliberation.

Miller, speaking on the second question, wished to drop the term, "compound atom," since there existed only atoms of elements. Opinions which differed widely were expressed by others and no agreement could be reached. The meeting adjourned. It is to be noted that in the report of Wurtz as given by both Engler and Anschütz there is no statement that the Congress passed the resolution on the clarification of the term equivalent (see letter of Mendeleev). In the report in *Le Moniteur Scientifique*, however, it is stated that the Congress voted to accept the distinction between atom and equivalent.

A second meeting of the committee, again with Kopp as chairman, followed the second session of the Con-

Carl Weltzien

gress. Kekulé spoke again on the topic of notation, followed by Cannizzaro. Kopp found it necessary to caution the speakers to avoid matters of theory and to confine their remarks to the topics decided upon by the committee. Many, however, agreed with Erdmann's comment that it is urgent to adopt a notation such that the symbols will represent a definite value in all formulas. Kopp then introduced the problem of atomic weights and their representation by symbols and proposed the following question to be put before the Congress: Is it desirable to bring chemical notation into conformity with the recent advances in the science by doubling a certain number of atomic weights?

Later the committee met again on Tuesday with Dumas as chairman. Kekulé continued the discussion of the question offered by Kopp. Strecker made a proposal to adopt in principle the notation based on atoms. Dumas called attention to the actual confusion existing in chemistry, which, he said, must not be prolonged because of its effect on the teaching of the subject. He advocated a return to the atomic weights of Berzelius. Wurtz was happy, he said, that Dumas had brought up this subject of the atomic weights and notation of Berzelius, as he (Wurtz) was not in favor of the adoption of all the atomic weights of Gerhardt, since recent advances in experimental chemistry should be taken into account. After further discussion the committee accepted the question and voted to leave the wording of it to the bureau (the president and secretaries). Wurtz in his report on the Congress gave no details about the discussion of the other two questions placed before the Congress at its third and last session.

The Congress met September 5 with Dumas in the chair. Dumas proposed the election of two vice-presidents. Will and Miller were elected and took their seats at the president's table. The secretaries then read the questions, the wording of which had been decided upon by the bureau:

(1) Is it desirable to bring chemical notation into harmony with advances in the science?

(2) Is it expedient to adopt anew the principles of Berzelius as they are concerned with notation, with some modifications?

(3) Is it desirable, by means of particular signs, to differentiate the new chemical symbols from those generally in use for fifty years?

Cannizzaro spoke against Question 2. This speech is written out in full in the record left by Wurtz. It is the celebrated address of the Congress in which Cannizzaro shows the great service which Gerhardt had rendered the science in basing his system of molecular weights on the theory of Avogadro and Ampère.[12] He speaks of the importance of the work by Dumas on vapor density determinations, of the value of the reasoning of Dumas' student Gaudin, and finally of Gerhardt's use of Dumas' work. Cannizzaro then explains the value of Avogadro's principle and shows that the system of Berzelius does not take it into account. This is followed by a discussion of the work of Deville on vapor densities as showing dissociation at elevated temperatures. He concludes:

Therefore, gentlemen, I propose to accept Gerhardt's system and thus to consider the changes in atomic weights of a number of metals as these become necessary. If in regard to a new system on such a basis we shall not be able to reach an agreement, we shall at least prevent the passage of a contrary judgment. No matter what you do you will not be able to prevent Gerhardt's system from daily winning new adherents. Today already it has been recognized by the majority of young chemists who have participated actively in the progress of this science. Let us therefore pass an agreement to prevent misunderstanding which, no doubt, would be caused by the simultaneous application of old and new formulae, and let us use, therefore, the crossed-through symbols for the new doubled atomic weights.

Many speakers followed Cannizzaro. Because of the diverse opinions expressed, Erdmann took the position that on questions of principle, such as were involved, no vote could be taken and that every scientist must be allowed full freedom. In this view he was supported by Wurtz, Kopp, and Boussingault. Odling then spoke against the use of barred symbols (implied in Question 3). Dumas put the question of the use of such symbols before the Congress and the assembly voiced the wish that henceforth those atoms, the atomic weights of which had been doubled, should be denoted by crossed-through symbols. With this resolution the

Congress ended except for a short speech by Dumas in which he expressed the gratitude of the members to the originators of the meeting and to his Highness, the Grand Duke of Baden, whose hospitality they had enjoyed.

There is one important incident of the Congress that is not reported by Wurtz. Lothar Meyar speaks of it in a letter to Kekulé and has included it in his remarks on Cannizzaro's paper, "Sketch of a Course of Chemical Philosophy," published in No. 30 of Ostwald's "Klassiker der Exakten Wissenschaften."[13] At the close of the meeting Angelo Pavesi, professor of chemistry in the University of Pavia and friend of Cannizzaro, distributed pamphlets of a paper written by Cannizzaro, and published it in 1858 in Volume VII of *Il Nuovo Cimento*, a journal edited by Piria as the organ of the University of Pisa. Lothar Meyer read the pamphlet on the return journey to Breslau and reread it later, and he says of it: "It was as though the scales fell from my eyes, doubt vanished, and was replaced by a feeling of peaceful certainty."[14]

Wurtz states that about 140 chemists attended the meeting but he listed in alphabetic order 127 names. I have rearranged the list of Wurtz by countries:[15]

Germany (57): Babo, Baeyer, Becker, Beilstein, Bibra, Boeckmann, Braun, Bunsen, Carius, Casselmann, Clemm, Erdmann, Erlenmeyer, Fehling, Finck, Finckh, Fresenius, Geiger, Gorup-Besanez, Grimm, Guckelberger, Gundelach, Hallwachs, Heeren, Heintz, Hirzel, R. Hoffmann, Keller, Knop, Kolbe, Kopp, Kuhn, Landolt, Lehmann, Ludwig, Mendius, L. Meyer, Mulhäuser, Müller, Naumann, Nessler, Neubauer, Petersen, Quincke, Scherer, Schiel, Schmitt, Schneyder, Schroeder, Schwarzenbach, Seubert, Strecker, Streng, Weltzien, Will, E. Winckler, Zwenger.

France (21): Béchamp, Boussingault, Dumas, Friedel, Gautier, Grandeau, Jacquemin, Ch. Kestner, LeCanu, Nicklès, Oppermann, Persoz, Reischauer, Riche, Scheuer-Kestner, Schlagdenhauffen, Schneider, Schützenberger, P. Thénard, Verdet, Wurtz.

Great Britain (18): Abel, Anderson, Apjohn, Crum-Brown, Daubeny, Duppa, Foster, Gilbert, Gladstone, Griffith, Guthrie, Miller, Noad, Normandy, Odling, Roscoe, Schickendantz, Wanklyn.

Austria (7): Folwarezny, Hlasiwetz, Lang, Lieben, Pebal, Schneider, Wertheim.

Russia (7): Borodin, Lesinskiĭ, Mendeleev, Natanson, Savich, Shishkov, Zinin.

Switzerland (6): Bischoff, Brunner, Marignac, von Planta, Schiff, Wislicenus.

Belgium (3): Donny, Kekulé, Staş.

Sweden (3): Bahr, Berlin, Blomstrand.

Italy (2): Cannizzaro, Pavesi.

Mexico (1): Posselt.

Portugal (1): Carvalho.

Spain (1): deLuna.

---

[12] This is the contribution of Auguste Laurent adopted by Charles Gerhardt and discussed in Vol. IV of his "Traité," 1856. See A. LAURENT, *Ann. de Chim. et de Phys.* [3], 18, 294–7, (1846); "Méthode de Chimie," 1854, pp. 79–97. W. ODLING, "Chemical Method," translation of Laurent's book, 1855, pp. 62–85.

[13] The paper has been translated into English and published as Alembic Reprint No. 18.

[14] Ostwald's "Klassiker," No. 30, p. 59. Lothar Meyer's treatise, "Modern Theories of Chemistry," in which the ideas of Cannizzaro are fully developed, was begun in 1862. The publication of this book in 1864 made Meyer's reputation in the world of chemistry.

[15] ANSCHÜTZ (*op. cit.*, p. 673) rearranged the list of Wurtz according to countries and the cities from which the chemists came. He omitted the name of Hermann Kolbe and placed J. H. Gilbert under Sweden. Joseph Henry Gilbert worked with John Bennet Lawes at the Rothamsted agricultural experiment station near Harpenden in Hertfordshire, England.

George E. Hein
California Institute
of Technology
Pasadena

# The Liebig-Pasteur Controversy
## Vitality without vitalism

I think . . . that the disputes between Mechanists and Vitalists are unsatisfactory . . . . One is never quite sure what is meant by "Mechanism" and by "Vitalism"; and one suspects that both names cover a multitude of theories which the protagonists have never distinguished and put clearly before themselves.[1]

The legacy of 19th century science includes not only sweeping advances in all major areas, but also heated controversies. This was the first century of "modern" science, of systematic experimentation by professional scientists. It was also the first century of "modern" disputes, in which careful, but selective, experimentation was added to age-old stubbornness. Famous is the debate between Liebig and Pasteur concerning the nature of fermentation and a general explanation of what are now called enzymatic reactions. For many years, this was a living issue and the arguments were vigorous and often bitter. Liebig gave full rein to his sarcastic, inventive mind against the solid Gallic logic of Pasteur.

Today, fermentation and related processes are believed to be due to the action of particular chemical substances: enzymes. Their relation to inorganic catalysts has been established in principle. Many of the theoretical concepts applied to catalysis in living systems are derived from studies on strictly chemical systems. Even a further serious question concerning the nature of enzymes has been resolved: they are now almost universally recognized as belonging to the class of proteins, either pure or combined with known structures. That is, they are members of a larger category of chemical compounds whose properties and behavior have been studied for many decades. It is perhaps worth mentioning that general agreement on this last point has only been reached since 1930. The ensuing 30 years have not been sufficient to dispel completely the air of mystery which surrounds discussions concerning enzymes, especially (but not exclusively) those in the nontechnical literature.

Indeed, in some sense the controversy lives on in two distinct although overlapping forms. On the one hand, historians of science and biographers of the protagonists prolong the debate in their accounts of 19th century events as well as in some of their interpretations of modern views concerning enzymes. On the other hand, the Liebig-Pasteur controversy can be considered as one example of the continuing unsolved mechanism-vitalism problem which dates back to the pre-Socratics. It is worth while examining the evidence in view of both current interests. Careful consideration can help to set the record straight: it can help to scrape bare the positions actually held by Liebig and Pasteur from the accumulated encrustations of almost 100 years of partisan commentary. Further, a new presentation can shed light on the kinds of arguments and opinions which are put forward by mechanists and vitalists.

## Historical

In 1839 Liebig published a paper in his *Annalen* (1) summarizing his views on fermentation, decay, and putrefaction. The extensive analyses which had been carried out in his laboratory afforded him ample evidence of the similarities between organic and inorganic matter. This view was supplemented by his own researches on natural products which had led to the isolation from bitter almonds of "emulsin," an obviously nonliving material which catalyzed the decomposition of amygdalin (2). Finally, Liebig had at his disposal Berzelius' recent discussion on "catalysis" (3) in which the latter made no attempt to distinguish inorganic and organic (in the wider sense) catalysts by any fundamental difference in composition or mode of action.

Liebig's theory compared fermentation and related phenomena to other decomposition processes. He assigned violent motion to the particles of the catalyst as it decomposed and assumed that the transmission of this motion to the reactants brought about their decomposition in turn. In modern terminology, catalysts were "energy rich" substances which could transfer their (translational) energy to certain chemically similar reactant molecules and enable them to undergo decomposition. The emphasis was on analogy to processes known from inorganic chemistry. He repeatedly compared the action of heat and acids to that of ferments. In several cases he pointed out the specificity of certain catalysts and tried to relate this to structural similarities between the activating compound and its "substrate." The theory accounted for catalyst specificity and neatly related observations in inorganic chemistry, organic chemistry, and general physiology.

In August of 1857 Pasteur presented a paper before the faculty of science at Lille and repeated it three months later before the Académie des Sciences (4). He reported that his observations on the fermentation of sour milk to produce lactic acid led him "to a completely different point of view" concerning fermentation. Subsequent papers on other forms of fermentation, as well as his concurrent interest in *génération dites*

Presented before the Division of History of Chemistry at the 139th Meeting of the ACS, St. Louis, March, 1961.
Contribution No. 2730 from the Gates and Crellin Laboratories of Chemistry, California Institute of Technology, Pasadena.
[1] BROAD, C. D., "The Mind and Its Place in Nature," Routledge and Kegan Paul Ltd., London, 1925.

*spontanées*, supported his original conclusions. In every case the chemical change observed was accompanied by the appearance and multiplication of large numbers of microscopic "globules." These appeared to be living cells, and were also components of the catalyst introduced to start the reaction. If they were destroyed by heat or removed by filtration, the fermentation process ceased. Also, various types of fermentation led to the production of optically active products; a fact, which, to Pasteur, indicated the involvement of living organisms. These observations sharply distinguished fermentation processes from other catalytic phenomena and suggested that the chemical changes brought about during fermentation were "correlative" with the growth of the globules, or bacteria. In his most extensive publication on the subject (5), Pasteur fit his theory into the general framework of cellular biological concepts and paid tribute to scientists who had previously suggested similar explanations, among them Cagnard de la Tour, Schwann, and Turpin.

These contradictory views provided the groundwork for the controversy. On the surface the sides seem clear. Pasteur is a vitalist; he claims that living organisms are necessary for the fermentation process. Liebig is a mechanist; he explains all catalysis, including fermentation, by a chemical-kinetic, mechanistic theory. For Liebig, Pasteur's bacteria were only an incidental event accompanying the breakdown of products and catalysts.

Who was right? There is general agreement today that enzyme action does not require vitalistic explanations; and, after Buchner's demonstration of extracellular, alcoholic fermentation in a yeast extract (6), the last doubts concerning the requirement of viable cells were dispelled. The answer appears clear-cut.

Yet, it all depends on which commentator you read. We may dismiss those biographies of Pasteur and Liebig which are by their partisans. There is no doubt for Vallery-Radot (7) in writing about his father-in-law nor for Volhard (8) writing about his teacher and benefactor! However, even Singer (9) concludes a brief discussion of this topic with the statement that, ". . . unlike Liebig, Pasteur *realized* that fermentation demanded the presence of living organisms" (9). This is hard to reconcile with Conant's terse conclusion, "Pasteur's generalization was wrong, but it was marvelously fruitful" (10). The issue is hardly clarified when one remembers that Liebig was actually a vitalist who publicly answered some of the ardent mechanists of his day.

## Vitalism

Some of the confusion described above results from the same causes that led to the original extended debates. An attempt to defend one champion against charges from the other side easily leads to exaggeration and sometimes to misstatements. However, by far the greatest problem arises from a poor understanding of the word "vitalism" and its application to biological and chemical theories.

The Oxford English Dictionary defines "vitalism" as "the doctrine that the origin and phenomena of life are due to or produced by a vital principle, as distinct from purely chemical or physical force." In similarly defining the word Webster's points out that it is opposed

to mechanism. The meaning of vitalism is clear: it refers to a theory, or a group of theories, which explains some or all manifestations of living organisms in terms of something other than the laws of chemistry and physics. Vitalism provides some form of explanation in non-mechanistic terms.

Since the "laws of chemistry and physics" and even the laws of mechanics are subject to change without notice, it is sometimes a little difficult to pin down the boundaries between mechanism and vitalism. C. D. Broad argues (11) that the only "pure" mechanistic explanation is one which elucidates all phenomena in terms of a single kind of stuff, which undergoes a single kind of fundamental change, which can be explained in terms of a single elementary causal law and which has only a single and simple principle of composition. This is rather limiting and makes just about every tenable theory a vitalistic one by default, a situation much to Broad's liking.

However, such fine points need not bother us here. It is enough to recognize that any mechanistic theory says that the laws of chemistry and physics, or the fundamental laws of physics, since today scientists agree that chemistry is a subdivision of one branch of physics, are enough to explain the behavior of living things. A particular vitalistic statement or a particular vitalistic argument is one which explains a phenomenon characteristic of a living thing in terms of something other than the laws of physics, something not reducible to a law of physics.

Although fairly obvious, it is important to note that it is not necessary to assume that all properties of living things require an explanation in terms of vital forces in order to hold a vitalistic position. On the contrary, it is only necessary to say that a single such property is not explainable in terms of the physical laws. Indeed, no vitalist would be likely to take the inclusive extreme position. If a mouse is dropped, it falls just as a stone does. I doubt that anyone has ever felt compelled to supply separate explanations for these observations on living and non-living matter. If a bat is substituted for the mouse, the result is quite different. Yet, even here, no sensible person nowadays would suggest that the flying creature violates the laws of gravity. In fact it is doubtful that for the last several centuries anyone would have suggested that the flight of the bat, or of any other winged creature, required anything but a mechanistic explanation. I am speaking here only of the act of flight, not of possible reasons why certain animals have the organs which enable them to fly.

What, then, is the essence of vitalism? Just how does it differ from mechanism? This depends on the view that is held; vitalistic theories vary widely.

Hospers (12) considers four ways of stating the issues between mechanism and vitalism. These involve discussions concerning a divine Creator of life, a non-material life force, emergence, and non-reducibility. The last of these is fundamental. At the minimum, any vitalistic position holds that the basic laws governing the behavior of living organisms are not reducible to the laws of chemistry and physics. Non-reducibility is a necessary condition for vitalism. Unlike the first three positions, an argument supporting only non-reducibility need not state explicitly how the laws of biology differ from the laws of physics. Since the "laws of biology" are not only subject to change but are as yet uncertain, this problem becomes extremely complex. Among others, many modern physicists interested in biology have struggled with it. For example, Delbrück (13) argues that it is possible that the fundamental laws of biology may be related to the fundamental laws of modern physics as the latter are related to the laws of classical physics. He draws an analogy between the present state of biology and the condition of physics in 1910, and suggests that the resolution of some impasses between various approaches to molecular biology may prove to require similarly drastic revisions of concepts as were suggested by the non-classical explanations offered as resolutions for problems in atomic physics half a century ago. An important part of any such argument is to say not only that we do not know the fundamental laws of biology, but also that a new conceptual framework may be required to establish sound laws. If a biologist accepts this suggestion and acts accordingly, he could be satisfied with explanations of biological phenomena which are not couched in the same terms as the present laws of physics, although they may be similar to them. I shall call such a position a minimum vitalistic position.

The first three issues listed above all have in common the introduction of some particular force or agent into explanations concerning living things, or, in the case of emergence, at least the introduction of purpose. Further, they all readily lead to positions which place complete explanations of the phenomena in question outside the realm of physical science. A vitalistic explanation based on one of these positions would be characterized by its reference to the particular alternative to mechanism chosen; it would be recognized by its invocation of a divine being, an *élan vital* or *entelechy*, or an emergent property such as purpose, as the cause of some phenomenon. In any case, it would be held that the phenomenon in question could not be fully understood by reference to the laws of physics, and also that one of the alternative postulates would provide an adequate explanation. Although emergence theories (those that hold that the whole is greater than the sum of its parts) are often couched in vague terms involving tendencies or the mysteries of life, on the whole all the above, which I shall call positive vitalistic positions, are readily recognized by their reference to some non-spatial and usually non-empirical principle.

The above brief outline of possible vitalistic positions emphasizes one important point: it is not reference to living things or to living processes which makes one a vitalist. If this were the case, every biologist would necessarily be a vitalist. Only the explanation of a phenomenon of life or of a process associated with living things by means other than the laws of chemistry and physics represents a vitalistic point of view. The minimum vitalistic position offers a particular explanation to account for the purported particular behavior of living things. The vitalism-mechanism issue is concerned with causes and origins.

## Liebig's View

Since Liebig's theory tried to explain all catalytic processes including fermentation by the same theory involving mechanical motion and chemical interaction, it is clearly not vitalistic. He even went further and first denied the existence of living cells in fermenting mixtures; later, when forced to concede their reality, he at least denied that they were causally related to the fermentation process.

Any attempt to reconcile this view with Liebig's vitalistic sentiments fails. Indeed, this phase of Liebig's life is difficult to integrate with his scientific work. One reason we revere Liebig today is because he extended chemistry to include a wide range of topics which had previously been within the preserve of biologists, often vitalists. With supreme confidence, Liebig approached problems in agriculture and physiology as strictly chemical tasks. In his sweeping researches in these areas he never had any doubts that the materials he isolated from living things were chemical substances, amenable to chemical study and subject to the laws of inorganic chemistry. His popular discourses in opposition to what he called "excessive-mechanism" must be attributed to other than scientific ways of thought.

## Pasteur's View

There is no doubt that Pasteur considered fermentation to be intimately connected with living cells. However, this is not enough to make his position a vitalistic one. To recognize (or assume) that some property or function is found only in living objects is simply to classify it, not to explain it. The question of causation still remains.

Further, it is important to distinguish between those phenomena which are part of the life process and those which are only found with it. Members of the former class are sometimes difficult to define, since the question, "what is life?" is involved here. However, members of the latter class are readily recognized. For example, no reasonable person would contend that the ability to fly is necessary for life to manifest itself. Yet only living things are capable of voluntary flight.

For Pasteur, fermentation was a process carried out only by viable cells during their growth and multiplication. He clearly recognized the metabolic significance of fermentation, that the products observed were remnants of the substrate after it had been utilized by the cell. However, he chose his words carefully; over and over in the many papers on this subject he repeats the same phrase, "*les fermentations sont correlatives d'un acte vital.*" This is a statement of the same kind as "only living things are capable of flight." Certainly it does not in any way imply a vitalistic hypothesis. In fact, it says nothing about the cause of fermentation or about the laws which govern living things.

Pasteur was a careful man. He stayed close to the facts, his facts. His experimental observations were that fermentations were chemical processes carried out only by living cells during their life cycle, and the experiments permitted nothing further. In fact, the papers entitled "*Sur la nature de la fermentation*" are disappointing in the sense that on this question they contain little more than reiterations that fermentation is correlative with the development of the cells. His repeated publications show forcefully and determinedly that living cells carry out the fermentation process, that they multiply and grow during it, and that there can be no fermentaion in their absence. Again and again, he admitted that he was ignorant of the true cause of fermentation. Probably his statement that "fermentation, properly so-called," required living cells was motivated more by a desire to restrict the term to experimentally similar situations than by an attempt to save his theory even at the risk of a circular argument. Also, without our wider framework of reference, it was impossible for Pasteur to realize that all his researches on fermentation, involving different bacterial species and leading to a variety of products, are only a small class of enzyme reactions. After working for 20 years and publishing more than 50 papers and notes, it was reasonable that Pasteur considered that his work encompassed the field of what we now call enzyme chemistry and that the known unorganized ferments (that is, extracellular enzymes) were peripheral examples not worthy of classification under the same heading.

One of the experimental results which seemed of particular importance to Pasteur was that fermentation could produce optically active compounds. Pasteur believed that only living organisms were capable of producing asymmetrical products from optically inactive starting materials. Since fermentation could bring this about, it must be related to a life process. This argument was crucial for Pasteur; it may have influenced his unshaking faith in the correctness of his theory, which was somewhat of a speculation when first advanced and certainly contrary to the most generally held view as exemplified by Liebig's paper. It may be significant that Pasteur's first contribution on the subject concerned itself with lactic acid fermentation, which produces an optically active product, rather than with the more common vinous fermentation, which produces the simpler inactive products alcohol and carbon dioxide. We can use Pasteur's interest in this point to trace his thinking concerning causes. Molecular asymmetry was something which Pasteur felt he understood very well and he speculated about it much more than he speculated on the nature of fermentation.

In examining his views on optical activity and molecular asymmetry we may first ask, how did the asymmetric molecules produced by fermentation arise? Pasteur was explicit on this point (*14*): the formation of asymmetric molecules must arise because the bacteria themselves contain asymmetric molecules. He considered that the chemical action of the ferment on its substrate involves the formation of a diastereoisomeric pair, only one member of which is capable of reaction. He clearly drew the direct analogy to the resolution of a racemic mixture of acids by an optically active base. Thus, the chemical action of yeast on its substrate involves the same principles as a chemical separation of inorganic optically active compounds. Note that nothing but the laws of chemistry is invoked. More than that, something about the nature of the living ferment is inferred by analogy to a non-living system.

However, Pasteur did not stop here. What is the origin of the asymmetry found only in nature, the asymmetric molecules produced only by living organisms? Pasteur believed that this was caused by strictly natural forces, forces known to physics. He commented that the earth is asymmetric because of its axial rotation and that this might provide a natural source of asymmetry. Pasteur felt that the existence of asymmetric force fields was a reasonable cause for the

production of asymmetric molecules; he even considered this a subject worthy of experimental work. He performed crystallizations in the presence of strong magnetic fields, expecting to demonstrate a kind of asymmetric induction. He hoped to grow plants in an environment where, by the use of mirrors, they were subject to the influence of an "inverted" sun that rose in the west and set in the east, thus producing plants containing compounds of "unnatural" configuration.

Neither the reasonableness of his theory nor the practicality of the experiments need concern us here. The only important point is that Pasteur felt that asymmetry was intimately related with living systems and yet he sought mechanistic causes for it! In this instance where he went beyond the facts and sought a fundamental explanation for a phenomenon of life, he turned immediately to physics. No alternative kind of interpretation was even suggested.

To summarize, Pasteur's theory of fermentation and related processes is not in any way vitalistic. He did not invoke positive vitalistic causes; he did not even take a minimum vitalistic position. His contribution to the controversy involved the report and reiteration of experimental results and not the proposing of causes. Where he did seek causes he looked for them within the known laws of chemistry and physics.

## Critique of Commentators

Despite the apparently forthright and clear stand Pasteur took, he is persistently dubbed a vitalist. It might be argued that the word "vitalism" is used synonymously with "vitality" to mean simply "involving life." Remarkably enough, this is often not the case. Those who call Pasteur a vitalist use the term correctly, although this does not detract from its erroneous application in this instance. A good example of this sort of argument is found in the influential biography of Pasteur by René Dubos (*15*). In introducing Pasteur's views on fermentation (p. 119) he wrote,

The 20th-century scientist does not know how to introduce life into his equilibrium reactions any better than the 19th-century chemist knew where to place yeast in the formula of alcoholic fermentation. However, so great were the triumphs of physicochemical science during the "wonderful century" that many scientists had enough confidence, or perhaps merely enough intellectual conceit, to ignore the difficulty, and to refuse to recognize the existence of an unsolved mystery in fermentation and putrefaction. Pasteur was willing to introduce mystery in the problem by stating that yeast was a living being and fermentation an attribute of its life.

A few pages later, in describing Pasteur's antagonists, he wrote (p. 123),

In the kingdom of science, there were probably many who did not share the official optimism, and who did not believe that the time had come when everything could be accounted for in terms of known physicochemical forces. But the priests of the new faith—Berzelius, Liebig, Wöhler, Helmholz, Berthelot and others—were the supreme rulers of scientific thinking... the new prophets had pronounced anathema on anyone who preached the doctrine of vitalism.

As those who had previously supported the vitalistic theory of fermentation and putrefaction he listed Cagnard de la Tour, Schwann, Kutzing, and Turpin. These passages clearly indicate that Dubos thinks of vitalism as the doctrine which opposes mechanism. They also suggest a leaning in favor of the vitalistic view of nature over the mechanistic one. However, this is not important to us except as perhaps supplying a motive for his entire discussion. What is more important is that the classification given puts people in the wrong camps! I have already pointed out that Pasteur's views on this question are not consistent with a vitalistic position. Similar arguments could be presented for Schwann. Although generally recognized as one of the founders of the cellular theory, he was an ardent and vocal mechanist. And these positions are by no means contradictory. The cellular theory makes a statement about a property of living matter: that it is always organized in complex units designated cells. It does not say anything about the origin of these units or the means by which their behavior may be explained. As a matter of fact, Schwann thought that cells could be precipitated out of solutions containing only inorganic materials, if all the right ingredients were present in the proper proportions. It is no mere coincidence that a generally available reprint of excerpts from Schwann's monograph on the cell theory (16) begins with a discussion of vitalistic (teleological) and mechanistic explanations of living matter and comes out firmly in favor of the latter view.

Contrariwise, Liebig definitely did not believe that "everything could be accounted for in terms of known physicochemical forces." I have already alluded to his vitalistic philosophy. A fuller discussion can be found in the comprehensive work by Metz (17). Even Whöler remained a vitalist, despite his reputation for having driven vital force out of organic chemistry. He too is misrepresented in Dubos' classification.

Curiously enough, Dubos referred at great length to Pasteur's fundamental mechanistic inclinations. However, he described them (p. 114) as the wild-eyed imaginings of a romantic mind.

Pasteur carried with him into the grave the dream of his scientific youth—the fantastic vision of developing techniques for the creation or modification of life by introducing asymmetrical forces into chemical reactions.

A man who believes that life can be created or modified in this manner by the action of physical forces can hardly be labeled a vitalist.

The influence of Dubos' work can be illustrated by a recent article in THIS JOURNAL (18) which essentially summarizes his discussion:

Turpin . . . Cagnard de la Tour, Schwann, and Kutzing were the unacknowledged (sic) forefathers of Pasteur's viewpoint. It was they who first eloquently expressed the sum and substance of Pasteur's dictum: The phenomena of alcoholic fermentation were inexplicable without resort to a vitalistic hypothesis.

## Nature of the Controversy

If neither Pasteur nor Liebig held vitalistic positions, why was there a controversy? An answer is possible, although perhaps not one as dramatic as might be hoped. As is so often the case in modern science, Liebig and Pasteur carried out different experiments, arrived at different conclusions based on these experiments and on their general outlook, and stuck with them. Each one refused to recognize the other's references and analogies. This situation must be familiar to every practicing scientist.

Liebig speculated about fermentation mainly on the basis of other experiments. His evidence was drawn from the then known extracellular enzymes; therefore he had no reason to try to overcome a deepseated inclination to avoid considering living cells. Pasteur insisted on working only with enzymatic systems which, during his lifetime, could not be separated from living cells. He in turn ignored the work on digestive enzymes, which dated back to the previous century.

It does not seem desirable to dwell for long on this short-sightedness exhibited by two great scientists, whose main bodies of work are immortal. Certainly larger issues were involved. Liebig was opposed to the germ theory, while Pasteur became its most famous and ardent supporter.

It is easy for us to criticize the protagonists in the light of our present scientific beliefs and general climate of opinion. Liebig's refusal to recognize the microscopic evidence concerning the existence of cells strikes us as extremely short-sighted. But this attitude must be viewed in the framework of his background and theoretical views. Liebig was a student of Berzelius and Gay-Lussac; like them, what he explained, he explained in terms of chemistry and physics. If that was not enough, then he attempted no interpretation at all. Or to put it another way, if an explanation of a group of observations was possible, then that explanation had to be in terms of chemistry. In any case, new facts are often not enough to destroy a theory; a different frame of mind, a new way of looking at things, is required. And such a transformation of thought is most difficult for someone intimately involved in supporting one side of an issue. The same kind of criticism and excuse can be made for Pasteur. He became deeply committed to the cellular, germ theory and this dominated his thinking.

Finally, in order to make perfectly clear the kind of position taken by Pasteur, it is worth while to consider a truly vitalistic explanation of asymmetry. Pasteur noted the asymmetry found in living things and attributed it to the action of blind asymmetric forces. He further hoped to show experimentally that asymmetry could be created by the use of available asymmetric forces.

Here is another view, taken from a recent book concerned with fundamental causes of natural phenomena (19):

It may be that life came on earth once, and once only, and that all life . . . has come from that one center. This seems suggested, if not proved, from the fact that certain chemical substances are known in two forms . . . known as dextro-rotatory and laevo-rotatory . . . if these substances be made synthetically in the laboratory of the chemist, they are almost invariably found to consist of equal quantities of either kind. If, on the other hand, they are prepared from the substances of living plants or animals, in which they occur naturally . . . they are found to be made up wholly of one type. This is by no means a conclusive argument—various ways of accounting for it may be imagined—but it does not by any means support the feeling, that there is an unholy and unending struggle between the creatures of the living world. It is, on the other hand, in general agreement with the evolutionary explanation, if it is thought that the whole of life comes from one original act, which may, in some sense, be identified with the religious idea of an act of creation by the Diety.

I shall not concern myself here with the validity or pertinence of this argument; what is important is its form. No attempt is made to explain the experimental "fact." Instead, the observation is used to bolster a particular view concerning evolution, a view which, by its very nature, is not amenable to experimentation. This approach is perhaps of little interest to the scientist, but it certainly illustrates a marked contrast to Pasteur's attempts to resolve a similar question. The above is the view of a man who believes in a positive vitalistic view of life and who uses experimental evidence to support this view. Pasteur used experimental evidence to draw conclusions which were amenable to further experiment, all within the framework of the then known laws of physics.

## Literature Cited

(1) Liebig, J., *Ann.*, **30**, 250, 364 (1839).
(2) Liebig, J., *Ann.*, **22**, 1 (1837).
(3) Berzelius, J. J., *Annales chimie physique*, **61**, 146 (1836), translated in Leicester, H. M., and Klickstein, H. S., editors, "A Source Book of Chemistry," McGraw-Hill Book Co., Inc., New York, **1952**, pp. 261–268.
(4) All quotations from Pasteur, L., are taken from "Oevres de Pasteur," reunies par Vallery-Radot, R., Masson et Cie., Paris, **1922**, Volume 2. This passage appears on pp. 3–14.
(5) Pasteur, L., *op. cit.*, pp. 51–125.
(6) Buchner, E., *Ber.*, **30**, 117–24 (1897).
(7) Vallery-Radot, R., "The Life of Pasteur," translated by Devonshire, R. L., Doubleday, & Co., Inc., New York, **1923**.
(8) Volhard, J., "Justus von Liebig," Verlag J. A. Barth, Leipzig, **1909**.
(9) Singer, C., "A Short History of Scientific Ideas," Oxford University Press, Oxford, **1959**, p. 462.
(10) Conant, J. B., "Pasteur's Study of Fermentation," Harvard Case History No. 6, Harvard University Press, Cambridge, **1952**, p. 36.
(11) Broad, C. D., "The Mind and Its Place in Nature," Routledge and Kegan Paul Ltd., London, **1925**, Chap. 2.
(12) Hospers, J., "An Introduction to Philosophical Analysis," Prentice Hall, Inc., New York, **1953**, pp. 282–294.
(13) Delbrück, M., *Trans. Conn. Academy of Arts and Sciences*, **38**, 173–190 (1949).
(14) Pasteur, L., *op. cit.*, p. 25.
(15) Dubos, R. J., "Louis Pasteur, Freelance of Science," Little, Brown & Co., Inc., New York, **1950**.
(16) Schwann, "Microscopic Researches," an excerpt in Gabriel, M. L., and Fogel, S., "Great Experiments in Biology," Prentice Hall, Inc., Englewood Cliffs, N. J., **1955**, pp. 12–20.
(17) Metz, J. T., "A History of European Thought in the Nineteenth Century," Blackwood, London, **1923**, Vol. 2.
(18) Feingold, H., this Journal, **31**, 403–406 (1954).
(19) Rowland, J., "Mysteries of Science," Werner Laurie, London, **1955**, p. 78.

——————◆——————

# ÉMILE CLAPEYRON (1799–1864)

## H. S. VAN KLOOSTER
Rensselaer Polytechnic Institute, Troy, New York

Among the founders of the science of thermodynamics two Frenchmen occupy a prominent place, *viz.*, Carnot and Clapeyron, both former students of the famous École Polytechnique, founded in 1794. This school owes its pre-eminent position to the fact that the number of entering students is limited to 250, chosen from over 1000 applicants from the best secondary schools in France. The curriculum extends over two years after which the graduates continue their studies in their chosen special fields.

Benoit Pierre Émile Clapeyron, a native of Paris, was born on February 26, 1799. He entered the École Polytechnique in 1816, four years after Carnot. Finishing his studies in 1818, he became a mining engineering student at the School of Mines and was graduated in 1820. The Russian government at that time was establishing a new school for public-works instruction and had asked for French engineers as instructors. Clapeyron and his friend Lamé, also a graduate of the School of Mines, were chosen and for ten years they taught pure and applied mathematics in Petrograd. The revolution of 1830 put a sudden stop to a successful career in Russia and Clapeyron returned to Paris, at the time when George Stephenson with his locomotive "The Rocket" opened up the prospects for railroad transportation on both sides of the Atlantic. Clapeyron drew up the plans for the first railroad from Paris to Saint Germain and applied his talents to the design of locomotives.

His later prominent role as a builder of railroads and bridges did not detract from his activities as a scientist and teacher. He was elected a member of the Academy of Sciences in 1858, occupying the seat of another famous alumnus of the École Polytechnique, *viz.*, Cauchy. For over 15 years (1849–64) he taught the course on steam engines at the École des Ponts in Paris. Early in his railroad career, when looking for a relation between power production and coal consumption, Clapeyron came across Carnot's 60-page brochure, "Reflexions sur la puissance motrice du feu," published in 1824. This was a revelation to Clapeyron and led to the publication in 1834 of his "Mémoire sur la puissance motrice de la chaleur" in which he first developed the graphical methods of cyclical processes, resulting in the well-known equation that bears his name:

$$\frac{dP}{dT} = \frac{\Delta H}{T(V_2 - V_1)}$$

This equation was first published in the *Journal de l'École Polytechnique* [**18**, 170 (1834)] and later also appeared in the *Annales de Physique* [(2) **59**, 446 (1843)]. Clapeyron died on January 28, 1864.

**Henry M. Leicester**
College of Physicians and Surgeons
of the University of the Pacific
San Francisco, California

# Some Aspects of the History of Chemistry in Russia

A consideration of the history of chemistry in Russia as an example of the general attitude of Russia toward science can be very instructive, both by explaining some of the features of Soviet science which have often puzzled Western observers and by indicating some of the possibilities for science in general which could ensue as a result of present policies in the modern world. This paper will attempt to develop a few of these points.

Probably the chief difference between the development of science in Western Europe and in Russia at the beginning of the eighteenth century[1] lay in the fact that Western science had grown gradually and naturally, arising from the mingling of many cultural streams, and was firmly based in the technical and intellectual lives of the people among whom it arose. In Russia, on the other hand, no such gradual development had occurred. There had been a technological expansion—in the manufacture of drugs, gunpowder, and assaying techniques—which was essentially the same as that of western Europe at the same period. This is not strange, for the technical processes were carried out almost exclusively by western artisans, imported for the purpose. Native Russians seldom had the training to carry on these processes. In the intellectual life of the highly stratified Russian society there was no interest in scientific problems, and very little even in the applications of science.

Thus when Peter the Great in 1724 decided that he could further his projects for the westernization of his country by creating an Academy of Sciences on the French model, he was forced to staff it entirely with foreigners brought to his new capital of St. Petersburg and given substantial material inducements to draw them to this raw, new city.

Science was thus imposed upon Russia by outsiders, just as technology had been. This characteristic domination of early Russian science by foreigners who acquired a vested interest in maintaining their special privileges was so strong that when a truly Russian scientific genius did appear in the person of Mikhail Vasil'evich Lomonosov (1711–65),[2] he was unable to exert an influence equal to his abilities on the scientific world of his time. Although his views on chemistry, physics, technology, and many other scientific fields were far in advance of his day, he was prevented from applying them to the full, largely because of his constant quarrels with his German colleagues in the Academy of Sciences. Most of his important work remained unpublished and unknown to the scientific world. It was only in his poetry that he was relatively free to express himself; and so, for nearly two hundred years he was

---

[1] LEICESTER, H. M., J. CHEM. EDUC., **24,** 438 (1947).
[2] FARBER, E., edit., "Great Chemists," Interscience, New York, **1961,** pp. 201–210.

---

Mr. Joseph Evans, Vice-president Dexter Chemical Corp., Dr. Leicester, and Prof. Aaron J. Ihde, Chairman Division of Chemistry

The 1962 Dexter Award winner, Henry M. Leicester, long has been a friend to readers of THIS JOURNAL. Two editors have sought his advise and counsel; for a decade (1949–59) he was a member of the Editorial Board. Numerous articles have come from his prolific pen. He also served as editor and contributor to the sixth edition of Mary Elvira Weeks' classic "Discovery of the Elements."

Prof. Leicester since 1950 has been the head of the Department of Physiological Sciences, College of Physicians and Surgeons of San Franciso. In addition to being a historian, he is a well-known biochemist contributing to an understanding of the chemistry of teeth.

His writings on Russian chemistry include works on Butlerov, Zinin, Markovnikov, Lowitz, Blokh, Mendeleev, and "The History of Chemistry in Russia prior to 1900." Through his knowledge of the Russian language and his personal contacts with Russian historians of science, Prof. Leicester has been responsible for drawing them closer to American historians of science.

Dr. Leicester received AB, MA, and PhD degrees in chemistry from Stanford University. He was one of the founders of *Chymia*, The International Journal of the History of Chemistry, and is presently its Editor-in-chief.

The Dexter Award includes a $1000 prize and a plaque. Previous winners of this award are: 1956, Ralph E. Oesper; 1957, Williams Haynes; 1958, Eva V. Armstrong; 1959, John Read (Great Britain); 1960, Denis I. Duveen; and 1961, James R. Partington (Great Britain).

known chiefly as a poet rather than as a scientist. It can be seen that even a man of undoubted genius cannot be effective when the atmosphere surrounding him is unfavorable.

Following his death, native Russian science languished, and only foreigners carried on the work of the Academy. This was an undistinguished period in the history of Russian science.

At the beginning of the nineteenth century a new wave of westernization swept over Russia and resulted in the foundation of a number of provincial universities. Here for the first time it became possible for young Russians to study the science of the West. At first progress was slow, since this new generation was only beginning to learn the actual conduct of research. As these men matured, however, and taught the next generation the ideas they had absorbed, the methods of western science spread through the universities; and research in the Western sense began to be carried out. Thus, for example, after 1830 the University of Kazan was a major center of chemical activity which for a time exceeded any activity at the Academy of Sciences, and where research was carried on by native Russian scholars.

This scientific research was, however, not completely free. The Russian universities were controlled by the government and a close watch was kept on the teachings of the professors. Too liberal ideas among the faculties or student bodies could result in closing the universities, sometimes for long periods. Especially in the later years of the nineteenth century, student riots and closed universities were quite common. Nevertheless the scientific fields were not as suspect as those subjects more closely related to politics and economics. The scientists were left to themselves, so long as they worked in scientific fields only. As a result, a true Russian science grew up, practiced by Russians in their own country and firmly based in the intellectual life of the nation. Thus science reached its highest point, at least in chemistry, in the years between 1840 and 1880—names such as Markovnikov, Butlerov, and Mendeleev stand out in the history of world chemistry.

The increasingly tense political situation after the assassination of Alexander II in 1881 resulted in more restrictive measures against even scientists, and both Markovnikov and Mendeleev, in spite of their scientific eminence, lost their university professorships because of their liberal political ideas. The succeeding generation of scientists, with few exceptions, did not measure up to the achievements of their predecessors.

This brief survey of the history of chemisty in Russia indicates quite clearly that, in order to achieve its greatest progress in a nation, a science must be firmly based in the life of that nation. Thus, the solid foundation of science in the culture of Western Europe certainly helps to account for the outstanding progress which it made after the Renaissance. The progress of Russian chemistry was marked, not when one genius attempted to further it but when it became part of the intellectual life of the nation, even though this intellectual life may have been but a small fraction of the total culture of that huge country.

Some further conclusions of interest can be drawn from the history of chemistry in Russia. It was formerly thought by many Westerners that Russia was a backward country intellectually, and that her science and technology were taken almost entirely from foreign sources. The spectacular advances in space research in the last few years startled those who held this view, but not those who were familiar with history. There had been no doubt as to the originality and ability of Russian scientists after the nineteenth century. At the same time, a knowledge of Russian history also helps to explain some of the other puzzling and contradictory features of present day Soviet science. Actually neither the ability shown by the space scientists nor the excesses of Lysenkoism and the rejection of the resonance theory should be surprising. Both aspects are a continuation of tendencies which have long been present.

Throughout its development, Russian science was regarded with mixed emotions by the governing class. As shown, science was never completely free from governmental supervision, and the supervisors always showed curiously ambivalent attitude in their work. The Czar might personally recognize the value of Mendeleev, the scientist[3]; but Mendeleev, the liberal, could never gain admittance to the Academy of Sciences,[4] which was controlled by the politically powerful and conservative German party. Thus he could be summarily dismissed from his university position when he supported the liberal views of some of the students. This distrusting of the scientist while at the same time valuing his work is not, perhaps, confined to Russia; but it was very pronounced there; and it may have been augmented because of the imposed character of Russian science in its early days. It seems to have been a continuous feature of Russian scientific life at all times.

When the tremendous expansion of scientific activity took place after the Revolution, this attitude did not change. The need for science was now even more obvious to the politicians, but the suspicion of it continued. It was probably intensified by the defection of such prominent chemists as Chichibabin and Ipatiev after World War I. Thus it was felt to be necessary that the scientist conform to the dominant ideology of the government before he could continue his work, just as had been the case in czarist Russia.

The scale of science in the Soviet Union today is vastly greater than it has ever been, but its roots lie in the past, and this must be considered in any evaluation of the present position or the future prospects. The study of the history of Russian science is as essential to an understanding of the Soviet Union as is any study of her political and economic policies.

[3] FARBER, E., *ibid.*, pp. 719–32.
[4] LEICESTER, H. M., J. CHEM. EDUC., **25**, 439 (1948).

+ + +

# THE GENESIS OF THE METRIC SYSTEM and THE WORK OF THE INTERNATIONAL BUREAU OF WEIGHTS AND MEASURES

**HENRI MOREAU**

International Bureau of Weights and Measures,
Sevres, France

*(Translated by Ralph E. Oesper)*

ON DECEMBER 10, 1949, the meter, the standard of length in the metric system, was 150 years old, and May 20, 1950, marked the 75th anniversary of the founding of the International Bureau of Weights and Measures. These two anniversaries, which were passed over practically unnoticed, recall important dates in the history of weights and measures, a history which to a great extent may be said to represent the history of civilization itself.

The history of the founding of the metric system is intertwined with that of the French Revolution of 1789. At various steps in the genesis of this system one encounters the names of eminent men of science and politics who played leading roles in this fateful period of French history. As for the Bureau of Weights and Measures, its creation was one of the consequences of the development of the metric system during the second half of the nineteenth century.

This paper will give the broad outlines of the origin of the metric system, that "enterprise whose result should belong some day to the whole world" (Talleyrand), and will describe the essential part of the work of that metrological institute of world-wide character, namely the International Bureau of Weights and Measures.

## DIVERSITY OF ANCIENT MEASURES

At all periods of social intercourse there has been a need for weights and measures so that commercial transactions can be carried on conveniently and honestly. This objective was far from attainment at the end of the eighteenth century, when a wide diversity of units produced inevitable confusion. Furthermore, there was considerable doubt as to the permanence of the standard weights and measures.

Without going into the detailed history of the ancient weights and measures, one dominant fact should be noted: the uniformity was illusory. The units varied, not only from country to country, and sometimes (as in France) from province to province, but even from city to city, and also according to corporation or guild. Of course, this state of affairs led to errors, frauds, and continual misunderstandings and disputes, to say nothing of the serious repercussions such a situation was bound to have on the progress of science. The multiplicity of names given to poorly determined units and the diversity in the multiples and submultiples of the principal measures increased the confusion.

To remedy this lack of uniformity and to obviate the consequent inconveniences, royal decrees relative to the unification and control of measures were issued at various times by the sovereigns, who, at the same time, hoped thus to increase their power over the whole country. Such decisions, which sometimes had real effects (Charlemagne, 789; Charles the Bald, 864, for instance) unfortunately did not outlive their sponsors.

The reform of the system of measures, which was neatly summed up in the motto "One King, one Law, one Weight, one Measure" occurring in more than one of the *cahiers* of the États Généraux (States General),[1] was constantly opposed by the interested resistance of the nobles, the influence of the guilds, and, in general, by all who profited by the prevailing disorder. Added to these hindrances was the innate indifference, if not the hostility, of those accustomed to their local units.

In Paris the principal units in use before the establishment of the metric system were the *Pied de Roi* (0.325 m.) for lengths and the *Livre poids de marc* (489.5 g.) for weights.[2] These two units were respectively represented by standards known as the *Toise du Châtelet* and the *Pile de Charlemagne*.

The Toise du Châtelet ( = 6 Pieds de Roi (1.949 m.)) was an iron bar that had been fastened in 1668 to the outer wall, at the foot of the staircase, of the Grand Châtelet.[3] At its ends were two notches or projections at right angles; a toise was supposed to fit precisely between them. This standard toise had served for the adjusting, among others, of the two famous toises, known as the *Toise du Pérou* and the *Toise du Nord*, which were used in measuring the arc of the earth's

---

[1] The États Généraux was the general assembly of the whole French nation; the representatives were sent by the clergy, the nobility, and the third estate (the commoners). The first of these États Généraux convened at Paris in 1302.

[2] The subdivisions of these units were:

| | |
|---|---|
| Toise = 6 Pieds de Roi | Livre = 2 marcs |
| Pied de Roi = 12 pouces | marc = 8 onces |
| pouce = 12 lignes | once = 8 gros |
| ligne = 12 points | gros = 3 deniers |
| | denier = 24 grains |

Other units of length in common use were: the *aune* (ell) of 3 pieds, 7 pouces, 10⁵/₆ lignes (1.188 m.); the *lieue* (league) of 2.283 toises (4.45 m.); the *perche royale* of 3.666 toises (7.15 m.).

[3] The Grand Châtelet was the name of a fortress of ancient Paris which, along with the Petit Châtelet, guarded the heads of the two bridges giving access to the Cité. The Grand Châtelet was torn down in 1802.

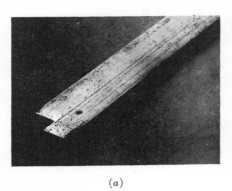

(a)

(b)

**The Toise du Pérou or de l'Académie 1735.**

(a) One of the ends, where the lines showing the subdivisions in lignes (2.256 mm.) and pouces (27.07 mm.) can be seen.

(b) The inscription on the cover of the case. This ancient French standard of length is preserved at the Observatory in Paris.

meridian in 1735 to 1737 below the equator by Bouguer, La Condamine, and Godin, and in Lapland by Maupertuis and Clairaut. In 1766 the Toise du Pérou replaced the Toise du Châtelet as the legal standard of measures of length in France.

The Pile de Charlemagne, constructed in the last third of the fifteenth century, consisted of a series of 13 copper weights, nesting in each other; the ensemble weighed 50 marcs (12.2375 kg.).

Despite votes by the États Généraux, all attempts to impose the Parisian units on the entire French kingdom came to a halt more or less rapidly; the successive governments recoiled before the immense task. Though at present it is somewhat difficult to visualize the difficulties to which the confusion in the measures led at the time—a disorder which the English economist Arthur Young described as the "infinite confusion of the French measures, which passes anything one can imagine," and which aroused the indignation of Talleyrand because the "variety was ghastly"—enough

**The Pile of Charlemagne and Its Case, Which Bears the Inscription:** "Poids original de la Cour des Monoyes." This Ancient French Standard of Weight is Preserved at the Musée du Conservatorie National des Arts et Métiers in Paris.

has been said to depict the state of anarchy which prevailed with respect to weights and measures in France prior to the establishment of the metric system.

It was necessary to wait for the great overturn accomplished by the French Revolution of 1789, whose great objective was the elimination of all traces of the feudal system and royalty, and for the influence of the French scientists, who realized the international import of such a forward step, before the problem could be put on a scientific basis and a complete reform brought about.

## CREATION OF THE METRIC SYSTEM

*Possible Bases of the New System.* The idea which guided the promoters of the reform of the weights and measures was to guarantee the invariability of the measures by relating them to a model taken from nature or to a standard whose magnitude was derived from natural phenomena. The new system would thus be based on a "natural universal unit," which would not belong to anyone and which could be adopted by all countries without arousing national jealousies.

When this problem was taken up in earnest, three propositions were advanced regarding the choice of the unit of length: a measured fraction of the length of an arc of meridian, or of the circle of the terrestial equator, or the length of a seconds pendulum.

The first proposition was a revival of that advanced in 1670 by the Abbé Gabriel Mouton, French astronomer and mathematician, who at the same time recommended a decimal division of the units. The idea of using the pendulum, which probably came from the Royal Society of London, had already been supported by Picard (1671), Huygens (1673), and Roemer. The real choice lay between the meridian and the length of the pendulum.

The project based on the pendulum, although attractive, was criticized at once. The length of the seconds pendulum depends on the intensity of the gravitational force and consequently is not the same at all points on the earth's surface. Moreover, the second, a unit of time, would enter into the definition of the unit of length.

Before proceeding farther with the study of the plan of reforming the system of weights and measures, the French authorities sought the cooperation of England to insure that the new system would have an international character. At this time the English were considering a reform of their own measures, and Sir John Riggs Miller had just proposed the length of the pendulum as the base (July, 1789). Accordingly, the time seemed eminently suitable for an *entente* in this matter between the Royal Society and the Académie des Sciences de Paris.

In March, 1790, Talleyrand, then bishop of Autun, laid before the Constituent Assembly a plan of the unification of weights and measures, likewise based on the length of the pendulum, and he requested England to collaborate with France in fixing the base of the new measures.

*The Adoption of the Meridian.* While awaiting the reply from the English, and after discussing the Talleyrand plan, the Académie des Sciences appointed a first commission, which adopted the decimal scale for all the divisions of weights, measures, and coinage (October 27, 1790).

A second commission, composed of Borda, Lagrange, Monge, and Condorcet, was charged with fixing the base of the unit of linear measure. Rejecting the length of the pendulum, for the reasons just given, this commission finally decided in favor of the quadrant of the earth's meridian, the ten-millionth part to be the actual unit of length. Since it was obviously difficult to consider the measurement of a quarter of the entire meridian, it was decided that they would limit themselves to measuring an arc extending between Dunkerque and Barcelona, the extremities of this arc of meridian, both at sea level, located to the north and south of the 45th parallel. This plan was adopted by the Assemblée Nationale on March 26, 1791, and the Académie immediately named the various commissions whose duty it would be to carry out the tasks necessary to the execution of this plan. Delambre and Méchain were placed in charge of the measuring of the arc of meridian, while Lavoisier and Haüy (later Lefèvere-Gineau and Fabbroni) were assigned the determination of the weight of a known volume of water from which to deduce the standard of weight.

*Attitudes of the English and the Americans.* The hoped-for cooperation of the English in the creation of the new system was not obtained. On December 3, 1790, shortly after the Riggs Miller project was placed before the House of Commons (April 13, 1790), the Duke of Leeds, Secretary for Foreign Affairs, replied to the Marquis de la Luzerne, the French Ambassador, that the British Government regretted that it could not accede to the proposals of the French Government, the arrangement being considered "impracticable."

As for the Americans, the reform of measures was also a matter then under consideration. In January, 1790, President Washington sent a message to Congress inviting that body to study the system of weights and measures. Secretary of State Jefferson proposed that a choice be made between two solutions: definition, simplification, and uniformization of the existing system of English units, or the establishment of a new system based on the seconds pendulum, with decimal multiples and submultiples of the fundamental unit taken equal to three-tenths of the pendulum's length.

Jefferson, though thoroughly enthused with the plan of seeing an invariable and universal standard adopted, nevertheless would not accept the meridian that was being supported by the Académie des Sciences de Paris, but adhered to the pendulum. He thought that the base of the new system should be a measurement that could be readily made in all countries; since the proposed meridional measurement could hardly be made anywhere other than between Dunkerque and Barcelona, France and Spain would thus have a monopoly on the checking of the unit of length.

This negative attitude was confirmed later when in 1795 Washington sent to Congress a communication from the Minister of the French Republic suggesting that the United States adopt the metric system of weights and measures. This proposal found little favor; a unit based on the ten-millionth part of the earth's quadrant was deemed less favorable from the point of view of its reproducibility than a seconds pendulum.

Thus, faced with the nonconcurrence of the most important foreign powers, the French proceeded alone toward the establishment of the new system, the system which "though conceived and created in France, will belong to all the nations."

Charles-Maurice de Talleyrand-Périgord, Prince of Benevent (1754–1838). Bishop of Autun 1788–91·, Member of the Constituent Assembly, then Diplomat, Noted Particularly for His Brilliant and Able Part in the Congress of Vienna (1814–15)

*The Determination of the New Units.* Almost ten years elapsed between the deposition of the Talleyrand proposal (March, 1790) and the definitive fixing of the value of the new unit (*mètre*) in December, 1799. This interval may appear excessive; but it should not be forgotten that all the operations requisite to the determination of the units of length and weight were carried out while the Revolution was in full swing. This unsettled atmosphere seriously hampered the progress of the work. Nor were the scientists in charge of the operations spared: loyalty tests, arrest, confinement, and even condemnation to death—such was the fate reserved for some of them during this period of political unrest and disorder.

Obviously, not all the labors of these ten years can be discussed here; the essential features will be outlined briefly.

*Unit of Length.* The measurement of the arc of meridian was divided into two parts: the northern sector, extending from Dunkerque to Rodez, was confided to Delambre; the southern part, from Rodez to Barcelona, was intrusted to Méchain. This geodetic operation—for which Delambre and Méchain employed the *repeating circle* (recently invented by Borda) which permitted a precision of one second in measurements of angles—consisted essentially of triangulation measurements and determinations of latitudes and azimuths.

Jean-Baptiste Delambre (1749–1822), Astronomer

The Arc of the Meridian Measured by Delambre and Méchain Between 1792 and 1798

Pierre-Francois Méchain (1744–1804), Astronomer

This important work was interrupted several times for various reasons; in the course of its execution numerous incidents and adventures occurred with Delambre and Méchain as their unfortunate victims, such as arrests and revocations of their right of passage, damage to and destruction of their work. Among other happenings, the markers which they used for their observations excited the distrust of the people; the white cloths—the royal color and hence counter-revolutionary—which were at the ends of these markers made the two scientists and their assistants suspect in the eyes of some of the local authorities, even though the scientists were fully provided with passports, permits, and the other necessary authorizations.

Begun in June, 1792, the determination of the length of the arc of meridian was not entirely finished until June, 1798. The results of this operation, approved by a commission of French and foreign scientists, gave the distance from the pole to the equator as 5,130,740 toises, or for the length of the meter 3 pieds, 11.296 lignes.

Antoine-Laurent de Lavoisier (1743–94), Chemist

Louis Lèfevre-Gineau (1754–1829), Physicist and Man of Public Affairs

Jean Valentin Fabbroni (1753–1822), Italian Chemist and Engineer

*Unit of Weight (Mass).* All the plans for reform emphasized that there must be a connection between the unit of weight and that of volume, and consequently with that of length. This part of the work, of course, was taken up by the Académie des Sciences.

The assignment, entrusted in 1791 to the academicians Lavoisier and Haüy, was almost completed in August 1793, when it was taken over entirely by the academician Lefevre-Gineau, assisted later by Fabbroni, deputy from Tuscany. The latter two scientists determined the weight of a known volume of water by weighing successively in water and in air a hollow brass cylinder whose dimensions had been carefully determined. These data yielded the weight of a cubic decimeter of distilled water taken at its maximum density (4°C.) and weighed *in vacuo*.

The results of this determination, likewise approved by a commission made up of French and foreign scientists, gave, with respect to the Pile of Charlemagne, the value 18,827.15 grains, which was adopted as the weight of the new unit: the kilogram.

Once these two important results had been obtained, all the elements requisite to the establishment of the standards of units of length and weight were at hand.

It should be noted however that prior to the delivery of the definite figures for the measurement of the arc of meridian and the determination of the unit of weight, two decisions were taken:

(1) A provisional system of measures was created in 1792 and sanctioned on August 1, 1793; a first nomenclature of the units was decided on and a provisional meter of brass, constructed by Lenoir, was sent to the Committee of Public Instruction on July 6, 1795; the length of this meter, deduced from the old (1740) measurements of the earth, was 3 pieds, 11.44 lignes.

(2) A little later, the law of the 18th of Germinal year III (April 7, 1795) instituted the decimal metric system in France and fixed the nomenclature of the new units, a terminology that is still in use: *mètre* for lengths, *are* for areas, *litre* for capacities, *gramme* (later *kilogramme*) for weights (masses); an article of this law also stipulated that the meter, which had been adopted as the fundamental unit of the entire system of measures, should be traced on a platinum rule.

*The Construction of the Standards.* In conformity with the provisions of the law of the 18th of Germinal, the standard meter and kilogram were constructed to give material form to the units whose magnitude had just been determined.

For the meter there was prepared, not a line standard but instead an end standard, i. e., a standard on which the length was not marked by the distance between two lines but by the distance between its terminal faces. The standard consisted of a straight rule, with a rectangular section 25.3 × 4 mm., and made of agglomerated platinum.[4] This rule was compared with the toise by means of the comparator constructed by Lenoir.

For the kilogram a platinum standard was prepared in the form of a polished cylinder, whose height was equal to its diameter. Its weight was probably adjusted with the aid of the balance and the provisional

[4] At that time platinum was obtained from spongy platinum produced by calcining ammonium chloroplatinate; the product was compressed, brought to white heat, and them hammered.

This Medal Almost Put into Effect the Plan of Issuing a Medal Which Was to Be Struck in 1799 "To Transmit to Posterity the Occasion at Which the Metric System Has Been Brought to Perfection, and the Operation Which Served as Its Base."

The Mètre des Archives and Its Case, Which Bears the Inscription:
Mètre
Conforme à la Loi du 18 Germinal an 3
présenté le 4 Messidor an 7

weights used in the determination of the weight of a known volume of water.

This prototype meter and kilogram were presented by a delegation of the Institut de France to the Conseil des Anciens and Conseil des Cinq-Cents[5] on the 4th Messidor year VII (June 22, 1799) and then deposited at the Archives de la République, which accounts for the name *Mètre et Kilogramme des Archives* which has been attached to these standards. The law of the 19th

[5] The Conseil des Anciens and the Conseil des Cinq-Cents were assemblies that made up the Corps Législatif organized by the Constitution of the year III (1795).

The Kilogramme des Archives and Its Case

Frimaire year VIII (December 10, 1799) finally assigned a legal value to them.

This brought to a close the gigantic plan of unifying the weights and measures, concerning which the illustrious Lavoisier—who took a leading part in all the preparatory labors of this reform until he went to the guillotine on May 8, 1794, during the Reign of Terror—could state: "Never has anything more grand and more simple, more coherent in all of its parts, issued from the hand of men."

### ADOPTION OF THE METRIC SYSTEM

The advantages of the simplicity and coherence of the metric system are widely recognized; a few words will suffice to recall its chief characteristics: First of all, it is entirely decimal, like the system of counting; the measures of area and volume are obtained by squaring and cubing measures of length; the weights are directly related to the measures of volume; the names of the multiples and submultiples are obtained by the simple addition of prefixes to the principal unit: kilo (k) = $10^3$; hecto (h) = $10^2$; deca (da) = 10; deci (d) = $10^{-1}$; centi (c) = $10^{-2}$; milli (m) = $10^{-3}$.

Despite the ease with which it is used, this system was not adopted immediately throughout the whole of France; its introduction was slow and difficult. The new system required a profound alteration in long established customs, and the various changes in the nomenclature re-enforced the opposition offered by the public.

The consular decree of 13th Brumaire year IX (November 4, 1800) re-establishing the old names of the measures (lieue, livre, once, perche, etc.), while retaining those of the meter and the decimal division, merely aggravated the situation by creating regrettable confusions: certain different units were found in effect to be bearing the same name. Then came the unfortunate imperial decree of February 12, 1812, authorizing, along with the legal system, the creation of measures called "usual" accommodated to the need of the people. For example, there was created a toise of 2 meters, a livre of 500 grams, a boisseau (bushel) of one-eighth hectoliter, etc., which were subdivided, according to ancient customs, into nondecimal units.

The reform had hardly been brought about before it found itself gravely menaced and the former anarchy began once more to reign among the measures. The resistance reorganized anew; besides satirical screeds and cartoons ridiculing the metric system, there were untoward incidents and even serious disturbances at various places. Immediate action was needed to safeguard the accomplished task.

The law of July 4, 1837, brought an end to this abnormal situation; it forbade, under the pain of severe penalties, the use of any weights and measures except those of the decimal metric system after January 1, 1840. The period of concessions, which had lasted a quarter of a century, was thus brought to a definite close, and the year 1840 marks the date of the beginning of the exclusive use of the metric system in France.

Becoming gradually known and appreciated in foreign countries, the metric system made rapid progress in the world, thanks to its simplicity and its logical and rational conception. Some of the Italian provinces adopted it at the beginning of the nineteenth century; in 1816 it was declared obligatory in the Low Countries; Spain accepted it in 1849. After 1860 the adoptions multiplied. In Great Britain, the law of July 29, 1864, authorized the use of the metric weights and measures concurrently with the imperial system; on July 28, 1864, the United States of America made an analogous decision. Despite its rejection of the metric system in 1795, the American Congress legalized the use of this system almost a century later by passing the Metric Act of 1886, declaring: "It shall be lawful throughout the United States of America to employ the weights and measures of the metric system; and no contract or dealing or pleading in any court shall be deemed invalid, or liable to objection, because the weights or measures

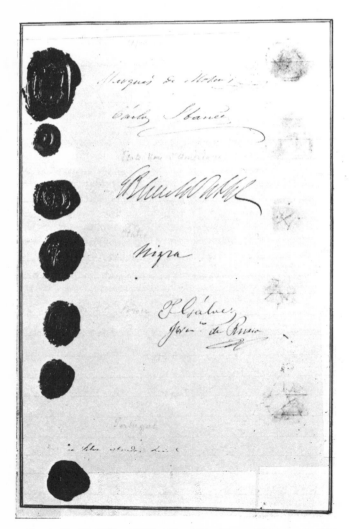

Convention du Mètre (1875): One of the Pages of Signatures. The Third from the Top Is That of the American Plenipotentiary, Elihu Benjamin Washburne, Envoy Extraordinary and Minister Plenipotentiary of the United States to Paris.

expressed or referred to therein are weights or measures of the metric system."

## THE INTERNATIONAL BUREAU

The first manifestations of the need for a world-wide unification of measures came to the fore on the occasion of the international expositions of London (1851) and Paris (1867). This thought was strengthened by the wishes uttered by various learned societies (Association Géodésique, Academies of Science of St. Petersburg, Paris, etc.), relative to the manufacture of new standards and the precise determination of their value in the metric system as based on the Mètre et Kilogramme des Archives in their actual contemporary condition. The international Geodetic Conference, held at Berlin in 1867, taking cognizance of the systematic differences that arose in the great European triangulations then in progress, recognized the need of fixing the common unit of measure for all the European countries; it also went on record as favoring the creation of an international bureau of weights and measures.

In response to these wishes, the French government in 1870 called together representatives of foreign countries. Twenty-four states responded to this invitation and their delegates constituted the *Commission Internationale du Mètre*. Interrupted by the Franco-Prussian war of 1870, the work of this body was resumed in 1872, with the participation of delegates from 30 countries, including 12 from the Western Continent. About 40 resolutions were passed dealing with the preparation of new prototypes, and the creation of an international bureau of weights and measures was recommended to the interested governments.

The members of this international commission, composed entirely of scientists, had no authority to commit their governments; it was only some years later that the establishment of this international bureau was officially sanctioned by the Conférence Diplomatique du Mètre, held at Paris in 1875 and which, through the signatures of the plenipotentiaries of 28 states, resulted in the *Convention du Mètre* (May 20, 1875). By this Convention (modified by the additional Convention of October 6, 1921) the signatory states bound themselves to set up and maintain at common expense a scientific and permanent International Bureau of Weights and Measures; its seat to be at Paris, the birthplace of the metric system.

The initial essential mission of this international bureau was to construct and preserve the definite standard meter and kilogram, to compare with them the national standards which were to be furnished to the various countries, and to improve the procedures of measuring in order to advance the progress in all fields of metrology. In proportion to the accomplishment of this program, the activity of the Bureau has been oriented toward the study of various metrological problems and of physical quantities entering into the accuracy of the measurements. During recent years, the

The Trianon or Pavillon de Saint-Cloud at the End of the Seventeenth Century

assignments of the Bureau have also extended into the field of electrical and photometric units.

## THE PAVILLON DE BRETEUIL

The choice of the site where the International Bureau of Weights and Measures would be located was finally decided in favor of the estate of the Pavillon de Breteuil, a peaceful spot, free of vibrational disturbances. This property was graciously put at the disposal of the International Committee of Weights and Measures by the French Government; with an area of 25,500 m., it thus constitutes a tiny international enclave within French territory.

Situated on the edge of the Parc de Saint-Cloud, close to the road from Paris to Versailles, and near the Manufacture Nationale de Porcelaine de Sèvres, the Pavillon de Breteuil is a structure with an historical past, built on the site of an ancient royal property.

Towards the middle of the seventeenth century Louis XIV, proprietor of this estate, presented it to his only brother, the Duc Philippe d'Orleans. The latter made some important improvements. The gardens were laid out by Le Nôtre—the famous landscape artist, to whom is due, among others, the magnificent gardens at Versailles—and this new estate became the Trianon de Saint-Cloud, a dependency of the Château

The Pavillon de Breteuil (Present Appearance). *To the Left:* the Laboratories. *To the Right:* Offices, Assembly Hall, Library, Residences

of this name that was destroyed during the war of 1870. In 1743 the Trianon de Saint-Cloud made way for a new pavilion erected by the Baron de Breteuil, Minister of the King's Household, thus giving this building the name Pavillon de Breteuil, which it has borne ever since. Badly damaged during the French Revolution, the Pavillon was restored by Napoleon I, who for a time gave it the name Pavillon d'Italie. Among those who lived in this rural retreat at that time were the Empresses Joséphine and Marie-Louise; the Queen of Naples, sister of Napoleon I; and Queen Hortense and her children, including the future Napoleon III. After the fall of the Empire the Pavillon de Breteuil was occupied by the Prussians, under Blücher, who did considerable damage to the property. Abandoned during the period of the Restoration (1814–30), the residence was restored by Napoleon III, who lodged his cousin Princess Mathilde, daughter of Jérôme Bonaparte, King of Naples, there in 1848. The Grand Duchesses of Baden and Marie of Russia also resided at the Pavillon.

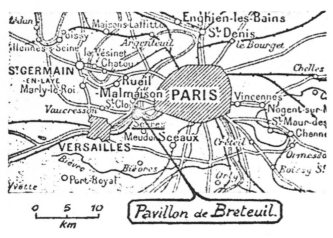

Geographical Location of the Pavillon du Breteuil. *Longitude:* 2°13'14'' (2.467 grades) east of Greenwich. *Latitude:* N 48°49'45'' (54.255 grades). *Altitude:* 65.9 m.

Just at the time it was planned to install a laboratory of celestial physics at the Pavillon, the Franco-Prussian War of 1870–71 was declared. During the siege of Paris the Pavillon de Breteuil once more sustained considerable damage. Consequently the property was in a rather run-down condition when it was turned over to the Comité International des Poids et Mesures on October 4, 1875. The latter made the necessary repairs, and a new building, designed to house the scientific apparatus, was finished in 1878. Many years later (1930), because of the extension of the duties of the Bureau, some new laboratories were built with funds supplied by the Rockefeller Foundation.

During the second World War the bombardments of the Paris region spared the Pavillon de Breteuil entirely. Only the air attacks, aimed at the Renault factories at Boulogne-Billancourt, especially that of March 3, 1942, did some damage to the buildings; fortunately, the scientific instruments escaped injury.

This, in brief, is the history of the Pavillon which, after having sheltered so many historic personages and having witnessed sumptuous fetes, is now the international sanctuary of the standards of the metric system.

## OPERATION OF THE BUREAU

From the point of view of organization, the supreme authority governing the Bureau emanates from the General Conference of Weights and Measures, made up of delegates from all the countries belonging to the Convention du Mètre.[6] This Conference normally meets every six years; the tenth is scheduled for 1954. The opening session, in the great Salon de l'Horloge of the Quai d'Orsay, is presided over by the French Minister of Foreign Affairs; the working sessions, headed by the President on duty of the Académie des Sciences, are held at the Pavillon de Breteuil. The duty of the General Conference is to discuss and initiate steps leading to the propagation and improvement of the metric system throughout the world, and also to sanction new fundamental metrological determinations, and to approve of the various scientific and administrative decisions that have arisen between the meetings.

The decisions of the General Conference are put into effect by a permanent International Committee of Weights and Measures, which controls the functioning and the management of the International Bureau. This committee meets every two years at the Pavillon. At present, it is composed of 18 members at the maximum—scientists or technologists of all nationalities—whose election is submitted to the General Conference for ratification. Between sessions of the Conference, the Committee fills by election any vacancies in its membership arising from deaths or resignations. It is understood that countries with large populations have a permanent seat, the other seats are assigned in rotation to the smaller nations. The present chairman of the International Committee is British (J. E. Sears); the secretary is a Belgian (M. Dehalu); the American member is E. C. Crittenden, of the National Bureau of Standards.[7]

The International Bureau, composed of a scientific, administrative, and technical personnel (17 in all at present) who may belong to any nationality, is headed by a Director (at present a Swiss, Ch. Volet), named by

[6] At present, 33 states belong to the Convention du Mètre; they are: Argentina, Australia, Austria, Belgium, Bulgaria, Canada, Chile, Czechoslovakia, Denmark, Eire, Finland, France and Algeria, Germany, Great Britain, Hungary, Italy, Japan, Jugoslavia, Mexico, Netherlands, Norway, Peru, Poland, Portugal, Rumania, Siam, Spain, Sweden, Switzerland, Turkey, United States of America, U.S.S.R., Uruguay. It should be noted that this list does not include all the countries that have adopted the metric system, but only those—metric or not—that are adherents of the Convention du Mètre.

[7] The preceding American members of the Comité were: J. E. Hilgard (1875–87), Director of the Coast and Geodetic Survey; B. A. Gould (1887–95), Professor at Harvard University; A. A. Michelson (1897–1905), Professor at the University of Chicago; S. W. Stratton (1905–31), President of the Massachusetts Institute of Technology; A. E. Kennelly (1933–39), Professor at Harvard University.

secret ballot cast by the International Committee, in which he has a vote *ex officio*. One of the regulations appended to the Convention du Mètre specifies that the President, the Secretary of the Committee and the Director of the Bureau shall be of different nationalities.

The expenses of the Bureau are guaranteed by contributions paid by each state belonging to the Convention du Mètre. The annual subscription, set at 175,000 gold francs (about $57,000) by the ninth general Conference, is apportioned according to the population of each country, with maximum limits of 15 per cent (countries of high population) and minimum of 0.5 per cent (countries with low population) of the total sum.

All of the countries which contribute to the support of the Bureau are co-proprietors of its furnishings; they are entitled to obtain standards of the first order and have the right to request metrological determinations and studies *gratis*. However, along with these privileges, the chief advantage is cultural and moral. The desire to collaborate in the advancement of metrological science is the motive that leads the nations to belong to the Convention du Mètre; by this adhesion they are acknowledging the duty of every cultivated country to participate in a task of world-wide progress, from which they themselves will benefit.

Directors of the International Bureau of Weights and Measures. (*a*) Gilberto Govi (1826–89), Italian physicist. Director 1875–77. (*b*) Ole Jacob Borch (1818–89), Norwegian mathematician. Correspondent of the Institut de France. Director 1879–89. (*c*) J. Rene Benoit (1844–1922), French. Correspondent of the Institut de France. Director 1889–1915. (*d*) Charles Èdoudard Guillaume (1861–1938), Swiss, Correspondent of the Institut de France. Nobel Prize in physics (1920). Director 1915–36. (*e*) Albert Perard (1880), French. Member of the Institut de France. Director 1936–51. (*f*) Charles Volet (1895), Swiss. Present director.

## THE INTERNATIONAL PROTOTYPES

In compliance with one of the articles of the Convention of 1875, the Bureau first of all took steps to assure the unification of measures by the construction and the determination of the international meter and kilogram, and also of copies to be distributed to all the countries that had requested them.

Pursuant to resolutions of the Commission Internationale du Mètre, study and research committees were organized in 1872 to produce the new standards and perfect the methods of comparing them. The details of all of these studies from 1872 to 1880 will not be given here. It will only be recalled that it was decided, among other things, that: (1) the international meter would be a line standard because of the advantages this construction offers with respect to comparisons and preservation; (2) the metal used for the standards would be an alloy composed of 90 per cent platinum and 10 per cent iridium; (3) the transverse section of the meter bars would be the X-shape computed by H. Tresca; (4) the value of the standard meter and kilogram would be deduced from that of the Mètre and Kilogramme des Archives in their existing condition.

The name of the French chemist H. Sainte-Claire Deville (1818–81) remains linked with the choice of platinum-iridium for the manufacture of the standards. This alloy is especially suitable because of its inalterability, homogeneity, hardness, high coefficient of elasticity, not too great expansibility (0.0086 mm./m./degree C.), and its ability to take a high polish.

The casting of a considerable quantity of platinum-iridium of well-defined composition was always a difficult task at that time. After many test castings, of which two were made in the presence of the French presidents, A. Thiers (May 6, 1873) and Maréchal de Mac-Mahon (May 1, 1874), these difficulties were all but overcome and a definitive casting of 250 kg. of this metal was made on May 13, 1874, at the Conservatoire National des Arts et Métiers in Paris, furnishing the supply of platinum-iridium known as the *Alliage du Conservatoire* or *Alliage de 1874*. After analyses had shown that this alloy contained small amounts of impurities, the Johnson Matthey Company of London was commissioned to cast a new and purer alloy (*Alliage Johnson-Matthey*) from which 30 metric bars were drawn.

The X-shaped section of the bars permits the engraving of lines on the surface of neutral fibers laid bare along the entire length of the bar, and thus makes the length of the standard independent of the effects of bending due to the action of its own weight, no matter how the bar is supported. For a limited quantity of material, this profile has the added advantage of possessing a high moment of inertia, which measures the resistance of the bar to deformations. (Actually, an X-shaped meter rule, supported at its ends and bearing a mass of 40 kg. at its center, does not suffer any permanent deformation.) This advantage is considerable if one takes into account the monetary value of the precious metal entering into the manufacture of a meter bar, whose mass is of the order of 3.3 kg.

After rejecting glass, quartz, and gold, the same alloy was adopted for the standard kilograms as was used for the meters.

The form of the Kilogramme des Archives was retained: a perfectly polished cylinder, the diameter (39 mm.) equal to the height, with the edges very slightly rounded.

Once the meters had been constructed, the Bureau proceeded, in 1888, to an important intercomparison of the bars, to which had been added a provisional prototype compared directly with the Mètre des Archives. A similar project was carried out for the kilograms, which were referred back to the weight *in vacuo*.

The comparisons finished, the international prototypes of the meter and kilogram were selected from among the standards whose values were closest to that of the Mètre and Kilogramme des Archives, respectively. These prototypes and their "*témoins*" (companion replicas) are preserved in the vaults of the Pavillon de Breteuil, 8 meters under ground; three keys, held by three different persons (the President of the International Committee, the Directeur des Archives de France, the Director of the International Bureau) are required to open this vault. Consequently, the international prototypes are not visible to the visitors who come to the Pavillon de Breteuil; for them are provided "factitious standards," which they may examine and handle without risk of damage to the actual standards.

During World War II, the international prototypes were not taken from the Pavillon de Breteuil; only the *témoins* and the working standards were temporarily moved (May to September 1940) to Brittany and the Vendée.

The first General Conference of Weights and Measures (September, 1889) approved the results of this important work and then proceeded to distribute, by

lot, the national prototypes among the various countries. It was thus that copies 21 and 27 of the meter and numbers 20 and 4 of the kilogram were alloted to the U. S. A.; they are preserved at the National Bureau of Standards, Washington, D. C. Likewise, at this time, approval was given to new definitions of the meter and kilogram, namely: The meter (or the kilogram) is the length at 0° C. (or the mass) of the international prototype in platinum-iridium, deposited at the Pavillon de Breteuil at Sevres.[8]

These definitions thus confer an agreed character on the metric system; it had in fact been difficult to maintain rigorously the original definitions of the meter and the kilogram, which would have led to new values for the standards each time the quadrant of the earth's meridian or the mass of the cubic decimeter of water is

[8] The seventh General Conference of Weights and Measures (1927) added some precisions to the definition of the meter, which now reads as follows: The unit of length is the meter, defined as the distance, at 0°C., between the axes of the two median lines traced on the platinum-iridium bar deposited at the International Bureau of Weights and Measures, and declared Prototype of the meter by the First General Conference of Weights and Measures, this rule being subjected to the normal atmospheric pressure and being supported by two rollers of at least one centimeter in diameter, situated symmetrically in a same horizontal plane and at the distance of 571 mm. from each other.

It should be noted that the International Meter, like the Mètre des Archives from which it was copied, is about 0.2 mm. shorter than the ten-millionth part of the quadrant of the earth's meridian, original definition of the meter. The same is true of the International Kilogram, which exceeds by 0.028 g. the mass of the decimeter cube of pure water, taken at its maximum density, original definition of the kilogram (see below).

**End of a Prototype Meter Identical with the International Meter**

Note the specular polished region on which is traced a group of three lines 0.5 mm. apart, the middle one, with its analogue at the other end, defining the length of the prototype. Two longitudinal lines about 0.2 mm. apart—not visible on the photograph because of the angle of illumination—cut across the three lines and thus outline their useful region. The X-shaped section is inscribed in a square of 2 cm. on the side. The total length of the meter rules is about 102 cm.; the width of the lines is around 5 μ.

redetermined.

The permanence of the unit of length therefore now depends on the stability over the years of a platinum-iridium bar. This stability has been confirmed up to now, within the limits of the precision in the comparisons of the line standards, with the help of *témoins* associated with the international meter. In addition to the three companion bars, likewise constructed of platinum-iridium, two other *témoins* of a different nature have been sought: a wave length of light and a material in the crystalline state. Hence, at present, the wave length of the red line of cadmium and a series of plane-end standards constructed from Brazilian quartz permit the checking of the permanence of the standard of length through the constancy of the relationship of these three magnitudes. (The wave length of the red line of cadmium, measured as a function of the meter on nine occasions between 1892 and 1940 in various foreign laboratories, gave results all lying within $\pm 2 \times 10^{-7}$ of the mean value.)

It is more difficult to check the stability of the international kilogram because at present there is no available "natural" reference permitting such control. It is only the constancy of the differences between the international kilogram and its replicas, likewise made of platinum-iridium, that testifies to the permanence of the unit of mass. To guarantee the best possible conservation of this unit, the International Kilogram has been used on only two occasions (1889 and 1946) since its construction, with the hope of reducing to a minimum the inevitable loss of material that accompanies use.[9]

The stability of the platinum-iridium standards of length and mass is clearly shown by the following com-

The International Kilogram. In the Foreground, the Holder Used for Handling the Standards

parison of the original values (1889) of the American primary standards and those found at the most recent of the periodic verifications.

| | 1889 | 1922 | 1948 | Difference |
|---|---|---|---|---|
| Meter No. 27 | 1 m. — 1.49 $\mu$ | 1 m. — 1.48 $\mu$ | | +0.01 $\mu$ |
| Kilogram No. 20 | 1 kg. — 0.039 mg. | | 1 kg. — 0.019 mg. | +0.020 mg. |

## THE YARD AND THE POUND

The foregoing discussion of the characteristics of the standards of the metric system leads logically to a like consideration of the yard and the pound, *i. e.*, the bases of the British system of measures—units which incidentally do not have the same value in Great Britain and the United States— and their relation to the metric units.

*Great Britain.* The ancient yards, the "Iron Ulna" from the reign of Edward I (1239–72), the one made in 1496 during the reign of Henry VII which served until 1588, and the one established under Queen Elizabeth I, which was used from 1588 to 1824, were all end standards.

In 1760 Bird constructed a yard which was recognized as the legal standard by an Act of Parliament in 1824; this line standard was lost when the Houses of Parliament burned in 1834. The Bird standard had been

The Storehouse of the Metric Prototypes. The International Kilogram, Under Its Triple Glass Bell Jar, Surrounded by Its *Témoins*. In the Metal Cases, the International Meter and Its *Témoins*

[9] Since the area of the base of the platinum-iridium kilogram is about 12 cm.[2], the removal of 0.1 mg. of metal would only require that a layer four-millionths of a millimeter (0.004$\mu$) be worn away over the entire surface of the base. Obviously, certain precautions are indispensable when the standards are handled.

related, in case of loss, to the length of a pendulum beating seconds at the latitude of London *in vacuo* and at sea level. However, this relationship was abandoned when the standard yard was remade, since the Kater measurements of the length of the pendulum were known to be unreliable because of errors, and the new yard was referred back to the old standard.

The metal chosen for the new standard was a bronze alloy containing 16 parts of copper, 2.5 of tin, and 1 of zinc (Baily's metal). Several rules were constructed and compared with ancient scales that had been verified against the 1824 yard. One of these rules was selected to be the standard of length at 62° F. (16.66° C.), and became the *Imperial Standard Yard*. Legalized by an Act of Parliament in 1855, this standard is now preserved at the Standards Department of the Board of Trade in London.

The Imperial Standard Yard, as well as its five Parliamentary Copies, is a line standard in the form of a bar 38 inches long (96.5 cm.) with 1 inch (25.4 mm.) square cross section; at one inch from each end there is a cylindrical cavity, 0.5 inch (12.7 mm.) deep, with a gold plug at the bottom on which are traced the lines defining the length of the standard.

The ancient pounds were replaced in 1844 by a platinum standard, the *Imperial Standard Pound*. This, like the four Parliamentary Copies, is in the form of a cylinder 1.35 inches (34.3 mm.) high and 1.15 inches (29.2 mm.) in diameter. This standard also is kept at the Board of Trade.

The legal relationships of the British units to the metric units are those approved in May, 1898:

$$1 \text{ yard} = 0.9143992 \text{ meter}$$
$$1 \text{ pound} = 0.45359243 \text{ kilogram}$$

The latest comparisons of the standard yard (1947) and the pound (1933) with the standard meter and kilogram gave:

$$1 \text{ yard} = 0.9143975 \text{ meter}$$
$$1 \text{ pound} = 0.453592338 \text{ kilogram}$$

which confirms a progressive shortening of the Imperial Standard Yard of the order of 2 parts in a million (1.7 $\mu$) in 52 years. A smaller ($2 \times 10^{-7}$) change, in the sense of a diminution, has likewise been observed in the Imperial Standard Pound.

*United States of America.* The situation regarding the system of weights and measures in the United States is rather peculiar: The metric system, which is employed almost exclusively in scientific work, has been legalized, whereas the system which is used in all daily transactions has never been officially approved in a formal manner.

The United States does not have any *legal* material standard yard or pound. These two units are directly related to the international meter and kilogram, as stated by the Mendenhall Order (1893): "The Office of Weights and Measures with the approval of the Secretary of the Treasury, will in the future regard the international prototype meter and kilogram as funda-

mental standards, and the customary units, the yard and the pound, will be derived therefrom in accordance with the act of July 28, 1866."

The relations of the U. S. A. yard and pound to the meter and kilogram are:

$$1 \text{ yard (U. S. A.)} = \frac{3600}{3937} = 0.91440183 \text{ meter}$$
$$1 \text{ pound (U. S. A.)} = 0.453592428 \text{ kilogram}$$

It is apparent that the U. S. A. yard is longer than the present Imperial yard by about four-thousandths of a millimeter (4.3 $\mu$) and that the U. S. A. pound is about 0.1 mg. heavier than the present Imperial pound.

This anomalous situation of the different values of the English and American standards has not escaped the notice of the metrologists of the two countries. Therefore, as a consequence of the proved instability of the English yard and pound, it has been proposed that the standards of length and mass of the imperial system be defined in terms of the international meter and kilogram by a fixed relation which, if adopted simultaneously by the United States, would result in agreement in the units of these two countries.

Canada has recently set an example along this line; the Canadian yard and pound have been given the legal values:

$$1 \text{ yard (Canadian)} = 0.9144 \text{ meter}$$
$$1 \text{ pound (Canadian)} = 0.45359243 \text{ kilogram}$$

## ACTIVITIES OF THE BUREAU

Limited at the start to a well-defined and relatively narrow program, the activities of the International Bureau have progressively extended into various fields. All of these studies cannot be examined here, even briefly; reference can merely be made to the many articles in the scientific and technical press, or the papers and notes contained in the 21 volumes of the "Travaux et Mémoires" of the Bureau and in the *Procès-Verbaux* of the International Committee. Leaving aside the studies on barometry, hygrometry, the construction of prototype standards of the mercury ohm, the resistance of mercury, the expansibility of solids and liquids, the density of water, the mass of a liter of air, the standards with plane and spherical ends, the methods of calibrating divided rules and series of masses, the elasticity and deformation of solids, the metrological properties of brasses, the thin layers and the oxidation of aluminum, etc., it will be possible to review only the principal studies carried out at the Bureau and those which constitute the essential part of its present activity.

*Lengths and Masses.* The periodic verification of the national meters and kilograms is one of the essential tasks of the Bureau. These comparisons, though they may be elementary in principle, represent a body of important work in view of the care applied to these measures and the number of observations they entail. Thus, a simple example, such as the comparison of three rules in all possible combinations and relative positions, requires 24 series of comparisons, carried out usually by two or three observers, or even four when national prototypes are involved.

With a view to increasing the precision of the measurements, studies have been made of improvements to be applied to measuring instruments, to methods of observation, and to the standards themselves. Along this line, notable progress has resulted from the researches of Ch. Volet through the use of micrometric microscopes, which can be revolved a half-turn on their vertical axes and thus allow the elimination of errors, sometimes quite significant, that hitherto could not be avoided. Certain prototype meters, whose markings did not provide sufficiently accurate settings, have been re-engraved with special attention to the correct edging of the lines, an important point that was not kept sufficiently in view when the rules were originally engraved. Repeated cleaning of the markings produces a change in the appearance of the lines. These modifications are the origin of certain abnormal variations in length observed in certain prototypes whose defective lines have doubtless been altered in form.

These improvements make it possible to compare the 1-meter standards with a precision of 0.1 $\mu$, *i.e.*, with a relative accuracy of one ten-millionth ($10^{-7}$), a limit slightly exceeded with standards that have very regular markings. It should also be pointed out that the recent development of the micrometric photoelectric microscope, devised by the Société Genevoise d'Instruments de Physique, adds a new considerable increase of the precision in the measurement of line standards.

An important series of comparisons of mass standards was made between 1946 and 1951. The international kilogram, its six *témoins*, two working prototypes of the International Bureau, and about 30 national prototypes were included in these measurements. The importance of this study is apparent from the fact that more than 300 weighings—at the rate of one per day—were made by A. Bonheure, who was in charge of this periodic verification.

These determinations have led to a systematic study of the methods of cleaning weights; it was found in fact that the method of cleaning precision weights may have a significant effect on the observed mass. The investigation showed that the most efficacious method is a jet of doubly distilled water vapor. (The importance of cleaning is evident if it is remembered that a 1-m$\mu$ film of moisture over the entire surface of a platinum-iridium kilogram would change its mass by 0.01 mg.)

The highest precision in measurements is obtained in weighings; when comparing two 1-kg. weights, the best balances permit a precision of the order of one-hundredth of a milligram, or a relative value of one-hundredth of a millionth ($10^{-8}$). (This precision has even been exceeded with the new balance of the National Physical Laboratory of England, where several thousandths of a milligram have been approached.)

The first-order primary standards of platinum-iridium are of course very expensive; they are used only as prototypes. The standards of the second order (working standards of the metrological laboratories and precision industrial standards) are constructed of less costly materials. Studies along this line were carried on at the Bureau by Ch. Ed. Guillaume with ferronickels and led to the discovery of the unknown properties of certain of these metals, notably *invar* (an iron alloy containing 36 per cent of nickel, with an extremely low coefficient of expansion); *elinvar* (54 per cent Fe, 36 per cent Ni, 10 per cent Cr, which has a zero coefficient); *anibal* (a nickel steel, used for compensating balance wheels of chronometers); *platinite* (a ferronickel containing 46 per cent Ni, whose expansibility is close to that of platinum); *baros* or *nichrome* (an amagnetic ferronickel containing 9 per cent Cr and 2 per cent Mn); the alloys containing from 42 to 58 per cent of nickel, whose expansibility is near that of the ordinary glasses or steel. All of these alloys have found application not only in metrology but also in industry.

The stainless steels, used for the construction of standards of length and mass, have also been studied with respect to their metrological properties.

**Setup (1951) for Determining "g" at the Pavillon de Breteuil**

*A.* Arrangement for the fall of the graduated rule. *B.* Apparatus for producing discharge sparks from a condenser (stroborama). *C.* Vibrating quartz regulating a light beam (about 35,000 cycles/sec.). *D.* Drum filmholder on which is recorded simultaneously the graduations of the rule during its fall and the chronometric track

Shortly after its founding the Bureau made a study of geodetic standards. The Jäderin method for the measuring of bases with the aid of stretched wires was brought to a high degree of precision by using geodetic wires of invar (wires 1.65 mm. in diameter, 24 m. long, provided at each end with a scale divided into millimeters, and used under a tension of 10 kg. force, or 98.1 newtons). Many geodetic wires are sent to the Pavillon de Breteuil by the various geographic services and their standardization is one of the important functions of the Bureau.

In the field of the unification of measures, the Bureau has had occasion to determine the relation between the metric units and certain national units, ancient or still legal. Examples are the Toise du Pérou and the rules of Borda; the toises of Bessel and No. 9 of the Prussian Geodetic Institute, the former having served as reference standard for all the geodetic operations in Central Europe at the middle of the nineteenth century; the double toise of Vienna; the double toise of Poulkovo; the yard and the pound of the British system.

*Thermometry.* Thermometry is the essential base of all metrology; it is impossible to conceive of any precise measurements that do not involve an accurate knowledge of the thermal conditions of the experiment. In view of the importance of temperature, one of the first tasks of the Bureau was therefore to study the improvements that might be applied to procedures used for its determination and the unification of the thermometric scale. This task was all the more indispensable because, toward the middle of the previous century, every phenomenon dependent on temperature was most often expressed on the scale peculiar to the thermometer of the experiments.

In the first place, the mercury thermometer really became a precision instrument when hard glass came into use for thermometers and after the studies by Guillaume had clarified the rules to be followed when using this type of thermometer. Correctly employed, the mercury thermometer permits the measurement of temperatures with a precision of a few thousandths of a degree in the interval from 0° to 100°C. The thermometers made by Tonnelot and Baudin between 1884 and 1913 have never been surpassed in quality of construction; they still serve as standards of the first order in many laboratories.

At the same time, the establishment of a unified temperature scale, to which the arbitrary readings of all the thermometric observations could be referred, was confided to P. Chappuis. His studies of gas thermometers (air, nitrogen, carbon dioxide, hydrogen) led to the adoption of the hydrogen thermometer as the normal temperature scale and the determination of corrections of the mercury thermometers in comparison with this scale.

Though limited until now to only slightly elevated temperatures, the thermometric studies of the Bureau have nevertheless contributed to the knowledge of the properties of toluene and other liquids as thermometric materials for measuring low temperatures. In 1897 P. Chappuis and J. Harker also compared platinum resistance thermometers with the hydrogen thermometer.

The measurements on the resistance thermometer had to be repeated at the Bureau as part of the plan to realize the *International Temperature Scale.* It must be remembered that this practical scale, which brings into actual being the absolute thermodynamic (Kelvin) scale, effectuates the closest possible agreement with the thermodynamic Celsius scale, as it is now known, by relying on a certain number of fixed points which serve as reference temperatures.

Although the resistance thermometer has now taken the place of the mercury thermometer in numerous experiments, the latter nonetheless remains a widely used instrument because of the ease with which it can be employed. Accordingly, studies of precision mercury thermometers are being continued at the Bureau on thermometers with bulbs and stems of fused silica, in the hope of producing instruments that are free from the familiar changes (secular change and depression after heating) of the "zero point." These displacements, which are not taken into account by many workers who are insufficiently informed, often lead to erroneous temperature measurements and are the chief cause of dissatisfaction with mercury thermometers.

*The Acceleration Due to Gravity.* The absolute value of the intensity of the gravitational force ($g$) is involved in the definition and absolute measurement of certain units. Therefore, an exact knowledge of the magnitude of this physical quantity, whose precise determination is a delicate procedure, is important.

Absolute determinations of this quantity have been made rather recently at Washington, Teddington, and Leningrad by the pendulum method. It was therefore of the highest interest that the Bureau likewise should participate in the determination of $g$, a measurement that moreover had been made at the Pavillon de Breteuil in 1888 by Defforges, using the pendulum method.

The new determination of $g$ undertaken by Volet at the Bureau replaces the classic pendulum method with a ballistic procedure, namely the fall of bodies, which is applied for the first time to a high-precision measurement. This venerable method, which can now be used with accuracy, thanks to modern techniques in the precise determination of very short time intervals, consists in taking moving pictures of a graduated rule in free fall and from them deducing its acceleration. The results of the first group of trials gave the following value:

$$g \text{ (Pavillon de Breteuil)} = 980.916 \text{ cm./sec.}^2$$

with a precision of several milligals.[10] Certain improvements, which deal chiefly with the production of flashes of light of the shortest duration, are now being applied to the initial setup and new measurements are planned.

This result, close to those obtained at Washington and Teddington, confirms the discrepancy observed with respect to the value found at Potsdam in about

---

[10] The *gal* (abbreviation of Galileo, the discoverer of the laws of the fall of bodies) is the cgs unit of acceleration; it corresponds to an acceleration of 1 cm./sec.²

1900—a value that was adopted internationally as a system of reference—which appears to be about 20 milligals too high.

The results already obtained, to which there has just been added the determination being made at Ottawa, which likewise employs the principle of the Volet method, leaves no doubt that the Potsdam value will have to be revised and a new point of departure set up for the relative determinations of $g$.

*Volume of the Kilogram of Water.* It will be recalled that the founders of the metric system based the unit of mass on the unit of length through that of volume. Their intention was to define the unit of mass by the relation: 1 kg. = the mass of 1 cubic decimeter of water at 4° C. Did the Kilogramme des Archives actually conform to this definition? Some doubts being raised on this point, the Bureau decided to undertake the determination of the volume of the kilogram of water. These delicate measurements were made several times between 1895 and 1907, using the general method of determining, by linear measurements, the volume of a body with a regular form, and then determining, by hydrostatic weighings, the loss in weight of the body when submerged in water. The linear dimensions of the bodies employed (bronze or brass cylinders, cubes of crown glass and quartz) were determined either by means of a caliper comparator (cylinders) or by interferential methods (cubes). The final result of this important study, with which is associated the names of Ch. Ed. Guillaume, P. Chappuis, Ch. Fabry, Macé de Lépinay, H. Busson and J. R. Benoît, led to the value 1.000028 cubic decimeters for the volume of a kilogram of pure air-free water at its maximum density (4° C.) and under normal atmospheric pressure.

The *liter*, which is equal to the volume occupied by the mass of a kilogram of water, therefore exceeds the volume of the cubic decimeter by 28 millionths, or 1 liter = 1.000028 cubic decimeters. This deviation represents the difference between the mass of the International Kilogram and that of the cubic decimeter of water, the original definition of the kilogram, and shows with what precision—aided perhaps by chance—Lefevre-Gineau and Fabbroni constructed the kilogram a century and a half ago.

This distinction between the *cubic decimeter* (unit of volume related to measures of length) and the *liter* (unit of capacity related to measures of mass), a distinction limited to measurements of high precision, is somewhat of a black mark against the impeccability of the metric system. Consequently, it might be desirable to have an international decision with the purpose of doing away with this duality, which the founders of the system certainly never envisaged.

*Interferometry.* As soon as methods were perfected for measuring the wave lengths of luminous radiations— those lengths which Fizeau declared constitute a *natural* micrometer of the greatest possible perfection—there was immediate appreciation of the possibilities offered by the phenomena of light interference for checking the permanence of the unit of length, as materialized in the platinum-iridium prototype, and for measuring the end standards with increased precision.

The production of a natural *témoin* of the unit of length and the assignment to spectroscopy of its definitive scale as a function of the metric unit, were the objectives of the studies made at the Pavillon de Breteuil in 1892–93 by A. A. Michelson and J. R. Benoît. They established for the first time the relation of the wave length of the lines of the cadmium spectrum to the international meter. In 1906 J. R. Benoît, Ch. Fabry, and A. Perot repeated these measurements by new procedures, which permitted the observation of fringes of superposition (Fabry-Perot standards) and confirmed the results of Michelson and Benoît obtained with the Michelson interferometer and standards.

As the result of these determinations, the wave length of one of the cadmium lines—$\lambda = 0.64384696\ \mu$ (the red line)— was finally selected to play the double role of *témoin* of the meter and fundamental standard for light waves.

Among the principal interferential researches carried out at the Bureau were the determination (with the Fizeau apparatus) of the coefficient of expansion of the platinum-iridium alloys of the prototype meters, and of various materials (pure platinum and iridium, bronzes, brasses, and various steels, gold, quartz, beryl, Iceland spar) and the index of air; the measurement with the Michelson interferometer of the end standards constructed of crystalline quartz, which constitute the third *témoin* of the metric unit; the study of the best monochromatic spectral lines with respect to their use in metrology; the perfection of the interference methods and the construction of an interferometer for the measurement of industrial gages of the Johansson type, etc. All of these studies, made by J. R. Benoît and A. Pérard, are now being continued by J. Terrien.

At present, the Bureau is particularly interested in the lines of single isotopes (nuclides); on one hand, the lines of mercury 198, a new element produced for the first time in the U. S. A. by the transmutation of gold bombarded with neutrons from an atomic pile; on the other hand, those of the two nuclides, krypton 84 and 86, produced in Germany by thermodiffusion. These new light sources, which give very fine lines that are perfectly monochromatic, are observable at large path differences and, from the metrological point of view, they doubtless are superior to the red line of cadmium. They are now the object of intense study at the National Bureau of Standards (U. S. A.), at the National Physical Laboratory (Great Britain), at the Physikalisch-Technische Bundesanstalt (Germany), and at the International Bureau.[11]

These recent studies have again brought to the fore the question of replacing the platinum-iridium bar (material standard) by a wave length as a *natural* standard of length. In 1948, the ninth General Con-

---

[11] Mercury 202, recently isolated in the U. S. A. by electromagnetic separation, has also been suggested as a source of perfectly monochromatic light.

ference of Weights and Measures considered a proposition along these lines, looking toward the abandonment of the present definition of the meter in favor of a suitably chosen wave length.

The idea of taking a wave length as standard of length is quite old, since it was first advanced in 1827. However it was fortunate that a too hasty decision was not made. Studies of spectral lines have progressively revealed the influence of various factors on the wave length of these lines. It was these latter reasons that caused the ninth General Conference not to make an immediate decision regarding the proposed change, and to wait until additional new studies of mercury 198 and krypton 84 and 86 confirm the results of the first experiments.

*Electric and Photometric Units.* The seventh (1927) and the eighth (1933) General Conferences of Weights and Measures directed the Bureau to establish and preserve electrical and photometric units, and to compare national and other precision standards with these standards, and also to make studies leading to the improvements to be applied to standards, to measuring instruments, and to methods of observation.

This new field of activity of the Bureau however presents a somewhat different situation than that of units of length and mass. The value of all the electrical quantities (which derive from the cgs system) is deduced from two of them, the ohm and the ampere, determined in absolute units, a determination which involves only the measurement of fundamental mechanical quantities: length, mass, time. For photometric quantities, the present primary standard is a black body functioning at 2042°K. (solidification point of platinum).

The determination of the ohm and the ampere in absolute units and the construction of a black body required many detailed preliminary studies and protracted and delicate measurements, which could only be made at more or less scattered periods in specially equipped laboratories. After these determinations were once accomplished in a national laboratory it became the function of material secondary standards to preserve the value obtained for each unit: standard ohm of manganine wire for the unit of resistance; Weston cell for the unit of electromotive force; incandescent lamps for units of luminous intensity and luminous flux at different color temperatures.

Up to the present the Bureau has not been given the task of measuring the absolute ohm and ampere nor of preparing the standard black body. Strictly speaking, there are no international primary electrical or photometric standards to which the units of each country may be related, as is the case with the meter and kilogram.

Accordingly, the international comparisons to be made by the Bureau will deal with the material electrical and photometric standards. To this end, six national laboratories[12] have been invited to send to the Bureau the secondary standards which represent the unit as it has been constructed in each of these laboratories.

One of the Laboratory Rooms of the International Bureau Showing Apparatus for Comparing National Standards of Electrical Resistance

Since the installation, in the new laboratories constructed for this purpose in 1930, of the necessary measuring instruments—bridge potentiometer, double Thomson bridge, photometric bench, Ulbricht sphere, etc.—these comparisons have been made periodically. The results have made it possible to assign to the national standards a value in terms of a *mean international unit.* All of the electrical and photometric standards preserved at the Bureau, restandardized in the "mean unit" at each comparison, now constitute international prototypes of the ohm, the volt, the candela, and the lumen. Just as the Bureau has been made responsible for the units of length and mass, it thus assures, though by different means, the world-wide unification of the units of electricity and light.

Although these international comparisons, together with the checks of standards requested by national and private laboratories, obviously make up the bulk of work of these two sections of the Bureau, research activities are none the less also pursued. In the field of photometry, for instance, J. Terrien, head of this section, has made many studies which among other things have resulted in raising the quality of the standard lamps, and improving the methods and measuring equipment and increasing the precision of the observations, the final goal of all the efforts of metrologists.

*The Three Advisory Committees.* When the electrical and photometric units were assigned to the Bureau, the members of the International Committee felt that it would be necessary to create for itself advisory committees on electricity and photometry composed of specialists in these fields from all over the world. It is the duty of these committees to coordinate all the stud-

[12] Physikalisch-Technische Bundesanstalt and Deutsches Amt für Mass und Gewicht (Germany); National Bureau of Standards (U. S. A.); Conservatoire National des Arts et Métiers and Laboratoire Central des Industries Electriques (France); National Physical Laboratory (Great Britain); Electrotechnical Laboratory (Japan); Institute of Metrology (U. S. S. R.).

ies on electrical and photometric matters and to suggest, in the form of recommendations to the International Committee and the General Conference, modifications of the definitions and values of the existing units. Later (1937) an Advisory Committee on Thermometry has been similarly instituted and its jurisdiction has been extended to calorimetry.

The latest investigations of these three committees were presented to the 1948 General Conference. The principal decisions and resolutions adopted were:

(1) *Electricity:* (*a*) Substitution, after January 1, 1948, of the system of *absolute units* for the so-called "international units," that had been defined by the conference of 1908; (*b*) Fixing of the conversion factors from the old to the new units:

Photometry Laboratory of the International Bureau. *Right:* Photometric Bench and Integrating Sphere for Comparing National Standards of Luminous Intensity and Flux. *Left:* Rheostats for Regulating the Electrical Supply to Standard Lamps

1 ohm (international mean)   = 1.00049 ohms (absolute)
1 ampere (international mean) = 0.99985 ampere (absolute)
1 volt (international mean)  = 1.00034 volts (absolute)

(2) *Photometry:* Adoption of the new unit of light intensity, the candela, defined from the luminescence of the integral radiator (black body) at the solidification temperature of platinum.

(3) *Thermometry:* (*a*) Publication and approval of the text of the "International Scale of Temperature," 1948. (*b*) Use of the word *Celsius* (° C.) to designate the degree of temperature, replacing the terms "centigrade" and "centesimal." (*c*) Resolution relative to substituting the melting point of ice by the triple point of water ($t = +0.0100°$ C.) as thermometric reference point of the Celsius thermodynamic scale and the adoption of an absolute thermodynamic scale related to only a single fundamental fixed point (triple point of pure water). (*d*) Use of the *joule* as the unit quantity of heat, replacing the "calorie."

In addition to all these researches and metrological studies, the Bureau is often asked to give advice on matters relating to measures and their organization. Several governments have consulted the Bureau regarding the revision of laws and the organization of their Departments of Weights and Measures.

Recently, the International Committee has also been placed in charge of an official inquiry concerning scientific, technical, and pedagogic circles, with the view of adopting, for international relations, a practical international system of units. With this objective, a plan of the units, meter-kilogram-second-ampere (Giorgi system) has been taken as the basis of discussion. The results of this inquiry are to be submitted to the next General Conference.

## CONCLUSION

Such, in brief, is the history of the origins of the metric system of weights and measures and the work accomplished by the International Bureau of Weights and Measures during the 77 years of its existence.

From the plan of the reform of measures laid down by Talleyrand in 1790 there has grown a quasi-universal system of measures, whose merits of simplicity and coherence have been recognized also by the two principal nonmetric countries, England and the United States of America, countries which themselves played an important role in the history of its foundation.

If the metric system, despite its continuous extension during a century, does not yet cover the entire globe, it nevertheless appears certain that its universality will eventually be completed. The report drawn up in 1951 by the "Committee on Weights and Measures Legislation" and submitted to the English Parliament justifies every hope in this sense. In large part, the United States will dictate the decision to be made: to give up the "Imperial System" and compel the adoption of the metric system, or to continue the coexistence of the two systems with all the attending inconveniences.

As for the International Bureau, it is not, as some may think, merely the place where the standard meter and kilogram are preserved; rather it is an international center of standardization, housing a metrological laboratory. Although many solidly established international organizations have not survived the upheavals of two World Wars, the Bureau has been able, despite some temporary difficulties, not only to continue its work but even to accept more assignments and thus pursue the mission confided to it in a disinterested scientific spirit and in close communion with the principal national metrological laboratories.

Looking forward to the years ahead, it may perhaps be asked whether the revolution that is shaping up in the development of fundamental standards of length and mass—the "atomic" standards, as they already are called—will not decrease the prestige of the International Bureau, perhaps endangering its very existence. However, it seems certain that whatever may be the standards of the future, the important part which the Bureau has filled in the global unification of the units of measure and in the improvement of metrological science will guarantee its continued existence.

It was this confidence in the future of the International Bureau of Weights and Measures that motivated the signatory countries of the Convention du Mètre to adopt unanimously, at the 1948 General Conference of Weights and Measures, a resolution designed to develop the future activity of one of the oldest international institutions.

# SOME FAMOUS BALANCES[1]

## RALPH E. OESPER

University of Cincinnati, Cincinnati, Ohio

*"Der Mann, der recht zu wirken denkt,*
*Muss auf das beste Werkzeug halten."*
GOETHE

WHEN Virgil wrote "*Arma virumque cano*" he set an example that could well be followed by the historians of chemistry. Without appliances the chemist is practically helpless, without equipment the science could never have developed beyond the stage of philosophical fantasy. Nevertheless, the histories have paid slight attention to the "arms" that made possible the victories won by the men of chemistry.

Artists commonly represent the chemist as addicted to the use of the retort. This is fair practice with respect to the alchemists, who customarily analyzed substances by subjecting them to destructive distillation, but it is absurd when continued by the modern commercial artist. He should know that the retort has long since gone out of style, that chemistry for almost two centuries has been typified by the balance.

"Nothing tends so much to the advancement of knowledge, as the application of a new instrument. The native intellectual powers of men in different times are not so much the causes of the different success of their labours, as the peculiar nature of the means and artificial resources in their possession."[2] The popular belief that the use of the balance was introduced into chemistry by Lavoisier has no foundation.[3]

"There is a certain justification for designating the period of chemistry since Lavoisier as the period of quantitative investigation, but this designation is superficial rather than factual. The distinction of the new from the old chemistry is not that it was only in the later period that men began to weigh or to use the balance—chemists have done this in all periods—but rather that in the earlier period chemical knowledge was not sufficiently advanced to make possible the determination of the weights of the constituents of the majority of the compound substances."[4]

"The conception of composition, as we now understand it, had not taken form. Careful and searching examinations of a few chemical occurrences were required, and precise statements of the results were

necessary before satisfactory hypotheses could be constructed, in terms of which fuller descriptions might be given of the facts established by experiment. What

*Courtesy of The Procter and Gamble Company*

THE VERDICT OF THE BALANCE
FROM AN OLD PROCTER AND GAMBLE IVORY SOAP ADVERTISEMENT, HARPERS' MAGAZINE, 1883.

This pen and ink sketch was again used in an Ivory Soap advertisement in the November, 1886, issue of the "Century," where it was stated, "The advantage of using an article that is pure and always uniform, is, you are always certain of having the same satisfactory results. Eight prominent professors of chemistry, of national reputation, have analyzed Ivory Soap, and the variation in each is so trifling that the quality of the Ivory may be considered reliably uniform."

The historical background seems to be that the slogan "99⁴⁴/₁₀₀% Pure" was obtained in a report submitted by a prominent Eastern independent laboratory about 1880. A little later a sample was sent to eight chemistry professors who, after analysis, gave their blessing to the new product. The illustration purports to show the jury of eight in action in the laboratory. This, of course, is pure imagination, as the men were in various colleges throughout the country, when they sampled and analyzed the soap.

was needed was not explanation but description; it is so easy to explain, so difficult to describe."[5]

"But, if, as is generally admitted, chemistry only took rank as a science when it made quantitative work its basis, then Lavoisier must be put before anyone else as having directed it into this road, and led it a considerable distance."[6]

[1] Presented before the Division of the History of Chemistry at the ninety-ninth meeting of the A. C. S., Cincinnati, Ohio, April 9, 1940.
[2] DAVY, "Collected works," London, **1840,** Vol. IV, p. 37.
[3] See, for instance, WALDEN's essay, "Mass, Zahl und Gewicht in der Chemie der Vergangenheit," *Ahren's Sammlung, N. F.,* **8,** (1931); KOPP, "Geschichte der Chemie," Vieweg, Braunschweig, **1844,** Vol. 2, p. 68.
[4] VOLHARD, *J. prakt. Chem., N. F.,* **2,** 20 (1870).
[5] MUIR, "History of chemical theories and laws," John Wiley & Sons, Inc., London, **1909,** p. 48.
[6] FREUND, "The study of chemical composition," Cambridge University Press, Cambridge, **1904,** p. 59.

Like religions, the natural sciences have relics, and among the relics pertaining to chemistry there are balances made famous either because of the men who used them or because these instruments played an important part in outstanding researches. Some years ago the writer began to collect photographs of such balances. The collection is far from complete; almost any chemist can suggest items that should be included.

The purpose of this paper is not to trace the history of the analytical balance or its use by chemists, but

(Reproduction by courtesy Science Museum, London)

FIGURE 1.—JOSEPH BLACK'S BALANCE (REPLICA)

rather to point out that a fairly good summary of the progress of chemistry can be obtained by emphasizing the arms rather than the man.

### I. JOSEPH BLACK (1728–1799)

It is fitting that this series of sketches begin with Black, whose classic study (1754) of the part played by carbon dioxide in the change from caustic to mild alkalies is "the first example we possess of a clear reasoned series of chemical researches where nothing was taken on trust, but everything was made the subject of careful quantitative measurement."[7]

"Others before him had used the balance for studying chemical reactions, but whenever a gaseous substance had, unknown to them, entered into the reaction as a

reagent or as a product, they had been defeated. Black, on the other hand, trusted first and foremost to his balance and to the principle of the conservation of mass, making search for chemical participants in the reaction only after the balance had showed him that they were there to be sought."[8]

"We may indeed regard Black's work as constituting the beginning of modern chemical science."[9]

Although Black had, so to speak, worked "balance in hand," his account[10] tells nothing of the weighing equipment used. The results were given no closer than one grain, so that a fairly rough instrument was adequate. A balance of this type, known to have been used by Black, is preserved in the Scotch Royal Museum at Edinburgh, but there is no reason to believe that it was used in the work on magnesia alba. A replica of this balance is exhibited in the Science Museum at South Kensington, London, and is pictured in Figure 1.

(Photograph by courtesy Science Museum, London)

FIGURE 2.—HENRY CAVENDISH'S BALANCE (NOW AT THE ROYAL INSTITUTION, LONDON)

It is of passing interest to note that Black devised a balance useful for weighing small quantities. He described this in a letter (Sept. 18, 1790) to James Smithson. The novel feature was a calibrated beam fitted to receive globules of gold of known weight and also brass rings, which by their position enable the operator to vary their effective mass. No examples of this early rider balance are known.[11]

[7] RAMSAY, "The gases of the atmosphere," The Macmillan Co., London, 1896, p. 60.

[8] MASSON, "Three centuries of chemistry," The Macmillan Co., New York City, 1926, p. 115.

[9] DONNAN, Introduction to RAMSAY's "Life and letters of Joseph Black," Constable and Co., Ltd., London, 1918.

[10] This is now readily accessible as No. 1 of the Alembic Club Reprints, Edinburgh, 1898.

[11] A sketch of the balance and the text of the letter may be found in the Annals of Philosophy, N. S., 10, 52 (1825). See also SPETER, Z. Instrumentenkunde, 50, 204 (1930).

## II. HENRY CAVENDISH (1731–1810)

"It has been said of Cavendish that his theory of the Universe seems to have been that it consisted *solely* of a multitude of objects which could be weighed, numbered, and measured, and the vocation to which he considered himself called was to weigh, number, and measure as many of those objects as his allotted three-score years and ten would permit. . . . . Whenever we catch sight of him we find him with his measuring-rod and balance, his graduated jar, thermometer, barometer, and table of logarithms, if not in his grasp, at least near at hand. Many of his scientific researches were avowedly quantitative. . . . . It seems indeed, to have been impossible for Cavendish to investigate any question otherwise than quantitatively." . . . . "He was indifferent to elegance of form in his apparatus, which, provided it were accurately constructed, might be clumsy in shape and of rude materials. He insisted, however, on its perfect accuracy."[12] At the

(*Photograph, courtesy of E. F. Smith Memorial Collection, Philadelphia, Pennsylvania*)

FIGURE 3.—JOSEPH PRIESTLEY'S BALANCE (NOW AT PRIESTLEY MUSEUM, NORTHUMBERLAND, PENNSYLVANIA)

death of Cavendish his apparatus passed to his cousin and heir, Lord George Cavendish, who presented much of it to Humphry Davy. Included was the balance (Figure 2) that had been constructed according to Cavendish's own design by Harrison. Although of unwieldy appearance it was used to produce results of considerable accuracy.[13] From Davy it passed to I. G. Children, then to Alexander Garden, from whom it was received (1868) by the Royal Institution, in whose museum it is now exhibited.

[12] WILSON, "The life of Henry Cavendish," printed for the Cavendish Society, London, **1851**, pp. 178, 186.
[13] "Cavendish produced results of an accuracy which would rank high even now, and which for that time was almost miraculous." FREUND, *op. cit.*, p. 59.

## III. JOSEPH PRIESTLEY (1733–1804)

"Priestley did not picture to himself chemical change as an orderly process occurring between definite substances, each of which had distinct properties. He did

(*Photograph from "Musée Centennal de la Classe 87. Arts chimiques et Pharmacie à l'Exposition Universelle Internationale de 1900 à Paris"*)

FIGURE 4.—LAVOISIER'S LARGE BALANCE (NOW AT THE CHATEAU DE LA CHAMFORTIERE, SARTHE)

not accurately weigh the materials he used and the products he obtained; he did not attempt to account for everything that took part in the transformation he examined."[14] However, he could do good quantitative work when he felt the necessity, and his unusual manipulative skill, both in chemistry and physics, makes it obvious that he could handle a balance with

(*Photograph, courtesy of Science Museum, London*)

FIGURE 5.—JOHN DALTON'S BALANCE, MADE BY ACCUM (NOW AT MANCHESTER LITERARY AND PHILOSOPHICAL SOCIETY ROOMS)

[14] MUIR, *op. cit.*, p. 38.

dexterity and certainty. If he did not make many weighings in his chemical investigations, the reason lay in the fact that he, like chemists in general, have no pleasure in the mere accumulation of data without apparent purpose.[15] The balance (Figure 3) brought to America by Priestley in 1794 was kept in the family for many years. It was then given to Edgar F. Smith by the Misses Annie and Jean Priestley, great-great-granddaughters of Priestley. In 1926 Professor Smith presented the balance to the Priestley Museum at Northumberland, Pennsylvania, where it is now preserved.[16]

### IV. A. L. LAVOISIER (1743–1794)

So much has been written about Lavoisier's recourse to the balance in solving chemical problems that it is sufficient for the present purpose to give no more than

*(Photograph, courtesy of Science Museum, London)*

FIGURE 6.—BALANCE USED BY SIR HUMPHRY DAVY. MADE BY FIDLER (NOW AT THE ROYAL INSTITUTION, LONDON)

the following. "Lavoisier brought to the study of chemistry the equipment most needed at this time—the habits and mental attitude of the trained physicist. We shall often have occasion to see that chemistry has gained enormously by the influence of those whose point of view has been preëminently physical, men who do not care to prepare new compounds or discover new reactions, but who prefer to weigh and measure, and in this way gain insight into the mechanism of chemical changes already familiar on the qualitative side."[17]

In one of his earliest papers, Lavoisier stated that the chemist had at his disposal a means of learning the precise quantities of concrete materials involved in their experiments. "La balance est une épreuve sure qui ne saurait les tromper."[18]

He wrote, "As the usefulness and accuracy of chem-

istry depends entirely upon the determination of the weights of the ingredients and products before and after experiments, too much precision cannot be employed in this part of the subject; and, for this pur-

*(Photograph by courtesy Swedish Royal Academy of Sciences)*

FIGURE 7.—BALANCE USED BY BERZELIUS (EARLY PERIOD). MADE BY SAUTER, STOCKHOLM (NOW AT BERZELIUS MUSEUM, FRESCATI, STOCKHOLM)

pose, we must be provided with good instruments. As we are often obliged, in chemical processes, to ascertain, within a grain or less, the tare or weight of large and heavy instruments, we must have balances

*(Photograph, courtesy of Royal Swedish Academy of Sciences)*

FIGURE 8.—BERZELIUS' BALANCE (LAST PERIOD). MADE BY LITTMANN, STOCKHOLM (NOW AT BERZELIUS MUSEUM, FRESCATI, STOCKHOLM)

made with peculiar niceness by accurate workmen—I have three sets, made by Fortin,[19] with the utmost nicety and excepting those made by Ramsden of

[15] HARTLEY, *J. Chem. Soc.,* **1933**, p. 918, gives a summary of those parts of Priestley's work that mark him as one of the earliest physical chemists.
[16] BROWNE, J. CHEM. EDUC., **4**, 197 (1927).
[17] MOORE, "History of chemistry," 3rd ed., McGraw-Hill Book Co., Inc., New York City, **1939**, p. 93.
[18] "Oeuvres de Lavoisier," Imprimerie Impèriale, Paris, **1865**, Vol. 3, p. 157.

[19] Jean Fortin (1750–1831) Parisian fine-mechanic, perfected and devised many physical and astronomical instruments. His balances, among the first of real precision, were prized highly.

London, I do not think any can compare with them for precision and sensibility. The largest of these is about three feet long in the beam for large weights, up to fifteen to twenty pounds; the second, for weights of eighteen or twenty ounces, is exact to one-tenth part of a grain, and the smallest calculated for weighing about one gros[20] is sensibly affected by the five-hundredth part of a grain."[21]

Lavoisier's apparatus since Madame Lavoisier's death (1836) has been in the possession of her heirs, the de Chazelles family. Some of the larger instruments are exhibited in Paris at the Conservatoire des Arts et

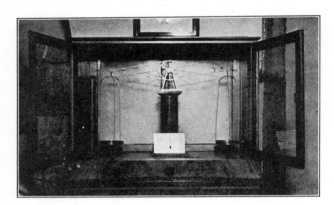

*(Photograph, courtesy of Gesellschaft Liebig Museum)*

FIGURE 9A.—LIEBIG'S "BRAUNSTEIN WAAGE" (NOW AT LIEBIG MUSEUM, GIESSEN)

Metiers, but the bulk of his appliances, including the three balances, are on view at the Chateau de la Chamfortière in the Sarthe, whither they were removed in 1935[22] from the Chateau de la Caniere in Auvergne, where they had been for many years, and where they were seen and described by Truchot[23] and by Lusk.[24]

The large balance (Figure 4) cost six hundred livres (approximately two hundred fifty dollars in present purchasing value). With a load of ten kilograms it will give an accuracy within twenty-five milligrams. The beam oscillates before two fixed scales, and the position of two marked points, one on each side of the central knife edge, is observed through telescopes. Speter, who has given a rather extended discussion of Lavoisier's balances and weights,[25] raised the interesting question, "Could Lavoisier have been able to gain his scientific triumphs so surely and so quickly if he had not possessed delicate balances and accurate weights and a knowledge of good weighing technic?" This thought is in line with Davy's statement, "Without

facilities for pursuing his object, the greatest genius in the experimental research may live and die useless and unknown."[26]

### V. JOHN DALTON (1766–1844)

"It would be unadvisable to claim for Dalton a high station in experimental chemistry. He possessed neither the mental habits and tastes for extreme exactitude nor the unrivalled manual expertness which characterized Davy, Wollaston, and Prout."[27]

"He was by no means gifted as an experimenter, and financial reasons long made it necessary for him to work with the crudest apparatus, often of his own construction; yet all these handicaps could not prevent him from discovering several of the laws which rest at the very foundation of the science."[28]

The balance (Figure 5) used by Dalton is of simple construction, unprotected by a case, and can be arranged for use as an hydrostatic balance. Dalton, by a codicil in his will, bequeathed "all his chemical and other philosophical apparatus" to his pupil and friend, Dr. Charles W. Henry, who, in turn, presented

FIGURE 9B.—DETAILS OF LIEBIG'S "BRANNSTEIN WAAGE"

the balance to the Manchester Literary and Philosophical Society. It is still in their possession.

### VI. HUMPHRY DAVY (1778–1829)

Davy never believed in atoms and substituted "proportions" for Dalton's word atom to avoid theoretical annunciations.[29] He made determinations of chemical proportions, basing his figures largely on experiments made by himself and his brother, John.

[20] 1 grain = 1/60 gross = 1/480 ounce = 1/5760 pound. 1 grain = 0.0729 gram. The French pound of that time = 375 grams.

[21] LAVOISIER, "Elements of chemistry," translated by Kerr, Creech, Edinburgh, **1790**, p. 297.—Lavoisier promised to acquaint the Academy with the details of his balances, but never did so.

[22] *Nouvelles de Chimie*, November, 1935.

[23] TRUCHOT, *Ann. chim. phys.*, [5] **18**, 289 (1879).

[24] LUSK, *Proc. Am. Med. Assoc.*, **85**, 1246 (1925).

[25] SPETER, *Z. Instrumentenkunde*, **54**, 56 (1934).

[26] DAVY, *op. cit.*, Vol. 8, p. 356.

[27] REILLY AND MACSWEENEY, *Sci. Proc. Roy. Soc. Dublin*, **19**, 139 (1929).

[28] MOORE, *op. cit.*, p. 115.

[29] GREGORY, "The scientific achievements of Sir Humphry Davy," Oxford University Press, London, **1930**, p. 131.

In his "Elements of Chemical Philosophy" (1812) he promised to publish the details of the labors "I have carried on during the last twelve years in analytical chemistry," but this promise was never kept.

The balance (Figure 6) used by Davy and also by Thomas Young (Professor at the Royal Institution, 1801–03) was described by both of them.[30] It was made for the Royal Institution by Fidler. Like many other balances of the time, it had a conically shaped hollow beam. Davy found that it would turn easily with one five-hundredth grain when loaded with one hundred grains on each pan. The balance is on view at the Royal Institution.

### VII.   J. J. BERZELIUS (1779–1848)

If anyone deserves the title "father of quantitative analysis," the honor must be given to Berzelius. Though analytic and synthetic methods existed before him, their precision was not of the order requisite for the solution of the problems raised by Dalton's laws. Even the notables were not in agreement as to the quantitative composition of even important compounds.[31] Reliable methods had to be created without regard to expenditure of time and labor. With inferior apparatus, with scarcely any help from chemical manufacturers in the supplying of pure materials and reagents, Berzelius, with undaunted patience, consummate skill, and most honest criticism of himself eventually produced the first trustworthy list of numbers repre-

senting the proportions in which the elements combine. He himself made atomic weight determinations of about forty elements and determined the composition of about two thousand compounds. His results were not without some errors which remained for correction by his successors—but it is not so remarkable that there

(*Photograph, courtesy of Professor Paul Pascal, University of Paris*)

FIGURE 12.—BALANCE USED BY DUMAS AND SAINTE-CLAIRE-DEVILLE IN THEIR STUDIES RELATIVE TO THE PREPARATION OF THE PLATINUM-IRIDIUM STANDARD METERS (NOW AT THE SORBONNE)

were errors as that these errors were on the whole so few and of such relatively small importance.[32]

[30] YOUNG, "Lectures on natural philosophy," London, **1845**, Vol. 1, pp. 97, 765; DAVY, *op. cit.*, Vol. 5, p. 17.
[31] For examples see SÖDERBAUM'S essay on Berzelius in BUGGE'S "Das Buch der grossen Chemiker," Verlag Chemie, Berlin, **1929**, Vol. 1, p. 431.

[32] MALLETT, "Chemical Society Memorial Lectures," Gurney and Jackson, London, **1901**, p. 18.

EDITORS' NOTE: Unfortunately, it was necessary to omit Figures 10 and 11 from this reprint collection because they could not be reproduced clearly.

(*Continued on page 72*)

---

### CHEMIKER-ANEKDOTEN

R. W. WOOD. "R. W. Wood pflegte sein Essen in einer kleinen Pariser Pension einzunehmen. Als es Geflügel gab, bestreute er zum Staunen der Tischnachbarn die Knochenreste auf den Tellern mit einem weiszen Pulver. Am nächsten Tag hatte er einen kleinen Spiritusbrenner mitgebracht und tropfte etwas von der Suppe in die Flamme. Als sie sich rot färbte, nickte er befriedigt mit dem Kopf. 'Das dachte ich mir,' erläuterte er den verwunderten Pensionsgästen, 'ich wollte nur wissen, ob die Knochen nochmals zur Suppe kommen. Darum habe ich sie gestern mit Lithium-chlorid bestreut. . . .' "

(*See page 76*)

The Berzelius Museum, assembled by the Swedish Academy of Sciences at Frescati near Stockholm, contains quite a few balances used by this master analyst. Two of these have been selected for inclusion in this discussion. Figure 7 shows the oldest instrument. It is of the simplest construction. The long beam and the suspension of the pans by threads reveal its early type. The balance used in the last period of Berzelius' life is shown in Figure 8. The beam is shorter and is of the now-common truss design. The readings were made with the aid of a magnifier. On the whole, this instrument does not differ greatly from some of the older balances still in use in certain laboratories.

### VIII. JUSTUS LIEBIG (1803–1873)

No chemist had a better appreciation of the value of analytical chemistry than Liebig. He was an expert in devising analytical procedures and equipment, and also

(*Photograph, courtesy of Professor Jean Timmermans, Brussels*)

FIGURE 13.—STAS' BALANCE (LARGEST) MADE BY SACRÉ, BRUSSELS (NOW AT UNIVERSITY OF BRUSSELS)

in making analyses. He was often asked to undertake important analyses, and his signature on a report carried real weight. The balance was an important item in the equipment of his laboratory. With its aid he did much to unravel the tangled skein of organic chemistry; by intelligent analyses he found means of furthering the progress of industrial, agricultural, and physiological chemistry. His own experience had taught him the latent power of this instrument; he knew whereof he spoke when he wrote ".... the balance, that incomparable instrument, which gives permanence to every observation, dispels all ambiguity, establishes truth, detects error, and shows us that we are in the true path."[33]

[33] LIEBIG, "Familiar letters on chemistry," 4th ed., Walton and Maberly, London, **1859**, p. 126.

The Liebig Museum at Giessen[34] has several balances that were used by Liebig. The best preserved is the one shown in Figure 9. It was used principally in the analysis of pyrolusite and so is known to the Museum authorities as the "Braunstein Waage." Liebig was

(*Photograph, courtesy of Professor Jean Timmermans*)

FIGURE 14.—STAS' BALANCE MADE BY SACRÉ, BRUSSELS (NOW AT UNIVERSITY OF BRUSSELS)

partial to long-beam balances, and it was a standing comment at Giessen that a cigar could be smoked between swings.

### IX. J. B. DUMAS (1800–1884)

Analytical chemistry is indebted to Dumas for an accurate method of determining nitrogen in organic materials; the physical chemists remember him chiefly for his method of measuring vapor densities. His greatest contribution along analytical lines was his determination of the relative atomic weights of about thirty elements. He was led into this field by the results obtained when the Berzelius value for carbon (76.432, O = 100) consistently gave impossible results. Dumas and Stas obtained the much better value 74.956. Encouraged by this correction, he decided that the whole list of Berzelius values needed revision. This work occupied him many years. Particularly important was his determination (1842) of the oxygen: hydrogen ratio in water. With Boussingault's aid he made accurate determinations of the ponderal composition of the air.[35] In these three studies Dumas used the balance shown in Figure 10. It was con-

[34] SOMMER, J. CHEM. EDUC., **8**, 211 (1931).
[35] For an excellent popular account of Dumas' work see THORPE, "Essays in historical chemistry," The Macmillan Co., London, **1923**, p. 318.

structed for him, and has a sensitivity of one milligram when loaded with one kilogram in each pan. The balance shown in Figure 11 was used for his work on vapor densities.

After the original French metric standards were found to be in error, an international commission was

FIGURE 15.—MENDELÉEFF'S SHORT-BEAM BALANCE MADE BY SALLERON, PARIS (NOW AT UNIVERSITY OF LENINGRAD)

organized in 1872 to supervise the preparation of new prototype meters. Dumas and Ste. Claire Deville were entrusted with the task of preparing the platinum-iridium ingots from which the bars were made. Their work was completed in 1882; the bars were made, the copies compared and finally delivered to the various governments in 1889.[36]

The tremendous balance (Figure 12) was constructed for this work. The height is 2.2 meters, the length two meters, the width 0.7 meter. Each meter bar was weighed in the horizontal and the vertical position. The sensitivity is one milligram with a load of ten kilograms in each pan. The three Dumas balances are now preserved in the laboratories of mineral chemistry of the University of Paris.

---

[36] *Cf.*, GLAZEBROOK, "Dictionary of applied physics," The Macmillan Co., London, **1923**, Vol. 3, p. 585, for a history of the revision of the metric standards. See also MATHEY, *Chem. News*, **39**, 175 (1879), for an account of the preparation of the bars.

## X.  J. S. STAS (1813–1891)

This great chemist introduced a new era into quantitative procedures; his approach to these problems was far superior to anything that had previously been attempted. Most of his time for forty years was spent in determining the atomic weights of a dozen elements. He was led to this work by the share he had had in determining with Dumas the atomic weight of carbon, and by belief in the validity of Prout's hypothesis. His experiments were conducted with a patience, care, and accuracy that are almost appalling, and nothing short of reading his own accounts can convey an adequate idea of the care and ingenuity he expended on the purification of all the materials used and the elabo-

FIGURE 16.—MENDELÉEFF'S BALANCE FOR WEIGHING GASES (NOW AT THE UNIVERSITY OF LENINGRAD)

rate precautions against mechanical loss. He studied the methods to be used with extreme rigor and found and applied refinements upon the older procedures. For him no pains were too great, no toil too severe that could render more accurate the results which others might take and trust, as the basis of their researches, however little the greater part of mankind might feel interested in or even know of his quietly pursued investigations. By his work he proved that the laws of constant proportions, of multiple proportions, of reciprocal proportions are mathematically accurate expressions of facts that hold good throughout the whole range of chemical interactions."[37]

---

[37] MALLET, *op. cit.*, p. 18.

Stas employed unusually large weights of interacting materials. For instance, 77–405 grams of silver were converted into nitrate and weighed as such; 139–259 grams of silver chlorate were converted into silver chloride; and so forth. The balances were of excellent construction and unusually satisfactory both as to sensitivity and steadiness. Stas seems to have been the first to apply *in full* to his weighings the proper correction for buoyancy in air.

Stas described his balances in his classic paper on his atomic weight determination.[38] "The largest [Figure 13] of the three balances, made expressly for my researches, will carry a load of five to six kilograms on each pan, and with this enormous load will indicate with certainty a difference in weight of one milligram. With a load of two to three kilograms on each pan, it turns in a very noticeable manner with a difference in weight of three- to four-tenths of a milligram." The other Stas balance shown here (Figure 14) has a capacity of five hundred grams on each pan, and indicates a difference under this load of two-tenths of a milligram. These balances are preserved at the University of Brussels.[39]

## XI.   D. I. MENDELÉEFF (1834–1907)

Mendeléeff was convinced that reactions are fundamentally connected with the physical and mechanical properties of the atoms and molecules. His chemical interest was largely in the field nowadays labeled physical chemistry. He made important experimental contributions to this field: specific volumes, specific gravities of solutions, elasticity of gases at low pressures, and so forth. For his ordinary work he used a long arm Oertling (London), capacity two hundred grams, sensitivity one-tenth of a milligram, or a Sartorius of the usual type. For special purposes he had available instruments of unusual design.

Figure 15 shows a balance made from Mendeléeff's own design.[40]

It has a short beam (twelve centimeters) and is capable of carrying considerable loads. With one kilogram on each pan, one milligram gives a swing of fifteen divisions on the scale placed behind the crosshairs at the end of the beam. The balance is small enough to be covered by a bell jar that can be evacuated. Obviously it cannot accommodate bulky objects and was designed for such special purposes as the verification of weights. The second balance shown (Figure 16) was used by Mendeléeff for work on gases. These balances are preserved at the University of Leningrad.

## XII.   E. W. MORLEY (1838–1923)

The publication of Morley's monumental "On the densities of hydrogen and oxygen and on the ratio of their atomic weights"[41] was the capstone of eleven

years of arduous toil. This indefatigable worker frequently spent the greater part of the night in the laboratory, and his health broke down under the strain of overwork before the researches were completed. These wonderfully accurate determinations, which are the peers of the results obtained by Stas for other elements, were attended by difficulties even greater than

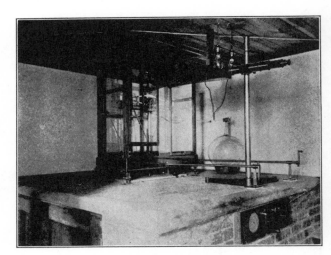

*(Photograph, courtesy of the Smithsonian Institution)*

FIGURE 17.—BALANCE USED BY E. W. MORLEY. MADE BY RUEPRECHT, VIENNA (NOW AT SMITHSONIAN INSTITUTION, WASHINGTON)

those encountered by the great Belgian chemist. Much time was spent in the detection of constant errors, in studying the details of the methods, in careful calibration of the instruments, and in making doubly sure as to the purity of the materials.[42]

Two balances were used. The first, made by Becker, Rotterdam, was presented to his alma mater by Morley and is still at Williams College. The second, and more interesting, (Figure 17) was constructed specifically for this work by Rueprecht, Vienna. The cost, five hundred fifty dollars, was borne by the Smithsonian Institution and the balance lent to Morley. After he completed his work it was returned to Washington. It had a capacity of twelve hundred grams in each pan, and the sensitivity was adequate. The gases were weighed in globes suspended from the pans and hung in an insulated closet under the balance. An ingenious long-distance mechanism enabled Morley to change the globes from one pan to the other, so that the Gauss method of reversals could be used without touching the globes. The parts of the dismantled apparatus can be seen at Western Reserve University, where this outstanding piece of work was carried out.

## XIII.   HEINRICH LANDOLT (1831–1910)

Lavoisier's enunciation of the law of conservation of mass during chemical reactions was far from justified

[38] STAS, "Oeuvres completes," Muquardt, Brussels, **1894**, Vol. 1, p. 315.
[39] TIMMERMANS, J. CHEM. EDUC., **15**, 357 (1938).
[40] SALLERON, *Compt. rend.*, **80**, 378 (1875).
[41] MORLEY, *Smithsonian Contributions to Knowledge*, **29** (1895).
[42] BOOTH, *Ind. Eng. Chem.*, **15**, 194 (1923); CLARKE, *J. Chem. Soc.*, **1923**, 3435; FREUND, *op. cit.*, 72, 192, 313.

by his own experiments, which deviated from the theoretical by 0.25 to two per cent. This fundamental tenet, whose origins are ancient, was established within 0.002–

(*Photograph, courtesy of the late Professor W. Marckwald, Berlin*)

FIGURE 18.—BALANCE USED BY H. LANDOLT MADE BY RUEPRECHT, VIENNA (NOW AT LABORATORY OF PHYSICAL CHEMISTRY, UNIVERSITY OF BERLIN)

0.004 and 0.01 per cent. by Stas and by Morley, respectively; but they assumed the validity of the law and took the minute deviations as proving the high purity of their reacting materials.

"But neither Stas's nor Morley's experiments were undertaken with a view to investigating the validity of the law of the conservation of mass, and as a matter of fact, they are particularly ill adapted to that purpose. . . . In experiments made by Landolt with the object of testing the law of conservation of mass, the conditions

report was not issued until after his death.[44] The reactions were carried out in sealed vessels, with a degree of care and consideration of details that probably has never been equaled. Of the last forty-eight trials, twenty-three showed an increase in weight, twenty-five a decrease, but the deviations in only three cases exceeded the maximal experimental error ($\pm 0.03$ mg.) and then by only 0.002 to 0.008 mg. Landolt concluded that, with respect to the fifteen reactions he studied, no change in the total weight had been established. Any deviation must be less than 0.01 or 0.001 mg. and so beyond the experimental limits of investigation.

The central point in this research was the balance (Figure 18). It probably is the finest instrument of its kind that has ever been made. Landolt, who knew what he needed, after extensive travels in Germany, France, and England, entrusted the commission (1901) to Rueprecht of Vienna. They discussed the details of the progressive refinements in fifty letters and frequent conferences. The capacity of the balance is six hundred grams in each pan, the beam is thirty centimeters long.[45] The work was carried out in a room provided with adequate temperature controls. Long-distance (three meters) controls made it unnecessary for the operator to enter the room to change the weights, reverse the loads, and so forth. An overload of one milligram with five hundred grams on each pan gave a scale reading of thirty-five to thirty-eight divisions (millimeters) that could be easily read to one-tenth through the telescope. It is reported that Landolt made more than 27,000 readings to establish the accuracy of "this beautiful instrument that gives me the greatest joy." The maximal weighing error was $\pm 0.001$–0.005 mg. Much of the work had to be done at night because of traffic vibrations.

The studies with this balance were carried out in Berlin, first (1901–05) at the Physikalisch-Chemisches Institut of the University, and then (1906–08) at the Physikalisch-Technische Reichsanstalt.

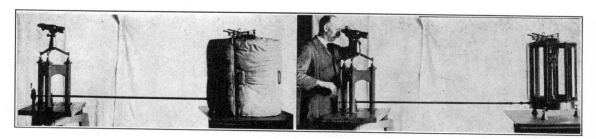

(*Photograph, courtesy of the late Professor W. Marckwald, Berlin*)

FIGURES 18A AND 18B.—BALANCE USED BY LANDOLT, DETAIL

could be specially adapted to this purpose, and hence a more rigorous proof given."[43]

Landolt's study of this problem extended over a period of almost twenty years (1890–1908) and the final

[43] FREUND, *op. cit.*, p. 102.

[44] LANDOLT, "Über die Erhaltung der Masse bei chemischen Umsetzungen," *Abhdl. Akad. Wissenschaften,* **1910,** Berlin, Phys.-math. Klasse. Abk. I. See also the detailed biography of Landolt by PRIBRAM, *Ber.,* **44,** 3337 (1911).

[45] A detailed technical description is given in FELGENTRÄGER, "Theorie, Konstruktion und Gebrauch der feineren Hebelwaage," Julius Springer, Berlin, **1907.**

## XIV. LORD RAYLEIGH (1842–1919)

Lord Rayleigh, like Stas, derived the inspiration for his epochal chemical work from a desire to test Prout's hypothesis. In 1882 he wrote, "The time has perhaps come when a redetermination of the densities of the principal gases may be desirable—an undertaking for which I have made some preparation."[46] This study, which promised to be a drab affair, turned out to be the basis of one of the most exciting chapters in the history of chemistry. The establishment of the fact that "chemical" nitrogen differed in density (1.2505

*(Photograph, courtesy of the late Baron Rayleigh)*

FIGURE 19.—BALANCE USED BY LORD RAYLEIGH MADE BY OERTLING, LONDON (NOW AT TERLING PLACE, ESSEX)

gm. per l.) from that of "atmospheric" nitrogen (1.2572) put Rayleigh on the track of some disturbing element that was present in the air in considerable amounts (1.3 per cent. by weight). The discovery of an unknown substance that had been under the very noses of

the chemists reads almost like a detective story. "At long last was captured the arch-eluder, who had escaped detection, though his haunts had been searched continually by chemists since chemistry began. He had taken the measure of Scotland Yard but had forgotten Sherlock Holmes, and when he appeared the game was up. What made the discovery especially remarkable was that it was made by the use of the balance, an instrument which is, and always has been, in every chemical laboratory, and in the use of which chemists are very expert. It was not discovered, though it might have been, by the spectroscope as so many other elements have been. . . . . The discovery of argon was much more important than the ordinary discovery of an element; it was the discovery of a new type of element, one which has been of fundamental importance in the development of the structure of the atom."[47]

No important work on the weighing of gases had been done since the time of Regnault (1845) and Rayleigh had detected a source of error in these measurements. Every precaution was taken, and years of toil were expended before he felt sufficient confidence to publish his first results. The work was done in the cellar of his house. The balance (Figure 19) was set up on a slate-topped cupboard in which hung the globes containing the gases. The room was waterproofed, and the atmosphere kept dry by the simple expedient of hanging in it well-dried wool blankets. Often these would gain two pounds in twenty-four hours.

The balance was left swinging overnight ready for the temperature to settle down, and the final readings taken the next morning. In his notes on the use of a balance[48] Rayleigh described a method of magnetic damping, but this was not used in this work. The methods of reading and illumination were, however. The balance, globes, and so forth, are still in the cellar at Terling Place, Chelmsford, Essex.

---

[46] RAYLEIGH, "Life of J. W. Strutt, Third Baron Rayleigh," Edward Arnold and Co., London, 1924, p. 158. An exceedingly readable, impartial, and detailed account of the discovery of argon is given in this biography of Rayleigh by his son. For the report of the discovery of argon see RAYLEIGH AND RAMSAY, *Chem. News*, 71, 51 (1895); *Smithsonian Contributions to Knowledge*, 29 (1896).

[47] THOMSON, "Recollections and reflections," The Macmillan Co., New York City, 1937, p. 397. Rayleigh, a physicist, once said, "If you wish a thoroughly troublesome job, pick out a chemical problem."

[48] RAYLEIGH, "Scientific Papers," Cambridge University Press, Cambridge, 1899–1920, Vol. 2, p. 226.

---

## CHEMIKER-ANEKDOTEN—R. W. WOOD

IN PARIS Professor Wood ate in a small boarding house. When there was fowl for dinner he astonished his tablemates by sprinkling a white powder on the bones left on the plates. Next day he brought along a small alcohol lamp and tested a drop of soup in the flame. Seeing a red flash, he chortled triumphantly, "I knew it!" Then he explained to his astonished audience, "I only wanted to know if the bones go into the soup, so yesterday I sprinkled them with lithium chloride."

*(See page 71)*

## XV. THEODORE W. RICHARDS (1868–1928)

Richards, the first American chemist to receive the Nobel Prize, was fond of making the following quota-

(Photograph, courtesy of Professor G. P. Baxter)
FIGURE 20.—BALANCE USED BY T. W. RICHARDS (1890–96) MADE BY TROEMNER, PHILADELPHIA (NOW AT HARVARD UNIVERSITY)

tion from Plato, "If from any art you take away that which concerns weighing, measuring, and arithmetic, how little is left of that art." He is most widely known for his work on atomic weights. For a long time the work of Stas was taken as the nearest approach to perfection that had ever been attained, but persistent discrepancies between his values and those of Richards led ultimately to the discovery that Stas's work was vitiated by appreciable errors that were not difficult to trace. Subsequent developments in Richards' laboratory have shown that Stas, though years ahead of his time, was in error by important amounts in nearly all of his work. A new era in analytical accuracy was thus inaugurated by Richards and the students who worked under him."[49] They redetermined the atomic weights of twenty-four elements in the laboratories at Harvard.

The balance (Figure 20) was employed by Richards in the period 1890–96, and presumably was used in the work on barium, copper, and strontium. For small loads it is accurate to 0.01 milligram, and up to fifty grams to 0.01–0.02 mg. It is not sturdy enough to carry its rated capacity, two hundred grams.

[49] BAXTER, Science, **68**, 333 (1928).

---

## ODD HASSEL

### RALPH E. OESPER
University of Cincinnati, Cincinnati, Ohio

ODD HASSEL, the eminent Norwegian physical chemist, was born at Oslo on May 17, 1897. After graduation from the University of Oslo in 1920, he continued (1922–25) his studies at Munich and then at Berlin. He held a Rockefeller Fellowship, 1924–25. The Ph.D. was conferred by the University of Berlin in 1924. From 1925 to 1934 Dr. Hassel was lecturer in physical chemistry at Oslo; in 1934 he was advanced to a full professorship, a position he has completely held up to the present day.

His researches have dealt mostly with various topics in physical chemistry. A steady stream of worth-while papers have come from his laboratory. His chief interests have centered around crystal structure and molecular structure. His conclusions have been based on X-ray diffraction studies, measurements of dipole moments, and investigation of scattering of electrons by vapors. Since 1939 the "rotating sector" method of electron diffraction has been developed in his laboratory and applied to a series of problems relating to the establishment of the configuration of "free" molecules. Papers dealing with the significance of van der Waals

distances in separate molecules, especially with reference to cyclohexane and its derivatives, decalin, and other six-membered rings, have been worthy of special notice. He has made an extensive study of the structure of cis decalin and a series of cyclohexane derivatives (including benzene hexachloride). In the field of preparative chemistry he has explored the preparation of the cyclohexane series and related compounds.

Professor Hassel's "Kristallchemie" was published at Dresden in 1934; following an urgent demand, an English translation by R. C. Evans, "Crystal Chemistry," was issued the next year.

A member of the Norwegian Academy of Science since 1933, Professor Hassel also belongs to the Norwegian Research Council for Science and Humanities, and since 1949 has been chairman of its Mathematics and Natural Science section. He has been Norwegian Editor of Acta Chimica Scandinavica since 1947.

Professor Hassel received the Fridtjof Nansen Award in 1946; in 1950 the University of Copenhagen conferred the Ph.D. honoris causa on this distinguished Scandinavian chemist.

# THE CENTENARY OF THE BUNSEN BURNER

**GEORG  LOCKEMANN**
Mühle Hollenstedt, Germany
*(Translated by Ralph E. Oesper)*

Aᴌᴍost all discoveries and inventions have a previous history, which in some instances extends over years, decades, and even centuries, as in the case of the discovery of oxygen; on the other hand, novel, unexpected, and even undreamed of events can occur, such as the discovery of X-rays, radium, and the fission of the uranium nucleus. Consequently, it is not surprising that there were forerunners to the Bunsen burner, whose centenary should have been one of the highlights in the 1955 calendar of historical celebrations. These predecessors represent unsuccessful attempts to use the same basic principle. Once brought to the stage of practical usefulness, this laboratory device was rapidly adopted in laboratories throughout the world and its adaptations to domestic and industrial needs followed in swift order. It would be hard to picture our present civilization without this efficient means of burning gas to produce heat. By this achievement alone, Bunsen became one of the great scientific benefactors of our era.

In 1852 Robert Wilhelm Bunsen (1811–99) was called from the University of Breslau to succeed Leopold Gmelin (1788–1853) as professor of chemistry at Heidelberg. Here he inherited an old laboratory, which, like the one he had just left in Breslau, had formerly been a monastery. It is not surprising that one of his stipulations when accepting the call was that a new laboratory was to be built according to his own plans. He moved into the new building at Easter, 1855. With its large auditorium, 50 working places, special rooms, etc., it was the largest and best equipped teaching laboratory in all Germany. It was soon filled to capacity with enthusiastic students, especially because Giessen, hitherto the Mecca of chemical training, had lost its appeal when the great Liebig had gone to Munich in 1852 with the express proviso that he be relieved of all laboratory instruction.

Like many other German cities, Heidelberg had acquired a gas works to light the streets. The plant went

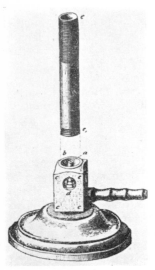
**Figure  1**

into production in October, 1852, *i. e.*, just when Bunsen took over his new chair. He had long wrestled with charcoal and coal furnaces, and with alcohol lamps, and was seeking a better means not only of lighting his laboratory, but also of providing better sources of heat for laboratory operations. Consequently, he included the necessary piping in the new laboratory. However, the devices for burning gas then available all suffered from the grave defect that they delivered luminous smoky flames of low heating power. Bunsen, a self-confident inventive genius, was sure that he could devise a suitable burner.

When his brilliant student Henry Roscoe (1833–1915) came back from his vacation, he brought from London an Argand burner, whose essential feature was a copper cone which could be slid up and down along the tube of the burner, and whose top consisted of wire gauze. Presumably this was closely allied to the burner described by Michael Faraday in his "Chemical Manipulations," published in 1827. Bunsen tried it out and rejected it. The flame was too large, it was difficult to regulate, and the gas was so diluted that the resulting temperature was too low. Furthermore, the flame flickered excessively. Bunsen set to work and in a short time came up with an astoundingly simple solution to this complex problem. Instead of feeding the flame with air from the outside, he prepared the gas-air mixture previous to the combustion. In this way he found that he could produce nonluminous flames of high heating value. He took his ideas to the university mechanic, Peter Desaga, and by the time Bunsen moved into the new laboratory in the spring of 1855, Desaga had manufactured enough burners for the Heidelberg students and soon was supplying the demands that came from all quarters of the chemical world.[1]

Bunsen did not publish an account of the burner until two years later. This description, accompanied by a cut, appeared in a joint paper with Roscoe,[2] the second in the series on their photochemical studies. He spoke of the burner in the modest terms so characteristic of all his descriptions of his own inventions and discoveries. He writes of the new heating device:

. . . which one of us has devised and introduced in place of the

[1] The author is indebted to Mr. Erich Fecht of Heidelberg, present owner of the firm C. Desaga, Factory for Scientific Apparatus (founded by Carl Desaga, the son of Peter Desaga) for information regarding the latter.
[2] *Poggendorffs Ann. Physik*, **100**, 84–5 (1857).

wire gauze burners in the laboratory here, and which is better suited than any other appliance for producing steady flames of different luminosity, color, and form. The principle of this burner is simply that city gas is allowed to issue under such conditions that by its own movement it carries along and mixes with itself precisely enough air so that the resulting air-bearing gas mixture is just at the limit where it has not yet acquired the ability to propagate the flame through itself. In Figure 6 [Figure 1 in this paper] $a$ is an ordinary cross cut burner rising in the center of the cylindrical space $b$ to the same height as the surface of the cube $cccc$. The cylindrical space $b$, which is 15 mm. deep and has a diameter of 10 mm., communicates with the outside air through the four holes $d$, which are 7 mm. in diameter. If the tube $ee$, which is 8.5 mm. wide and 75 mm. long, is screwed into the cylinder, and the city gas is allowed to flow into it through the burner $a$, it sucks in so much air through the openings $d$ that it burns at the mouth of the tube $e$ with a nonluminous, perfectly soot-free flame. The brightness of the gas thus mixed with air hardly exceeds that of a hydrogen flame. After the openings $d$ are closed, the bright and sooting illuminating gas flame reappears.

The burner evidently was used for some years in the form described and pictured here, namely, with four air holes in the square block. In any case, the illustrations (Figure 2) in the papers entitled "Lotröhrversuche" ("Studies with the blowpipe") and "Chemische Analyse durch Spektralbeobachtungen"[3] still show the same model. When it was desired to obtain a somewhat or completely luminous flame, it was necessary to stop up several or all four holes. There is no record of the date at which the four holes in the cubical base of the burner were replaced by the now general two larger holes in the burner tube along with the rotatable perforated ring. It is quite likely that this improvement was contributed by Desaga.[4]

Neither Bunsen nor Desaga applied for patent protection on the new burner. As was to be expected, it was not long before others produced imitations of the strikingly useful appliance, and some went so far as to claim the invention as their own. As early as 1855 Desaga found it necessary to send a note to the *Dingler Polytechnische Journal* refuting the allegation by the firm Julius Pintsch of Berlin that the burner was their brainchild. On May 22, Bunsen sent Desaga a written declaration that the latter had employed a principle outlined by Bunsen as the basis for the construction, in a very ingenious manner, of a gas burner whose mechanical details were developed by the apparatus maker himself. With this it was possible to obtain a sootless, nonluminous flame. In his (Bunsen's) opinion, Mr. Desaga had constructed a burner which doubtless has contributed materially to the use of illuminating gas for heating purposes.

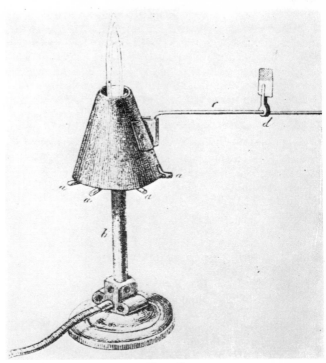

Figure 2

A second attempt to pirate the invention was made by R. W. Elsner, a gas engineer of Berlin, who went so far as to obtain a patent on the burner in the Kingdom of Hannover. The patent was dated January 4, 1856, and had a life of five years. Desaga, of course, attacked this procedure. He stated[5] that as early as the fall of 1854 he had received from the "Herrn Hofrath Bunsen" a commission to construct, in accord with the latter's specifications, a gas burner without a wire gauze and delivering a completely soot-free flame, and that when he finally succeeded after many trials, he equipped the new laboratory at Heidelberg with 50 such burners.

The further spread of the use of the burner is common knowledge. It soon rendered invaluable services to Bunsen himself. It was an essential tool in the photochemical studies he carried out with Roscoe from 1855 to 1862. It likewise made possible the joint researches with Gustav Kirchhoff (1824–87) which resulted in their spectral analytical triumphs (Figure 3).

If the centennial of the bunsen burner brings once more to our minds the memory of the brilliant scientist, gifted inventor, and lovable gentleman, Robert Wilhelm Bunsen, who generously donated all the fruits of his wonderful skill and mind to the whole civilized world, we should certainly not forget to include in our gratitude his worthy technical collaborator, Peter Desaga.

[3] *Ann.*, **111**, 257 (1859); *Poggendorffs Ann. Physik*, **110**, 161 (1860).

[4] The three illustrations accompanying this paper were kindly provided by Dr. Rudolf Sachtleben, section chief in the Deutsches Museum in Munich. Unfortunately, neither the museum nor the Desaga firm in Heidelberg has any specimens of the original Bunsen burner.

[5] *Dingler Polytechnische Journal*, **143**, 340 (1857).

EDITORS' NOTE: The Figure 3 referred to is reproduced on page 83 of this reprint volume.

# CHEMISTRY AND THE SPECTRUM BEFORE BUNSEN AND KIRCHHOFF[1]

**TILLMON H. PEARSON and AARON J. IHDE**
University of Wisconsin, Madison, Wisconsin

PRODUCTION of colors by refraction was known to Seneca (1). Kepler (2) made use of an equilateral glass prism for the study of the subject. The Archbishop of Spalatro, Marco Antonio de Dominis (3), explained the rainbow by postulating that the light reflected from the inner surfaces of raindrops was colored by passing through different thicknesses of water. Descartes (4) improved the explanation and made it in terms of refrangibility. He also calculated the angle of the bow.

It was Newton (5), however, who recognized the significance of the phenomenon. He wrote: "I procured me a Triangular glass-Prisme to try therewith the celebrated *Phoenemena of Colours*." After sunlight from a circular hole in the shutter had passed through his prism he observed, as others had before him, an elongated and rainbow-hued spot on the wall. His search for understanding was aided by a second prism which revealed that the various colors of the spectrum could be refracted again but without further change in color. The colors of the blue end were refracted most and those of the red end least, just as had happened when the light passed through the first prism. Newton also observed that the second prism could be used to recombine into white light the colors separated by the first prism.

The ideas of Newton on light were immediately attacked. Robert Hooke, who had a color theory of his own as the result of his work on thin films, was especially vociferous in his denunciation. The reception of his first scientific paper caused Newton to withdraw from scientific discussion. Most of his later publications came only after prolonged persuasion on the part of his friends. It is of interest to note that his book, "Optiks," was only published in 1704, the year after Hooke's death.

The eighteenth century saw little progress in the further understanding of light. Scheele (6) in 1777 reported the effects of spectral colors on the darkening of silver chloride. It was well known among silver miners that a certain ore found as a white mineral, horn silver, turned dark upon exposure to sunlight. Scheele exposed samples of the chloride to the various colors of the spectrum, noting that the darkening was most rapid at the violet end. His results were verified and extended in 1801 by Johann Wilhelm Ritter (7) who found the dark region beyond the violet portion of the spectrum still more effective in producing darkening

than the visible violet. The same discovery was made independently by William Hyde Wollaston (8).

It was the discovery of the infrared region of the spectrum a year earlier which had prompted Ritter to investigate the possible existence of radiant energy beyond the violet. The famed astronomer, William Herschel (9) in studying the illuminating and heating power of the various colors of the spectrum observed a steady increase in heating power from the violet to the red. He used the arrangement illustrated (Figure 1). The blackened bulb of thermometer 1 was placed in the color range under test while thermometers 2 and 3 to the side of the spectral area served as controls. When the bulb of thermometer 1 was placed in the dark region beyond the visible red it showed an even faster temperature rise than it did when the red color fell upon it, revealing the passage of radiant heat of low refrangibility through the prism.

Wollaston's paper (8) verifying the existence of ultraviolet light also reported the presence of dark lines in the spectrum of sunlight. Up to this time investigators had been working with highly impure spectra resulting from circular openings or wide slits admitting the beam of light. Wollaston used a narrow slit, not more than a twentieth of an inch in width. When he viewed the light from the slit at the distance of 10 or 12 feet, through a flint-glass prism held near the eye, he saw the beam separated into red, yellowish

Figure 1. Herschel's Recognition of Infrared

[1] Presented before the Division of the History of Chemistry at the 118th Meeting of the American Chemical Society, Chicago, Illinois, September, 1950.

green, blue, and violet. In the resulting spectrum he reported seven dark lines. Five of the lines were reported as being on the boundaries of the colors observed, but the other two were observed within the yellowish green and the blue regions.

These lines, plus many additional ones, were independently rediscovered in 1814 by Fraunhofer (10). The young lens manufacturer, in studying the refractive index of glass samples for particular colors, noticed a bright double line (of sodium) in the spectrum of the flame which he was using. This same double line was observed in alcohol and sulfur flames as well as in oil and tallow light in exactly the same position and was therefore useful in the determination of indexes. In order to find out if a similar line could be observed in the solar spectrum, he allowed sunlight to pass through a narrow slit and fall upon a flint-glass prism set in front of a telescope. Instead of a bright yellow double line he observed countless vertical lines darker than the colored parts of the spectrum in which they occurred. Eight of the most prominent lines were labeled $A$ to $H$, and nearly 600 lines were observed, all but the less definite ones being mapped (Figure 2).

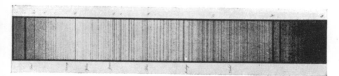

Figure 2. Fraunhofer's Map of the Solar Spectrum

He reported on the effect of slit width and types of prisms on spectral purity. His experiments convinced him that the lines were due to the nature of sunlight rather than to diffraction caused by the slit or to optical illusions. During the remaining years of his life he continued his studies of spectra without ever realizing the significance of the lines which today bear his name.

The spectra of light from several of the heavenly bodies were also observed by Fraunhofer (10, 11). The spectrum of moonlight showed the stronger lines of sunlight in the same place. The planets Venus and Mars showed fainter spectra with lines $D$, $E$, $b$, and $F$ being positively identified. Study of the spectra of the stars was difficult but revealed a lack of similarity with the solar spectrum. It was not possible to distinguish lines in the orange and yellow for Sirius but there was a strong streak in the green and two streaks in the blue which seemed unlike any of the lines in planetary spectra. Castor showed a spectrum similar to Sirius. The $D$ line was identified in the spectrum of Pollux and Betelgeuse and possibly in that of Procyon.

In 1821 Fraunhofer (12) reported experiments with diffraction gratings. His first gratings were made of wires wrapped closely around a flat frame. Later he made gratings by ruling lines on glass covered with gold foil. With his gratings he determined the wave length of the line labeled $D$. With gratings made of wires ranging between 0.04 and 0.6 mm. in thickness he obtained values lying between 0.0005882 and 0.0005897 with a mean of 0.0005888 mm. The accepted modern value is 0.0005896 mm. for $D_1$ and 0.0005889 mm. for $D_2$ (13).

The phenomenon of diffraction, first reported in 1665 in the posthumous treatise of the Jesuit mathematics professor at Bologna, Francesco Grimaldi (14), had received little attention during the century in which Newton's corpuscular theory of light had been dominant. Now, with the re-emergence of the undulatory theory as a result of the work of Young and Fresnel, diffraction took on a new significance and the diffraction grating was destined to play an important role in the study of spectra.

The extension of Fraunhofer lines into the infrared was shown by John Herschel (15), son of William, in 1840. He covered a paper with gum and lampblack to make it readily absorptive of heat. After dipping in alcohol the paper was exposed to the spectrum of the sun. The alcohol, instead of evaporating evenly in the dark region beyond the visible red, as would have been the case if the spectrum were continuous, evaporated unevenly, leaving several moist patches which indicated that the dark lines apparently carried beyond the visible spectrum. Later experiments with more refined techniques soon verified this assumption.

David Brewster (16) reported in 1834 on lines produced by sunlight passed through "nitrous acid gas." He stated as the object of his inquiries, "the discovery of a general principle of chemical analysis in which simple and compound bodies might be characterized by their action on definite parts of the spectrum." After first observing that sulfur attacked the violet end of the spectrum of lamp light and iodine vapor the middle part, he turned his attention to the brown oxide of nitrogen. The spectrum was crossed by hundreds of lines or bands. Upon increasing the thickness of the gas the lines grew more distinct in the red and yellow region and broadened in the blue and violet. The same effect was noted when the thickness of the gas remained constant but the gas was heated, an experiment with attendant dangers since the tubes frequently exploded. Brewster reported the noncoincidence of the lines with the lines of the solar spectrum and the absence of the lines in Fraunhofer's map.

Brewster's work was immediately extended by John Frederic Daniell and William Hallows Miller (17) who passed the light of a gas lamp through halogen vapors before examining the prismatic spectrum with a small telescope. In the spectrum of bromine vapor in air they observed the colors interrupted by more than 100 lines. When the concentration of bromine was increased, the blue end disappeared while the lines in the red grew stronger. They also investigated the absorption of iodine vapor and chlorine.

The investigation of absorption spectra was resumed some years later by William Allen Miller (18). None of the fourteen colorless gases studied showed lines. When colorless elements were united, however, they might form colored gases which did show lines while colored elements like iodine might show no lines when in gaseous compounds.

The characteristic bright lines in the spectra of certain metallic salts on heating were first observed by Thomas Melvill (19) in 1752. This young Scottish investigator died during the next year and his observations apparently went unnoticed. The difference in flame colors given by sodium and potassium salts appears to have been used as a means of distinguishing salts of these elements by Marggraf (20) by 1758. John Herschel (21) reported in 1822 that the flame colors of the chlorides of strontium, calcium, barium, and copper, and that of boric acid were resolved on passing through a prism, bright lines being apparent on a dark background. He believed the bright lines would be useful in detecting small quantities of a substance and touched upon the subject in his "Treatise on Light."

Henry Fox Talbot (22) suggested in 1833 the use of common salt in the flame of a spirit lamp to obtain homogeneous light. If a stream of oxygen were directed on the salt through a blowpipe a light of great intensity might be obtained. "Strontian and barytes" were also suggested as sources of homogeneous light. During the next year this same investigator (23) pointed out that lithium and strontium, both giving red flames, could be distinguished by passing their light through a prism. The strontium flame revealed many red lines plus an orange and a blue line whereas the lithium gave only a single red line. In a subsequent paper (24) Talbot referred to the fixed character of the lines of sodium and reported that the spectrum of copper was full of dark lines. Here he was mistaking bright lines for dark lines. He also observed lines in the spectrum of the boric acid flame.

In 1835 Charles Wheatstone (25) published the results of his experiments on the spectra of electric arcs produced by metallic electrodes. He noted that bright lines were produced which were characteristic of the metal making up the electrode, observations being made on mercury, zinc, cadmium, tin, bismuth, and lead.

The developments of Niepce, Daguerre, and Talbot, which were leading to photography, naturally found their way into studies of spectra. In 1842 A. Edmond Becquerel (26) photographed the solar spectrum with nearly all of the lines registered by the eye of Fraunhofer plus extension into the ultraviolet. John William Draper (27) photographed the spectrum only a few months after Becquerel. Draper, occupant of the chair of chemistry and physiology at New York University, had introduced the daguerreotype into portraiture in the United States (28). In 1843 he photographed the diffraction spectrum using a grating ruled on glass by John Saxton, a mechanician at the U. S. Mint.

In 1847 Draper (29) published results of studies on hot bodies, reporting that all solids become incandescent at the same temperature. Below 525°C. invisible rays were emitted. Above that temperature rays of progressively greater refrangibility were emitted as the temperature increased. All spectra of incandescent solids were continuous.

During all of this period there was no real recognition of the relationship between bright-line and dark-line spectra. Fraunhofer had observed that the bright lines of the sodium flame corresponded to the position of the D line in the solar spectrum. Investigators were encountering confusion, however, on at least two scores. On the one hand they were not obtaining bright-line spectra free of the continuous spectrum. Their flames contained sufficient organic material to provide incandescent carbon giving white light. Draper (30), in his study of flame spectra, reported that all flames gave a continuous spectrum. On the other hand their flames and even their electric arcs were contaminated with sodium so that the D line was present regardless of the element under study.

In spite of this, the decade preceding Bunsen and Kirchhoff's successful work saw a number of investigators groping in the right direction. Foucault (31) examining the spectrum of an arc between charcoal electrodes, noticed a line similar to the D line of the solar spectrum. Lacking suitable instruments for independent measurement of the lines, he attempted to superimpose the two spectra by passing the sun's rays through the arc and through the prism. This proved that the lines were indeed identical in position. Further, the D line of the sunlight was strengthened by passage through the arc. If the sunlight was shut off the D line was in the arc source as a bright line. Foucault wrote, ". . . the line D appears darker than usual in the solar light . . . Thus the arc presents us with a medium which emits the D rays on its own account, and which at the same time absorbs them when they come from another quarter." Foucault failed to follow up his observations on spectra when he devoted his energies to other researches.

In America, David Alter (32) was investigating the spectra of numerous metals and gases by 1855. In describing the spectra of hydrogen and other gases he stated that each element had a characteristic spectrum and that "the prism may also detect the elements in shooting stars." William Swan (33), in 1857, called attention to the extremely minute quantities of sodium necessary to bring out the D line.

In spite of the findings which anticipated the report of the Heidelberg scientists in 1859, it was the collaboration of Bunsen, the chemist, and Kirchhoff, the physicist, which attracted attention to the significance of the spectrum. Collaboration of these two workers representing different training and objectives, paved the way for a new impetus in chemistry, in physics, and in astronomy.

Bunsen had been making use, in qualitative analysis, of the flame colors imparted by different metallic salts to the colorless Bunsen burner flame. In order to distinguish between similar flames he had viewed them through colored solutions or glasses. One of his

English students, R. Cartmell (34), acknowledged Bunsen's valuable suggestions in a paper on the subject. Kirchhoff, at about this time, pointed out that one might better pass the light through a glass prism and view the spectrum. In acting upon the suggestion the pair (35) developed their spectroscope for viewing flame colors. The instrument represented no new principles or devices which had not been in use for years, but brought together on one stand the necessary collimating and viewing telescopes with the prism enclosed inside a blackened box (Figure 3).

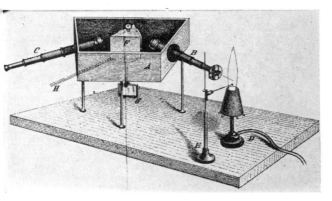

Figure 3. Bunsen and Kirchhoff's Spectroscope

Kirchhoff had already turned his attention to the solar spectrum and published a paper (36) on the relation of bright lines to the Fraunhofer lines. When common salt was heated in a flame the characteristic bright line was observed but when white light from incandescent lime, which was known to show a continuous spectrum, was passed through the sodium flame and then through the prism a dark line appeared in the D position. Kirchhoff grasped the fact that hot gases absorbed the same kind of light which they emitted. Sodium vapor must be present in the outer atmosphere of the sun, absorbing the D line present in the white light coming from the incandescent surface of the sun. When the sun's light was passed through a lithium flame before entering the spectroscope, a new dark line appeared between the Fraunhofer B and C positions which could not be identified with the known lines of Fraunhofer. Hence, no lithium was present in the sun's atmosphere. Kirchhoff reserved to himself and Bunsen the right to further investigate these phenomena. The first paper was soon followed (37) by a long mathematical treatment of the relation between the radiating and absorbing powers of substances for heat and light.

The spectroscope, together with the Kirchhoff laws of spectroscopy, thus provided a powerful new tool for the study of the chemical composition of solar and stellar atmospheres. Astronomers quickly brought the instrument into widespread use. At the same time the earthly uses of the instrument were not overlooked. Bunsen and Kirchhoff (38) quickly reported the discovery of the alkali metals cesium and rubidium.

William Crookes (39) reported evidence for thallium at about the same time. In subsequent years the spectroscope loomed large in the discovery of new elements as well as in more prosaic qualitative analysis.

Immediately after the report of Kirchhoff in late 1859 it was pointed out by E. Verdet (40) and by George Gabriel Stokes (41) that Foucault had anticipated his discovery. Kirchhoff (42) denied prior knowledge of the work of Foucault. William Thompson (Kelvin) (42), in correspondence with Kirchhoff, pointed out that Stokes had been offering essentially Kirchhoff's explanation to his students at Cambridge for a number of years but had never bothered to publicize his ideas. Stokes (43) later verified this but insisted that, "I have never attempted to claim for myself any part of Kirchhoff's admirable discovery, and cannot help thinking that some of my friends have been overzealous in my cause." John Tyndall (44) reiterating the fact that Foucault, Stokes, and Thompson had been close to the discovery, also considered himself on the right track in 1859 if his experiments had not been interrupted, and considered Ångström (45) closest to having made the discovery. Crookes (46) put forth claims of priority for W. H. Miller.

Kirchhoff (47) persistently defended the originality of his own work and attempted to show that the earlier investigators were guilty of misinterpretation of results or confusion of objectives. Nevertheless, in reviewing the growth of understanding of chemistry and the spectrum, it again (48) becomes evident that discovery is a cooperative enterprise. Bunsen and Kirchhoff represent the culmination of a long series of steps toward understanding. As a pair they were able to draw together the threads of tradition in order to make the final synthesis. Together they were able to carry their synthesis into new and fruitful investigations in the fields of chemistry and astronomy. Earlier workers had not seen the picture in its broader aspects, had not received suitable publicity for their results, and had not carried on to the point of significant application.

## LITERATURE CITED

(1) SENECA, L. A., "Quaestiones Naturales," Book I, Chaps. 2–8, about A.D. 63. J. CLARKE, "Physical Science in the Time of Nero, being a translation of *Quaestiones Naturales* of Seneca," Macmillan, London, 1910, pp. 16–32.

(2) KEPLER, J., "Dioptrice," Augsburg, 1611; "Dioptrik," Ostwald's Klassiker der Exacten Wissenschaften, W. Ostwald, Ed., No. 144, W. Engelmann, Leipzig, 1904, p. 12.

(3) DE DOMINIS, M. A., "De Radiio Visus et Lucis," 1611. ERNST MACH, "The Principles of Physical Optics," E. P. Dutton and Co., New York, 1925, pp. 84–5.

(4) DESCARTES, R., "Discours de la Méthode, les Météores, la Dioptrique, la Géometrie," Leyden, 1637. C. ADAMS AND P. TANNERY, Eds., "Ouvres de Descartes," Vol. VI, Leopold Cerf, Paris, 1902, pp. 93–105.

(5) NEWTON, I., *Phil. Trans. Roy. Soc.* (London), 6, 3075–87 (1672).

(6) SCHEELE, C. W., "Chemische Abhandlung von Luft und Feuer," Erusius, Leipzig, 2nd ed., 1782, p. 66.

(7) RITTER, J. W., *Gilbert's Ann. Physik*, **7**, 527 (1801).

(8) WOLLASTON, W. H., *Phil. Trans. Roy. Soc.* (London), **92**, 365–80 (1802).

(9) HERSCHEL, W., *ibid.*, **90**, 255–92 (1800).

(10) FRAUNHOFER, J., *Denkschr. Akad. Wissenschr. Munchen*, **5**, 193–226 (1817). J. S. AMES, "Prismatic and Diffraction Spectra," Harpers, New York, 1898, p. 4.

(11) FRAUNHOFER, J., *Gilbert's Ann. Physik*, **74**, 337–78 (1823).

(12) FRAUNHOFER, J., *Denkschr. Akad. Wissenschr. Munchen*, **8**, 1–76 (1821).

(13) LANGE, N. A., "Handbook of Chemistry," 7th ed., Handbook Publishers, Inc., Sandusky, Ohio, **1949**, p. 1089.

(14) GRIMALDI, F., "Physico-Mathesis de Lumine, Caloribus, et Iride" Bologna, **1665**. J. JEANS, "The Growth of Physical Science," University Press, Cambridge, **1947**, p. 202.

(15) HERSCHEL, J. F. W., *Phil. Trans. Roy. Soc.* (London), **130**, 1–59 (1840).

(16) BREWSTER, D., *Trans. Roy. Soc. Edinburgh*, **12**, 519–30 (1834); "Second Report of the British Assoc. for the Advancement of Science," Murray, London, **1833**. D. BREWSTER AND J. H. GLADSTONE, *Phil. Trans. Roy. Soc.* (London), **150**, 149–60 (1860).

(17) MILLER, W. H., *Phil. Mag.*, [3] **2**, 381–2 (1833).

(18) MILLER, W. A., *ibid.*, [3] **27**, 81–91 (1845).

(19) MELVILL, T., *Edinburgh Physical and Literary Essays*, **2**, 36 (1752).

(20) FÄRBER, E., "Geschichtliche Entwicklung der Chemie," Springer, Berlin, **1921**, p. 210.

(21) HERSCHEL, J. F. W., *Trans. Roy. Soc. Edinburgh*, **9**, 445–60 (1822).

(22) TALBOT, H. F., *Phil. Mag.*, [3] **3**, 35 (1833).

(23) TALBOT, H. F., *ibid.*, [3] **4**, 112–114 (1834).

(24) TALBOT, H. F., *ibid.*, [3] **9**, 1–4 (1836).

(25) WHEATSTONE, C., "Notices of Communications to the British Assoc. for the Advancement of Science," Murray, London, **1836**, pp. 11–12. Published and bound with "Report of the Fifth Meeting of the British Assoc. for the Advancement of Science held in Dublin in August, 1835."

(26) BECQUEREL, A. E., *Bibliothèque universelle Genève*, **40**, 341 (1842).

(27) DRAPER, J. W., *Phil. Mag.*, [3] **21**, 348–50 (1842). J. F. W. HERSCHEL, *ibid.*, [3] **22**, 120–32 (1843).

(28) DRAPER, J. W., *ibid.*, [3] **17**, 217–25 (1840).

(29) DRAPER, J. W., *ibid.*, [3] **30**, 345–60 (1847).

(30) DRAPER, J. W., *ibid.*, [3] **32**, 100–14 (1848).

(31) FOUCAULT, L., *L'Institut*, 1849, 45–6.

(32) ALTER, D., *Am. J. Sci. Arts*, **18**, 55–7 (1854); **19**, 213–214 (1855).

(33) SWAN, W., *Trans. Roy. Soc. Edinburgh*, **21**, 411–30 (1857).

(34) CARTMELL, R., *Phil. Mag.*, [4] **16**, 328–33 (1858).

(35) KIRCHHOFF, G., AND R. BUNSEN, *Pogg. Ann. Physik*, **110**, 161–89 (1860); *Phil. Mag.*, [4] **20**, 89–109 (1860).

(36) KIRCHHOFF, G., *Monatsber. Akad. Wissensch. Berlin*, **1859**, 662–4; *Pogg. Ann. Physik*, **109**, 148–50 (1860); *Phil. Mag.*, [4] **19**, 193–7 (1860).

(37) KIRCHHOFF, G., *Monatsber. Akad. Wissensch. Berlin*, **1859**, 783–98; *Pogg. Ann. Physik*, **109**, 275–301 (1860); *Phil. Mag.*, [4] **20**, 1–19 (1860).

(38) KIRCHHOFF, G., AND R. BUNSEN, *Pogg. Ann. Physik*, **113**, 337–81 (1861); *Phil. Mag.*, [4] **22**, 329–49, 498–510 (1861).

(39) CROOKES, W., *Phil. Mag.*, [4] **21**, 301–5 (1861).

(40) VERDET, E., *Ann. chim. phys.*, **58**, 476–8 (1860).

(41) STOKES, G. G., *Phil. Mag.*, [4] **19**, 193–7 (1860).

(42) KIRCHHOFF, G., *ibid.*, [4] **20**, 19–21 (1860).

(43) STOKES, G. G., *Nature*, **13**, 188–9 (1876).

(44) TYNDALL, J., *Phil. Trans. Roy. Soc.* (London), **151**, 1–36 (1861); *Phil. Mag.*, [4] **22**, 147–56 (1861).

(45) ÅNGSTRÖM, A. J., *Pogg. Ann. Physik*, **94**, 141–65 (1855).

(46) CROOKES, W., *Chem. News*, **5**, 234 (1862). W. A. MILLER *ibid.*, **5**, 201, 224 (1862). H. E. ROSCOE, *ibid.*, **5**, 218, 261, 287 (1862).

(47) KIRCHHOFF, G., *Pogg. Ann. Physik*, **118**, 94–111 (1862); "Researches on the Solar Spectrum and the Spectrum of the Chemical Elements," Cambridge and London, **1862**; *Phil. Mag.*, [4] **25**, 250–62 (1863); "Gesammelte Abhandlungen," Barth, Leipzig, **1882**, p. 625 ff.

(48) IHDE, A. J., *Sci. Monthly*, **67**, 427–9 (1948).

---

# JOHANNES DIDERIK VAN DER WAALS

**RALPH E. OESPER**
University of Cincinnati, Cincinnati, Ohio

BORN at Leiden on November 23, 1837, van der Waals studied at the University there from 1862 to 1865. He then taught physics at Deventer and The Hague. His doctorate was awarded in 1873 and his dissertation "On the continuity of the gaseous and liquid states" attracted much attention. It was subsequently translated into English, French, and German. This topic was the *leitmotif* of all his important work.

He is best known for his improvement of the equation of state, taking into account the attraction between the particles of the gas and their own proper volume. In other words, the internal pressure of the gas is greater than the observed pressure by the amount $a/v^2$. He calculated the pressure inside a drop of water to be about 10,000 atmospheres. The second factor responsible for the deviation from the ideal gas law was introduced in the well known correction $(v - b)$. The most important development of this work was the van der Waals law of corresponding states, which enables the operator to calculate the state of any gas or liquid at any temperature and pressure if the state at the critical temperature is known.

The Nobel Prize was awarded to this great theoretician in 1910 "for his work concerning the equation of state of gases and liquids." In subsequent studies he found that $b$ varies with temperature and Clausius found that $a$ is not constant for a given material but varies with temperature. However, the van der Waals equation was a most valuable approach to a very difficult problem and it has been a great aid in the liquefaction of gases and the theory of the modern freezing technique.

Van der Waals died at Amsterdam on March 9, 1923, and is buried there. The plain stone covering his grave is already quite weather-beaten and the inscription is becoming hard to read.

# Bergman, Klaproth, Vauquelin, Wollaston[1]

**ELSIE GRUEBER FERGUSON**   Newcomb College, New Orleans, Louisiana[2]

THE chemists whose lives and work are very briefly discussed in this paper are men whose names are not as familiar as are those of Lavoisier, Gay-Lussac, Proust, Scheele, Berzelius, Cavendish, Priestley, or Dalton, contemporaries of our characters, but whose importance in connection with the development of analytical chemistry is unquestioned. Bergman was the first of that great trio of which Sweden is so justly proud, Klaproth was without a rival the greatest chemist in Germany of his time and was everywhere respected, Vauquelin was the greatest analytical chemist in France at the turn of the century (1800), and Wollaston held the same position in England.

In order to evaluate their contributions properly it is necessary that we think of chemistry as it had developed up to about 1700. Since Mr. Hooke's advanced ideas were not generally known, the phlogiston theory was gaining supporters. With Boyle, chemists thought of fire as a "weighable element," though if they read Boyle further they found that he defined an element as a substance incapable of further chemical decomposition by fire or other means. Of the ninety-two elements known to us today exactly one dozen (antimony, arsenic, carbon, copper, gold, iron, lead, mercury, phosphorus, silver, sulfur, tin) were known in 1700. Chemical reaction was explained on the basis of chemical "affinity," a term employed by Hooke and defined by Thomas Thomson as "the power by which the ultimate particles of bodies are made to unite together and are kept united."[3] It was commonly believed that only those substances possessed affinity for each other which had something in common with each other. Not until about 1800 did Newton's term "attraction" find common usage. The term attraction was up to that time confined to cases of forces acting at sensible distances, such as between planets and stars, and was not applied to forces acting between minute particles of matter. Oxygen was unknown, the fundamental laws of weight were unknown. Seldom was attention paid to the balance and even when it was considered, the results as obtained were misleading. Thus Homberg, friend and student of Otto von Guericke and later a colleague of Lemery, found in the late seventeenth century that equal amounts of all acids change the weights of various samples of tartrates by the same amount.

The analytical chemistry of the time was of interest to the mineralogist, the pharmacist, and to a few industries. There were, of course, no formal courses in analytical chemistry. Some of the methods used then are familiar to us now—they included the processes of filtration, sublimation, crystallization, distillation. Steam distillations were carried out in wooden vessels

*From Weeks's "Discovery of the Elements"*
TORBERN BERGMAN, 1735–1784

since the glass vessels were thick, crude, and not very strong. Crucibles were made of metals or, more frequently, glazed earthenware. Porcelain crucibles were unknown before 1778. Oil lamps were the source of high temperatures, but not until 1773 were several of these lamps together used to heat an oven. The microscope had been used by Duclas in 1670 to distinguish between crystals of table salt and gypsum in mineral waters. Duhamel had, in 1700, not yet distinguished soda from potash. Analysis in the dry way and analysis in the wet way were both in use, but it was not assumed that these two methods should yield similar results.

What did Bergman, Klaproth, Vauquelin, and Wollaston do to further the growth and development of chemistry? One of these was the son of a tax collector, another of a merchant, a third of a serf, and the last the son of a clergyman. One was very poor and one came from a family which had enjoyed education, culture, and wealth for generations. One was not only discouraged from entering a scientific career but was forbidden to do so; the others were encouraged. Two were married, two not. Yet these four men coming from four different countries with widely differing backgrounds are considered the four greatest analysts of the the eighteenth century. We shall consider briefly the life and work of each of these four men.

[1] Delivered before a seminar in the History of Chemistry at Tulane University, New Orleans, Louisiana, April 27, 1939.
[2] Present address: 3432 North Washington Road, Fort Wayne, Indiana.
[3] THOMSON, "A system of chemistry," 5th London ed., Abraham Small, Philadelphia, Pa., **1818**, Vol. III, p. 9.

85

Torbern Bergman was born on March 20, 1735 (one hundred years after Hooke, four years after Cavendish, two years after Priestley) in Catherinberg, West Gothland. His mother was the daughter of a merchant, his father a receiver of revenues—a post of uncertain duration, depending upon the political swing of the diet in power. In order for his son to be in a remunerative as well as a permanent position, he urged him to study law or divinity, for which purpose he was sent to the University of Upsala at the age of seventeen and placed under the care of a relative who was a "magister docens" at Upsala. Bergman had already displayed remarkable interest and ability in physics and mathematics at the gymnasium in Skara, so that the relative was charged with the duty of weaning him away from these interests. He was therefore found studying law whenever the "magister docens" made his rounds, but at the end of the call Bergman rapidly found his favorite books. In his attempt to do well in law to please his family, and well in mathematics and physics to please himself, he neglected to get exercise or diversion. After two years his concentrated efforts and lack of sleep (a maximum of five hours a night was all that he allowed himself) told on his health and he was obliged to leave the university.

At Upsala at that time Linnaeus was kindling a great interest in natural sciences in all the students. Bergman was no exception. While he regained his strength at home, he took long walks and collected many plants and insects, some not listed by Linnaeus. His health restored, he returned to Upsala, this time with full permission to study his favorite subjects. His first paper was published in the *Memoirs* of the Stockholm Academy in 1756 and concerned the ovum of a leech which contained a dozen young animals. The paper was autographed by Linnaeus who signed it "Vidi et obstupui," since he had not believed what Bergman had recorded until he saw it himself. Bergman then published other papers on the history of the insects that attack fruit trees, the means of recognizing them from their larvae, and on the methods of guarding against these insects. He proudly related that in one summer in one garden seven million destructive insects had been destroyed by his method.

In 1758 Bergman got his master's degree, his dissertation being on a mathematical problem in astronomy. He was made "magister docens" in natural philosophy at the University of Upsala, and in 1761 became adjunct professor in mathematics and in physics. This post he held until 1767. During this time he published papers in the *Memoirs* of the Stockholm Academy on the rainbow, twilight, the aurora borealis, and the electrical phenomena of iceland spar. He was one of the first to view the transit of Venus over the sun in 1761.

Professor of chemistry at Upsala at that time was Wallerius. He was retired in 1767 and intended that one of his relatives should be his successor. It was a surprise to nearly everyone that Bergman applied for this position in chemistry, since his interests seemed to be entirely in other fields. To prove his qualifications he immediately published two dissertations on the manufacture of alum. Wallerius formed a party to oppose Bergman and was joined in this by all who, according to Thomas Thomson, "despaired of equalling his reputation and industry."[4] Thanks to the personal plea of Gustavus III of Sweden, whom a friend of Bergman had influenced, Bergman was appointed Wallerius' successor.

His excellent background in mathematics, physics, and natural science proved most helpful to him in his position, enabling him to see more clearly some of the weaknesses of the science of chemistry of his time. He was convinced of the need of a new nomenclature and of the necessity of establishing chemistry on an experimental basis. Bergman's lectures were described as exceedingly valuable. If the sign of a good teacher is the number of good students he produces, Bergman passes the test well, for Gahn, Hjelm, Gadolin, and the Elhuyars all called him "professor." That Bergman was a leader among his colleagues is shown by his selection as Rector of the University, an honor bestowed soon after his appointment to the Chair of Chemistry, and one of the greatest of the many honors which came to him. Since the University of Upsala owned a tremendously large estate which the faculty managed under the guidance of the rector, a successful rector needed to be an excellent business manager, a person of foresight enough to keep a safe balance between good teachers and good business managers on his staff, and, as always, a person of tact and wisdom in dealing with people. The period in the life of the University of Upsala, when Bergman was at the helm, is remarkable for the smoothness with which the affairs of the University were conducted.

His reputation rapidly spread abroad both as a chemist and as an administrator. Honorary membership in many foreign scientific societies attested to the importance of his contributions; these came freely in spite of his double duty as administrator and professor, which was steadily undermining his strength. In 1776 Frederick the Great of Prussia invited him to come to the Berlin Academy of Sciences at a greatly increased salary with greatly reduced duties. For the sake of his health Bergman was tempted to accept. Hearing that his leaving would pain the King of Sweden who had earlier befriended him, Bergman declined the offer and begged the King not to spoil his sacrifice by raising his salary—a plea to which Gustavus III lent no ear.

In 1771 Bergman married Margaret Catherine Trast, a widow, daughter of a clergyman near Upsala. They had two sons, both of whom died in infancy. Bergman himself never enjoyed good health after his first two years of intensive work at Upsala. From 1769 on his health failed constantly, from 1780 on very rapidly. It is not surprising, therefore, in view of his poor health and active life, that Bergman died at the

[4] THOMSON, "History of chemistry," Colburn and Bentley, London, **1830**, Vol. II, p. 33.

age of forty-nine years on July 8, 1784, at a bath in Sweden near Wittern.

The twenty-eight years allowed him after the publication of his first paper in 1756 were richly productive; though his research activity was confined mainly to the field of chemistry, within that field his interests were broad. His publications include a book on the doctrine of affinity published in 1773, an enlarged edition of which followed in 1783; a book on blowpipe analysis published in Vienna in 1779; "Sciographia regni mineralis," a new classification of minerals based on chemical constitution, 1782; three volumes of collected works called "Opuscula physica et chemica" appearing 1779–83; and the last three volumes of his works published in Leipzig in 1787–90 after his death. The first four volumes are devoted entirely to chemistry, the others also to natural history, electricity, and astronomy. These volumes contain all of his works except the "Sciographia." All of these books except that on the blowpipe were translated from the original Latin into French and German, the "Sciographia" also into English.

The blowpipe was first used by Florentine glass blowers in 1660, then by goldsmiths for soldering. In 1679 Kunkel first described the use of bellows and charcoal blocks. In 1739 Cramer, like Kunkel a metallurgist and mineralogist, used a copper blowpipe. It was introduced into purely chemical processes by the Swedish chemist Cronstedt who, incidentally, used minerals in amounts as small as a pinhead and directed the flame of a candle against these small portions. Though Wallerius in 1750 mentions it as part of the essential equipment of an analyst, Bergman gives the first complete description of it, distinguishing between the inner and outer flame, giving directions for its use with soda, borax, phosphate, etc., and reporting the behavior of earths, salts, combustible materials, calxes, metals, and ores with the blowpipe. He used the blowpipe with charcoal blocks, with gold and silver spoons. Gahn, his pupil, was much more successful in the use of this important tool than Bergman himself and suggested many improvements.

Up to the time of Bergman, minerals were classified according to their hardness, color, crystal form. Bergman tried to classify them according to their constitution. In order to do this he had to develop the first complete method of analysis of minerals in the wet way. He identified metallic constituents by their precipitation reactions rather than by reducing them to their metallic form, and is first again in pointing out that most minerals will dissolve in hydrochloric acid after they are finely powdered, and that those insoluble in acid even at high temperatures can be "opened up" with potassium carbonate. He was the first to emphasize the importance of the choice and the function of a reagent. Many of our routine reagents he also used: barium chloride for sulfuric acid and sulfates; lime water for carbon dioxide; litmus paper to detect the presence of free acids; potassium ferrocyanide to detect iron and copper; silver nitrate for hydrochloric

acid, chlorides, and hydrogen sulfide; oxalic acid for lime; and ammonium and alkali carbonates for the precipitation of metals and earths. Bergman's "Treatise on Mineral Waters," published in 1778, contained the first general method of water analysis ever published, a method used for over twenty years until Kirwan improved on it by developing a shorter, easier, and more accurate system.

Bergman's greatest contribution to quantitative analysis was the idea that a constituent did not necessarily have to be determined in its elemental condition but that it could be isolated in the form of a well-known compound. For many of his fusions he used iron crucibles rather than the more readily corroded earthenware. He analyzed qualitatively and quantitatively an amazing number of ores, stones, mineral waters, and minerals. But little can be said for the accuracy of his analyses. Other chemists using Bergman's method and the same reagents obtained better results, but the chemical world, respecting the name of Bergman, attempted always to check his results and ignored those of superior analysts, such as Wenzel, whose name was almost unknown.

Although Bergman's name is not mentioned in the "Handbook of Chemistry and Physics" in connection with the discovery of a single element, yet he had a share in the early study of several. He suspected a new metal in pyrolusite, could not find it, and asked Gahn to continue the problem, resulting in the discovery of manganese in 1774. With Scheele he believed that the minerals tungsten and wolfram contained a new element and gave that problem to the Elhuyar brothers in 1784. Bergman just missed finding zirconium in zircon and molybdenum in native molybdenum sulfide. His student Hjelm isolated molybdenum six years after Bergman's death.

A brief mention of some of the subjects of his papers other than those already mentioned might be of interest: on the difference between cast iron, wrought iron, steel; on products of volcanoes; on the aerial acid (in which he gives Cavendish no credit for work he had already published); on oxalic acid (in which he again omits the name of Scheele, whose work on this acid had already been done and was undoubtedly known to Bergman); on magnesia (in which he does mention Black); and on silica, which he did not know to have acid properties. Bergman's close adherence to the phlogiston theory is decidedly disappointing. Though he was among the first to apply quantitative methods to the study of combustion processes, the fact that a metal gained in weight while losing phlogiston troubled him not a moment. He even determined the relative phlogiston content of all the metals by their reactions with acids. Thus Bergman performed the first experiments that could have emphasized the idea of equivalents, which neither he nor Lavoisier did. His figures were used by Lavoisier with his own explanations, but until his death Bergman believed in the phlogiston theory.

Throughout his career Bergman was interested in reforming the nomenclature of chemistry. It was through his influence that Guyton de Morveau returned to Paris in 1782 with the express purpose of establishing a uniform system of nomenclature based on the phlogiston theory. The French schools, headed by Lavoisier, were naturally opposed to such a system. Through their influence Bergman lost the support of Morveau, who was converted to antiphlogistic views. Since, in addition to this, Bergman was quite inconsistent in the use of the system he proposed, it was not generally adopted. Bergman also tried to introduce a general system of symbols. He suggested that metals be represented by varying crowns, salts and alkalies by circles, and acids by crosses. Of importance in this connection is the fact that Bergman was the first person to use a combination of symbols to indicate at a glance the nature of the compound. However, his inconsistency here, too, was at least partly responsible for the fact that although the system received much attention it was never generally used.

Bergman's reputation in chemistry rests as much upon his work on affinity as upon his development of methods of analytical chemistry. Up to 1775 there had arisen two distinct schools of thought on affinity. According to one group, headed by Geoffroy, "any substance $a$ has a definite intensity of affinity by which it is united to another body $x$. When a third body $b$, having a greater affinity for $x$ than $a$ has, is presented to the compound, $a$ is displaced and $b$ unites in its stead with the body $x$."[5] The other group held, of course, that no difference in intensity of affinity exists, that is, that $b$ might displace $a$, but that $a$ in turn could displace $b$ under proper conditions. Geoffroy's views were given great weight and popularized by the fact that Bergman adopted and taught them in his "De attractionibus electivis" which first appeared in the *Memoirs* of the Royal Society of Upsala in 1775 and was later translated into English by Dr. Beddoes, Davy's friend. In this thesis Bergman stated that all bodies capable of combining chemically with each other have an attraction for each other which is a definite and fixed force capable of being represented by a number. He then proceeded to draw up his famous fifty-nine tables of affinity, each headed by one substance under which were placed all the bodies that reacted with it in order of affinity. Bergman's tables differed from others of their kind in that they were based on more accurate analyses, were more complete, and also for the first time, following a suggestion made by Baumé, made a distinction between affinities for reactions in solutions at room temperature and in the dry way at elevated temperatures. Every chemist of the time was convinced of the correctness of Bergman's views in this respect, and nearly everyone used his tables. A new element or compound had to find its place in these tables before it could be considered a legitimate substance. Until Berthollet's dissertation on affinity was published in 1803, Bergman's views were unchallenged. Berthollet, who believed that affinity was not elective but was dependent on the mass and shape of bodies, and that increased mass meant increased affinity, was logically led to the conclusion that substances must be able to unite with each other in all proportions, while Bergman held that substances could unite in certain proportions only.

As Davy is credited with the discovery of Faraday, so Bergman is often thought of as the discoverer of Scheele. Although Scheele was greatly indebted to Bergman in many ways, Bergman can hardly be given the honor of having found Scheele. Actually it is Gahn to whom credit is due here, too, as in so many other cases, although to Bergman was given the first opportunity of recognizing the talents of Scheele. When the latter had written his first paper, the result of his first research on tartaric acid and its compounds, he sent it to Bergman, expecting that it would be read before the Stockholm Academy of Sciences and published in its *Memoirs*. Bergman, a very busy man, set this paper by an unknown author aside without reading it, intending to study it later. However, he forgot all about it. Scheele then sent a copy of the paper to Retzius, who shortly thereafter incorporated the information contained therein into a paper of his own without ever mentioning the name of Scheele. Naturally, this experience made Scheele very bitter. It appears that Scheele may have tried on another occasion to send a paper to Bergman, that it was read but not published, probably on account of a certain awkwardness of style. Bergman's attention was drawn to Scheele in quite another manner. Bergman had purchased from the apothecary Lokk some potassium nitrate, which to his amazement behaved quite differently after ignition than before. He was unable to explain the formation of brown fumes on addition of acetic acid to the ignited salt. Neither could Lokk nor Gahn account for these facts. It was Gahn who then discovered that the young apprentice in Lokk's shop, Scheele, understood the reaction perfectly. When Gahn informed Bergman of this fact, the latter was intensely eager to meet Scheele, who, however, did not share this enthusiasm, due to his earlier disappointing treatment at Bergman's hands. It required repeated efforts on the part of Bergman and persistent persuasion by Gahn to make Scheele willing to meet the great Bergman. Finally Scheele did consent to a meeting, which led to a friendship between these two men that lasted until Bergman's death. Scheele benefited socially from Bergman's support and Bergman suggested many of the investigations that Scheele carried out, such as the study of pyrolusite which led to important theoretical and practical results. Retzius writes of their friendship: "It is difficult to say whether Scheele or Bergman was *docens* or *discens*, for unquestionably Bergman obtained the greatest part of his practical knowledge from Scheele, while on the other hand Scheele is indebted to Bergman for the fact that in later years his understanding was clearer than earlier."[6]

---

[5] THOMSON "History of Chemistry," *op. cit.*, Vol. XI, p. 9.

[6] BUGGE, "Das Buch der Grossen Chemiker," Verlag Chemie, Berlin, 1929, Vol. I, p. 276.
Translations from the French and German are the author's.

Bergman's most striking scientific characteristic is his perpetual emphasis on continued investigation. He deplored any inclination to be carried away with an enthusiasm for explaining more than had been definitely experienced. One could wish, however, that several other facts might be reported differently: that he of analytical chemistry. Unlike Bergman, Klaproth is noted for the superb quality of his work rather than its quantity; for finishing, improving, refining existing methods rather than opening fields for others to continue; for being himself a master analyst, excelled by none of his contemporaries and equalled by few; for

MARTIN HEINRICH KLAPROTH, 1743–1817

had given more credit where credit was due, particularly to Gahn and Scheele; that he could himself have been a better experimenter and thus actually, instead of only nearly, have discovered a few elements; that he had been a leader in antiphlogistic thinking; and that he could have carried through some of his reforms. However, Bergman was a pioneer in analytical chemistry and as such he built for it a firm foundation which has not as yet been changed in essential respects.

While Bergman is considered the founder of analytical chemistry, and deservedly so, Klaproth, the greatest German chemist of his time and one of the greatest in all Europe, is often referred to as the creator of the art

making it possible to have analyses duplicated with much greater accuracy than before his time.

Martin Heinrich Klaproth was born in Wernigerode, in the Harz, on December 1, 1743, when Lavoisier was three months old. Eight years later a fire destroyed all of his father's property and goods, leaving the family impoverished. Martin and his two brothers helped to earn their education in the village school. The older brother later became a clergyman, the younger a private secretary and Keeper of the Archives of the government in Berlin. Martin sang in the village choir to earn money for a schooling which he hoped would prepare him for service in the church (he remained all his life a deeply religious man) but the "unmerited hard treatment he met at school so disinclined him to study"[7] that, at sixteen, he decided to learn the apothecary's trade. Why Klaproth was harshly treated is not stated. For five years he was an apprentice and for two more years an assistant in the laboratory at Quedlinberg. From 1766-8 he assisted in the public laboratory at Hanover. Here he had access for the first time to some books on chemistry which so stimulated his intellectual interest that he became eager to go to Berlin to study under Henkel, Rose, Pott or Marggraf. In 1768 he went to Wendland's laboratory in Berlin (at the sign of the Golden Eagle in the Street of the Moors) where he continued studying chemistry and where he also studied Latin and Greek with the help of a clergyman. At the end of 1770 he went to Danzig where he worked in a laboratory for several months, returning to Berlin in March, 1771, to the laboratory of Valentine Rose. In June of the same year Rose died, requesting on his deathbed that Klaproth be made his successor. Klaproth characteristically not only felt it his duty to take over the direction of the laboratory, but also to care for the two young sons of Rose. The younger of the two died; the other, Valentine Rose the younger, became Klaproth's assistant, with whom he published many papers. This Valentine Rose was the father of Heinrich Rose, the third great chemist in that family.

In 1782 Klaproth passed a brilliant examination for an apothecary's license and presented a paper on "Phosphorus and Distilled Waters." In the same year he bought the Flemming Laboratories and shortly thereafter married Sophie Christiana Lekman. They had three daughters and one son, the famous orientalist Heinrich Julius Klaproth, who became adjunct in Oriental Languages to the Academy in St. Petersburg. In 1800 Klaproth bought the room of the Academical Chemists where he experimented, lectured, and kept his mineralogical and chemical collection. His laboratory soon became a model "conducted upon the most excellent principles and governed with the most conscientious integrity."[8]

During these years Klaproth was a frequent contributor to the *Memoirs* of the Berlin Academy, Crell's *Annalen*, Köhler's *Journal*, and Gehlen's *Journal*. Each paper represented a definite contribution either correcting a false impression, extending views of the time, presenting new analyses, or reporting on new elements. By 1800 Klaproth was Professor at the Royal War School, Professor at the Royal Mining Institute, member of the College of Sanitation, the Berlin Academy of Arts, the Berlin Academy of Sciences. All of Europe knew him as a great chemist. It was not surprising, therefore, that in 1811 the King of Prussia conferred on him the Order of the Red Eagle or that in 1810, when the University of Berlin was founded, Klaproth was appointed as its first Ordinary Professor of Chemistry, although he was then sixty-seven years old.

[7] THOMSON, "History of chemistry," *op. cit.*, Vol. II, p. 192.
[8] *Ibid.*, Vol. II, p. 230.

This post Klaproth filled successfully until his death on January 1, 1817. The post was then offered successively to Berzelius, who declined it because he was satisfied with conditions at home, to Leopold Gmelin, who remained instead in Heidelberg, and to Mitscherlich, who accepted it.

Klaproth devoted his entire life to scientific pursuits. The brief discussion here presented concerns his most important contributions. Just as his actual analyses were characterized by extreme accuracy so, for the first time, was his method of reporting results an accurate one. Where in the analysis of minerals the per cent of the constituents did not exactly sum up to one hundred, it was the habit of analysts, Bergman included, to make corrections either by recalculating the per cent determined in order to have a summation of exactly one hundred per cent or by changing the per cent found according to a preconceived notion of what had been gained or lost. Klaproth was the first person to report in his publications the actual "uncorrected" data obtained, giving the weight of the mineral employed and the weights of the constituents obtained. Thus errors in the analyses were no longer hidden, and attention was focused on the source and elimination of errors, amounting usually to about 0.5 to 2 per cent. This practice, introduced by Klaproth, called attention to small amounts and has led to the discovery of many substances, from Klaproth's own discovery of potash in minerals to the discovery of the inert gases. As his method of recording results is our model even today, so his actual methods of analyses served as a model for many years. Those minerals which failed to yield to the carbonate treatment of Bergman, Klaproth ground to a very fine powder, digested in potash, and fused in a silver crucible. Where potash was contained in the mineral, Kalproth substituted the use of barium carbonate. He placed a great deal of emphasis on knowing the purity of the reagents used, of purifying them if necessary, and on the careful choice of apparatus. He was also the first person to bring precipitates to constant weight by drying or igniting them. For grinding he used either flint or agate mortars, in extreme cases diamond mortars. He substituted silver crucibles for iron wherever the temperature required would allow it. He determined the actual amount and nature of the loss suffered by the mortar or the crucible and made appropriate corrections.

In the course of his analyses Klaproth contributed to the early history of a fair number of elements, discovering two, verifying the discovery of two others, and assisting in the study of several others. In 1789 he found that pitchblende, which was thought to contain only zinc or iron, must contain another element which, in honor of Herschel's recently discovered planet, he called "uranium." The element was isolated by Peligot fifty years later when platinum crucibles were available. Because of its similarity to alumina, zirconia was overlooked in mineral analysis until 1789 when Klaproth discovered it in zircon. In 1795 he found it in hyacinth, called "jacinth" in Revelations where it is mentioned as one of the precious stones decorating the walls of Jerusalem. Berzelius isolated zirconium. In 1793 Klaproth first distinguished between barium carbonate and strontium carbonate. In 1795 he separated from iron oxide the oxide of an element which he named titanium. Rose later improved the method. Klaproth, a great reader of the literature, realized that the oxide described by Gregor of Cornwall in 1791 was the same as his oxide and gave full credit for its discovery to Gregor of Cornwall. This element was not isolated until 1910. In 1798 Klaproth delivered a paper before the Berlin Academy of Sciences on Transylvanian gold ore. In this ore he had found a new white metal. Müller von Reichenstein had suspected a new element in this ore in 1782, and sent a specimen of it to Bergman who, however, reported only that the element was not antimony. Klaproth, crediting Müller with the discovery, named this element tellurium. In 1804 Klaproth discovered an oxide in yttria which he called cereria. He confirmed the discovery of chromium and glucinum by Vauquelin and of ytterbium by Gadolin. As Hofmann said, "If one considers how rarely it is the fortune of a chemist to find a single element, it can be understood how greatly Klaproth's discovery of four elements must have impressed his contemporaries."[9]

In 1795 was published the six volume collection of his works, "Beitrage zur Chemischen Kentnisse der Mineralkörper." Klaproth assisted also in the translation by Fischer of Berthollet on affinity and chemical statics, in the publication of a chemical dictionary, and in editing Gren's "Manual of Chemistry," to which he made remarkable corrections rather than additions.

Phlogistic ideas had taken an especially strong hold on German chemists because of strong nationalistic feeling, particularly against the French. Though he had been a student of Marggraf, disciple of Stahl, Klaproth, free from all prejudice, suggested to the Berlin Academy in 1792 that experiments on combustion and calcination be subjected to exact revision. The results confirmed Lavoisier's conclusions and the Berlin Academy was itself converted, which brought about the conversion of other German groups to antiphlogistic doctrines.

Klaproth, like Vauquelin, tacitly assumed the Law of Definite Proportions and helped to settle the controversy of 1801–7, in which Berthollet and Proust led opposite camps.

To quote again from Thomas Thomson: "Amidst all these labours it is difficult to say whether we should most admire the fortunate genius which, in all cases, easily divined the point where anything of importance lay concealed; or the acuteness which enabled him to find the best means of accomplishing his object; or the unceasing labour and incomparable exactness with which he developed it; or the pure scientific feeling under which he acted, and which was removed at the utmost possible distance from every selfish, every avaricious, and every contentious purpose."[10] He had

[9] BUGGE, op. cit., p. 338.
[10] THOMSON, "History of chemistry," op. cit., Vol. II, p. 232.

the valuable gift, according to Kopp,[11] of knowing how to keep scientific discussions impersonal. The only recorded instance of any unpleasantness between Klaproth and his fellow scientists is found in Berzelius' autobiography.[12] Berzelius and Hisinger had found in

Courtesy of the Fisher Scientific Company

SINTERING URANIUM, WHICH WAS DISCOVERED BY KLAPROTH, IN HIGH-FREQUENCY VACUUM APPARATUS AT THE WESTINGHOUSE LAMP COMPANY

heavy spar a new substance having two stages of oxidation, one colored and one not, had called this substance "cerium" and sent a report on it to Gehlen's *Journal*. Gehlen responded that Klaproth had preceded them in discovering a new substance in the same mineral, that Klaproth's paper would be published in the current issue of his journal, and Berzelius' in the following. Honors for the discovery were to be shared between Klaproth and Berzelius. When this news reached Paris, an enthusiastic group of the Swedish chemists working there were eager that Berzelius' priority should be established. Their feverish activity lead Vauquelin to write in the *Annales de Chimie* that "Klaproth's reputation makes very unlikely the idea that Klaproth wished to attribute to himself the work of another." Klaproth, reading this, was incensed. Berzelius writes: "Klaproth, who must have been a somewhat gruff man, anathemized me in a very forcible letter, saying that he and Valentine Rose had known this substance since 1784 and that he wanted to know through which correspondent in Paris such a shameless untruth had arisen." Berzelius answered that he was a new chemist, had no correspondents in Paris, and was ignorant of the statement made until so informed by Klaproth himself. To this explanation Berzelius received no answer. He writes: "That was the only thing I ever had to do with

[11] KOPP, "Geschichte der Chemie," Friedrich Vieweg und Sohn, Braunschweig, 1843, Vol. I, p. 344.
[12] BERZELIUS, "Autobiographische Aufzeichnungen," in KAHLBAUM, "Monographien aus der Geschichte der Chemie," Leipzig, 1903, Vol. VII, p. 36.

this great chemist." Klaproth objected to the name "cerium," and suggested "cererium" instead. For some time either name was used depending upon the direction of allegiance of the particular chemist. Thus in 1825 Wöhler, writing from Berlin to his former professor, Berzelius, mentions the fact that Leonhard, for whom Wöhler was translating Hisinger's "Mineralogy," used the form "cererium" but that he would much prefer to use "cerium."[13] A final impression of Klaproth we have in the memorable words of A. W. von Hofmann: "with a modesty far removed from vainglory, ready to recognize fully the merits of others, considerate of their weaknesses but of unrelenting severity in the criticism of his own work, Klaproth has furnished us for all time with a model of the true scientist."[14]

[13] WALLACH, "Briefwächsel zwischen Berzelius und Wöhler," Engelman, Leipzig, 1901, Vol. I, p. 31.
[14] BUGGE, *op. cit.*, p. 341.

(*Part 2 of this paper begins on page 93.*)

# OTTO HÖNIGSCHMID

DESPITE the imperative necessity of agreement on atomic weights, it was not until December, 1893, that an official table was issued. This was prepared by F. W. Clarke at the request of the American Chemical Society, which also sponsored his succeeding annual reports. In 1898, the German Chemical Society published its first table of approved values. Pursuant to a suggestion by its committee, an invitation was sent from Berlin in March, 1899, to the chemical societies and other interested organizations asking their coöperation in preparing and issuing a table of correct atomic weights. More than fifty representatives were appointed; they organized by mail and in due course named a working committee: Clarke, Seubert, Thorpe. In 1904 Moissan was added; Seubert was succeeded by Ostwald in 1906, and at Moissan's death (1907) Urbain took his place. This International Committee on Atomic Weights issued annual tables from 1903 on. In 1913 it was placed under the aegis of the Council of the International Association of Chemical Societies. The last report signed by the full committee was that of September, 1915. The war then interfered with free correspondence, personal hostilities intervened, but the so-called International Tables were put out regularly (except in 1918), though in fact they were little more than re-promulgations of the pre-war values, because the committee members were chiefly employed in war activities and atomic weight work had largely been interrupted. Ostwald, isolated, proclaimed the 1916 table for 1917, 1918, 1919. At the close of the war, coöperation was not resumed, the committee functioned without German representation.

A newly organized German Atomic Weight Commission issued its first table in 1921. The International Union of Pure and Applied Chemistry, successor to the Association of Chemical Societies which was dissolved during the war, in 1921 created an International Committee on Chemical Elements, one of whose three divisions was to prepare the table of atomic weights. The only report was issued in 1925. In 1921, the Swiss Chemical Society had a table prepared that, except for unusual changes, was to be valid until 1930. Three tables, 1922–4, were issued by a Spanish committee. In 1927, Baxter, who for many years had prepared an annual report on atomic weight measurements for the American Chemical Society, put out a table over his own signature. The Chemical Society (London) issued a table in 1929. Consequently, in 1929 there were current no less than six atomic weight tables: three discordant and rather out of date, and three recent which agreed closely with each other. This ridiculous situation was relieved in 1930, when the International Union of Chemistry united all countries and created its Committee on Atomic Weights to present yearly a table based on the best evidence.

Otto Hönigschmid, after Ostwald's retirement in 1922, became chairman and leading spirit of the German Atomic Weight Commission; he has been a member of the International Committee since its creation in 1930. Hönigschmid was born at Horowitz, Bohemia, on March 13, 1878. He studied chemistry at the German University of Prague (Ph.D. 1901) and supplemented this training in Moissan's laboratory at the Sorbonne (1904–06), at Harvard (1909–10) under Richards, and at the Radium Institute in Vienna (1910–11), where he made the first accurate determination of the atomic weight of radium.

In 1908 he was privatdozent at his alma mater, in 1911 he was appointed ordinarius and director of the laboratory for inorganic and analytical chemistry at the Technical High School in Prague. His real life work was begun in 1918 when he went to the University of Munich, where he founded and has since directed the German Atomic Weight Laboratory.

Professor Hönigschmid and his collaborators have determined the atomic weights of no fewer than forty elements, including the first figures for rhenium and hafnium. Their results are reflected in numerous revisions of the values adopted in the official tables. These accomplishments have involved remarkable refinements in preparative and analytical procedures. The accuracy of the results and the exceptional attention even to minute details betray the expert knowledge, the persistence, and the devotion of this master analyst.

One of Hönigschmid's specialties has been the application of atomic weight determinations to radioactivity and isotopy. His exact work on radium, uranium, uranium lead, thorium, ionium, and thorium lead furnished striking confirmation of the hypothesis of atomic disintegration advanced by Rutherford and Soddy. In 1934, when he re-examined the atomic weight of radium, the Belgian Radium Corporation lent him the enormous weight, five grams, of radium bromide, whose market value was about $240,000.

Although it is now known that most elements present themselves as mixtures of two or more isotopes, these are usually so resistant to segregation, and almost always occur in such unvarying proportions, that the mean (chemical) atomic weights are still the most fundamental values for stoichiometry. The results given by the mass spectroscope and by the balance are mutually stimulating. Hönigschmid was the first to establish by atomic weight determinations the shift in the isotopic ratio of ordinary elements (potassium, mercury) that had been subjected to "ideal distillation" by von Hevesy.

Many deserved honors have come to Otto Hönigschmid, but invitations to head chemical departments elsewhere have been declined because he feels that he can serve science and education best by remaining as chief of what the Müncheners call the "Atomlabor." On the occasion of his sixtieth birthday, a Festschrift of the *Zeitschrift für anorganische und allgemeine Chemie* was published.

—*Contributed by Ralph E. Oesper, University of Cincinnati*

# Bergman, Klaproth, Vauquelin, Wollaston[1]

ELSIE GRUEBER FERGUSON Newcomb College, New Orleans, Louisiana

KLAPROTH'S services to analytical chemistry and mineralogy in Germany were performed nearly equally well in France by Vauquelin, twenty years Klaproth's junior. Vauquelin was greatly indebted to Klaproth, his model, but among his countrymen he had no equal in analytical skill. After the death of Lavoisier, Vauquelin, Fourcroy, Guyton de Morveau, and Berthollet were the chief representatives of French chemistry. Said one Frenchman about the relative importance of the first three mentioned: "Lavoisier was creator, Fourcroy apostle, Vauquelin disciple."[2]

Louis Nicolas Vauquelin was born May 16, 1763, in St. André-d'Hébertot, a Normandy village, the son of a farmer on the estate of a Madame d'Aguesseau. When not in the village school, the boy assisted his father on the farm. He readily mastered the subjects taught at the school and also distinguished himself as a student of religion, taught him by the village curé, who became very fond of Vauquelin and who urged him at the age of fourteen to follow his inclination and apprentice himself to an apothecary. He started at Rouen but after a few months there went to Paris, where he was under the protection and friendship of Madame d'Aguesseau and the priests of the order to which the curé of d'Hébertot belonged. For three years he found work in various pharmacies, finally in that of Cheradame, a cousin of Fourcroy. It was there that the latter became interested in him. Shortly after their first meeting Fourcroy, to Vauquelin's great joy, asked the latter to come to his laboratory to work and live with him. Vauquelin soon won the respect and love of Fourcroy as well as of his two sisters, who treated Vauquelin with the greatest kindness. His life here was a very happy one.

Not only was Vauquelin an unusually apt apprentice, but at the same time he continued his studies, really not begun until he went to Rouen, since the schooling at d'Hébertot was of a decidedly inferior rank. He made excellent progress in Latin, Greek, botany, chemistry, physics, natural history, and philosophy. Fourcroy, now his best friend and adviser, insisted on his presenting himself for a master of arts degree at the Athenaeum, a decidedly painful prospect for the very timid Vauquelin, who always spoke hesitatingly and occasionally stammered. However, he passed the ordeal and soon succeeded Fourcroy in teaching the course in chemistry at the Athenaeum. At about the same time, Vauquelin, now about thirty, became a licensed pharmacist and directed a laboratory in the Rue St. Anne.

In 1793, as a result of events following the revolu-

tion, Vauquelin was forced to leave Paris. He went to Melun as pharmacist, but fortunately his exile was of short duration. In 1794, probably through the influence of Fourcroy, he was back in Paris as Assistant Professor of Chemistry under Fourcroy and Guyton de Morveau at "L'École Centrale de Travaux Publics," a year later renamed "L'École Polytechnique."

*From Weeks's "Discovery of the Elements"*
LOUIS NICOLAS VAUQUELIN, 1763–1829

1795 saw him Inspector of Mines. He was asked to give a course in the school of mines in "docimasie," the art of testing the purity of a metal. For the first time he was not living with friends but in the spacious apartment furnished him at the school of mines. On Fourcroy's death in 1811, Vauquelin gave up the greater part of this apartment to Fourcroy's two sisters, who lived there until he died.

After the death of Robespierre on July 20, 1794, Vauquelin was also made a member of the National Institute, now called the Academy of Science. In 1801 he was made Professor of Chemisty in the College of France. Shortly after this Brongniart, member of the Institute and Professor of Chemistry applied to arts at the Jardin des Plantes, died, and Vauquelin became his successor. His selection for this post was distinguished by the remarkable fact that he was unanimously nominated for the position by the Institute, the administration, and the inspector of studies. His lectures covering this three-year course were exceedingly valuable, for he had gathered together information from his years of intensive study and research. Unfortunately, they were not published. Berzelius remarks in his autobiography that listening to lectures of Vauquelin, Biot, and Gay-Lussac convinced him that

[1] Delivered before a seminar in the History of Chemistry at Tulane University, New Orleans, Louisiana, April 27, 1939. Continued from the December, 1940, issue.

[2] BUGGE, "Das Buch der Grossen chemiker," Verlag Chemie, Berlin, 1929, Vol. I, p. 356.

lecturing was an art which required special study, as well as a natural gift for clearness and ease of expression. Vauquelin had undoubtedly made a special study of it, for although he lacked a natural ease of expression, his students were always most enthusiastic about his lectures.

At the same time that he was lecturing at the Jardin des Plantes, serving as Inspector of Mines, and making for the use of chemists the most difficultly obtainable substances, like phosphorus, he was also Director of the School of Pharmacy. When the Legion of Honor was founded in 1802, Napoleon made him a member.

In 1811 Fourcroy suffered an attack of apoplexy, leaving the Chair of Chemistry at the School of Medicine vacant. Several applied for the position but all others withdrew their applications when they realized that Vauquelin was also seeking it. Soon after this Vauquelin received his doctor's degree, his thesis being a comparison of the composition of human and animal brains. Vauquelin taught at the School of Medicine for eleven years. Then, in 1822, the spirit of reaction after the revolution was responsible for the fact that he and nine others lost their positions. Vauquelin was fifty-nine years old at this time. According to Kopp he was pensioned when he lost his position. He continued working at his other interests, however, and received many honors, including membership in several foreign organizations. Finally in 1828 his home area elected him a deputy, in which position he distinguished himself not by his oratory, but by his diligence, his fine spirit, his determination to make progress without disorder or anarchy, and his devotion to the interests of his country. These same personal traits had characterized all of his dealings and activities. From 1822 on Vauquelin suffered from a "grave malady" which afflicted him for seven years. He died at his birthplace October 1, 1829, at the age of sixty-three.

Vauquelin's career was an unusually successful and fruitful one. His reputation rests on the research he published either alone or with Fourcroy, Humboldt, Klaproth, Chevreul, and Thomson, on his public works, and on his career as educator. Unfortunately there is no collection of his works. They appear mainly in *Annales de Chimie* which, for a time, he edited, and in other French journals, in the *Journal de Physique*, in "l'Encyclopedia Methodique." Vauquelin was interested in many organic substances, including such organic acids as pyromucic and tartaric, and their occurrence in plants. These researches were usually carried out with Fourcroy. It is in inorganic chemistry that his most important contributions were made, however. Kopp, in his discussion of Vauquelin, deplores the fact that although Vauquelin was always alert for new methods of inorganic analysis, he was not as keen at developing or using new analytical methods, nor as able to produce results of the same degree of accuracy, as Klaproth. Many of the mineral analyses of Vauquelin were made on samples that Haüy, who was at the school of mines, gave him. Perhaps the poor analyses made by Vauquelin were not so much due to a lack of preci-

sion or technic as to impurities in the reagents and poor specimens presented him by Haüy for analysis. That Vauquelin was, however, an analyst of unusual skill, is seen from the records of his achievements, from which the following selection contains only a small fraction of his contributions.

In 1797 while analyzing a Siberian ore of lead he discovered chromium and described its most important properties and those of its compounds. A year later he isolated this element. The protoxide of chromium was immediately used in painting green on china, and lead chromate was used to dye cotton and calico. In 1798 he discovered in Siberian beryl the oxide of beryllium or "glucinum." This element was isolated by Wöhler and Bussy in 1828. In 1803 he studied platinum, his experiments leading to the discovery of iridium and osmium a year later. In 1813–14 he worked out a method for the separation of lead, palladium, rhodium, iridium, and osmium.

With Fourcroy he found that bones contain magnesium phosphate, fish brains contain phosphorus. He also published papers on alum, on the efflorescence of salts, on tungstic acid, on the ignition of phosphorus in hydrochloric acid, on the combustion of hydrogen in closed vessels, on the respiration of insects and worms, on the volumetric and gravimetric composition of water, on the coloring matter in animal bloods, on the decrease in solubility of one salt due to the presence of another, on dimorphism, and on many other topics. Vauquelin was one of the most versatile chemists. With Fourcroy he proposed one of the most unique varieties of affinity, an "affinité disposante." This exists, they believed, when a substance "acts chemically by means of affinity towards a compound which is not yet formed, but present in the mixture only in the form of its widely separated constituents."[3] For many years chemists in general accepted the existence of a "predisposing affinity."

As Fourcroy had befriended Vauquelin, the latter in turn helped Thenard when he came to Paris. Among his students, who always had the greatest respect and devotion for Vauquelin, can be mentioned: Chevreul, Orfila, Humboldt, Leopold Gmelin, and Stromeyer, a great contributor to mineral analysis. Although he was always shy under normal conditions, he was courageous and bold when occasion demanded. Twice, at the risk of his own life, he rescued unfortunate victims of revolutionary activities. He saved the life of a Swiss soldier who escaped the massacre at the Tuileries but fell into the hands of an infuriated populace. On another occasion, Vauquelin, garbed in the official costume of a member of the Institute, rescued his student Orfila who, along with other Spaniards, had been thrown into prison by Bonaparte. Vauquelin calmly, politely, and successfully merely demanded his release.

Vauquelin thus rose from his very humble beginning to the enviable position of being the greatest analyst in

_____

[3] KOPP, "Geschichte der Chemie," Friedrich Vieweg und Sohn. Braunschweig. **1843**, Vol. II p. 306.

country, and one of the greatest in Europe. He was
tunate in that he could claim as friends both the
é d'Hébertot, who first encouraged him, and Four-
y, without whose help the rise of Vauquelin would no
bt have been considerably slower. He was gifted
h a fine appreciation and a mind which delighted in
classics, history, and music as well as in science, and
h a personality which won for him universal respect
esteem.

t seems difficult to doubt that there is a destiny
ich guides our paths when we find ourselves discuss-
in the same classification as ranking chemists of
ir day men of such diverse backgrounds as Vauque-
and Wollaston. The Dictionary of National Biog-
hy lists four Wollastons, beginning with the great-
at-grandfather of our William Hyde Wollaston.
o a family which over a period of at least two hun-
d years had numbered among its members men of
church, poets, members of the House of Commons,
losophers, lawyers, writers, professors, and scien-
ts was born in Norfolkshire on August 6, 1766,
gland's first great analytical chemist, the third son
an Episcopal clergyman. Unlike most clergymen,
llaston's father had inherited a great deal of money
ich, also, had been in the family for generations.
e many of his forebears, William Hyde was sent to
mbridge. He was especially proficient in languages,
turing as senior fellow in Greek and Hebrew.
rough his friendship with John Brinkley, the As-
nomer Royal of Ireland, he became interested in
ronomy. In 1788 he took a degree in medicine, be-
ning to practice it in 1789 in Huntingdon and then
Bury St. Edmonds. Here he formed one of the
sest friendships of his life—that with the Reverend
nry Hasted. In 1793 he took an M.D. degree from
mbridge. The next year he was made a Fellow of
Royal Society, his certificate having been signed by
illiam Heberden the elder, the most eminent physi-
n of eighteenth century England (who was also, in-
lentally, Wollaston's uncle), the Honorable Henry
vendish, Sir William Herschel, and others. In 1797
set up practice in London, living at 18 Cecil Street
the Thames. No sooner had he built up a very
ccessful practice in London than he abruptly ended
career as a physician by retiring—at the age of
rty-four. The reason for this unexpected decision
ay have been the fact that another, less able than he,
s granted the position in St. George's Hospital for
ich he had applied, but it may also have been the
t that he was oversensitive and overanxious over his
tients, as seen from a letter written to his friend
sted on December 29, 1800: "Allow me to decline the
ntal flagellations called anxiety, compared with
ich the loss of thousands of pounds is as a fleabite."[4]
Wollaston's problem now was to find an income to re-
ace the thousands he had given up, for although his
ther was monied, the fact that he had fourteen

grown sons and daughters besides William Hyde made
the share of each a relatively modest one. He therefore decided that he would swell his income through
chemistry, bought a home at 14 Buckingham Street,
built a laboratory in the rear of the house and before
long realized returns on inventions of various kinds.
His interests were more varied than anyone else's at

*From Weeks's "Discovery of the Elements"*

WILLIAM HYDE WOLLASTON, 1766–1828

the same time except those of Cavendish. The most
important of these interests—from a financial standpoint for him and an analytical standpoint for us—was
the development, about 1805, of a process for working
spongy platinum into a malleable, useful form. This
process he kept a secret until shortly before his death
when he sold it for 30,000 pounds.

As early as 1800 began the failure of his eyesight, so
unusually fine that with his steady hand he could write
with a diamond on glass in handwriting so small that
the ordinary eye required a microscope to read the
beautifully formed letters. Partial blindness in both
eyes resulted. In 1827 his left arm became numb, in
1828 his left pupil became insensitive. When he was
told that his symptoms probably indicated a tumor on
the brain, he immediately began to dictate papers on
his unpublished work. From his bed he directed experiments in progress in the adjoining laboratory until
his death on December 22, 1828, at 1 Dorset Street, at
the age of sixty-two.

This manuscript prepared just before his death has
been lost. However, the other fifty-six papers Wollaston had published are a record of fine achievement in
pathology, physiology, chemistry, optics, mineralogy,
crystallography, astronomy, electricity, mechanics, and
botany. He laid the foundation for the Pulfrich and
Abbé refractometers, first drew attention to what is
known as Fraunhofer lines (he thought they separated
the four colors of the spectrum), invented the reflecting

4 "Dictionary of national biography," Oxford University
ess, London, 1921, Vol. XXI, p. 783.

goniometer which made possible the exact measurement of crystals, immediately used by mineralogists, carried out experiments that finally led to Davy's safety lamp for miners, showed galvanic and frictional electricity to be the same, studied chemical effects of light, wrote papers on methods of comparing light from the sun with that from fixed stars, on calculi of the bladder, on the finite extension of the atmosphere, and on the nature of the triple phosphates. Wollaston's suggestion to the House of Commons in 1814 regarding a standard gallon led to the imperial gallon of the Weights and Measures Act of 1824; he also served on the Royal Commission on Weights and Measures which rejected the decimal system, and with Young as commissioner of the Royal Society on the board of longitude.

These illustrations indicate amply the phenomenal fertility of Wollaston's active mind. Analytical chemistry is indebted to him particularly for the development of a useful form of platinum without which the composition of most minerals would still remain unknown. Wollaston was by no means the first to work on platinum. In 1784 Achard fused arsenic and platinum, got a malleable residue; in 1787 Jeanetty made platinum crucibles, but their cost prevented a general use. In 1800 Richard Knight published a method for preparing malleable platinum by igniting the double chloride of ammonia and platinum. A method similar to this was used by a London firm (Messrs. Johnson, Matthey and Co.), who for many years furnished platinum vessels to laboratories and industries all over the world. It was their method which Wollaston elaborated and his modification which was used for about fifty years. Gentle heating of the chlorides was followed by a manual rubbing of the platinum until it became exceedingly fine. It was pressed while cold in a brass barrel, then compressed with levers. Next it was placed on a charcoal fire and heated to redness to drive off moisture. Finally it was heated at the highest obtainable temperature in a wind furnace for twenty minutes. Then it was placed upright on an anvil, and struck while hot with a heavy hammer. By this method the first platinum vessel for concentrating sulfuric acid, weighing 423 ounces, was made in London in 1809.

Wollaston's work on platinum resulted in his discovery of palladium in platinum ores in 1803. Since he was unwilling to have it known at this time that he was working in platinum, the discovery of palladium was announced in an unusual fashion. He sent to a Mrs. Forster who had a shop in Soho an anonymous note with some palladium asking her to sell this palladium. There was in London at that time an Irishman named Chenevix. During the reign of terror he had been in Paris and was imprisoned there by chance with some chemists who aroused in him an active interest in this science. On his release from prison he distinguished himself as an analyst in a very short time, yet made many enemies because of his crude manner of opposing current philosophical ideas. The unusual method of announcing this element palladium caused him to sus-

pect a fraud which he aimed to uncover. He bough[t] some of this element, studied its properties, and the[n] bought out all of Mrs. Forster's supply. Soon he read [a] paper before the Royal Society in which he stated tha[t] palladium was not, as had been "shamefully a[n]nounced," a new simple metal but that it was an allo[y] of platinum and mercury. Wollaston was Secretary [of] the Royal Society at the time and had made since[re] efforts to prevent Chenevix from reading this pape[r] which was also published in the *Philosophical Transa[c]tions.* Wollaston sent another anonymous note, offe[r]ing a reward of twenty pounds to anyone who woul[d] produce a metal like palladium. Interest in this el[e]ment ran high. Chenevix had prepared an alloy whi[ch] he found to have the properties the unknown discover[er] claimed for palladium and sent samples for analys[is] to other chemists, all of whom reported that they cou[ld] not check Chenevix' work. At about that time, 180[3] Wollaston was ready also to announce the discovery [of] rhodium and to have himself known as the discoverer [of] palladium; the argument over palladium ended—[as] did, sad to say, the career of Chenevix as chemist.

After 1813 Wollaston busied himself with "equivale[nt] weights," a term which he introduced. In a paper d[e]livered before the Royal Society he defended his use [of] equivalent rather than atomic weights by saying tha[t] although chemical reactions are best explained [by] means of Dalton's atomic theory, yet for all practic[al] purposes a consideration of equivalents is more impo[r]tant. So in preparing his Synoptic Scale of Chemic[al] Equivalents he says, "I have not been desirous of war[p]ing my numbers according to an atomic theory b[ut] have endeavored to make practical convenience my so[le] guide."[5] This scale of equivalents made it possible [to] obtain results of calculations concerning equivalen[ts] quite mechanically. A table published in 1814 i[n]cluded values obtained by other chemists, such [as] Berzelius. Whereas Dalton had used as a standard f[or] his weights H = 1, and Berzelius used O = 100, Wolla[s]ton selected O = 10. This was quite a complete tab[le] including equivalent weights of many elements and als[o] of acids, bases, and salts. Wollaston's work did mu[ch] to draw attention to Dalton's theory but also, unfo[r]tunately, helped considerably in confusing still furth[er] the minds of chemists in regard to the distinction b[e]tween equivalent, combining, and atomic weights— a confusion which lasted until after the Karlsrü[he] meeting of 1860.

Wollaston, were he living today, would undoubted[ly] take an active interest in the field of crystal structur[e]. More than one hundred years ago he wrote, "It is pe[r]haps too much to hope that the geometrical arrang[e]ment of primary particles will ever be perfectly known— yet, until it is ascertained how small a proportion t[he] primary particles themselves bear to the interval b[e]tween them, it may be supposed that surrounding co[m]binations, although themselves analogous, might di[f]

---

[5] WOLLASTON, "A synoptic scale of chemical equivalents[,]" *Trans. Roy. Soc.,* Nov. 4, **1813,** p. 7.

rb that arrangement, and in that case the effect of ch interference must also be taken into account before y theory of chemical combination can be rendered mplete."[6]

As officer in the Royal Society for many years, Woll- ton knew either personally or by correspondence a eat many chemists. Berzelius enjoyed his company his visits to England. He helped to convert Sir mphry Davy to Dalton's theory to which he him-

self readily subscribed, since it offered an explanation for the facts now stated in the Law of Multiple Propor- tions—facts that he realized but could not explain. He knew Faraday. He was one of the few with whom Cavendish was at ease. However, he was as cautious in forming friendships as he was in the statements he made. This extreme caution, combined with the fact that when he made a statement he knew it to be correct, gave him the nickname "The Pope." The friendships he did allow himself were warm and lasting. It seems that this great man, like Vauquelin, was never married.

WOLLASTON, "On super-acid and sub-acid salts," Alembic print No. 2, p. 40.

---

# GEORG-MARIA SCHWAB

RALPH E. OESPER
University of Cincinnati, Cincinnati, Ohio

EORG-MARIA SCHWAB, eminent physical chemist, sents a fine example of a scientist who was not over- ne by the force of adverse circumstances. With d held high, he has always kept his eyes steadily his life's objective: to teach chemistry effectively d to contribute to its progress by first class writing d research.

Son of the well-known journalist Joseph Schwab, org-Maria was born at Berlin on February 3, 1899. ter World War I he entered the University of Berlin d received the Ph.D. degree in 1923. His disserta- n, prepared under the guidance of E. H. Riesenfeld Nernst's famous Institut, described the first prepara- n of pure ozone, its solidification, and the determina- n of its physical constants. Dr Schwab served as sistant to Nernst's successor, Max Bodenstein,[1] til 1925. In Nernst's school he was trained in classi- l physical chemistry; under Bodenstein he became a icticist. However, he was not a mere follower of denstein but, from the start, worked on his own oblems, such as the thermal decomposition of thane, reactions in cold discharges, and the dis- lution velocity of gases. In 1925 he migrated to the iversity of Würzburg and habilitated as Privatdozent 1927. There he studied the catalytic decomposition ammonia, active hydrogen, dissolution of gases, and otochlorination.

In 1928 Wieland invited him to the University of unich; he was promoted to extraordinary professor 1933. The work on heterogeneous catalysis was oadened with the aid of a number of collaborators. me of the fields which engaged him and his students re: the kinetics of heterogeneous catalysis, the

nature of the heat of adsorption, the poisoning of catalysts, the distribution of active centers, the prop- erties of atomic chlorine and bromine, the influence of organic radicals on parahydrogen. During this period came his invention of inorganic chromatography.

Numerous papers record his findings. Among his books are "Physikalisch-chemische Grundlagen der chemischen Technologie" (1928) and "Katalyse vom Standpunkt der chemischen Kinetik" (1931). The latter text has been translated (with additions) by H. S. Taylor and R. Spence, and is used widely in American universities. Professor Schwab edited the monumental international "Handbuch der Katalyse," of which 7 volumes have appeared.

In 1939 the increasing racial persecution forced this distinguished chemist to leave his fatherland. He emigrated to Greece where for 11 years he headed an industrial research laboratory. Fortunately he was allowed to continue his purely scientific work, though difficulties arose during the German occupation. This troubled period was nonetheless fruitful. In addition to incidental studies (adsorbing carbon, turn-over transitions, parahydrogen, chromatographic studies) his kinetic studies led him to a conclusive theory of the electronic mechanism of metal catalysis.

He was appointed Professor of Physical Chemistry at the Athens National University of Technical Sci- ence in 1950. The next year he was recalled to Munich to take over the chair of physical chemistry, a post previously occupied with distinction by Fajans and then by Clusius.[2] However, Professor Schwab, im- bued with the importance of active scientific coopera- tion, continues to give courses twice each year at Athens.

OESPER, R. E., J. CHEM. EDUC., 15, 151 (1938); SCHWAB, G. ., Wien. Chem. Ztg., 46, 9 (1943).

[2] OESPER, R. E., J. CHEM. EDUC., 28, 321 (1951).

# JOHANN NEPOMUK FUCHS

**WILHELM PRANDTL**

University of Munich, Munich, Germany

(*Translated by Ralph E. Oesper*)

THE term "isomorphism," coined by Berzelius, denotes the fact that similar compounds of various elements may have like crystal forms. This phenomenon was discovered early in 1819 by Eilhard Mitscherlich in Berlin, first with the salts of phosphoric and arsenic acid, then with sulfates of bivalent metals.

Isomorphous elements can replace each other in their respective corresponding compounds in indefinite proportions and form homogeneous mixed crystals, in which they occur together in nonstoichiometric ratios. This fact had been known several years prior to Mitscherlich's first observations.

Since 1807, the chair of chemistry and mineralogy at the university, which was founded at Ingolstadt in 1472 and moved to Landshut in 1800, had been occupied by Johann Nepomuk Fuchs. As a pupil of Klaproth and the Paris school, and in conformity with the demands of this stage of chemical development, he had occupied

**Johann Nepomuk Fuchs in 1844**

"Science is the lodestar of practice, without it the latter easily loses itself in the murky and infinite ranks of possibility."

himself at first with the analyses of minerals in order to find out whether their compositions were in accord with the laws of definite and multiple proportions. The atomic theory and the chemical system of symbolic notation were just taking form. It was still the fashion to follow Lavoisier and regard all chemical compounds and minerals as simple or compound oxides. About this time, Berzelius determined "the weight of the elementary quantity compared with that of oxygen gas," whose quantity or volume he represented by O and arbitrarily set equal to 100, *i. e.*, he determined the atomic weights of the elements referred to O = 100. The procedure was to determine by quantitative methods the percentage content of the simple oxides in a natural or artificial compound and then to calculate the volumes of oxygen which must have been contained in these oxides. In chemical compounds these volumes are in the ratio of small whole numbers; for example, in sulfates 1:3, in nitrates or chlorates 1:5, and so forth.

Fuchs conceived the plan of analyzing as accurately as possible whole groups of similar minerals, *e. g.*, garnets from various regions. Beginning in 1813, he and his friend Adolph Ferdinand Gehlen, professor of chemistry at the Bavarian Academy of Sciences in near-by Munich, studied zeolites. This name (Gr. *zeein* = to boil, and *lithos* = a stone) had been coined in 1756 by the Swedish mineralogist Axel von Cronsted (1722–65) as a collective term for hydrous, acid-decomposable silicates, which foam under the blowpipe because of the evolution of steam and then melt to a glass. Later, these silicates were classified, according to their appearance, as fibrous-, foliated-, and needle-zeolites, mesotype or natrolite, stilbite, analcite, etc. The two friends soon discovered that several varieties of mesotype had the same composition as Klaproth's natrolite, whereas others with the same oxygen ratios contained lime in place of soda. Since these warped under the blowpipe they called them scolecites (Gr. *scolio's* = curved). However, they subsequently found a scolecite which contained considerable proportions of soda along with lime. In 1815 Gehlen (b. 1775) died prematurely as a result of arsine poisoning. Fuchs carried on alone and published the findings in Schweigger's *Journal für Chemie und Physik* [**18**, 1 (1916)]. Since the lime-soda-bearing zeolite was intermediate between natrolite and scolecite with respect to composition and properties, he proposed that it be named mesolite (Gr. *mesos* = in the middle). In modern terms, all three minerals form an isomorphous mixed series.

In addition to this study of zeolites Fuchs analyzed a new mineral which had recently (1814) been found uth Tyrol. He suggested that this lime-alumina silite be called gehlenite, in honor of his late friend and worker. In his report[1] he stated that the results of e best analyses "agree, as may be seen from the ccompanying quantities of oxygen, fairly well with the eory of definite chemical proportions. . . . However e situation is peculiar with respect to the lime and n oxide; neither one or the other taken by itself fits o the series of ratios, but if they are taken together, a antity of oxygen is obtained which is almost exactly ur times that of the oxygen of water, and almost equal the oxygen of alumina. Nevertheless, I do not rerd the iron oxide as an essential constituent of this riety, but merely as a *vicariating constituent,* if I may permitted to employ this expression to designate a ostitute for almost as much lime, which in the abce of the iron oxide must be present to make up the l complement in order to enter into the proper ratio th the other constitutents; and I believe that in the ure varieties will be discovered which will contain ch less or no iron oxide at all, but instead a greater antity of lime. The whitish crystals, which merely n a light yellowish grey in the fire, and which appear be somewhat more refractory, seem to constitute the nsition to this.

"The results of several analyses of mineral compounds st be looked at from this viewpoint if it is desired, on e hand, to bring them into accord with the theory of oportions, and on the other if it is desired to avoid ving the varieties unnecessarily dispersed too much . . Aluminum sulfate forms an alum with amnium as well as with potash, or with both of these alies at the same time; would it be really expedient look on these three different combinations, which do t differ at all in their physical characteristics, as ee different species of salt? The ammonium can rece the potash here altogether or in part, and vice sa."

Fuchs also cited the case of feldspar, in which the tash can be replaced by soda. Therefore, Fuchs was e first (1815) to state that in minerals, and also in ificially prepared chemical compounds, certain contuents can substitute for one another, *i. e.,* vicariate, hout any noticeable change in their crystal form. is new fact was not the result of a chance observation t rather was derived from wide experience with neral analyses.

In the course of his studies of zeolites, Fuchs also instigated a mineral from Amberg, which had been desated as a fibrous zeolite. He immediately recoged that the specimen was not a zeolite but that as ll as alumina and water it contained phosphoric acid per cent). Since no previous case of such mineralized osphate had been reported Fuchs believed that he l discovered a new mineral. However, in 1818 he lized that this material was identical with wavell, which had been studied by Humphry Davy (1805) l Klaproth (1810), but that its high content of phos-

Birthplace of J. N. Fuchs in Mattenzell in the Bavarian Forest

phoric acid had completely escaped both of these eminent chemists. Fuchs also found (1818) that lazulite, a blue mineral from the Salzburg region and Styria, which had hitherto been considered a silicate, likewise is a phosphate containing almost 42 per cent phosphoric acid, which Klaproth had missed entirely. Another rare mineral, hitherto considered to be topaz, was recognized by Fuchs as a fluoriferous magnesium phosphate; he named it wagnerite. In 1834 he discovered, at Bodenmais in the Bavarian forest, a lithium-bearing iron-manganese phosphate which he named triphyline, in allusion to its containing three bases.

Johann Nepomuk Fuchs was born on May 15, 1774, in the Bavarian village community of Mattenzell. His parents were poor peasants, who lived in a miserable hut where he was born. His first schooling was obtained in the nearby monastery and he proved so superior among his fellow pupils that he was destined for the clergy. Consequently, in his 17th year he was sent to the episcopal Gymnasium at Regensburg. After the usual humanistic preparatory course, at the age of 20 he was enrolled in the Bavarian university at Ingolstadt where he took up philosophical studies. However, he felt no inner urge for the clerical profession and found patrons who made it possible for him to study medicine at the University of Vienna. He was attracted to science more than to medicine, and chemistry interested him particularly. Natural history, especially botany and chemistry, had been taught at Vienna since 1768 by Nicolaus Joseph Freiherr von Jacquin, whose son Joseph Franz had assisted him since 1791 as adjunct and from 1797 as professor. Under the influence of these men, who at that time were the chief representatives of Austrian sciences, Fuchs turned more and more to chemistry and mineralogy. However, he completed

Schweigger's *Journal für Chemie and Physik*, 15, 377 (1815).

Adolph Ferdinand Gehlen, 1775–1815

the medical course and took his Doctor of Medicine degree at the then Palatinate-Bavarian University of Heidelberg. He passed his state medical examination at Munich but then decided not to enter the practice of medicine because he wished to devote himself exclusively to chemistry and mineralogy. The need for chemists was urgent at the time and it was not difficult to secure a government grant to further his plans. He was thus able to visit the centers where his chosen fields were being practiced in the best manner: Freiberg in Saxony, where lived the great "teacher of mineralogy for all Europe," Abraham Gottlob Werner; Berlin, where the German past-master of chemistry Martin Heinrich Klaproth was active; and finally Paris, where were gathered the leading French chemists Guyton de Morveau, Fourcroy, Berthollet, and Vauquelin, as well as the founder of crystallography, René Just Haüy. After Fuchs had also acquired practical experience on several mineralogical and geological expeditions, he returned to Munich and passed an examination before a committee of the Bavarian Academy of Sciences, with the result that in the fall of 1805 he was installed at the University of Landshut as teacher of chemistry and mineralogy. Georg Augustin Bertele had been active there since 1794 as professor of chemistry, general sciences, botany, pharmacy, and materia medica. Fuchs now held lectures in chemistry and mineralogy in Bertele's fairly well-equipped laboratory. From 1807 on he held the rank of professor. He assembled a collection of chemical preparations, arranged and enlarged the mineral collection, and improved various pieces of laboratory equipment. From 1820 on he also gave a course in analytical chemical exercises, which was open to a maximum of eight students who must have previously shown their merit. In addition, he carried on the mineral studies described above.

In 1810 Fuchs married the daughter of one of the most prominent citizens of Landshut, the owner of the inn at which the university professors held their evening social gatherings. Fuchs thus became well-to-do and acquired a house of his own. He was of good stature, but made no pleasant impression at first contact. It was necessary to become accustomed to his characteristic inquiring look, which was combined with nearsightedness and an ironical smile. As a result of the privations and exertions during his boyhood and student years his lungs were weak when he came to Landshut; at times he brought up blood, so that his friends were fearful about his life. Although this condition improved, Fuchs was always sickly and had to be careful of himself. Nevertheless, by following a strict regimen, conserving his forces, and avoiding all detrimental influences, he reached the ripe age of almost 82 and, within the limits set by his constitution, was indefatigable to the very end of his life. Because of his nearsightedness he bent low over his writing desk, his arms drawn close to his body, and he often had in front of him a little bowl containing chloride of lime and a rod for stirring it up. His lectures, interspersed with frequent coughing, were not attractive, but they were well prepared and sincere; his experiments seldom failed. Accustomed to privations from his youth, he held economy to be one of the principal virtues, and he practiced it in the laboratory with respect to apparatus and chemicals. The loss of a vessel, through the carelessness of a co-worker, could put him into a state of great agitation. He was painfully exact and reliable in the fulfillment of the duties he assumed. A pious, strict Catholic, Fuchs was lovable and always ready to help his fellow man.

Joseph Franz Freiherr von Jacquin, 1766–1839

Although not fond of scientific disputes, he was perfectly capable of putting up a forceful, stubborn, fact-filled defense when he was drawn into such debates.

His poor health hampered his teaching, and his chief merit was as an investigator. Here, as in his daily life, he was extremely conscientious and trustworthy. The results of his researches were highly regarded in professional circles because they invariably proved to be correct.

In the fall of 1823, Fuchs was called to the Bavarian capital as curator of the national mineralogic collections and to become a member of the Academy of Sciences. The president of this learned body was the well-known philosopher Friedrich Wilhelm Schelling, and its chemist was Heinrich August Vogel, who had succeeded Gehlen in this post in 1816. Fuchs inaugurated his activities in Munich with a public lecture "The Mutual Influence of Chemistry and Mineralogy," in which he pointed out that chemistry was indispensable to the founding and progress of mineralogy, since a classification of minerals is only possible on the basis of their chemical constitution and crystal form.

The University of Landshut was moved to Munich in 1826, and Fuchs was again installed as ordinary professor of mineralogy, while Vogel was appointed to the corresponding chair of chemistry. Fuchs held his lectures in the Academy headquarters on Neuhauser-strasse, where the collections were housed. The building also contained a small chemical laboratory in which he continued his chemical investigations, with the sole assistance of a hireling whose pay was 50 kreutzers (25 cents) per day. In these modest circumstances Fuchs carried out the significant researches which will now be described.

Beginning in 1821, Fuchs turned his attention to the origin of china clay, i. e., kaolin. He showed that the clay from Obernzell near Passau was not a product of the weathering of the difficultly attackable feldspar, as was generally assumed, but that it came instead from a much more readily decomposable lime-soda-alumina silicate, which he named porcelain spar (porcelainite). Under the action of water and carbon dioxide this clay had lost all of its soda, almost all of its lime, and a third of its silica, and had thus been converted into kaolin.

In the course of this study Fuchs also took up the synthesis of silicates through the mutual action of alkali silicate and alkali aluminate solutions. He found that the resulting precipitates contained not only alumina and silica but also alkali, and that the latter is replaced by lime when the precipitates are treated with lime water. Consequently, he had observed the base-exchange of zeolites as well as the artificial production of natrolite, scolecite, and other zeolites. In this way he became familiar with the chemistry of silicic acid and arrived at one of his most important discoveries, namely water glass.

At that time only two artificial compounds of silicic acid with the alkalies were known. The first (insoluble) was ordinary glass, which, with no regard to its lime content, was thought to be an alkali silicate containing excess silica. The second was the so-called silica liquor, which was prepared by fusing silica with excess alkali and then dissolving the melt in water, or allowing it to deliquesce in moist air. As early as 1818, Fuchs had prepared a new product from finely divided silica, which he obtained by boiling silica liquor with ammonium chloride solution. Concentrated caustic soda or potash was then saturated with this silica powder and the solution evaporated to a thick syrup. On cooling, it congealed to a rigid, translucent glasslike mass which was stable in the air; when powdered it dissolved in water. Fuchs called his product *water glass*. He worked out a method for preparing it on a commercial scale and recommended it as a fireproofing agent for scenery, as an artist's primer, adhesive, lute, etc. As late as 1855, i. e., just one year before his death, he issued, as a sort of testament of his lengthy experience, a collected account of the "Preparation, Properties and Practical Application of Water Glass, including Stereochromy." He coined the latter term (Gr. *stereos* = solid, *chroma* = color) to designate a procedure in which the artist uses water glass as a binding agent for the colors and the background, a method which he had tested in conjunction with well-known Munich painters. It was claimed that this process yielded more durable murals than the old traditional frescoing.

The analytical investigation of silicates and the in-

Neuhauserstrasse in Munich about 1830—the Academy building to the left

vention of water glass, together with its technical utilization, led Fuchs into the study of building materials, such as limestone, clay, marl, and particularly the binding agents prepared from these, namely, lime, mortar, and hydraulic cement. He instituted experiments on the burning of limestone and the quenching of lime, the behavior of lime cream toward the ingredients of mortar, especially toward the various kinds of silica and silicates. Therefore he was well equipped to offer a ready and excellent answer to the prize question submitted in 1830 by the Society of Sciences at Haarlem: "Quels sont les caractères, auxquels on reconnaîtra les ciments, qui s'endurcissent sous l'eau? Quels sont les principes constituans et quelle est la combinaison chimique, qui s'opère pendant leur solidification?" In his "Über die Eigenschaften, Bestandteile und chemische Verbindung der hydraulischen Mörtel," which was awarded a gold medal, Fuchs stated for the first time the scientific foundations of the requirements which are necessary for the production of a good hydraulic cement, and he proved that its hardening under water is due essentially to a chemical union of opened-up silica with lime, a reaction which proceeds gradually under the influence of the water.

Abraham Gottlob Werner, 1750–1817

During the course of his many studies of mineral natural products Fuchs made a number of remarkable observations. As early as 1809 he distilled petroleum from St. Quirin on the Tegernsee in the Bavarian Lower Alps, and in addition to naphtha obtained a fatlike, unsaponifiable, colorless, odorless, and tasteless substance which was insoluble in water and soluble in alcohol or ether. This material was later (1830) found in wood tar by Karl von Reichenbach at Blansko in Moravia, and again in 1835 by J. B. Dumas in coal tar. Reichenbach was the first to recognize the technical and economic importance of this product, which was subsequently named *paraffine*. In 1822, Fuchs visited the salt works at Hall, near Innsbruck, and found iodine in the mother liquor. He also found this element in various Bavarian mineral waters, and likewise bromine and lithium. He discovered that rose quartz from Rabenstein near Zwiesel, Bavaria contains about one per cent of titanium dioxide and attributed the color of the stone to this foreign constituent.

Through his observations on silica and its natural compounds, Fuchs in 1833 came to the realization that not all of the so-called dense or compact substances, in which no crystalline structure could be discerned, were to be regarded as aggregates of crystals which were so small as to elude perception. Instead, and contrary to this general belief, there are also certain dense substances which really have no trace of crystallization and which accordingly must be designated as being without form or *amorphous*. He contrasted the crystalline condition of solids, *crystallism*, with *amorphism*, and showed that one and the same chemical substance may have different chemical and physical characteristics depending on whether it is in one or the other condition. Pure opal is essentially nothing other than formless amorphous, and compact silica, whereas quartz (rock crystal) represents definitely shaped silica. Opal is comparable to liquids in that it is a continuum with the same cohesion in all directions. Like liquids and all amorphous materials it exhibits only single refraction. Opal differs from quartz not only in physical characteristics but also in chemical behavior. For example when ground to a powder with hydrated lime, opal combines with the latter and sets under water; it dissolves in cold dilute caustic solutions, a behavior not shown by even the finest quartz powder. Chalcedony and flint are mixtures of opal with crystalline silica. "Accordingly we must distinguish two states of solidity, that of the shaped and that of the shapeless, and we may not regard solidification and crystallization as being identical." Many materials are known only in the shaped state, some only in the shapeless condition; many can be put into both states. Amorphous materials, which Fuchs also designated as rigid liquids, may arise by dry methods through vitrification or by wet methods through coagulation. Opal is produced by coagulation ordinary glass from a melt. Under certain conditions glass may crystallize, whereby it becomes cloudy because of the separation of innumerable tiny crystals—a process known as devitrification. Amorphous antimony sulfide (kermesite) can be obtained from crystalline antimony trisulfide (antimonite) by keeping the latter in the fused state for a long time and then rapidly cooling the melt. The black mercuric sulfide, prepared by either a wet or dry method, can be converted into red cinnabar by sublimation and crystallization, and the latter can be changed into the black sulfide again by heating and rapid cooling.

As examples of vitrified minerals, Fuchs cited not only obsidian, pumice, pitchstone, perlite, but also leucite and gadolinite. Coagulated minerals were exemplified by allophane, psilomelane, pitchblende, etc. organic coagula by the resins, gums, hard coals, animal glues, and so forth. The glowing displayed by many amorphous materials when they are heated to a certain temperature was attributed by Fuchs to "the awakening of the force of crystallization."

He regarded "the infinite face, the sphere, the mother form of the corporeal world" as the elementary building stone of amorphous materials. He pointed out that mechanical forces, such as pulverization, can never convert a crystalline substance into an amorphous one *i. e.*, diamond into lampblack; this change can be accomplished only by arousing the internal forces by chemical means. He used the term *deformation* for the process which is the contrary of crystallization, and he was convinced (1833) that every chemical synthesis must be preceded by a deformation, that every material which combines with another must pass through a state of shapelessness, that it must sacrifice its individuality to the chemical product. "Every inorganic compound likewise must put off its form, if it wishes to enter the organic realm and be assimilated in an organic body. Crystallization and life are absolutely incompatible with each other, and as soon as any substance in an organic body begins to take on a crystalline shape, at that instant it falls into the inorganic realm. The crystal is, so to say, the landmark between the organic and the inorganic realms." Fuchs used this occasion to point out how important easily attackable silica is to plant nutrition.

In 1837, and hence several years before the appearance of Liebig's "Die organische Chemie in ihrer Anwendung auf Agricultur und Physiologie" (1840), Fuchs set forth in a lecture his views on the development of the terrestrial sphere. He expressed his conviction that the carbon of fossil coals and resins and that of the entire animate nature had been derived from the atmosphere and that the oxygen of the air had thereby originated at the same time.

During his many years of experience with mineral analysis Fuchs devised new analytical and preparative procedures, and some of these are still in use. At that time the simple ammonium molybdate test for phosphoric acid was not yet known, and occasionally even eminent chemists overlooked the presence of this acid or its salts. Fuchs worked out a method of detecting phosphate by means of the blowpipe. He found that

René Just Haüy, 1743–1822

phosphates, particularly after being moistened with sulfuric acid, impart a bluish green color to the blowpipe flame. He used alkali silicate solution to separate phosphoric acid from alumina. This reagent precipitates the latter quantitatively as alkali aluminum silicate (artificial zeolite) from a solution containing both phosphate and aluminate, the phosphate remaining in solution. In 1831 he proposed the use of barium or calcium carbonate for the separation of tervalent from bivalent iron and other bivalent metals such as manganese, zinc, nickel, and cobalt. This precipitation procedure is still widely used. In 1839 he showed that tervalent iron may be quantitatively determined in the presence of phosphoric acid in hydrochloric acid solution by means of the loss of weight suffered by a strip of pure copper foil used to reduce the ferric solution. If titanic acid is present it is revealed through its reduction to violet titanous chloride.

In 1832 Fuchs prepared tin sesquioxyhydrate by boiling stannous chloride solution with freshly precipitated ferric hydroxide; the hydrochloric acid solution of the product yielded purple of Cassius on reaction with gold chloride solution. The recipe using a mixture of stannous chloride and ferric chloride solution for the preparation of this gold purple goes back to Fuchs, who also expressed the opinion that the product contains amorphous gold.

All of his accomplishments demonstrated that Fuchs was a thoroughly independent investigator, who not only accumulated factual material but also recognized relationships and opened new paths along which others could make still further progress. His chemical studies

Heinrich August Vogel, 1778–1867

(*Concluded on page 109*)

**Petr Zuman**
Czechoslovak Academy of Sciences
Prague
and **Philip J. Elving**
University of Michigan
Ann Arbor

# Jaroslav Heyrovsky:  Nobel Laureate

The 1959 Nobel Prize in Chemistry was awarded to Professor Jaroslav Heyrovsky of Czechoslovakia for his discovery of polarography and for his role in the development of this technique which has become such an important theoretical and practical tool in electrochemistry, analytical chemistry, and many other areas of science and technology.

Although most chemists are acquainted with Heyrovsky's name, few know much about his life and personality. The purposes of the present paper are to reveal him as a man and as a chemist, and to indicate in some measure why the award of the Nobel Prize to him was so widely acclaimed as a most justified reward.

## The Role of Polarography in Chemistry

It is interesting to note that whereas many physical methods were brought to an applicable form by the joint or independent efforts of a number of scientists with sometimes even the attribution of priority being questionable, the discovery of polarography is the achievement of one person, even though the development of the method was effected by the efforts of many individuals, including pupils, co-workers, and friends.

The connection of polarography and its originator is unusual in the annals of science. It is rare that a discoverer of a scientific approach is able to force the expansion of the method he developed towards the world-wide reception accorded polarography. It is furthermore rather exceptional that a man should be able to remain for almost forty years among the top investigators in a field which he first opened: a field whose magnitude is indicated by the approximately nine hundred papers published each year which deal with polarography.

With some important experimental approaches, considerable periods of time have elapsed between the discovery of the physical effect and its extensive practical application, e.g., over a century passed after the discovery of infrared spectra at the beginning of the nineteenth century before the method was used for the study of the structure of organic compounds. Polarography, on the other hand, found rapid application and within 20 years of its discovery was extensively used.

Polarography is currently one of the most frequently applied methods of analytical chemistry (1) both in research laboratories and in production control. The first field of broad practical application was metallurgy, where the speed and sensitivity of polarographic methods were early appreciated. These same advantages were soon recognized in the pharmaceutical industry and in the areas of food chemistry and pollution con-

trol. In medicine (2), where the method is widely used in clinical analysis, toxicology, and industrial hygiene, another advantage of polarography—the relatively small sample necessary—is also of prime importance; polarography is more extensively used in medicine in Europe than in the U.S.A. Other industries using polarography extensively as a method of both qualitative and quantitative analysis include the heavy chemical industry as well as the petrochemical, photographic, insecticide, rubber, and plastics industries. One of the recent trends in the application of polarography is to the continuous analysis of process streams.

In basic research, polarography has enabled investigators to gain further information on electrode processes, to elucidate their mechanisms, to distinguish chemical reactions preceding and following the electron-transfer process proper, and, in some instances, even to obtain rate constants characterizing some of the steps in such processes. In fact, polarography is sometimes said to have caused a "renaissance" in electrochemistry, e.g., polarographic studies of transport phenomena brought the interest of electrochemists back to important fields of electrochemistry which were supposed to have been "solved" and "closed" in the 1920's.

In other areas of physical chemistry, polarography permits evaluation of thermodynamical constants such as oxidation-reduction potentials and equilibrium constants of chemical reactions in solutions, as well as of such kinetic data as the rate constants of chemical reactions occurring at the electrode surface or in the bulk of the solution.

Polarography has been useful in both inorganic and organic chemistry in the elucidation of reaction mechanisms and equilibria, including the detection of reaction intermediates. Application of polarography often offers a convenient way of choosing the best conditions for synthetic reactions, separations, and isolations. Studies of the correlations between polarographic data and structure and other characteristics of chemical species are of importance not only for the expanding fields of theoretical inorganic, organic, and physical chemistry, but also because they form a sound basis for the initial attempts at using polarography in the elucidation of chemical constitution.

In biochemistry polarography is extensively used both as an analytical tool and for determination of reaction rates and mechanisms of biochemically important reactions; here, the possibilities of selectivity and of continuous measurement, sometimes even in very complicated and turbid solutions, are of importance.

## Heyrovsky and the Development of Polarography

Jaroslav Heyrovsky was born on December 20, 1890, in Prague, where his father was Professor of Roman Law at the Czech University, at that time called Charles-Ferdinand University (see reference *3* for a biography). Interested in mathematics and physics even while attending secondary school, Heyrovsky concentrated on chemistry, physics, and mathematics on entering the University of Prague in 1909. Inspired by the achievements of Sir William Ramsay, he transferred in 1910 to University College in London, where he was mainly influenced by Ramsay's successor, the well-known physical chemist and electrochemist, Professor F. G. Donnan. After attaining the B.Sc. in 1913, Heyrovsky started a doctoral thesis under Donnan's guidance on the determination of the electrode potential of aluminum. Due to the passivity phenomena observed with this metal, Donnan suggested that Heyrovsky use an amalgam dropping electrode similar to that used in Donnan's studies of membrane equilibria in which such an electrode had been used to determine the activity of sodium ion. This was Heyrovsky's introduction to the dropping electrode, a type of electrode which was to persist throughout all of his subsequent scientific career.

These studies were interrupted by World War I. Heyrovsky was home on a visit when war broke out in the summer of 1914. For a few months he was able to continue experimental work at the Chemical Institute of the University of Prague. In January, 1915, he was called up for military service in the Austro-Hungarian army. Due to his delicate physical constitution he spent the major part of his service as a dispensing chemist and roentgenologist in a military hospital. This allowed him to continue work on his thesis, which he submitted in the autumn of 1918 to the University of Prague.

As partial fulfillment for the doctorate degree, Heyrovsky took an examination in physics, which profoundly influenced his scientific career. During the examination, the examiner, Professor B. Kucera, called Heyrovsky's attention to the anomalies of the electrocapillary curves obtained with a dropping mercury electrode in a dilute electrolyte solution and suggested that he study these phenomena. As a result, during the following years, Heyrovsky, who became first an assistant and later the first lecturer (Docent) in physical chemistry at Charles University (1920), spent all of his available time in weighing the mercury, which flowed out of the capillary electrode at different potentials. He also submitted a habilitation thesis on aluminic acid, the constitution of aluminates, and amphoterity; these studies, which were influenced by Professor B. Brauner, resulted in three papers, which enabled Heyrovsky to gain the D.Sc. degree at the University of London in 1921.

Becoming somewhat tired by the troublesome and not always reproducible measurements of electrocapillary curves, Heyrovsky tried to follow the current flowing during the electrolysis between the dropping mercury electrode and a reference electrode. In the course of those experiments, in which the first current-voltage curves were obtained with the dropping mercury electrode, the principles of polarography were discovered. This new approach to the problems of electrolysis was described in papers published in Czech (*4*) and English (*5*), and during the General Discussion on Electrode Reactions and Phenomena, held by the Faraday Society in 1923.

Heyrovsky now devoted all of his time, efforts, and interests to following up his important discovery by studying the electrolytical processes which occur on the tiny mercury drop. He investigated hydrogen overvoltage, using polarographic measurements. With a Japanese collaborator, M. Shikata, he developed in 1925 the polarograph, an instrument for the automatic recording of current-potential, i.e., polarographic, curves. This instrument, which was one of the first examples of automatized laboratory apparatus, avoided the tedious manual point by point measurement of the current-potential curves, and thereby represented a scientific revolution in electrochemistry and chemical analysis. In their paper (*6*) Heyrovsky and Shikata coined the words, "polarograph" for the instrument and "polarography" for the new type of measurement and the new branch of electrochemistry. The names were chosen to emphasize the characteristic role of the polarizing electromotive force in the curves obtained by such measurements.

In 1922 Heyrovsky was appointed assistant professor and was also made the director of the then newly established Department of Physical Chemistry of the Charles University, Prague, which became a center of polarographic research. In 1926 he became professor *ordinarius* of physical chemistry.

After the fundamental experiments with the dropping mercury electrode in the early twenties, Heyrovsky soon recognized the importance of limiting currents. In his laboratory originated the concepts of diffusion-controlled currents (Ilkovic) and of half-wave potentials and their shift with complex-formation, the equation for the polarographic current-potential relation (Heyrovsky-Ilkovic), the existences of migration currents (Heyrovsky, Bures, Kemula), capacity currents (Ilkovic), catalytic currents (Herasymenko, Slendyk, Heyrovsky, Babicka, Brdicka), and many other important contributions to polarographic theory and practice. His co-workers, K. Wiesner and R. Brdicka (Fig. 1), recognized the importance of kinetic-controlled currents in which the electrode reaction is accompanied by a fast

Figure 1. Professor Brdicka (far left) and Professor Laufburger, vice president of the Czechoslovak Academy of Science, congratulating Professor Heyrovsky on the occasion of the announcement of the Nobel Prize.

chemical reaction; Brdicka also first observed and explained adsorption-controlled currents.

The efforts of Professor Heyrovsky to demonstrate the importance and usefulness of polarography were not always easy. For a long period, patience and endurance were necessary before the method was accepted and found its way into chemical laboratories. However, after an induction period of about 10 years, there occurred a steady growth in the number of papers on polarography published annually; the present rate, as mentioned, is about 900 papers yearly. The start of this growth can be traced to a book and two lecture trips, which apparently triggered the world wide dissemination of polarography. The book was a volume of Böttger's treatise (7) on physical methods of analysis, which contained a section by Heyrovsky on polarography. In 1933 Heyrovsky lectured on polarography for six months as a Carnegie Visiting Professor at the University of California (Berkeley), Stanford University, and the California Institute of Technology. At the same time, he formed his first links with American scientists by visits to other universities in the central and eastern states. In 1934 Heyrovsky was invited to deliver a lecture on polarography in Leningrad on the occasion of the Mendelejev centenary celebration.

Additional stimulus to the growth of polarography was provided by the visits of students and guests from abroad to Heyrovsky's laboratory. Usually, infected by the enthusiasm of Professor Heyrovsky, they helped to spread the knowledge of polarography throughout the world; many started active centers of research in their home countries, e.g., Shikata in Japan, Kemula in Poland, Breyer in Australia, and Semierano in Italy. From among American chemists, O. H. Müller, now at the State University of New York Medical Center at Syracuse, worked with Professor Heyrovsky for some time and then published an early and influential set of introductory papers on polarography in the JOURNAL OF CHEMICAL EDUCATION in 1941 (8), which is now available in revised book form (9). An early and influential visitor was I. M. Kolthoff of the University of Minnesota (Fig. 2) who visited Professor Heyrovsky several times before and after World War II, and whose treatise on polarography with J. J. Lingane, now in its second edition (10), is the important reference work in the area.

Figure 2. Dr. Pribil, Dr. Kolthoff, and Dr. Heyrovsky (from left to right) in front of the old building of the Department of Physical Chemistry of Charles University in Prague, where polarography was born.

## Postwar Scientific Activities

The busy scientific life of the Prague Department of Physical Chemistry was interrupted in 1939 by the Nazis. Although deprived of co-workers and pupils, Heyrovsky was able to continue his work on the expansion of polarography due to the friendly efforts of the German anti-Nazi scientist, Professor J. Bohm, who arranged to have Heyrovsky's laboratory left at his disposal.

Figure 3. Professor Heyrovsky studying oscillographic curves with his son, Michael.

In 1941 Heyrovsky began to investigate the oscilloscopic observation of polarographic electrode processes, which enabled him to gather additional information concerning the distinct electrolytic and adsorption processes which occur during the growth of a single mercury drop; this method of investigation has become his principal interest in recent years. Using the $dV/dt - V$ curves obtained at an applied current, Heyrovsky tried mainly to explain the differences in the rates of electrode processes for certain types of depolarizers and the influence of surface-active substances on electrode processes. For these studies, he developed the streaming mercury electrode, which was later successfully used for solving some problems in classical polarography. Professor Heyrovsky explains his interest in "oscillographic polarography" with the statement that a new method always brings new findings and new approaches for the solution of old problems.

After the end of World War II Professor Heyrovsky continued his research activities at the Department of Physical Chemistry with students who were hungry for science after six years of separation from their studies. In 1950 the Polarographic Institute was founded as a state-supported research center; Heyrovsky, who became its first director, left the University, becoming an honorary professor and still delivering lectures on polarography in the Department of Physical Chemistry, now headed by his former pupils, M. Kalousek and J. Dvorak. After the reorganization of the Czechoslovak Academy of Sciences in 1952, the

Polarographic Institute was incorporated into the Academy as part of the Chemical Section and one of the Academy's first institutes.

During the 1940's, Professor Heyrovsky became interested in derivative and subtractive differential polarography, which led to further analytical applications of polarography. The last problem in classical polarography which he investigated was, in 1949, the polarography of aldoses in heavy water solution. Recently, he has again become interested in polarographic maxima. These effects which may be due to a stirring of the solution in the neighborhood of the mercury drop also cause the anomalies on the electrocapillary curves, observed by Kucera, which, as indicated earlier, led to the discovery of polarography; this effect is still not yet completely understood.

Another old problem of Heyrovsky's which remains unsolved is that of the polarography of aluminum; this problem is now under study by his son, Michael, who in recent years has helped his father greatly in experimental work (Fig. 3).

The laboratory of Professor Heyrovsky is in an ancient mansion in a quiet street of Prague. The coauthor of this paper, a recent American visitor to Professor Heyrovsky (Fig. 4), described the Polarographic Institute and its director as follows (11):

At the present time the Polarographic Institute, which has grown considerably, is located at two different spots in Prague. The more interesting of these locations is a former palace which has been adapted for use as laboratories. Actually, I was surprised to see how well this has worked out. At the time I was in Prague the building was being completely rewired for an adequate supply of electricity. One pleasant part of the building

Figure 4. Discussion in the Polarographic Institute: Professors Heyrovsky (right) and Elving, 1959.

is the garden which makes a delightful place for discussion. I would guess that there are about 20 people, most of whom are independent professional-level investigators, in this location. The other group has equally well-equipped laboratories on the upper floor of an office building in the center of the city.

I was much impressed by the intellectual vigor of the people in the Institute. They are well informed regarding work in the areas of their interests and enjoy discussing mutual interests. Personally, I found them a most delightful group of people, socially and professionally.

Professor Heyrovsky himself devotes only a minimum amount of time to administrative matters. Most of his time is spent in

writing and in personally carrying out laboratory work investigating further developments and applications in the oscillographic presentation of polarographic measurements.

Professor Heyrovsky is obviously very much interested in the young men associated with him in the Academy and encourages their emergence as independent investigators. For example, Professor R. Brdicka (Fig. 1), who was formerly associated with him, is now head of the Institute of Physical Chemistry, another part of the Chemical Section of the Academy.

Professor Heyrovsky is a delightful person with whom to discuss things. It is evident that he keeps up not only with the polarographic literature but with a vast variety of other chemical literature. He remembered with great interest his trip to the United States in 1933 and contrasts the amazing change in the interest in polarography then, when such interest was practically non-existent, with the present interest when polarography is one of the most active fields of investigation in chemistry as is clearly indicated by the large number of papers dealing with polarographic theory, methodology, practice, and applications which are published, for example, each year in the *Journal of the American Chemical Society* and in *Analytical Chemistry*. He is clearly both a scientist and a scholar, as well as a great man in character and in influence.

## Heyrovsky the Scientist

Posted on the walls of Heyrovsky's laboratories is a quotation from Faraday, "Work, Finish, Publish." In furtherance of this goal, the founder of polarography has always stressed the importance of the printed dissemination of scientific ideas and findings. Besides his more than 170 original scientific papers, Heyrovsky has written a number of review articles as well as several important treatises and textbooks on polarography and derived techniques. The influence of these has already been indicated.

Of primary importance for the extension of the understanding of the polarographic method was his earlier mentioned article on polarographic analysis in Böttger's "Physikalische Methoden der analytischen Chemie (7)." It is interesting to note in view of the present-day acceptance of polarography as a standard analytical technique that in 1932, before asking Heyrovsky for a contribution, Böttger, himself a noted analytical chemist, spent a fortnight in Heyrovsky's laboratory to acquaint himself with the method and its analytical importance. Perhaps of even greater scientific influence was Heyrovsky's large textbook, "Polarographie" (12), which was published at the same time as the first edition of the monograph by Kolthoff and Lingane, "Polarography" (13), which contributed so much to the acceptance of polarography in English-speaking countries. A Russian translation (14) of the Czech book on polarography by Heyrovsky's pupil, Varasova, helped to spread a knowledge of polarography in the U.S.S.R.

Professor Heyrovsky has never forgotten that advances in any area of science depend not only on the experienced scientists, but also on the suitable indoctrination of beginners in that area. Consequently, he wrote a detailed elementary laboratory manual (15) on polarography which has since been revised (16) and published in some eight languages.

More specialized works include one on oscillographic polarography written with Dr. Forejt (17), the German edition of which has just appeared with the cooperation of Dr. Kalvoda, and an introduction to theoretical polarography, which is being written with Dr. Kuta.

Early in Heyrovsky's career, it became clear to him that a suitable publication medium for the work of

Czech polarographers and other chemists was urgently needed. In 1928, Heyrovsky and his friend, Professor Votocek, founded an Anglo-French bilingual journal, *Collection of Czechoslovak Chemical Communications;* the journal is now tetralingual (English, German, Russian, French). Until 1947 these two were not only editors of the journal but also its publishers and often the translators of its papers. Most of the polarographic work done in Czechoslovakia has been published in this journal in English or in German.

Professor Heyrovsky also early recognized the importance of systematic documentation work and periodically summarized bibliographical data on polarography in the *Collection of Czechoslovak Chemical Communications*. In the preparations of these bibliographies he has been aided by J. Klumpar (1938) and O. H. Müller (1948–1952); in recent years there has been an unnamed co-author, Mrs. Heyrovsky. These data were first collected in his monographs (*7, 12*) and later (1951) as an independent publication covering the period from 1922 to 1950 (*18*). Since 1951 the "Bibliography of Publications Dealing with the Polarographic Method" has appeared annually as a supplement to the journal. Recently, a subject index to these bibliographies appeared (*19*). Documentation in polarography is thus, as a result of this work and the bibliography (*20*) published by E. H. Sargent and Co. of Chicago, much more accessible than in most other branches of chemistry.

Professor Heyrovsky has always worked very intensively; he still adheres to the habit of spending weekends in the laboratory (in his opinion those are the only days when he is certain not to be disturbed during work). His working day in the Institute is from 8 A.M. to 7 P.M., interrupted only by a short nap after lunch. All of his own studies were and still are made by Heyrovsky without the support of any assistant or technician. He is an excellent example of another motto, found on the walls of the Institute: Newton's "A man must resolve either to produce nothing new or to become a slave to defend it."

Heyrovsky's main interest has always been in the experiment. His strength has consisted of finding new phenomena, of designing new experiments, which enable him to decide among existing ideas, and of being able to distinguish important from unimportant ideas. One of his collaborators compared him to a genial mushroom picker, who is able to find a mushroom even on the highway. He is often ingenious in the explanation of experimental facts, but frequently leaves the more quantitative treatment of the problem to his co-workers. He is fond of theory, but only of theory verified by experiment. When he was the editor of the *Collections*, the journal refused to publish purely theoretical papers without any experimental verification. When Heyrovsky becomes convinced that a theory is in accordance with experiment and explains important findings, he is ready to accept it, admire it, and support it, e.g., his admiration for the work on kinetic currents of his best known co-worker, Professor Brdicka, and the latter's collaborators.

Professor Heyrovsky's scientific success is reflected by the many honors given him. He has been elected to the Czechoslovak Academy of Sciences, the American Academy of Arts and Sciences, and the German, Hungarian, and Indian Academies of Sciences; he is an honorary member of the Czechoslovak, Polish, and Austrian Chemical Societies, of the Society for Analytical Chemistry (England and India), and of the Polarographic Society (London). He has received honorary doctorate degrees from the Universities of Dresden, Warsaw, and Marseilles. He was awarded the Czechoslovak State Prize (1951), the Order of the Czechoslovak Republic (1955), the first Medal of the Polarographic Society (1959), and the Nobel Prize (1959).

Since the end of World War II, Heyrovsky has delivered lectures on one or more occasions in England, Germany, Poland, Austria, the U.S.S.R., Hungary, Sweden, Denmark, Bulgaria, China, and Egypt.

## Heyrovsky the Teacher

It was both the possibility of work in a promising and new field and the personality of Professor Heyrovsky that have attracted so many students and co-workers to him. Heyrovsky's devotion and enthusiasm, his modest and polite behavior, his efforts and patience have made him an outstanding practical example for young people. In his kind manner, he always tries to help anybody interested in polarography. He follows the problems of his pupils just as eagerly as his own, but, when it comes to publication, his name rarely appears on the paper. When it does, more than half of the work has been carried out by him.

Most of his present co-workers in the Polarographic Institute came with him in 1950 from the Department of Physical Chemistry of the Charles University. He does not believe in regulated, forced teamwork, and, consequently, research teams are organized in the Institute only occasionally. Most of the investigators are allowed to choose their own problems, since, in Professor Heyrovsky's opinion, this is the most fruitful approach in basic research. However, when a complex problem is to be solved, the cooperation of specialists in diverse fields is available. At the weekly Institute discussion meetings, no one hesitates to express an opinion, even when it is in disagreement with that of the Director.

Heyrovsky is justly proud of the attachment of his pupils, co-workers, and friends, as reflected, for example, in the numerous letters he receives from all over the world and which he conscientiously answers.

## Heyrovsky the Man

In sacrifice to the major interest of his life, polarography, Professor Heyrovsky has given up most of his early interests. Once a pianist and a member of a student chamber music orchestra, he is today only a listener of music; he is fond of attending opera and still knows long parts of many by memory. At one time a well-known reviewer of books, today he hardly finds time to read novels, although when he wishes to brush up his knowledge of languages which is always admired by foreigners, he reads crime stories. He often repeats David Hume's critical comment that a book which does not contain any mathematical formulae is good only to be thrown into the fire.

Always interested in sports and once a mountaineer, soccer and tennis player, skier, and swimmer, Professor Heyrovsky has now, following the order of his physician, limited himself to two short walks weekly. Nevertheless, he still makes a kick-off at the traditional soccer match between the Polarographic Institute and the Institute of Physical Chemistry. Every day he acknowledges his childhood love for animals and the outdoors by spending some time in the garden of the Institute (Fig. 5).

Figure 5. Sir C. Raman (Indian Nobel Prize winner) with Professor Heyrovsky in the garden of the Polarographic Institute, Prague.

Professor Heyrovsky is fond of guests, his hospitality having become proverbial. He likes good jokes, red wine, and good cooking, but dislikes smoking (the smokers in the Institute have to go out of the building to smoke; even then, they occasionally hear some sarcastic remarks). His pleasant sense of humor is most characteristically expressed during the annual Institute parties, where his speeches are spiced with good jokes; until a few years ago he and Professor Brdicka used to perform short improvised satirical plays based on scientific life. At these latter occasions, he showed his ability in make-up, usually involving long beards.

Mention has been made of Heyrovsky's son, Michael, who is now an active investigator in polarography.

Another member of Heyrovsky's family who steadily supported and encouraged Professor Heyrovsky during his whole scientific career is his devoted and charming wife, Marie, who, after serving for a long time as his unofficial secretary, · became that officially in 1951. Their daughter Jitka (Czech for Judith) is a biochemist in a research institute.

## Literature Cited

(1) FISCHER, R. B., ET AL., *Anal. Chem.*, **28**, No. 12, 9A (1956).

(2) BREZINA, M., AND ZUMAN, P., "Polarography in Medicine, Biochemistry and Pharmacy," Interscience Publishers, Inc., New York, **1958** (also published in Czech (1952) and German (1956)).

(3) BRDICKA, R., *Collection Czech. Chem. Communs.*, **15**, 691 (1950).

(4) HEYROVSKY, J., *Chem. listy*, **16**, 256 (1922).

(5) HEYROVSKY, J., *Phil. Mag.*, **45**, 303 (1923).

(6) HEYROVSKY, J., AND SHIKATA, M., *Rec. trav. chim.*, **44**, 496 (1925).

(7) HEYROVSKY, J., in BÖTTGER, W., ed.; "Physikalische Methoden der analytischen Chemie," vol. II, Akademische Verlagsgesellschaft, Leipzig, **1936**, pp. 260–322; *ibid.* vol. III, **1939**, pp. 422–77.

(8) MÜLLER, O. H., J. CHEM. EDUC., **18**, 65, 111, 172, 227, and 230 (1941).

(9) MÜLLER, O. H., "The Polarographic Method of Analysis," 2nd ed., Chemical Education Publishing Co., Easton, **1951**.

(10) KOLTHOFF, I. M., AND LINGANE, J. J., "Polarography," 2nd ed., Interscience Publishers, Inc., New York, **1952**, 2 vols.

(11) ELVING, P. J., *Anal. Chem.*, **31**, No. 12, 52A (1959).

(12) HEYROVSKY, J., "Polarographie," Springer Verlag, Vienna, **1941**, reprinted by Edwards Brothers, Ann Arbor, Michigan, **1944**.

(13) KOLTHOFF, I. M., AND LINGANE, J. J., "Polarography," Interscience Publishers, Inc., New York, **1941**.

(14) HEYROVSKY, J., "The Polarographic Method, Its Theory and Applications" (in Russian), *Onti Chimteoret*, Leningrad, **1937**.

(15) HEYROVSKY, J., "Polarographisches Praktikum," Springer Verlag, Berlin, **1948** (published also in Russian (1951), Bulgarian (1954), and Chinese (1955)).

(16) HEYROVSKY, J., AND ZUMAN, P., "Einführung in die praktische Polarographie," Verlag Technik, Berlin, **1959** (also published in Slovak (1950), Czech (1953), Hungarian (1955), and Polish (1956)).

(17) HEYROVSKY, J., AND FOREJT, J., "Oscillographic Polarography," (in Czech), SNTL, Prague, 1953; HEYROVSKY, J., AND KALVODA, R., "Oszillographische Polarographie mit Wechselstrom," Akademie Verlag, Berlin, **1960**.

(18) HEYROVSKY, J., *Proc. First. Internat. Polarograph. Congr.*, part II: Polarographic Bibliography from 1922 to 1950, Přirodoved. vydav., Prague, **1951**.

(19) HEYROVSKY, J., AND HAN, J. E. S., "Subject Index to Polarographic Literature, vol. II, 1951–1955," (in English and Chinese), Academia Sinica, Peking, **1958**.

(20) "Bibliography of Polarographic Literature: 1922–1955," E. H. Sargent and Co., Chicago, **1955**.

---◆---

## Johann Nepomuk Fuchs   *Continued from page 103*

of zeolites and mineral phosphates, in conjunction with the discovery of vicariation, fundamentally advanced the systematization of minerals on a chemical basis. He provided the first scientific foundations for the technology of the silicates, hydraulic cement, artificial zeolites, and glass. His theory of amorphism pointed the way to research in the vast region of the noncrystalline materials, from which there has since developed the chemistry of colloids.

In Landshut as in Munich, Fuchs acted as adviser to industry and agriculture; he was consultant to dyers, paper and tobacco manufacturers, to starch makers and brewers. He introduced the manufacture of sugar from beets into Bavaria.

His services as teacher, scientist, and consultant re-

ceived proper recognition from the state authorities. In 1833 he was appointed chemist in the Upper Medical Council; in 1835 he was named Adviser to the Board of Mines and Salt Works, with retention of his other offices; in 1849 he was raised to the rank of nobleman; and in 1853 he was given the title Privy Councillor. His colleague Schafhäutl, in 1842, honored him by naming a chromiferous muscovite from the Ziller valley, fuchsite.

Johann Nepomuk Fuchs died at Munich on March 5, 1856, of general exhaustion of his vital forces. His "Gesammelten Schriften" together with a biography was issued in 1856 by his student and last assistant at Landshut, Cajetan Georg Kaiser, who later was professor of technology at the University of Munich.

# WILHELM OSTWALD

*A Study in Mental Metamorphosis*[1]

**FLORENCE E. WALL**
New York, New York

To THE average student of chemistry of this generation, the name of Wilhelm Ostwald means simply "the founder of physical chemistry." A second thought, if any, associated with the dates of books on chemistry with which he may be familiar, might leave the same student with the impression that Wilhelm Ostwald must have died long, long ago.

To the student of art, the same name would stand for the originator of the most thoroughly scientific and comprehensive scheme for the classification of colors that has ever been devised. In fact, so good is this system—so much better than the competitive system which is given the preference in American schools—so sufficient to establish the fame of the originator of it, that the two students might well engage in a friendly argument that this Wilhelm Ostwald could not possibly be the same person.

Some chemists, especially those that never knew him, are willing to concede Ostwald's contribution to physical chemistry and to electrochemistry, but they then dismiss him with some remark—patronizing, pitying, or contemptuous—about his "throwing over chemistry for philosophy." A few with similar leanings who had studied in Germany (and some Germans, themselves), perhaps imbued with the idea of *omne ignoto pro magnifico*, are awed into thinking that in making such a divagation, Ostwald had "chosen the better part." And still others, snap-judging the man by the products of that glorified trade-training which passes for "education for [some of] the professions" today, are inclined to dismiss him as a high-class "jack-of-all-trades" who, "if he really dabbled so seriously in all those other fields could not have been much of a chemist, after all."

So it was with mixed feelings, aroused by this welter of confusing opinion, that this study was undertaken,[2] to determine who and what Wilhelm Ostwald really was, as a scientist, as a philosopher, and especially as a *person*. The tendency to gloss over Ostwald's life and accomplishments after he abandoned his work in pure chemistry—done with a finesse that varies in effect between gently drawing a veil and slamming an iron door—served only to whet curiosity, fan a desire to reconstruct the fabric of the work of his mind and hands, and thus trace, if possible, the evolution of mental processes that led to so unusual a shifting of interests.

For such intimate matters, no better source of information could be found than "Lebenslinien" (*18*). This 3-volume autobiography of Ostwald, was published in 1927, just five years before he died. Not in mere vanity, but in unselfconscious, objective appraisal of his great contributions to human culture, he dedicated the first two volumes *To German Youth* and the third *To the German People*. Together they constitute a remarkable memorial to another of that group of "Titans of Chemistry," along with Wöhler, Liebig, Hofmann, Baeyer, and the many others who established 19th century Germany as the Fatherland of Science. Certainly this work shows that the author should not be considered as "dead [even] to science after 1905."

It is not the purpose of this paper to present just another biographical sketch of Ostwald. The details of his personal life and his contributions to science have been too well presented by others, better qualified (*1, 4, 5, 6, 35, 36, 38, 39*), but a few facts should be reviewed as background.

## EARLY LIFE

Friederich Wilhelm Ostwald was born of German parents in Riga, Latvia, in 1853. He was the second of three sons, and to anyone that dedicated his life to a study of exact science and certainty, it must often have been subconsciously if not actually disturbing that the date was not fixed. Latvia, being at that time a province of the Russian Empire, followed both the calendar of the Greek Catholic Church (Schismatic) and the old Julian Calendar which was still official for Russia. According to the earlier reckoning, the date was August 21; by the newer reckoning, it was September 2, and the latter date is generally given.

Students of genetics might find material for research in Ostwald's intellectual heritage. His grandfather and father were coopers—the latter also a minor local official—and his mother was the daughter of a poor baker. They both, however, made the most of native gifts and good intelligence and strove to give their boys opportunities that had been denied to themselves. They read a great deal, followed the theater and other arts, and sent young Wilhelm, at the age of six, to the best available school.

[1] Presented before the Division of History of Chemistry at the 111th Meeting of the American Chemical Society, Atlantic City, New Jersey, April 14–18, 1947.

[2] This paper was originally prepared as a special assignment for a class in *Philosophy of Education* at New York University. It has been considerably revised and enlarged for presentation here.

Successively he attended an elementary State school, the Realgymnasium at Riga, and the Technische Hochschule at Dorpat. Curricula and subject matter seem to have been at the mercy of divided and strongly competitive authority, for the older so-called cultural education of old Russia was struggling to maintain supremacy in face of a rising tide of favor for the more modern, so-called practical methods of Germany. Students were thus tossed about like a political football, emerging with an odd combination of a little physics, chemistry, and mathematics; four languages (Latin, Russian, French, and English); and a little natural history. The school at Riga was the only one of the prevailing "Latin schools" to offer even a smattering of science. The poor quality of this was forcibly brought home to the young Ostwald by the early death of a dear chum, which made him realize how inadequate and biased was an "education" that gave students no practical knowledge of physical and mental health and of the mere facts of living.

Deficient as it was, Ostwald's early education—and his extracurricular interests in music and art—laid the foundations for practically all the interests he was to follow in later life. His first contact with chemistry was through an old text, "Die Schule der Chemie" by Stöckhardt (1846), but the almost catastrophic results of an amateurish attempt to make fireworks taught him that to accomplish anything worthwhile he needed much more than a recipe and an earnest desire. Toward the sketching and painting which later became his most beloved hobby, he made his earliest contribution in the paints that he had to compound for himself, with the help of a friendly neighboring pharmacist. To foster his interest in photography he had to make everything from the collodion for his plates to his camera itself. Even the writing, through which as author and editor he has made an indelible mark in the history of science, fulfilled the promise shown in an early handwritten periodical and an abortive attempt to compose a deathless romance.

To one seeking first causes and trends, all these varied interests and tendencies indicated one thing in common—an abundance of that *energy*, the study of which in all its manifestations and transformations was to become one of his major interests in life.

Ostwald spent ten years at Dorpat, as student, assistant, and finally *privat-dozent*. He has made some shrewd—frequently caustic—comments on the various teachers to whom he was obliged to look for wisdom in many branches of study. For two of them, however, he always had only the best and deepest feelings of esteem and gratitude: Karl Schmidt, who taught him chemistry, and Arthur von Oettigen, who taught him physics. Later he was successively an assistant to both.

## BEGINNING OF HIS SCIENTIFIC WORK

His work at the *Dorpatsche Hochschule* was mostly in inorganic chemistry, yet Schmidt, who admittedly knew practically nothing of the then newly developing organic chemistry, assigned him a problem in the synthesis of indigo. This was sent for criticism to Adolf Baeyer in Germany, but when the latter rejected it, Ostwald forthwith dropped all interest in synthetic organic chemistry.

**WILHELM OSTWALD AT 50**

Frontispiece of Vol. 46, *Zeitschrift für physikalische Chemie*

His first published writing was "On the chemical mass action of water," which appeared in the *Journal für praktische Chemie* in 1875 (Vol. 120).

Ostwald's studies in physics showed him the need for considerably more knowledge of higher mathematics. To the textbook of Karl Snell, from which he undertook to tutor himself, he cheerfully gives credit not only for most of the sound mathematics he acquired but also for being directed toward his later study of philosophy. His interest in chemical transformations led him to measure densities, loss of heat in solutions, and equivalents of heat and chemical activity. In the total lack of devices and methods, he created his own. His knowledge of mathematics showed him both that his results were correct and that he was actually engaged in a field of research that had never been touched by previous investigators. This gave him his first taste of success and earned him a Master's degree in 1876.

As a *privat-dozent* he could join the inner circle of scientists at Dorpat. He became interested in the dual system of harmony in music and took up the study of such different instruments as the violin and the bassoon. Before long, however, he was forced to admit that his zeal was much greater than his ability and he finally yielded to the urging of his colleagues that he stick to science. He had already established his pattern—not to expend any energy on any interest or occupation once he learned he could not excel in it.

## ORIGIN OF PHYSICAL CHEMISTRY

Physical Chemistry came formally into existence in

the course of lectures that Ostwald established at the *Dorpatsche Hochschule* in 1876. The designation was not new as it had been used for a textbook as early as 1857 (*2*). After the very first lecture he began to collect notes for a textbook of his own, based first on his lectures and experiments and then broadening them to cover all available references in both chemistry and physics, in German, French, and English.

Continuing his investigation of physicochemical problems Ostwald undertook an exhaustive study of the measurements of density, refractive index, and chemical affinity of all the acids known and available to him. No one had ever even conceived the idea of such a study, much less ever had the glimmer of an idea of how to go about anything of the kind. Again he had to devise all his own apparatus and methods. For his accomplishment, and the publication of the orderly table which set forth the whole project, he was granted his coveted Doctor's degree in 1878.

Although he had solemnly promised himself that he would never marry, he became engaged the following year to Helene von Reyher, whom he had met through evenings of musical recreation. Marriage was out of the question, however, until he should be earning more money. He tried to combine a commercial laboratory position with his teaching, but was so disgusted with the antiquated, self-satisfied incumbent of the directorship and the extremely backward working conditions that he felt obliged to abandon the post almost at once. A happier choice of a position in one of the public secondary schools, although it deprived him temporarily of the companionship of older minds and potential research workers like himself, did at least improve his financial status, and he was married in the spring of 1880.

Contact with younger minds, however, gave Ostwald the opportunity he never quite had at the *Dorpatsche Hochschule*, namely, the chance to instill his newer ideas into his pupils, and thus assure the broadening of his own beliefs on chemical theory. This may well have been the secret of his wonderful ability to explain things, as manifested in the simplicity and clarity of all his writings. His published articles had gone far, but for years they seemed to make no impression. He wrote rather bitterly of the treatment accorded his work by Berthelot, the French leader, who made free use of his publications with little or no credit. Until this time, the French had sincerely believed that chemistry was a French science (was it not the heritage of their own eminent Lavoisier?), and they always looked with scorn or suspicion on any new ideas about chemistry that might emanate from any other country.

### REMOVAL TO RIGA

In 1881, Ostwald was appointed as professor of chemistry at the University of Riga. He had a miserable laboratory in the basement of a building but he made the best of it. He once more devised all his own apparatus and methods, and wrote a laboratory manual for his students.

Through a strong desire to see how other laboratories were constructed and conducted, and because the professorship at Riga seemed to demand a broadening of his contacts in scientific circles, Ostwald made his first trip to Germany during the winter holidays of 1882–83. Years before, when he had applied for a traveling fellowship and been denied it, he had felt slightly crushed at first, but then reacted rationally. He fully realized that, had he gone, he would have been caught in the maelstrom of experimental organic chemistry which was then whirling through Germany, would have become just another satellite of Baeyer or Hofmann, and sacrificed recognition for his own original and unique work. His fame having spread through publications, he could afford to visit his learned contemporaries, most of whom were well known to him through his study of the history of chemistry and their published contributions to science.

The recounting of this journey and of the famous learned ones whose acquaintance he made reads like a conducted tour through a portrait gallery of "Who's Who in 19th Century Chemistry." He made it a point to attend classroom lectures of some of the most famous of the teachers; and before he left Berlin he was honored with an invitation to address a regular meeting of the German Chemical Society—on his own subject. The meeting was an agreeable disappointment to most of his audience, the secret of this being that although most of the famous organic chemists of the day knew nothing of his branch of physical chemistry, Ostwald had a good grasp of, and had actually done considerable work in organic chemistry. He met Helmholtz, also this great teacher's greatest pupil, Hertz, and attended meetings of the Physical Society.

The importance of physical measurements in chemistry, the relationships of chemical activity, heat, and other forms of energy, and the gradually increasing momentum of a body of thought toward *energy* as a common source of scientific phenomena, were not new. In fact, it was "in the air." An English investigator, M. Pattison Muir, at Cambridge University, had published in the *Philosophical Magazine* (September, 1879) a review of all the work that had been done on chemical affinity from the time of Torbern Bergmann, the Swedish chemist of the late 17th century, and Berthollet (1803), to and including the work of Ostwald. Further early work had been done by J. R. Mayer, who first, in 1842, published his fundamental discovery of the mechanical equivalent of heat, thus establishing the study of thermodynamics—which Ostwald in his own time soon translated into Energetics.

Others whose earlier or contemporary investigations were all converging toward a common objective were: Robert Clausius 1822–88, who stated the second law of thermodynamics; William Thomson (Lord Kelvin, 1824–1907) who developed it; and the American, J. Willard Gibbs (1839–1903), whom Ostwald helped to bring into deserved public recognition, through a translation of Gibbs' "Thermodynamic Studies" (1892).

## ASSOCIATION WITH ARRHENIUS AND VAN'T HOFF

Until about a year after Ostwald's first visit to the outer world he was practically alone in his field of investigation, but in 1884 he was suddenly made conscious of the brilliant paralleling researches of a young Swede, Svante Arrhenius, of Stockholm. On the same day when he was suffering from a bad toothache, and his wife was presenting him with a new daughter, he received by post the reprint of an article entitled "Studies on the conductibility of electrolytes."

From the first two disturbances he recovered in due time, but the last persisted for many days and caused him many sleepless nights. Finally his scientific and and personal curiosity prevailed and he set out to visit Arrhenius and learn more of his work. The friendship thus established continued in happy personal and professional association until the death of Arrhenius in 1927. The visit marked another broader circle of contacts with the scientific world, because from Upsala and Stockholm, Ostwald returned home by way of Norway and Denmark, where he made the acquaintance of many other famous professional colleagues in both chemistry and physics, who had heretofore been known to him only by name.

Ostwald prevailed on Arrhenius to go to Riga and work with him, and from this fortunate association resulted much advancement of their joint interests. After nearly a year had passed the similar chance arrival of the reprint of another article, "Studies of chemical dynamics," brought these two into contact with Jacobus H. van't Hoff, of whom neither of them had heard, but, who was to become the third member of a later famous triumvirate of scientific crusaders. In fact, the introductory reprint showed Ostwald that in the applications of thermodynamics to chemical problems, the author of it had already progressed farther than he had.

In 1885, after many years of labor, the first part of Ostwald's "Lehrbuch der Allgemeinen chemie" (19) appeared. It was a completely new organization and presentation of the subject matter. As always happens in any attempt to force unwelcome scientific truths on an unready world, Ostwald's "New chemistry" met with considerable concerted opposition, both through being silently ignored by those that could have helped to promulgate it, and by open ridicule and shabby treatment in public sessions of scientific meetings. The battling had the unavoidable result of making him better known, so, whether or not they liked him, his professional colleagues could not honestly oppose the appointment of Ost-

wald as editor of the newly established *Zeitschrift für physikalische Chemie*, of which the first number appeared in February, 1887, with the name of J. H. van't Hoff as co-founder and editor.(15).

## CALL TO LEIPZIG

Editorial work by remote control—that is, trying to edit a periodical printed in Leipzig from a desk in Riga—promised to be both arduous and unsatisfactory. After one issue, however, Ostwald was invited to Leipzig, and he soon saw himself, at thirty-four about to continue his career from the acknowledged vantage point of one of the greatest universities of Europe.

Ostwald remained at Leipzig for eighteen years, during which period he firmly established both the delimitations of his field of physical chemistry and the relationships of this field to other branches of science which border on it. He accomplished a prodigious amount of original work and his laboratory became a mecca for enterprising graduate students from all over the world. The first American to arrive was Morris Loeb; Arthur A. Noyes was next. Some other well-known students from this side of the Atlantic among Ostwald's earliest students were Wilder D. Bancroft, G. W. Coggeshall, William J. Hall, W. Lash Miller, James L. R. Morgan, Theodore W. Richards, and J. E. Trevor. Some of the later group were S. L. Bigelow, Frederick G. Cottrell, Colin G. Fink, Arthur B. Lamb, G. Victor Sammet, E. C. Sullivan, Willis R. Whitney, and J. H. McBain.

As these and many others brought his teachings back to their own students or to their own continued re-

Courtesy of The Chemists' Club, New York

**MEETING OF SOCIETY OF CHEMICAL INDUSTRY, NEW YORK, 1912**

Front row: Eustace Carey, Charles F. Chandler, Rudolph Messell, William H. Nichols, William Ramsay, Thomas Tyrer, Thomas J. Parker.
Second row: Frederick B. Power, Ira Remsen, Wilhelm Ostwald, S. Lewkowitsch, Herman A. Metz, Virgil Coblentz.
Top row: Marston T. Bogert, Sir Max Muspratt.

search, he saw his influence permeating into many un-anticipated applications. He always felt that the number of teachers among his graduates gave him a great advantage over Berzelius, who often expressed regret that most of his students had come as older men with their ideas fixed and their minds not receptive. His research in thermodynamics—or energetics—continued, supported by the force of continued discoveries of van't Hoff, Arrhenius, and others, and the unexpected corroboration of such famous mathematicians as Max Planck and Georg Helm.

The new learning also permeated Ostwald's own lectures, articles, and textbooks, necessitating frequent revisions or rewriting to fit established knowledge to the newer theory, and vice versa. Following the last part of the "Lehrbuch" in 1887 (the "Great Ostwald") came the "Grundriss der Allgemeinen Chemie" in 1889 (the "Little Ostwald"), which has appeared in five editions to date, and has been translated into many languages, including Russian and Japanese.

## CATALYSIS

Beginning in 1891, after being interested in it since 1883, Ostwald devoted several years to the study of catalysis which, happily, he could associate with energetics. Despite disagreement among his followers, he is generally believed to be the first to understand the nature of catalytic reactions. Ostwald, himself, considered this his greatest contribution to chemistry, and for this work he was awarded the Nobel prize for chemistry in 1909.

One vitally important industrial application of Ostwald's work on catalysis was the synthesis of ammonia (1900) and of nitric acid (1901). These accomplishments freed Germany from the fear of being cut off from Chile, source of the natural nitrates, in event of war.

In 1893 appeared "Die wissenschäftlichen Grundlagen der analytischen Chemie," the work that was to revolutionize the study of analytical chemistry. Whether or not it was admitted openly at the time, all analytical chemistry soon was taught in terms of physical chemistry; such topics as the conductivity of solutions, electrolytic dissociation, heat equivalence, and the transference of heat and chemical energy soon became an integral factor of the patter of general chemistry. Within a few years a continuous stream of books was either in press or in plan.

In 1894, a new interest was offered, through the establishment of the Electrochemical Society, of which Ostwald became the first president. Through the activities of this new society in its attempts to place university graduates in industrial positions, official State Examinations were initiated, which made minimum standards compulsory for all technical schools, and thus helped to ensure competence in those that were to be employed in industry.

## CLASSIFICATION OF THE SCIENCES

Of increasing importance as a sideline of interest was a study of the organization or order of the sciences.

From his hobby of studying the history of science Ostwald had evolved a scheme of his own, quite different from the artificial and arbitrary classifications passed on from Aristotle and Newton. This interest inspired him to start (1889) the publication of his famous "Klassiker der exakten wissenschaften," of which two hundred and forty-three little volumes had been published by 1938. The first in the series is "Über die Erhaltung der Kraft," by Helmholtz, originally published in 1847. Others cover various phases of different branches of science from mathematics to physiology.

Ostwald's own classification grouped the sciences in three divisions: *order, energy,* and *life* (14). To the first group belong: logic (within mathetics,) mathematics, geometry, and kinematics; to the second: mechanics, physics, and chemistry; and to the third: physiology, psychology, and sociology. These were arranged as follows:

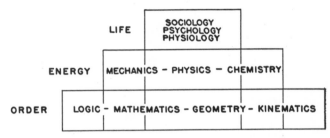

OSTWALD'S PYRAMID OF THE SCIENCES

In this concept the breath of each layer corresponds to extent and the height corresponds to content, of each.

Further considerations bring out that each branch of science exists in the *pure* and in the *applied* form, the second presupposing a knowledge of the first. Each general science is prerequisite for those with richer content that stand higher. Thus, to practice physics one must know mathematics; but one may be an outstanding chemist without a knowledge of the sociological sciences, and a good mathematician or logician without knowing chemistry. The diagram raises many interesting questions and suppositions.

## PHYSICAL BREAKDOWN

So much pure "head work"—thinking—without any of the physical work that accompanies chemical investigations or any least bit of physical exercise in recreational sports, led inevitably to a state of exhaustion, which, if Ostwald would have admitted it, actually amounted to a complete breakdown by the end of 1895. His father had always taught his sons that "the will makes everything possible." As his own thinking on the nature of mental reactions had not been completely codified and clarified, he failed to recognize the warning symptoms as physiological, which they really were. Never having known any change of mental activity except from one kind of work to another, he proceeded to aggravate his condition by forcing his "will" to continued thinking. Only the persuasive powers of a kind medical friend saved him from certain disaster, and caused him to regain his balance by a change of interest and occupation.

Drawing on one of his many hobbies, Ostwald liked to find his recreation and "change of mind" in painting and sketching from nature. Wherever he went his box of paints went along, and he considered a trip lacking if he could not produce something tangible as a remembrance of things seen. At this time he took several months' leave of absence, extended his circuit of travel, visiting all corners of Germany, and later Austria, Switzerland, and Italy—even the far-off Isle of Wight.

He recovered his physical health and returned to the university in September, 1896, but he soon began to realize that he was losing—had actually lost—his desire for work in chemistry. This was at first quite distressing, but he rationalized it by recalling that many distinguished scientists—notably both members of that famous devoted pair of chemists, Liebig and Wöhler—had experienced and weathered similar feelings of being "tired of chemistry." He was only glad that he had laid a firm foundation in other interests.

## BIRTH OF ENERGETICS

The first of these was energetics. Ostwald's own story of his development of the ideas of energetics places the hour of its birth in 1890. As mentioned before, the concept was not new, even to him, because he had learned and taught the laws of the conservation of energy in his earliest days. The more he thought about it, however, the more important it became, and the more he tried to organize his thoughts on it. Finally, to set a stamp of some sort on all his thinking, he had chosen as his opening lecture at Leipzig, the subject: "Energy and its transformations" (13).

The association of energetics with physical science had come about logically through application of the work done by "the triumvirate" (Arrhenius, van't Hoff, Ostwald), but the association with biological science was not so easily determined. Ostwald found himself thinking more and more about early work of J. R. Mayer, who first conceived the idea of such an association through watching the hard labor, and noting the resultant sweating of slaves at work, and even of draught animals. Further concrete aid came through a visit to the physicist, E. Budde, in Berlin, who was planning to write a textbook of physics in terms of Ostwald's theories. Following a long evening's conversation with Budde, as he could not sleep much, he rose early, went to the neighboring zoo, and sat alone in the beautiful morning sunshine. He claims to have experienced his "flash of genius" in one of those golden moments—"a veritable descent of the Spirit"—which gave him insight into the whole concept of world order,"... as if he had suddenly landed in paradise with an exhaustive treatise from which he could give everything its right name..."

Feeling—and according to his friends also looking—completely transfigured, he started quietly but rapidly to reorganize his thoughts on his work in terms of his new enlightenment. Everything seemed to fit perfectly. He proceeded still cautiously, but seized the opportunity afforded by the demand for a second edition of his great textbook to revise it completely in terms of his new thinking. It brought together for the first time a unified concept of electricity and electrochemistry, making possible a continuity of thought on this subject from the earliest theories to the latest provable discoveries of his friends, Arrhenius and van't Hoff.

His organized thinking led him into the whole study of reality, of the nature of matter, and all related concepts. *Reality* had formerly been associated only with material substances and objects; but Ostwald believed that after order, number, time, and space, *energy* logically followed as a general concept. If, he argued, his pen, paper, desk, room, house, and the earth were all realities, why was not also the light, by which he could illumine the darkness of his room with one flip of his finger? And if so, why not also the thoughts that he could generate in the cells of his brain, by which he activated what his hand wrote with the pen on the paper, etc.? He associated the whole flow of thought with Mayer's law of the conservation of force (energy) which could be applied to everything, whether or not it could be seen, measured, or otherwise fitted into the earlier accepted standards. To the question, "What properties has energy?" he answered, "Everything there is." The thought that he early formulated as his *Energetic Imperative*—that is "Squander no energy; utilize it!"—was, he felt, his best help through his daily living (11, 13, 20).

He expected opposition, and he found plenty of it. The feeling that existed between the professors of science and of natural philosophy at the time brought doubt, questioning, and unfavorable criticism from both sides. Aside from the interpolation of certain passages in the introduction to his textbook, Ostwald felt he could bide his time, and his reward came in the gradual realization that the work of Planck, Clausius, Hertz, Maxwell, Gibbs, Röntgen, and other all fitted into the general scheme, and actually tended to turn into the same theory.

## EXCURSION INTO PHILOSOPHY

The broadening of his interests brought Ostwald into friendly contact with his professional associates in the other faculties of the university, notably Wilhelm Wundt, the founder of physiological psychology. They had become acquainted by correspondence several years earlier, and closer association strengthened Ostwald's interest in philosophical considerations and in the applications of his theory of energetics to biology and psychology. Through the fame of his lectures and laboratory work, Ostwald's influence increased both at home and abroad. He was invited to take part in scientific meetings in England and eventually became as well known there as in his own country. Through usage, his early difficulties with the language were overcome, and he was soon willing to lecture in English.

Ostwald placed his public espousal of philosophy in the year 1900, when he first gave a lecture on Natural

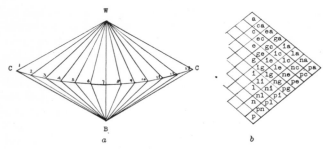

**OSTWALD'S SYSTEM FOR CLASSIFYING COLORS**

(a) Cones, in which the triangles represent one pure shade and two variations in the complete cycle of eight basic colors: yellow, orange, red, violet, ultramarine blue, turquoise blue, sea green, leaf green. *W*, white; *B*, black; *C*, color.

(b) Cross section of half of figure at left. Single letters represent succession of values from white through grays to black; *pa*, pure color at periphery. All intervening combinations mean variants in shade, each designating some specific proportion of white, black, and color. Opposite side of cross section would show same letters in corresponding positions for complimentary color; *i. e.*, yellow-ultramarine, orange-turquoise, red-sea green, violet-leaf green.

Philosophy. From a set of such lectures, he wrote two books which were well received, and one was soon translated into English (*23*). This work brought him the attention of William James, of Harvard, and there followed many invitations to attend and address the meetings of philosophical societies and to contribute to their publications.

He brought to these expressions the same kind of serious thinking that he had devoted to chemistry and physics. He undertook even more seriously to formulate some order of the sciences and determine interrelationships among them. Philosophy, for example, as a major field of study comprises logic, aesthetics, and ethics, and he proceeded to subject these to careful analysis. He considered aesthetics a field of applied psychology; and ethics a field of applied sociology. To confirm his interest in his new studies, he established and became editor of a new periodical, the *Annalen der Naturphilosophie* (1901). His book of "Lectures on Natural Philosophy" (1902) (*30*) is dedicated to Ernst Mach, whom he considered to be the one, of all the persons he then knew, that had most strongly influenced him.

### AMERICAN VISITS

Ostwald was made an honorary member of the American Chemical Society in 1900, one of the earliest of many honors conferred on him by foreign countries. He first came to the United States in 1903 at the invitation of Jacques Loeb, to visit the University of California and deliver a lecture. In deference to the interests of Loeb, the subject chosen was "The relations between physical chemistry and biology" (*28*). He returned the following year (1904), to take part in the International Congress of All Arts and Sciences during the St. Louis World's Fair, where he addressed one of the philosophical groups.

All these distractions and jauntings from his position at Leipzig caused dissatisfaction on all sides—the

Administration, his colleagues, the students, and in himself—so he decided to make a clean break and resign from the university. Just as a major crisis was developing, Ostwald was appointed by the Kaiser himself as the first Exchange Professor to be sent to Harvard. This was the result of a growing criticism of an "imbalance in education," caused by the preponderance of American students that went to Germany for graduate work, as against practically none that came to this country for the same reason.

Early in 1905, Ostwald, his wife, and their two daughters arrived in Cambridge. There he gave general and special lectures at the university and numerous others at various colleges and before scientific and philosophical organizations.(*17*). His associates at Harvard were William James, Josiah Royce, and Hugo Münsterberg. Of all of these, as well as of President Eliot, his own former pupil, Theodore W. Richards (of the department of chemistry), and others, the record gives good descriptive sketches of their appearance and personality.

### VARIED INTERESTS

The year was soon over and he returned to Germany, first to settle his family in a lovely new home, *"Landhaus Energie,"* at Gross-Bothen in Saxony; and then to devote himself to his various professed interests—energetics, school and university affairs, scientific methods, organization of science, world language, internationalism, pacifism, and color. His interest in each and every one of these subjects was not the superficial smattering of the dilettante, but the sober and wholehearted participation of the trained investigator who makes each study a major problem to be solved to the best of his ability.

During the next few years—until the outbreak of the World War in 1914—Ostwald drew most, perhaps, on his remarkable ability as an organizer. Although he was not teaching chemistry and was primarily occupied with philosophy, his interest in science had not abated. His first great project was the establishing of a National Bureau of Chemistry which was eventually realized in 1910 as the Kaiser Wilhelm Institute.

Another interest was an organization called briefly *Die Brücke*, which was planned to foster closer cooperation among branches of industry and between pure and applied science. Among the results of these efforts, the format of technical journals was standardized, and a system was devised for naming and classifying colors.

### INTERNATIONAL ASSOCIATIONS

Ostwald served for years on the International Commission for Atomic Weights. Two systems had been observed (based on H = 1 and O = 16) but in 1906 the single standard, O = 16, was adopted. Ostwald served on this Commission continuously, publishing the tables himself from 1916 to 1932.

Further evidence of his great interest in internationalism was shown by his cooperation in the establishing

(1911) of the International Association of Chemical Societies. Initiated by representatives of England, France, and Germany, it attracted representatives from most of the other countries and plans were soon laid for standard chemical nomenclature, standard format for journals, and a world language for science.

As part of the Association of Chemical Societies, Ostwald planned an International Institute of Chemistry. He found in Ernest Solvay, the Belgian industrialist, a kindred soul who offered to endow the proposed Institute and who also was interested in "social energetics."

The idea of a world language was nothing new. By Ostwald's time two—Volapük and Esperanto—had been introduced. In him the realization of a great need for something of the kind had evolved through his teaching of so many foreign students, and his visits to so many international meetings. The study and use of foreign languages seemed a serious waste of energy. Ostwald had always been extremely critical of the German schools for their over-emphasis on the study of languages. He felt this was responsible for considerable mental aberration. While he was at Harvard he had studied Esperanto. As this later proved to be unsuitable he created a new artificial language, called *Ido*. This was intended to be the international medium for standard scientific nomenclature and literature. He donated· half of his Nobel prize to the furthering of this work, and it was progressing slowly when the start of the War swept it all away.

Associated with Ostwald's interest in philosophy was that aroused by the movement for *Monism*,[3] founded by Ernest Haeckel in 1906. He was the leader of the group of Monists from 1910 to 1914. He wrote many essays and sermons on problems of ethics, formal religion, and antiquated philosophy (*22, 27*). The *Monistenbund* of Austria celebráted his 60th birthday (1913) by publishing a commemorative issue, recounting his many accomplishments (*8*). All this activity, too, was swept away by the War.

As an ardent pacifist, Ostwald considered war the most horrible waste of energy. He had regularly attended all the great peace congresses and had addressed several sessions. His most earnest plea was for voluntary disarmament. The outbreak of the World War was a great shock to him. He took no part in it, al-. though his plant for making nitrates was taken over by the government.

## PROFESSION OF ART

With the world around him shaken to its foundations, Ostwald found consolation in peaceful pursuits and, beginning in 1914, he started on the last phase of his active creative life—the scientific study of color. Having long been interested in the art he now studied the history and the theory of color, devised units for measurements, invented the necessary instruments, set the standards, wrote his own texts (*9, 10, 40*), and introduced a curriculum for the study of color in the elementary schools. On this one subject he wrote sixteen books, and established and edited a periodical. He considered his work on color his greatest contribution to human culture. If there were many that believed that Ostwald should have received the Nobel prize for peace, even he believed his work on color merited the same prize for physics.

In writing of his reasons for abandoning his research in pure science and giving up the university, Ostwald said that when one reaches the top of any profession, there are only two ways to proceed: either to try to stay at the top and run the risk of falling off and being crushed by the rushing feet of younger, active followers; or while still at the top to step aside from such a dangerous place and, if one feels sad at giving up what has taken the best years of one's life, to be prepared with other means of using one's mind and time. He, himself, certainly need never have feared that he would find either his mind or his time idle. The riches of his mental resources always ensured copious reserves.

## CONCLUSION

No one should call Wilhelm Ostwald merely a jack-of-all-trades, or a dilettante in anything he undertook. His native German thoroughness made him study anything exhaustively, once he considered it worthy of his attention. He had a remarkable memory and an exceptional gift for grasping a concept or a project as a whole. Although he had great personal charm—a magnetic personality—there seems to have been little relieving lightness in him, little real sense of humor.

In testimony of this is an incredibly heavy analysis, complete with mathematical equations, of the nature of *happiness*. In one version,[4] $G$ stands for the amount

$$G = k(A - W)(A + W)$$

of happiness; $A$ for procedures (energy expended) welcome to the will; $W$ for unwelcome disagreeable experiences associated with resistance; and $k$ the factor for transforming the energetic process into the psychological. The explanation is certainly something that has to be seen (and studied intently) to be believed; but Ostwald adduces proof that it works, and for such different conditions as the desire for drink and the ecstasy of religious belief.

If Ostwald never apologized for what many thought (and think) was a defection, a perfidious abandoning of a sacred trust and responsibility, he was always willing to explain it. He firmly believed that life can be prolonged by a change of mental activity, and from his study of history and of men, he had many examples to prove it. His book, "Grosse Männer" (*16*), is an original, extremely interesting, and thought-provoking study of the biology of genius.

Wilhelm Ostwald's life was his own, and it was his

---

[3] The doctrine (1) that there is only one kind of substance or ultimate reality; (2) that reality is one unitary organic whole with no independent parts.

[4] This is in "Lebenslinien," Vol. III; Slosson (*36*) gives another formula, $G = E_2 - W_2$. The explanation and deductions are about the same.

privilege to do as he wished. If he had retired from chemistry to the top of a column, like St. Simeon Stylites of old, or, like some modern celebrities, to sit on a flag pole or stagnate in a mausoleum full of junk, one might condemn him as a renegade who gave up something for nothing. His prolific writings are eloquent testimony against any such accusation. By the time he left the University of Leipzig (1906) he had written about twenty-five books and literally thousands of articles, reviews, abstracts, etc. (4). That output would be considered a full career by many a healthy professor and researcher. What many of the older generation—those that have been ignoring Ostwald as "dead to science after 1905"—may not know is that he wrote about ten more books on chemistry after that date. He continued to edit his *Zeitschrift* until 1922; his editorial "swan song" is a fine review of the period covered by the first hundred volumes.

Other publications include about twenty books on philosophy and energetics; about thirteen on biography and biology; and as mentioned before, sixteen on art. Too few of the long list of his books have been translated, which is unfortunate because almost without exception each work is excellent of its kind. His last book, "Goethe the Prophet," was published in 1932, just before Ostwald died. It was characteristic of him that when he left his home on March 31, 1932, to go to the clinic at Leipzig, all his painting equipment was left in perfect order, ready for work when he should return. But he was not to return to it; he died on April 4.

Today, almost exactly fifteen years afterward, may be too soon to try to appraise this truly great mind and its truly prodigious contribution to the life and living of his time. This investigator—of the middle generation and without prejudice—who undertook this study originally by request, has continued to read on and on whenever time permits, and almost envies the now upgrowing and future generations to whom Wilhelm Ostwald is merely a name on a textbook. Sooner or later some of them will have to rediscover the treasury of "Ostwaldiana" in the libraries and draw on it for a whole series of dissertations on this or that phase of the life and accomplishments of this man whose versatility was greater than that of Leonardo da Vinci with whom he has been compared (35).

Viewed objectively, as presented by himself through his autobiography and his other voluminous writings, Wilhelm Ostwald stands out as a phenomenal combination, not only of the scientist and the philosopher, also of artist, linguist, and writer, who squandering no energy, but conserving it, applied his major interests to one another. As the founder of both a branch of science and a system of philosophy he seems to be quite unique—at least this slice of history will probably not see his like again.

## LITERATURE CITED

(1) BANCROFT, W. D., J. CHEM. EDUC., **11**, 539–42, 609–13 (1933).

(2) GRAHAM-OTTO, "Ausfuhrliches Lehrbuch der Chemie," Band I. (H. BUFF, H. KOPP, and F. ZAMMINER), "Lehrbuch der Physikalische und Theoretische Chemie," F. Vieweg, Braunschweig, **1857**.

(3) HELM, GEORG, "Die Energetik," Veit, Leipzig, **1898**, 366 pp.

(4) VAN'T HOFF, J. H., *Z. physik. Chem.*, **46**, v–xvi (1903).

(5) JAFFE, BERNARD, "Crucibles: The Lives and Achievements of the Great Chemists," Simon and Schuster, New York, **1930**.

(6) VON MEYER, ERNST, "A History of Chemistry," Macmillan, London, **1892**.

(7) MEYER's Lexikon, "Energetik" (7th ed.), **1925**.

(8) MONISTENBUND-ÖSTERREICH, "Wilhelm Ostwald: Festschrift . . . 60 Geburtstagsfeier," Wien, Leipzig, **1913**.

(9) OSTWALD, WILHELM, "Color Album," Winsor and Newton, London, **1933**.

(10) OSTWALD, WILHELM, "Colour Science" (trans. J. SCOTT TAYLOR), Winsor and Newton, London, **1931**.

(11) OSTWALD, WILHELM, "Die Energetische Imperativ," Akad. Verlagsges., Leipzig, **1912**.

(12) OSTWALD, WILHELM, "Die Energie," Barth, Leipzig, **1908**.

(13) OSTWALD, WILHELM, "Die Energie und Ihre Wandlungen," Engelmann, Leipzig, **1888**.

(14) OSTWALD, WILHELM, "Die Pyramide der Wissenschaften" Cotta Buchhandl., Stuttgart, **1929**.

(15) OSTWALD, WILHELM, *Z. physikal. Chem.*, **100**, 1–8 (1922).

(16) OSTWALD, WILHELM, "Grosse Männer," Akad. Verlagsges., Leipzig, **1909**.

(17) OSTWALD, WILHELM, "Individuality and Immortality" (Ingersoll lecture), Harvard, **1906**.

(18) OSTWALD, WILHELM, "Lebenslinien," 3 vols., Klasing, Berlin, **1926–7**.

(19) OSTWALD, WILHELM, "Lehrbuch der Allgemeinen Chemie," Engelmann, Leipzig, **1885–7**.

(20) OSTWALD, WILHELM, "Les Fondements Enérgetiques de la Science de Civilization," Giard, Paris, **1910**.

(21) OSTWALD, WILHELM, "L'Evolution d'une Science, La Chimie," trans. by M. DUFOUR, Flammarion, Paris, **1916**.

(22) OSTWALD, WILHELM, "Monism as the Goal of Civilization," Int. Cong. of Monism, Hamburg, **1913**.

(23) OSTWALD, WILHELM, "Natural Philosophy," Henry Holt & Co., New York, **1910**.

(24) OSTWALD, WILHELM, *J. Am. Chem. Soc.*, **15**, 421–30 (1893).

(25) OSTWALD, WILHELM, "Outlines of General Chemistry," London, **1889**.

(26) OSTWALD, WILHELM, "Principles of Inorganic Chemistry" (4th ed.), Leipzig, **1907**.

(27) OSTWALD, WILHELM, *La Vie Internationale*, **4**, 113–65, Bruxelles (1913).

(28) OSTWALD, WILHELM, "The Relations of Biology and the Neighboring Sciences," University of California Publications, Physiology, **1**, #4 (1903).

(29) OSTWALD, WILHELM, "The System of the Sciences," Rice Inst. pamphlet, November, **1915**.

(30) OSTWALD, WILHELM, "Vorlesungen uber Naturphilosophie," Engelmann, Leipzig, **1902**.

(31) PERRY, ROBERT, B., "Approach to Philosophy," Scribner, New York, **1905**.

(32) PERRY, ROBERT B., "Philosophy of the Recent Past," Scribner, New York, **1926**.

(33) REEVE, SIDNEY A., "Energetics," Crawford, Nyack, **1938**.

(34) DEROBERTY, E., *Rev. Philos.*, **69** 1–38 (1910).

(35) SACHS, A. P., *Chemist*, **10**, 11–21 (1933).

(36) SLOSSON, E. E., "Major Prophets of Today," Little, Brown & Co., Boston, **1914**.

(37) TREVOR, J. E., *J. Am. Chem. Soc.*, **15** 430–48 (1893).

(38) WALDEN, PAUL, "Wilhelm Ostwald," Engelmann, Leipzig, **1904**.

(39) WALDEN, PAUL, *Ber.*, **65²**, 101–41(1932).

(40) ZEISHOLD, HERMAN, "Wilhelm Ostwald's Color Theory," Board of Education, City of New York, **1938**.

**Paul Harteck**
Rensselaer Polytechnic Institute
Troy, New York

# Physical Chemists in Berlin, 1919–1933

In the period from 1919 to 1933, many of the outstanding physical chemists of Germany were centered in Berlin. These included Nernst, Haber, Bodenstein, Volmer, and Bonhoeffer. At the same time many renowned scientists in allied fields were also present. Therefore a center of physical chemistry developed which was unequalled anywhere in the world at that time. In allied fields, Max Planck was working on thermodynamics, von Laue on crystal interference, and Schrödinger and London on development and application of wave mechanics. Simon and Meissner were working on low temperatures. For spectroscopy there was Paschen at the Physicalisch-Technicallische-Reichsanstalt and also Warburg who made the experimental foundation of photochemistry. Still other outstanding groups were present; for example, Otto Hahn and his co-workers on radiochemistry and G. Hertz who worked on the separation of isotopes by gaseous diffusion. The factors which brought about and made such a possible concentration of scientific talent were singular.

It would almost be presumptuous of me to try to review the great era of physical chemistry which occurred in Berlin after World War I and extended until 1933. However, I may speak of famous men whose names can never be forgotten in the history of natural science and make comments regarding their personality and work because I am one of the few who can speak from his own personal experience. I must be allowed, however, to make two limitations: first, I shall speak in detail of only those scientists who were connected with physical chemistry and whose work has been important in this field. Secondly, I would prefer to speak more about the scientists who are no longer among us because their places in history are rather well established.

## Scientific Atmosphere in Berlin

Berlin in the year 1919 was the capital of a country which had just lost World War I, but even in those times of revolution, inflation, and uncertainty in politics, intellectual life and scientific culture started to develop. The technical and exact natural sciences and even the scientists themselves were held in high esteem. There was a very well-educated and cultured class which was not too large, but was able to produce scientists who became world-famed. At the same time scientists from other countries who could speak German and had German cultural ties were accepted in Berlin; thus there was an intellectual exchange with the whole world. There still exist friendships and relationships begun during this time among scientists all over the world.

Since most of the institutions were government-sponsored, it was very important to have high government officials who were broad-minded and intelligent people. The funds for the institutions were adequate, although not excessive, but the most important thing was the scientific atmosphere and the scientific enthusiasm which was unique during this period. It was very important for the development of physical chemistry in Berlin of those days that exceptionally good scientists headed the institutes of physical chemistry of the University, the Polytechnic Institute in Berlin-Charlottenburg, the Kaiser Wilhelm Gesellschaft (now the Max Planck Society), and the Physikalisch-Technische Reichsanstalt (equivalent to the Bureau of Standards in the United States). W. Nernst held the chair for physical chemistry at the University from 1905 till 1922 when he became President of the Physikalisch-Technische Reichsanstalt. He was succeeded in the chair of physical chemistry by Max Bodenstein. The institute for physical chemistry of the Kaiser Wilhelm Gesellschaft was headed by Fritz Haber, and the institute of physical chemistry of the Polytechnic Institute was headed by Max Volmer, a specialist on the kinetics of phase formation. In addition, G. Hertz was head of the experimental physics at the Polytechnic Institute, and in these years he performed his classic work in the field of isotope separation, which was actually a development in physical chemistry. The presidents of the Physikalisch-Technische Reichsanstalt before and after Nernst were O. Warburg and Paschen. Noddack, the discoverer of rhenium, with his low temperature laboratory worked in fields which were allied to physical chemistry at the Physikalisch-Technische Reichsanstalt. In the old Nernst institute of the University there was a lucky combination of the Nernst tradition, represented especially by F. Simon, with the experimental skill of the new director Max Bodenstein in the field of reaction kinetics. The atmosphere at Kaiser Wilhelm Gesellschaft in general and the institute for physical chemistry in particular was certainly novel. The possibilities of working in a well equipped institution, under very favorable conditions, and devoting full time to research were very unusual in those days in Germany. In the interval after World War I till 1933 these men controlled almost all the physical chemistry in Berlin. They were Walter Nernst, Fritz Haber, and Max Bodenstein, and therefore I may be allowed to enlarge upon each of these three scientists.

Read by Gene G. Mannella as part of the Symposium on Inorganic Chemists in the Nuclear Age before the Division of History of Chemistry at the 134th Meeting of the American Chemical Society, Chicago, September, 1958.

### Walter Nernst (1864–1941)

The education of young Nernst was the usual one of a young German physicist. Since his first scientific achievements were made under the guidance of the physicist Friedrich Kohlrausch in Werzburg and Boltzmann and Ettinghausen in Graz, the most important event for his future life was his decision to go to Wilhelm Ostwald in Leipzig in 1887 as an assistant. Even though he was much younger than the three dominating figures of Arrhenius, Ostwald, and van't Hoff, who at this time were in Leipzig, he soon developed as one of the founders of the new discipline, physical chemistry.

*Jr. Walther Nernst.*

In 1891 he became associate professor in Göttingen, in 1895, full professor and department head in Göttingen, and in 1905, professor of physical chemistry in Berlin. In 1922 Nernst became president of the Physikalisch-Technische Reichsanstalt, and in 1924 he returned to pure physics and became the professor of physics of the University of Berlin. So we may say that at the end of his career he turned back to pure physics, but his really important works were practically exclusively devoted to physical chemistry.

His works during his lifetime must be considered overwhelming and, therefore, I must confine myself only to the enduring highlights of his career. I shall draw from Max Bodenstein who wrote some very excellent articles on Nernst and his work. Even his first independent research became an important achievement for electrochemistry. From the assumption that a metal which is immersed in an electrolyte behaves like a reservoir of ions under a characteristic "electrolytic solvation pressure," it was possible to calculate the maximum electric work for this procedure and to bring this in line with the experiments. Along such lines he performed many investigations which are still fundamentals of electrochemistry.

The problem of chemical equilibrium was the second and perhaps even more important achievement of Nernst, and the research in this area led him to discover the third law of thermodynamics, which brought him immortality. The assumption that at the absolute zero the free energy and the heat of formation become identical together with a series of ingenious experi-

ments and theoretical analyses led him to this eminent discovery. Since much needed data were not available, for example, the specific heats of solid substances and gases, he developed for this purpose the vacuum calorimeter and constructed a small hydrogen liquefier so that the desired data could be obtained down to a temperature from which it was possible to extrapolate safely to absolute zero. If anybody did not agree to call his "theorem" the third law of thermodynamics, but only a way of calculating chemical equilibrium from thermodynamic data, combined with much from quantum theory and quantum mechanics (the latter having in principle nothing to do with thermodynamics)—if anybody was bold enough to make such a remark, Nernst would visualize such a man as his very personal enemy. Still, as far as I know, no biography of Nernst has been written which measures up to the performance of such a unique man of genius. His textbook of physical chemistry was first edited in 1893 with many editions following. It was, in the German language, *the* textbook for physical chemistry. Only after 1925 other textbooks came into the foreground like those by A. Eucken and J. Eggert, both of whom were pupils of W. Nernst. The majority of his outstanding works were done before World War I, and with his return to pure physics, his productivity began to fade. His dominant influence in physical chemistry, however, was unchallenged, and it would have been hard for a scientist in Germany who was not accepted by Nernst to succeed.

Nernst was an unusually gifted personality. His combined imagination, objectivity, technical skill, and the theoretical mastery of his material were almost

---

### W. NERNST

Walter Nernst hatte eine Abneigung gegen die Einführung von neuen Einheiten. Als das "Hertz" als Einheit der Schwingung eingeführt wurde, erklärte er ungehalten: "Ich würde vorschlagen, eine Einheit für die Durchflusgeschwindigkeit von 1 Liter pro Sekunde zu wählen und sie ein 'Falstaff' zu nennen."

*From "Chemiker-Anekdoten" (new edition entitled "Was nicht in den Annalen steht"), published by Verlag Chemie, Weinheim/-Bergstrasse, Germany.* (See page 123)

unparalleled even by the outstanding physical chemists in those days. In addition, if he liked, he could be a brilliant teacher or speaker and improvise speeches, but he had certain pecularities which will have to be mentioned. For example, in his lectures he related practically everything to his own work, or works of his pupils, so that a student who attended his lectures got the impression that most of physical chemistry and related fields were worked out by Nernst. I heard the following with my own ears:

The first law of thermodynamics is due to the experience in natural science that we cannot make energy or heat from nothing and that to a certain amount of heat a certain amount of energy is equivalent. The second law of thermodynamics is due to the investigation of a group of very eminent scientists who have shown to what extent under determined conditions heat can be transformed into work. And concerning the third law of thermodynamics—this I have just done myself alone.

But his eloquence and his mastery in discussion sometimes misled him to defend a standpoint which he himself did not accept. Sometimes it seemed that he only enjoyed demonstrating his superior dialectic.

In the physics colloquium in Berlin which was chaired by Max von Laue there were, among other outstanding participants, Einstein and Planck. Nernst obviously had the correct feeling that, compared to the gigantic performances of Einstein and Planck, even his third law of thermodynamics was not entirely equal in importance and, true to his nature, he would not miss an opportunity to object when one of these two scientists made a statement, or to try to direct the discussion to a field in which he felt himself superior. He could do this with so much wit and charm that all, and even those involved, were very amused. Nernst was able to invent a story or innuendo on the spur of the moment and if there was a meeting with scientists who knew him, or with his pupils, at which he did not tell a story or make witty remarks they would be a little disappointed. Because he passed away during the war, there is no adequate biography of Nernst and there is danger that all these anecdotes may become forgotton. It would be a pity if they were lost. Despite all his stories and jokes at the expense of other people, Nernst was a typical "Geheimrat," and I wonder if in his later years, he was close to even one of his pupils. If you met one of the former pupils of Nernst it did not take long before he began to speak of the unique times he had had under Nernst, who inspired him; but his admiration was always superior to his devotion.

## Fritz Haber (1868–1934)

At the same time another of the really great physical chemists was in Berlin. It was of interest for me to learn from Wilstätter's autobiography in which he dedicated a chapter to his old friend Haber, that during his studies, and during the time he worked toward his Ph.D. as an organic chemist, and even in the years afterwards when he was assistant professor, Haber was just a young man with unusual energy and activity. No one who knew Haber at this time would have thought that he would develop into such an outstanding personality. Haber's friend Wilstätter called this period "seven years of detours and errors," and he thought that the reason for this was that Haber was a man who could not fit into poor surroundings. When he came to Karlsruhe where he spent seventeen years of his life (obviously too many), he at least had the influence of Bunte and Engler to whom he was deeply devoted the rest of his life. Haber succeeded in doing a very unusual thing in Karlsruhe. From his base in organic chemistry, he taught himself physical chemistry and performed highly-rated research work in electrochemistry. The greatest moment in his life came when he succeeded in performing his ammonia synthesis from nitrogen and hydrogen in the years before World War I. At this time Haber was a highly esteemed scientist to whom the directorship of the institute of physical chemistry of the Kaiser Wilhelm Gesellschaft was given. Now he became a man of world-wide prestige and after the war was awarded the Nobel Prize for chemistry. In World War I the ammonia synthesis was an important factor because by this means it was possible to compensate for the loss of the nitrates imported from Chile. The nitrates produced from the ammonia by the Haber-Bosch method were not only important for the warfare, but in addition they were needed as fixed nitrogen for fertilizers. This fact saved many millions of people of Germany from near-starvation during World War I. Haber liked to assume this use even more important than the fixed nitrogen for warfare. Haber also played an important role in other fields of the war economy and in the warfare with poisonous gases. He considered

Dr Fritz Haber

himself to be a good German and the defeat affected him very deeply. Above his desk in his home in Berlin hung the picture of Kaiser Wilhelm the Second, with a personal signature of the Emperor; it remained there until 1933, when he left Germany for England.

After World War I he started another huge endeavor—trying to recover gold from sea water since Germany had to pay reparation in foreign currency and gold, which was obviously impossible. This work was not successful because the assay of gold of the waters of the seas as reported in the literature was much too high. Ironically, Haber succeeded in developing a method which would have economically produced gold from the waters of the seas if the data in the literature had been correct. This type of enormous project was probably more in line with his energy and talent for organization than pure research under limited subsidy.

It was, therefore, very fortunate that this technologically-great deed gave him real and ideal backing to develop his institute and organize it in such a way that it became, without a doubt, the leading institution for physical chemistry in those days. Scientists, young and old, and many guests were in contact with Haber's institute. To mention them and to weigh their merits would be difficult and go far beyond the scope of this paper.

The publications of Haber's institute which appeared in various periodicals were edited in book form. · This impressive volume contained progress in almost all fields of physical chemistry. Haber, by his personality, gave tone to the institute. He was wise enough to know that one has to give to the group leaders and also to keen young members of the institute far-reaching scientific freedom to develop an atmosphere of free scientific thinking and enterprise. In later years he made trips away from the institute for weeks or months; when he came back he would call all his pupils and ask them "While I was away who did some nice work that an old man would enjoy?"

In Haber's institute there were different departments. Freundlich headed the department for colloid chemistry, Ladenburg, spectroscopy, Polanyi, kinetics, and to a certain extent all departments did pioneer work in their field. Kallmann was the right hand of Haber in the administration of the institute. His research work included mass spectroscopy and high voltage particle acceleration which tended toward nuclear physics. K. F. Bonhoeffer joined the institute in 1922 after working with Nernst for his Ph.D. in physical chemistry.

Up to this time the problems of thermodynamics had been in the foreground not only in teaching but also in research. But to far-seeing people it became obvious that the problems of pure thermodynamics could not answer many important and interesting questions. It is obviously one of the most noble duties of physical chemistry to make use of the discoveries in pure physics for solving problems of chemistry. This field, on the boundary line between physics and chemistry, which was developed by Ostwald and his contemporaries, and which is always in a state of development, has attracted outstanding scientists, sometimes from the field of physics and sometimes from chemistry. It was obvious after World War I that the time was ripe for some change in attitudes in applying the approaches of new fields to physical chemistry. Band spectroscopy and quantum mechanics became attractive for solving chemical problems in general, and photochemistry and reaction kinetics, to some problems in particular. The combination of nuclear physics and chemistry opened up new directions of investigation. Spectroscopy and quantum mechanics were developed to a large extent in Germany during these times.

Bonhoeffer took full advantage of this situation and as a young scientist produced much outstanding work in a few years on different lines at the institute. I would like just to mention his work on hydrogen atoms, predissociation, parahydrogen, OH radicals, and the paper with Haber in which spectroscopy was used for problems of combustion. Bonhoeffer was perhaps the pupil whom Haber liked most, and Bonhoeffer could not

have shown greater gratitude to Haber than by his last efforts to re-establish in Germany the new institute of physical chemistry of the Max Planck Society at Göttingen. In West Germany this is the successor of Haber's institute in Berlin-Dahlem. Bonhoeffer developed this institute in Haber's spirit and brought it to international recognition in a few years. Each young man who had the opportunity of working close by with Haber had, in addition to his scientific gains in knowledge, the opportunity to learn things which frequently became increasingly important to him in a more general way. From all his advice I have just two comments that I would like to recall. Once Haber said:

It is too bad there are so many people who think only a few days on what problem they will work, then they will work hard for two years and write the whole thing together in one month, instead of spending about equal amounts of effort on these three points.

It is perhaps easier and certainly much more gratifying to work in fields which are entirely novel, if a man can do so. The difficulty of reading through and evaluating the enormous amount of work of others in an older field may stifle any creative productivity.

No one who had ever been in contact with Haber would ever forget his personality. I would like to mention that one of his long-time assistants became so influenced by thoughts and ways of Haber that he not only started to speak and act like Haber but that his handwriting became so similar that it could hardly be distinguished from Haber's. The end of Haber's institute in 1933 was a great loss for physical chemistry and an almost unparalleled shame in the history of natural sciences. It was not only an unparalleled ingratitude with respect to the unique merits of Haber, but there was also a full misunderstanding of the singularity of this institute and the impossibility to regenerate it by will alone.

After the war it was one of the duties of the Kaiser Wilhelm Institute (now Max Planck Society) to honor the memory of Haber. I think his former pupil, J. Jaenicke, is now writing Haber's biography.

## Max Bodenstein (1871–1942)

The third outstanding physical chemist in Berlin at this time was Bodenstein. Bodenstein did not have the brilliance of Nernst, and I think to a certain extent he looked up to Haber. In these days theoretical physics was most highly regarded in Germany, especially in Berlin, perhaps because of the outstanding theoretists like Einstein, Planck, Schrödinger, and von Laue. I think Bodenstein was himself a little under the influence of this almost overemphasis on theory. Even a young scientist who performed practically nothing but was very good in theory was highly esteemed by Bodenstein, but at the same time he himself was one of the most outstanding experimenters, and his skill is still admired. It is hard to understand how Bodenstein was able to study reaction kinetics with almost absolutely pure gases fifty years ago. In those times one did not have dependable high vacuum pumps; liquid air and dry-ice were seldom available. Stopcock grease which had almost no vapor pressure did not exist, and the quality of the glassware was poor compared with the standards of today. Despite all these handicaps

Bodenstein and his pupils performed outstanding work. The reactions which he investigated, like the formation and decomposition of hydrogen iodide, the formation of hydrogen bromide, and in later years the formation of hydrogen chloride and the formation and decomposition of phosgene, were studied in such manner that the results stand today.

He had many pupils who became famous scientists. I would just like to mention S. C. Lind, the dean of radiation chemistry, and G. Kistakowsky at Harvard, who are both very well known. I also appreciate the

good fortune of having been accepted as a Ph.D. candidate by Bodenstein, who gave me the basis for my further experimentation. As time goes on and as kinetics becomes more and more important, I hear people complain sometimes that Bodenstein is one of those who should have received a Nobel Prize.

I would like to mention that Nernst, Haber, Bodenstein, and Bonhoeffer all came from very wealthy families, like the majority of the scientists in physics and chemistry in those days in Germany, especially in Berlin. In those days a professor who was world-famous had an outstanding position in Berlin. He ranked high in society and money was no problem to him. In his wealthiest years Haber was considered to be a multimillionaire.

For an outstanding professor, especially in Berlin, life was full of work which could almost kill a man without exceptional strength. People always expected an outstanding scientific performance from him; he was a member of the Academy of Science in Berlin, had to give lectures, make up examinations, do his share of committee work, and write textbooks. When I was a young student in Berlin I was shocked, watching such a performance.

In those times, even when Berlin was the center of gravity for physical chemistry, the rest of Germany was rich in outstanding scientists and institutes. In Hamburg, Otto Stern developed molecular ray research techniques to a degree of perfection which has not been surpassed today. This was in a city where the University in general and research in particular were not accepted by a large part of the influential people. The institute in Leipzig founded by Ostwald, followed by Leblanc and then by Bonhoeffer, was second only to Berlin and at about the same high level as the Institute in Göttingen. There, following Nernst, Tammann did his pioneer work on metallurgy and was followed by A. Euchen. Euchen was one of the most outstanding pupils of Nernst.

## Today's Perspective

Today it is hard to understand that in the early thirties some prominent scientists thought that physical chemistry had reached a certain endpoint, that the fields which belong to physical chemistry had been developed in their main lines and there were only small remainders. It looked as if it would soon be necessary to look only for complicated unsolved problems. The Raman effect, parahydrogen, and isotope work more or less appeared to be very interesting residues. The field of radioactivity was not acknowledged a discipline belonging to physical chemistry at that time. The work of Otto Hahn and his group in Berlin-Dahlem, of G. von Hevesey, and F. Paneth had not been in the usual trend of research, and only a few may have surmised that this was pioneer work in preparation for future developments. The stagnation in physical chemistry was only temporary. In a short time discoveries like the artificial splitting of atoms, the neutron, deuterium, artificial radioactivity, practical methods to separate isotopes, and the application of electronics for experimentation in physical chemistry were made. These gave a feeling that in the near future things would be in a realm of possibility not previously imagined. Indeed in the early thirties a new wave of problems came from physics to physical chemistry with the only difference being (as seen from the German point of view) that in all these discoveries and developments Germany was participating to only a minor extent. This may have been just a little fluctuation. But I do not think that it would be correct to explain this fact in this way. I had the opportunity in the years 1933–34 to work in Rutherford's Institute, at Cambridge, England, and when I looked at the way people performed their experiments and the way they overcame experimental difficulties, I got the impression that there was nothing superior in Germany and that the discovery of deuterium by Urey did not just come about by good luck. Perhaps people in Germany had become a little too self-complacent and underestimated the ability of foreign countries. This would certainly have been overcome and Germany would have regained her role if the "Third Reich" had not created a discontinuity in scientific development which has not been overcome even today. I think it is a real lesson for other countries to realize this and not forget it.

———————— ✦ ————————

CHEMIKER ANEKDOTEN. Nernst had a phobia against dragging in new units. When the hertz was introduced as a unit of frequency, he boldly proposed, "Let's have a unit for rate of throughput, 1 liter per second, and let's call it 1 falstaff." (See page 120)

**Maurice W. Lindauer**
Valdosta State College
Valdosta, Georgia

# The Evolution of the Concept of Chemical Equilibrium from 1775 to 1923

The explanation of the wide diversity of chemical change has long challenged man's ingenuity as it continues to do to this day. A large part of the history of chemistry is the result of man's attempts to meet this particular challenge, and much of our present knowledge of chemistry grew out of such investigations. Although chemical equilibrium is no longer looked upon as a revelation of the forces which control chemical change, much of its development arose out of just such an expectation. It is the purpose of this paper to trace some of the major attitudes and ideas which led to the present concept of chemical equilibrium.

## Chemical Affinity and Early Methods of Its Evaluation

The idea of affinity, as an expression of the tendency of substances to enter into chemical combination, was introduced sometime during the 13th century by Albertus Magnus, who reflected the earlier view of Hippocrates that chemical action is the result of a similarity or kinship between the reacting substances (1, 2). Walden (3) reported that the alchemist Geber, also about the 13th century, arranged a number of metals in several primitive activity series according to their behaviors toward sulfur, mercury, and oxygen; later, Paracelsus, Stahl, and others employed similar series. In 1718, E. F. Geoffroy enunciated his "Tables des differents rapports" (affinity table) in which substances were arranged in vertical columns in order of decreasing affinity, going down the column, with respect to the substance at the head of the column. A considerable amount of affinity data was compiled during the 18th century, and this activity was climaxed with the concept of elective affinity as enunciated by T. Bergman in 1775, in a treatise entitled "De Attractionibus Electivis." Bergman concluded that chemical combinations were the result of the elective affinities which depended solely upon the nature of the reacting substances. Bergman further unified this concept by specifying that affinities were to be determined on the basis of displacement reactions. That is, if the addition of a substance, C, to another substance, AB, produced the substance AC and eliminated substance B, then it can be concluded that substance C has a greater affinity for substance A than does substance B. Bergman also noted that in some displacement reactions, the elimina-

tion of B from substance AB required several times the stoichiometric amount of substance C; but considering the basic requirement of displacement, Bergman still maintained that the affinity of substance A for substance C was greater than that for substance B. Bergman's concept of elective affinity was widely accepted, and it did much to systematize the knowledge of chemical reactions of that day. It is interesting to note that the displacement reaction still finds use in modern inorganic chemistry, although not as a method of first choice, in classifying the stability order of coordination complexes (4).

## C. F. Wenzel and the Influence of Quantity

In 1777, two years after Bergman's publication, C. F. Wenzel published a paper entitled "Lehre von der chemischen Affinität der Körper" in which he attempted to estimate chemical affinities by noting the rate at which different metals were dissolved by various acids. In his experiments, Wenzel observed that the rate at which metals were dissolved was influenced by the quantity of acid as well as by the nature of the acid. However, Wenzel's observations did not attract the attention of his contemporaries, and his work was forgotten.

Wenzel's work illustrates several of the principles which J. B. Conant, in his book "On Understanding Science," calls the "tactics and strategy of science." Two principles which are among the requirements for the acceptance of an idea or concept are (1) the proposal must fit the times, and (2) the proposal must be better than its predecessor. Thus, in spite of the limitations of the elective affinity concept, it is still more general, and hence more acceptable, than the fact that the quantity of acid influences the rate at which metals are dissolved. This illustrates the second of Conant's principles in that calling attention to the shortcomings of a concept is not sufficient, in itself, to displace an established mental construct or concept. Furthermore, Wenzel's observations preceded the similar one of Wilhelmy, made in a much more sophisticated era, by some 70 years, and even Wilhelmy's observation was not fully appreciated until later. In view of the supporting concepts (which were developed long after Wenzel) that were necessary for the acceptance and understanding of the influence of the quantity of reactants on the outcome of chemical reactions, there is little reason to credit Wenzel with a significant foresight in the matter of chemical equilibrium. Instead, it is to his credit that he published an objective report of his observations in spite of the contradiction with the then popularly accepted idea of elective affinity.

The author is indebted to the National Science Foundation for the opportunity to attend the Academic Year Institute at Harvard University, where this work was undertaken; and he especially wishes to acknowledge the advice and encouragement offered by Dr. Leonard K. Nash of the Harvard Chemistry Department.

## C. L. Berthollet and the Influence of Quantity

In June of 1799 during Napoleon's Egyptian campaign, Claude Louis Berthollet, one of Napoleon's most trusted advisors, read a paper before the National Institute of Egypt in which he called attention to the fact that chemical combinations are also influenced by other principles in addition to that of chemical affinity. Among the many principles which he noted, Berthollet is remembered mostly for his emphasis on the influence of the quantity of reactants upon the course of chemical combinations.

J. W. Mellor (5) strongly suggested that Berthollet's ideas on the effect of quantity stem from Berthollet's proposed explanation of the large trona (sodium carbonate) deposits found on the shores of the Natron Lakes in Egypt. Mellor explained that Berthollet recognized in this natural phenomenon the reaction

$$CaCO_3 + 2NaCl \rightarrow CaCl_2 + Na_2CO_3,$$

as being the reverse of that predicted by the elective affinities, and that Berthollet concluded that this reversal was the result of the large quantity of calcium carbonate present on the shores of these lakes which reacted with the sodium chloride brought in from the rivers. Upon examining Berthollet's later writings, it does not seem reasonable that the trona episode was entirely responsible for his ideas on the effect of quantity. Berthollet stated, in a footnote on the opening page of his short treatise entitled "Recherches sur les lois de l'affinité" ("Researches"), which was published in 1801 upon his return to Paris, that "The reading of this Treatise was commenced in the Institution of Cairo, June, 7th year" (6), but he does not give any direct indication of the origin of his ideas. In this treatise, he gives but little attention to the problem of the trona deposits, and this is discussed rather late in the book. Furthermore, he discussed the natural trona deposits in connection with the influence of efflorescence on the outcome of chemical reactions. In this discussion, which he also repeated in a somewhat modified form in a lengthy two-volume exposition of his ideas (published in 1803 under the title, "Essai de statique chimique"), Berthollet mentioned three and possibly four requirements for the formation of natural trona deposits; these are "1st, a sand containing a great quantity of carbonate of lime; 2nd, humidity; 3rd, muriate of soda. I have also remarked that reeds contribute much to its (i.e., trona) formation" (7) Berthollet went on to say that a small amount of trona is formed in solution as a result of the action of the large quantity of calcium carbonate and the sodium chloride, but he emphasized that the large trona deposits are the result of the trona being removed from further action (e.g., the decomposition into calcium carbonate) by the process of efflorescence. If the trona episode was singularly responsible for his ideas, as Mellor implied, then it seems that he would have devoted much more attention to the subject than he did. It is interesting to note that in his "Researches" but not in his later "Essay," Berthollet described an unsuccessful attempt to demonstrate the formation of sodium carbonate under laboratory conditions. Berthollet rationalized the failure of the trial on the basis of insufficient time; the deposition of trona, he explained, required a long period of time. He therefore dismissed the experiment—but not his conclusions. Thus, it appears that Berthollet did not attach the significance to the trona episode which Mellor implied, and it seems reasonable that his ideas on the influence of quantity on chemical reactions were at least in the embryonic stages of development before he ever went to Egypt. His presence in Napoleon's retinue indicates the extent of his prominence even at a time preceding the events for which he is best known. Early in his "Researches" (Art. I, No. 3), Berthollet criticized Bergman's failure to consider the influence of the quantity of substance required to accomplish displacement. It appears that Berthollet was fairly well acquainted with Bergman's theory before he went to Egypt, and his ideas may well have originated from an earlier dissatisfaction with Bergman's ideas. The fact that his writings call attention to many principles which influence chemical combinations indicates his general dissatisfaction with the single principle of elective affinity as Bergman proposed and lends support to the contention expressed above.

Whereas Bergman's theory was a collection of independent affinities, Berthollet attempted in his "Researches" (Art. I, No. 1) to unify the understanding of chemical phenomena by the consideration of all of the forces which effect such phenomena. In order to emphasize the existence of such forces, he called attention to experimental results which were contrary to the predictions of the elective affinities. In an attempt to explain these contradictions, Berthollet performed a number of experiments whose results he interpreted as being due to the effect of the quantities of substances. In Art. I, No. 5, Berthollet stated:

It is my purpose to prove in the following sheets, that elective affinity, in general, does not act as a determinate force, by which one body separates completely another from a combination; but that, in all combinations and decompositions produced by elective affinity, there takes place a partition of the base, or subject of the combination, between the two bodies whose actions are opposed; and that the proportions of this partition are determined, not solely by the difference of energy in the affinities, but also by the difference of the quantities of the bodies; so that an excess of quantity of the body whose affinity is the weaker, compensates for the weakness of affinity.

In Article II of this same treatise, he cites a number of experiments which, according to him, prove the above assertion. These experiments are summarized in Table 1. The second and fourth experiments are obvious misinterpretations in the light of present chemical knowledge, but this is characteristic of early work in all fields; as a whole, Berthollet's experiments were quite reasonable. Berthollet did not indicate the

### Table 1. A Summary of Article II of Berthollet's "Researches"

*Experiments which prove that in Elective Affinities, the Bodies whose Powers are opposed, divide between them the Body which is the subject of the Combination.*

| Expt. | Reactants and their proportions | Products |
|---|---|---|
| 1. | 1 part $BaSO_4$, 1 part $KOH$ | $K_2SO_4$ |
| 2. | 1 part $K_2SO_4$, 1 part $CaO$ | $CaSO_4$ and $K_2SO_4$ |
| 3. | 1 part $CaC_2O_4$, 2 parts $KOH$ | $K_2C_2O_4$ |
| 4. | 1 part $CaC_2O_4$, 2 parts $HNO_3$ | $Ca(NO_3)_2$ |
| 5. | 1 part $Ca_3(PO_4)_2$, 2 parts $KOH$ | $K_3PO_4$ |
| 6. | 1 part $KOH$, 1 part $CaCO_3$ | $K_2CO_3$ |
| 7. | 1 part $NaOH$, 1 part $K_2SO_4$ | $Na_2SO_4$ and $K_2SO_4$ |

quantities of the products obtained in these experiments, except for the first experiment in which he stated that the amount of barium sulfate decomposed was small. This omission of the quantity of product seems odd in view of Berthollet's emphasis on this principle, but then the concept of elective affinity adequately explained that aspect (i.e., the reverse of Berthollet's reactions) so that further explanation was deemed unnecessary.

Berthollet must be given credit for having devised a clever experimental scheme. It must be remembered that he regarded salts as combinations of the entire acid and the entire base, and not as combinations of parts of the acid and base as we now regard them to be. In the fourth experiment, he demonstrated the partition of a base between two acids by the isolation of calcium nitrate from the mixture which still contained some of the original calcium oxalate; therefore, he concluded that both the nitric acid and the oxalic acid had divided the base between them. One is tempted to wonder what Berthollet might have concluded had he used an excess of nitric acid in this experiment. In other experiments, he demonstrated the partition of two bases between a single acid. In his attempt to establish the universal validity of his idea, Berthollet was careful to demonstrate that the idea applied to a number of different situations.

Toward the end of Article II of his "Researches," Berthollet gave an explanation (No. 10) of chemical reactions that bears a remarkable resemblance to the present concept of the dynamic nature of chemical equilibrium:

It follows as a consequence of the preceding observations, that the action of a substance which tends to decompose a combination, diminishes in proportion as its saturation advances; for this substance may, in such case, be composed of two parts, one of which is saturated, and the other free. The former may be considered as inert, and as unconnected with the latter, the quantity of which diminishes according as the saturation advances; whilst, on the contrary, the action of that which has been eliminated, increases in proportion to the augmentation of its quantity, until equilibrium of the contending forces ends the operation, and limits the effect.

As Berthollet's statement indicates, the term equilibrium was used to denote a balance of chemical forces, exactly as the term is used in mechanics. Having demonstrated such remarkable foresight, we may wonder why the ideas of chemical equilibrium were mired for over 50 years before another significant advance appeared.

In his emphasis on the effect of quantity of substance, Berthollet concluded that it was possible to obtain combinations of different compositions simply by varying the proportions of reactants. For example, in Volume 2 of his "Essay," he regarded mercury(I) and mercury(II) compounds as the extremes of oxidation and that all intermediate compositions were also possible. It was over this "law of variable composition" that Berthollet became involved in the famous controversy with Proust, in which Proust and the law of definite proportions emerged victorious. Several years later, Dalton published his famous atomic theory which readily explained the law of definite proportions and the law of multiple proportions, but not the law of variable composition. With this, Berthollet's law of variable composition fell into disrepute, and as a result, chemists no longer seemed to give any serious consideration to Berthollet's ideas. Several writers have expressed regret over the rejection of Berthollet's valid ideas on mass action along with his erroneous idea of variable composition (8, 9).

While it is true that Berthollet's ideas were generally ignored by his contemporaries, the idea of the effect of quantity on chemical reactions was kept alive well into the middle of the 19th century through the efforts of a number of prominent chemists. The first of these to perpetuate this idea was Gay-Lussac, who had formerly worked under Berthollet and who is mentioned in both the "Researches" and the "Essay." Gay-Lussac's articles (10) continued to remind chemists of this effect as late as 1839. In the early 1830's, Berzelius (11) also commented favorably on Berthollet's ideas of mass action. In the 1840's, H. Rose (12) demonstrated the same effect of quantity that Berthollet mentioned 40 years earlier. Rose demonstrated that alkaline earth sulfides were decomposed by water into hydrogen sulfide and calcium hydroxide in contradiction to the predictions of their elective affinities.

At this point, it is worth while to compare briefly the contributions of Wenzel and Berthollet. Whereas Wenzel simply called attention to a phenomenon which was inconsistent with elective affinities, Berthollet attempted to rationalize such phenomena in terms of a more inclusive theory. It must be remembered that Berthollet was not trying to completely discredit and supplant Bergman's theory; he simply insisted that chemical combinations were affected by other principles in addition to that of elective affinity. The chemical literature of the first half of the 19th century contains many papers dealing with Berthollet's idea of mass action, and the interested reader is directed to an excellent study of this subject by Holmes (13).

### The Influence of Quantity in the Period 1850–1864

The first widely accepted demonstration of the effect of mass action was reported in 1850 by Ludwig Wilhelmy, who showed that the rate of inversion of cane sugar in the presence of a large and essentially constant amount of water is proportional to the amount of sugar. This work is generally regarded as one of the earliest instances of a quantitative study of chemical kinetics and a serious consideration of the effect of mass action on chemical reactions. In 1855, Gladstone (14) studied the now-classic reaction of iron(III) ion and thiocyanate ion, and he noted that changes in the amount of the colored substance resulted from changes made in the amounts of the reactants.

In 1862, attention was again drawn to the effect of mass action by M. Berthelot and Pean de St. Giles, who studied the esterification of acetic acid by ethanol. In these studies, they showed that the rate of formation of the ester is proportional to the amount of the reacting substances, and that the same equilibrium point is reached by the hydrolysis of ethyl acetate, the reverse of the esterification reaction.

The experiments performed in this period constitute an important milestone in the development of the concept of chemical equilibrium, because from this point on, mass action was recognized and accepted as an important factor in the outcome of chemical reactions. It is interesting to note that the experiments of Wilhelmy, Gladstone, and Berthelot and St. Giles can still be found in many of the current chemistry laboratory manuals of general and physical chemistry.

## Guldberg and Waage's Law of Mass Action

In 1864, C. M. Guldberg and P. Waage of the University of Christiania published a general law of mass action in their native Norwegian, and later, in 1867, they republished this article in French (15). In this paper, Guldberg and Waage introduced a new term called "active mass," which is essentially the same as the present term, concentration. Berthollet introduced the term mass into chemistry, and he defined mass as the product of the weight of substance required to produce a certain degree of saturation (16). In terms of acid-base reactions, Berthollet's mass was simply proportional to the present equivalent weight. Berthollet also spoke of a "sphere of action" in connection with chemical combinations, which referred to a proximity requirement of the reactants. Both the sphere of action and mass were important in the work of Guldberg and Waage who effectively combined these two ideas in their law of mass action. Guldberg and Waage reasoned that the effect of quantity was due to the amount of reactant within a sphere of action in which the combination could take place. Not knowing exactly how to estimate this sphere of action, Guldberg and Waage decided to use the space in which the masses of reactants was contained. Hence, the term active mass merely refers to the mass per unit volume.

Guldberg and Waage applied their ideas to incomplete or easily reversible reactions, for which they stated that the chemical forces which give rise to combination, are proportional to the active mass product of the reactants, and the state of equilibrium results from an equality of the chemical forces exerted by the opposing reactions, i.e., the forward and reverse reactions. For example, in the general reaction,

$$A + B \rightleftharpoons C + D \qquad (1)$$

the chemical force in the forward direction is

$$k(A)(B) \qquad (2)$$

and the chemical force in the reverse direction is

$$k'(C)(D) \qquad (3)$$

and the condition of equilibrium is

$$k(A)(B) = k'(C)(D) \qquad (4)$$

where $(A)$, $(B)$, $(C)$, and $(D)$ represent the respective active masses of the substances A, B, C, and D. The constants $k$ and $k'$ were called coefficients of affinity, following a usage established by R. W. Bunsen (17) in 1853. It should be noted that these equations represent chemical force, and not reaction velocity which was later represented by these same equations.

The influence of Newtonian mechanics appears throughout this early work on chemical equilibrium, and the idea that chemical combinations are the result of mutual attractive forces acting between the reactants is implicit in the term affinity. Berthollet regarded these forces as being similar to gravitational force. The primary interest was in chemical affinity, the driving force responsible for chemical reactions. While

it was well known that velocity is related to force, there do not seem to have been any significant attempts before 1865 to relate velocity of chemical reactions with the affinities of the reactants (18).

The law of mass action, as expressed in equation (4), aroused considerable interest in the evaluation of the affinity coefficients. After all, this expression offered for the first time some promise of the quantitative evaluation of affinity, a goal which had defied measurement for many years. In fact, much of the scientific activity of the 19th century can be characterized by the determination of coefficients of all sorts, such as coefficients of linear expansion, of cubical expansion, of resistivity, of electrical and thermal conductivities, and many others. Most of these coefficients proved to be of greater value to technology than to science. Underlying the determination of these coefficients was the hope that, somehow, a grand synthesis of some sort could be derived which would explain these phenomena. Likewise, the determination of affinity coefficients held forth the promise of explaining the mysterious phenomenon of chemical affinity.

## M. Berthelot and J. Thomsen and Their Ideas

The chemical forces implied by the law of mass action, and hence the related affinity coefficients, were not directly measurable, and therefore a considerable effort was devoted to a search for an indirect method of evaluating these coefficients. W. Ostwald, in his Masters dissertation (19) in 1877, pointed out that the ratio of the affinity coefficients, (approximately the equilibrium constant) could be computed readily from the active masses present under equilibrium conditions. However, at that time, such a ratio was of only secondary importance; the values of the coefficients themselves were of primary interest. In this connection, it is necessary to mention the ideas of M. Berthelot in Paris and J. Thomsen in Copenhagen, who regarded the heat evolved by chemical reactions as a measure of the chemical affinities.

In order to appreciate the contributions of Berthelot and Thomsen, it is worth while to consider the general methods by which forces can be measured. One method of measuring force is the relatively direct static method, and another method is the more indirect dynamic method. In the static method, the force to be measured is connected to a known and variable force, such as a spring, and the system is allowed to come to equilibrium. In the equilibrium condition, the two forces are equal in magnitude, and the amount of the unknown force is determined directly by observing the amount of known force required to effect an equilibrium. Weighing objects with a simple spring scale is an example of the static method. Chemical reactions, however, are not amenable to this type of measurement. In the dynamic method, a force is allowed to do work, and the amount of work done is measured, and the force can then be computed from the amount of work done. Around the middle of the 19th century two important relationships were established which enabled workers to measure the amount of work done by a chemical reaction; these were Hess's law of constant heat summation, and Joule's mechanical equivalent of heat. It occurred to both Berthelot and Thomsen that the heat evolved by a chemical reaction was due to the operation of the chemical forces, and therefore, this heat of reaction should be a measure of the chemical affinity. Thomsen pointed out that Hess's law followed as a consequence of the law of conservation of energy, and that the heat of reaction is the result of the difference of energy content of a chemical system before and after a chemical reaction. As such, the heat of reaction reflects the chemical affinity involved in the reaction. Berthelot expressed a similar view, which he called the "principle of maximum work," in which heat was liberated only from reactions which occurred spontaneously. The erroneous ideas of Thomsen and Berthelot seem understandable and pardonable when it is considered that the second law of thermodynamics, the basis of our present understanding of chemical equilibrium, was being formalized by Clausius at this time (ca. 1867).

Relative to the earlier discussion of Berthollet's contributions, it is interesting to note that during the 1860's there was a revival of interest in his writings. Lothar Meyer's widely used textbook, "Modern Theories of Chemistry," includes a six-page discussion of Berthollet in the introduction, and many references are made to him in connection with the effect of mass action. Julius Thomsen was also very much aware of Berthollet's work as is indicated by a paper which he published in *Poggendorff's Annalen* in 1869 entitled "On Berthollet's 'Theory of Affinity'." There is also a certain similarity in the work of Thomsen and Berthollet in that both workers devoted a lot of attention to reactions of acids and bases.

Thomsen did a great deal of experimental work on the thermic effects, as he called them, of neutralization reactions and mixtures of salt solutions, but his interests were focused more on chemical affinity than on chemical equilibrium. Both Thomsen and Berthelot are now regarded as the founders of thermochemistry, but they should also be remembered as important contributors in the development of the concept of chemical equilibrium.

## J. G. van't Hoff and Chemical Equilibrium

Among the many important contributions to chemistry made by van't Hoff, his ideas concerning chemical affinity and chemical equilibrium are perhaps the most significant, but strangely enough, these contributions are among the lesser known works of this great chemist. The mention of his name immediately brings to mind his great contributions to structural chemistry and osmotic pressure, but usually not chemical equilibrium. In fact, our present concept of chemical equilibrium differs little from the form in which it is presented in van't Hoff's "Studies in Chemical Dynamics," which was published in 1884. His contributions in this area range from the double-arrow innovation, still universally used to indicate the dynamic nature of chemical equilibrium, to the well-known van't Hoff equation which described the variation in the equilibrium constant as a function of the temperature.

Although Guldberg and Waage are generally credited as the first to have developed the law of mass action, van't Hoff also developed this same law independently and from a different basis. Van't Hoff derived the law of mass action on the basis of reaction velocities, the velocities of the forward and the reverse reactions being equal at equilibrium. This is exactly the explanation of the dynamic nature of chemical equilibrium and the derivation of the law of mass action that is found in practically every introductory college chemistry textbook. Guldberg and Waage also used the reaction velocity concept, but their original concept of chemical equilibrium involved the idea of a balance of opposing forces (20). Through the consolidation of chemical kinetics and thermodynamics, van't Hoff provided the law of mass action with a more logical basis than it previously had.

The first two sections (120 pages) of van't Hoff's "Studies in Chemical Dynamics" are devoted to a thorough discussion of chemical kinetics in a treatment that differs little from that in many present day physical chemistry textbooks. The third, fourth, and fifth sections of this book deal with "The Influence of Temperature on Chemical Change," "Chemical Equilibrium," and "Affinity." We must recognize that van't Hoff was equipped with the very powerful tool of thermodynamics, which was unavailable to many of the earlier workers.

In this treatise, van't Hoff asserted that the maximum work done by a chemical process could be regarded as a measure of the chemical affinity. At long last, the illusive affinity had been objectively defined! Van't Hoff defined chemical affinity as the maximum amount of work, $A$, that could be obtained from a chemical process minus the amount of work required to maintain the system at constant volume. The symbol $A$ has long been used to represent the Helmholtz work function, but Sackur (21) wrote that this symbol represented affinity. It is often believed that this symbol was introduced as an abbreviation of the German word for work, *arbeit*. It seems that during the latter part of the 19th century this symbol was used somewhat loosely to represent either work or its chemical equivalent, affinity. Van't Hoff certainly used the symbol $A$, but he called it ". . . the work which can be done by the force of affinity which brings about a chemical reaction. . ." (22). Van't Hoff also recognized that the second law of thermodynamics imposed certain restrictions upon the nature of the process by which the maximum amount of work can be obtained, namely, that the process must be carried out reversibly and isothermally; van't Hoff was careful to consider both of these restrictions, particularly the influence of temperature. He pointed out that the law of mass action is valid only for constant temperature conditions, and that the influence of temperature on the equilibrium constant can be determined from considerations involving the second law of thermodynamics. By considering equilibria in terms of a reversible cycle of operations, van't Hoff derived the equation,

$$\frac{d\ln K}{dT} = \frac{q}{2T^2} \qquad (5)$$

where $q$ is "the quantity of heat which is absorbed when a unit quantity of the first system (i.e., the reactants) is converted into the second (i.e., products) without any external work being performed" (23). In his "Studies," van't Hoff applied the law of mass action and the "van't Hoff equation," equation (5), to a variety of situations such as heterogeneous and homogeneous equilibrium of several kinds and also reactions for which $q = 0$, and others for which $q \gtrless 0$. Later in this same work, he enunciated his "principle of mobile equilibrium" in the following statement: "Every equilibrium between two different conditions of matter (systems) is displaced by lowering the temperature, at constant volume, towards that system the formation of which evolves heat" (24). He also showed that this principle applied to all possible cases of both chemical and physical equilibria.

By making the appropriate substitutions for the case of physical equilibria (i.e., changes of state) the van't Hoff equation becomes identical with the special form of the Clausius-Clapeyron equation. Van't Hoff also showed that the conclusions of both Berthollet and Arrhenius were only special cases of his more general formulation. However, van't Hoff's greatest triumph was in the derivation of the well-known reaction isotherm, which states that for the general reaction,

$$aA + bB \rightarrow cC + dD, \qquad (6)$$

the maximum work is

$$A = RT \ln K - RT \ln \frac{C_C{}^c C^d{}_D}{C_A{}^a C_B{}^b} \qquad (7)$$

where $C_A$, $C_B$, $C_C$, and $C_D$ represent concentrations, or partial pressures of the substances A, B, C, and D respectively. Thus in the case where all of the substances are present at unit concentration, the equilibrium constant, $K$, is a direct measure of the maximum work, $A$, and the related affinity. By partial differentiation of the reaction isotherm equation, followed by appropriate substitution, van't Hoff obtained the familiar Helmholtz equation,

$$A = q - T \frac{\partial A}{\partial T} \qquad (8)$$

The reaction isotherm and affinity were the subjects of the great interest in the study of equilibria of every imaginable sort during the late 19th century; and it should also be mentioned that van't Hoff, along with Helmholtz, did much to stimulate the great interest on the potential measurement method of determining maximum work.

Chemistry is indebted to van't Hoff for his consolidation of chemical kinetics, thermodynamics, and physical measurements in the elucidation of chemical phenomena; and therefore he must be regarded as one of the greatest founders of physical chemistry.

### J. Willard Gibbs and Chemical Equilibrium

It is well known that Gibbs, in the 1870's, conceived an even more general approach to chemical equilibrium than van't Hoff's; but his work was obscured, for the most part, by the abstract form in which it was presented. It was several years after van't Hoff had published his "Studies," that a few workers, notably Roozeboom, recognized the significance of the work of Gibbs and showed that the earlier conclusions of van't Hoff and others could be derived on the basis of the thermodynamic potentials of Gibbs. By and large, chemical equilibrium is still presented along the lines

of van't Hoff's arguments; and it is only recently that thermodynamic potentials have appeared in undergraduate physical chemistry textbooks.

### G. N. Lewis and Chemical Equilibrium

In 1923, G. N. Lewis and M. Randall published their now classic "Thermodynamics" which was largely responsible for the widespread application of thermodynamics to the study of chemical reactions and chemical equilibrium in this country. The "maximum work" of van't Hoff later gave way to the term "free energy" which was coined by Helmholtz. Because of the chemist's greater interest in constant pressure than in constant volume (in earlier years), the so-called Gibbs free energy was introduced. At the suggestion of G. N. Lewis this free energy was defined as "the work available for use"; therefore when a system at constant temperature passes spontaneously from one state to another, the maximum useful work which becomes available represents the decrease in the free energy of the system. This decrease can be taken as a measure of the affinity of the chemical process (25). Lewis actually makes very little reference to the term affinity; in many respects, the term free energy has replaced chemical affinity as the driving force of chemical reactions.

In 1907, Lewis introduced the concepts of activity and fugacity to replace the less adequate one of concentration, in the rigorous definition of chemical equilibrium (26). Lewis defined the condition of equilibrium as the state of a system in which the fugacity, and hence the related activity, of a given substance is the same in each phase or part of the system. The concepts of activity and fugacity were devised to take into account the fact that mass action generally does not vary linearly with concentration as was assumed by earlier workers.

The concept of activity is responsible for the attempts of a number of workers, such as Debye, Hückel, Onsager, Harned, and others, to devise better theories of solutions; and in this respect activity played a role analogous to that of Berthollet's mass. Thus, this brief historical account illustrates another of Conant's principles, namely, that an important function of a concept is to suggest and stimulate further investigations.

### Conclusion

In the historical development of the concept of chemical equilibrium there are a number of events which stand out as significant contributions to our present understanding of the concept. These are (1) the recognition and acceptance of the influence of the amount of reactant on chemical reactions, (2) the quantitative formulation of this effect in the law of mass action, (3) rationalization of the effect of mass by chemical kinetics and thermodynamics, (4) refinement of the law of mass action with the introduction of activities, and (5) the wide application of chemical thermodynamics to equilibrium situations.

There is a tendency among many students of chemistry to regard the ideas and activities of the 19th century workers as being entirely obsolete and therefore worthless as far as understanding of modern chemistry is concerned. Such an attitude indicates a gross misunderstanding of the objective of a historical study; the purpose of a historical study is to improve our understanding of the present. For example, if we consult almost any college general chemistry textbook, we find that both Bergman's theory and Berthollet's idea of mass action are, in essence, present in the discussion of the factors which affect the extent of equilibrium-type chemical reactions. To say, as do modern textbooks, that the extent of reaction depends on the nature of the reacting substances is simply restating Bergman's statements about elective affinities. To say that the extent of chemical reaction depends on the concentration of the reacting substances is simply a refinement of Berthollet's statements on mass action. In a sense the late Wendell M. Latimer's book, "Oxidation Potentials," is the 20th century equivalent of Bergman's 18th century classic on elective affinities. The term affinity is still encountered occasionally, and its usage today seems to be more prevalent among British chemists. However, this is not to say that the concept of chemical affinity has fallen into disuse. Instead, the concept of affinity still survives in more sophisticated forms and under a variety of names. For example, the terms nucleophilic, electrophilic, dienophilic, and electron affinity are all widely used to designate specific types of combinations.

The concept of chemical equilibrium developed as a byproduct of studies directed toward the understanding of chemical affinity, and today this concept serves many important utilitarian roles in both chemical science and technology. Certainly chemistry would not be the science it is today without the concept of chemical equilibrium; on the other hand, its progenitor, chemical affinity, continues to challenge the minds of chemists and physicists to new heights of understanding of the age-old phenomena of chemical combinations.

## Literature Cited

(1) PARTINGTON, J. R., "A Short History of Chemistry," Harper and Brothers, New York, 1960, p. 322.
(2) FINDLAY, A., "A Hundred Years of Chemistry," The Macmillan Co., New York, 1937, p. 110.
(3) WALDEN, P. (translated by R. Oesper), J. CHEM. EDUC., 31, 27 (1954).
(4) COATES, G. E., "Organometallic Compounds," 2nd ed., Methuen and Co., Ltd., London, 1960, p. 346.
(5) MELLOR, J. W., "Chemical Statics and Dynamics," Longmans, Green, & Co., New York, 1904, p. 177.
(6) BERTHOLLET, C. L. (translated by M. Farrell), "Researches into the Laws of Chemical Affinity," Philip H. Nicklin and Co., Baltimore, 1809, p. 1.
(7) BERTHOLLET, C. L. (translated by B. Lambert), "Essay on Chemical Statics," J. Mawman, London, 1804.
(8) MELLOR, J. W., op. cit., p. 178.
(9) MEYER, L. (translated by P. P. Bedson and W. C. Williams), "Modern Theories of Chemistry," 5th ed., Longmans, Green, & Co., New York, 1888, p. 452.
(10) MELLOR, J. W., op. cit., p. 179.
(11) PARTINGTON, J. R., op. cit., p. 323.
(12) MELLOR, J. W., op. cit., p. 180.
(13) HOLMES, F. L., Chymia, vol. 8 (in press).
(14) MELLOR, J. W., op. cit., p. 182.
(15) MELLOR, J. W., op. cit., p. 183.
(16) BERTHOLLET, C. L., "Researches into the Laws of Chemical Affinity," Philip H. Nicklin and Co., Baltimore, 1809, p. 5.
(17) MEYER, L., op. cit., p. 458.
(18) GUGGENHEIM, E. A., J. CHEM. EDUC., 33, 544 (1956).
(19) MEYER, L., op. cit., p. 423.
(20) MOORE, F. G., "A History of Chemistry," 3rd ed., McGraw-Hill Book Co., New York, 1939, p. 372.
(21) SACKUR, O. (translated by G. E. Gibson), "Thermochemistry and Thermodynamics," The Macmillan Co., London, 1917, p. 317.
(22) VAN'T HOFF, J. H. (translated by T. Evan), "Studies in Chemical Dynamics," Chemical Publishing Co., Easton, Pa., 1896, p. 251.
(23) VAN'T HOFF, J. H., op. cit., p. 148.
(24) VAN'T HOFF, J. H., op. cit., p. 123.
(25) LEWIS, G. N. AND RANDALL, M., "Thermodynamics," McGraw-Hill Book Co., New York, 1923, p. 584.
(26) LEWIS, G. N., Proc. Amer. Acad. Arts. Sci., 43, 260, 261, 284 (1907).

## American Students in Ostwald's Lab

The American contingent at Ostwald's laboratory in Leipzig (1904–05). Reading left to right: Colin G. Fink, Samuel C. Lind, W. T. Metcalf, John P. Mitchell, Arthur B. Lamb, G. V. Sammet, William C. Bray, Thomas F. Rutter, and William H. Sloan. [Reprinted from J. CHEM. EDUC., 36, 262 (1959).]

# *A* STUDY *of* EQUATIONS *of* STATE

## GEORGE WOOLSEY

Valencia High School, Placentia, California

THE study of the changes of volume of liquids and gases with changes of pressure and temperature has been the subject of experimental and theoretical investigation for many years. As the technic for work with higher pressures and with lower and higher temperatures has improved, the range of experimental determinations has increased tremendously. With this increased experimental range, the labor of completely covering the entire experimentally possible field for all liquids and gases has become prohibitive. Consequently, the use of equations of state for the purpose of interpolation and, in some cases, for extrapolation from experimentally known values becomes increasingly important. And, as the number of known fluids becomes greater it becomes increasingly desirable, if possible, to devise equations which are applicable to all normally acting substances.

That this subject of pressure-volume-temperature relationships is of considerable importance is shown by its many theoretical and practical applications. Many thermodynamic investigations depend upon a knowledge of change of specific heats with changes of pressure or temperature, and this knowledge in turn depends upon accurate values of coefficients of expansion. Designers and operators of distillation and compressor equipment, refrigeration engineers, and, in fact, everyone concerned with the properties of liquids and gases over wide ranges of pressure and temperature have need for as much exact and definite information on this subject as can be obtained. Precise molecular weight determinations from vapor density measurements can be made only in case that the deviation of the gas measured from perfect gas conditions is known.

It is not planned in this paper to study all of the equations of state which have been proposed. Such a procedure would hardly serve a useful purpose. For those interested, Partington and Shilling in their "Specific Heats of Gases" list fifty-six equations of state published prior to 1924 and give references to them. A few of the more recent ones will be mentioned later in this paper. Only those which show a marked advance in viewpoint are to be considered here. Those equations which are studied critically will, in many cases, be studied from a modern viewpoint impossible at the times they were proposed. This is, of course, no reflection upon their value at the time, but it is the only course possible in evaluating their present-day usefulness.

## HISTORICAL (*1*)

Robert Boyle (1627–91) published in 1660 a paper on "New Experiments Physico-Mechanical touching the spring of air and its effects." While answering Franciscus Linus, a critic of this paper, he first (1662) enunciated the law that the volume of a gas varies inversely as the pressure (temperature remaining constant). In continental Europe this law is usually attributed to E. Mariotte who did not publish it until 1676.

The next general law for gases was not discovered until one hundred twenty-five years later. In 1787 Charles and in 1802 Gay-Lussac showed that the temperature rate of change of the pressure-volume product is the same for all gases whose molecular complexity does not change with the temperature. This law leads directly to two other concepts of great importance. In 1811 Avogadro made the hypothesis that equal volumes of all gases at the same temperature and pressure contain the same number of molecules. In addition, the idea of an absolute scale of temperature was evolved from the law of Charles and Gay-Lussac. Since the pressure-volume product decreases linearly with decreasing temperature it is evident that if this linear decrease continues without change a temperature (about −273°C) will be reached at which the pressure-volume product will be equal to zero. This temperature is called the absolute zero.

Though it has long been known that liquids evaporate or boil with the formation of vapor, it was thought for a long time that there must be a fundamental difference between these "vapors" and the permanent gases. Lavoisier was the first to express the opinion that the so-called permanent gases might be liquified. He thought that if the earth were cooled to the temperature of outer space at least a part of the atmosphere would liquify. His associates, Monge and Clouet, were the first to succeed in this direction experimentally by liquifying sulfur dioxide. About the same time (1790) van Marum and Paets van Troostwyk, compressing ammonia to see if it obeyed Boyle's law, found that at a certain pressure the volume decreased rapidly and drops of liquid appeared. In 1799 Guyton de Morveau liquified ammonia by cooling and in 1805 Northmore appears to have liquified chlorine. In 1823 Davy and Faraday liquified chlorine. In 1834 Thilorier developed a method for the manufacture of soda water and applied it to the condensation of carbon dioxide in large quantity.

The next notable advance concerning the relation between liquids and gases was in the development of the idea of the critical point. In 1822 Cagniard de la Tour observed that if a sealed tube about two thirds full of liquid alcohol and one third full of the vapor were gradually heated the meniscus between the two phases became flatter and less distinct and finally disappeared.

The temperature and the pressure at which this occurs are now called the critical temperature and the critical pressure, and the density, at this point the same for both the liquid and the vapor, is called the critical density. It is evident, therefore, that at the critical point there is no difference between the liquid and the gas. At temperatures higher than the critical temperature no amount of pressure exerted on a gas can cause condensation to a liquid. This phenomenon has been found common to all substances, but of course, it occurs at different temperatures, pressures and densities for different substances.

The work of Cagniard de la Tour was lost sight of and was not generally known until Andrews repeated the experiment. Andrews' discovery of the critical temperature was first made public in the 1863 edition of Miller's "Chemical Physics" and in 1869 it formed the subject of his Bakerian lecture of the Royal Society, "On the continuity of the gaseous and liquid states of matter."

The fact that gases can be condensed to liquid requires that the picture of gases as given by the perfect gas law be modified considerably. The formation of liquids can be accounted for only upon the assumption that attractive forces exist between the molecules, and moreover, since the volume does not go to zero, the volume occupied by the molecules themselves must be appreciable.

Correction for the volume occupied by the molecules was first made by Clausius (2) in connection with mean free path studies. He deduced the equation $p(v - b) = Rt$ for one mole of gas where $b$ is four times the volume of the molecules themselves.

In 1854 Rankine (3) suggested the equation $\left(p + \dfrac{a}{tv^2}\right)v = Rt$ to allow for the attractive forces between the molecules. The quantity, $a$, is a constant and the term $\dfrac{a}{tv^2}$ represents the decrease in pressure due to the attraction of molecules near the surface upon molecules about to strike the wall of the containing vessel.

The greatest advance in the subject of equations of state was made by van der Waals (4) in 1873 when he took account of both of the effects just discussed and proposed his celebrated equation $\left(p + \dfrac{a}{v_2}\right)(v - \cdot b) = Rt$. This equation represents quite accurately the conditions at the critical point and represents qualitatively the behavior of fluids at other points. It has been, in fact, the starting point for most of the subsequent work on equations of state.

Discussion of equations which have been developed since that of van der Waals will be made in later sections of this paper, where they will be discussed critically as they are given. Before continuing the critical study of equations of state for real gases it is desirable to give the development of the concepts of perfect and of ideal gases, and also to point out some of the properties of real gases.

## LAWS OF PERFECT AND OF IDEAL GASES

The laws of Boyle and of Charles and Gay-Lussac are well expressed by the equation of state for a perfect gas.

$$pv = NRt$$

where $p$ = pressure of the gas
  $v$ = volume of the gas
  $N$ = number of gram molecular weights (moles) of the gas
  $R$ = universal gas constant
  $t$ = temperature of the gas on the absolute scale
    (°C. + 273.16)

The picture of a gas which obeys this law is that of perfectly elastic spheres of negligible volume compared to the total volume occupied by the gas and exerting no appreciable forces of attraction or repulsion upon each other.

Such a gas, as has been indicated, is called a perfect gas. These molecules must be colliding with each other and with the walls of the containing vessel, thereby producing a pressure,

$$p = \frac{MNu^2}{3v} \tag{5}$$

where $M$ = the molecular weight of the gas (or the average molecular weight if a mixture of gases is involved) and $u$ = square root of the average square of the velocities of the molecules.

This picture of a gas is, of course, excellent for many purposes where the pressures involved are not great and the temperatures are far above the temperatures at which it tends to liquify.

Since real gases, under the conditions mentioned, do obey the perfect gas laws over limited regions, it is convenient to express the perfect gas equation in terms of the constants of the real gas.

The constants of the real gas can be expressed as

  $t_c$ = the critical temperature on the absolute scale
  $p_c$ = the critical pressure (atmospheres)
  $v_c$ = the critical molecular volume (liters)
    $= \dfrac{M}{1000 d_c}$

where $d_c$ is the critical density (G/c.c.)

A most useful derived constant, the critical coefficient, is defined as

$$n = \frac{Rt_c}{p_c v_c}$$

It is evident that if the real gas obeyed the perfect gas law at the critical point the value of $n$ would be unity. However, since all real gases have critical coefficients ranging in value from 2.89 for carbon bisulfide to over five for the cyanides and nitriles, the critical coefficient is a measure of the departure from the perfect gas law at the critical point. That is, the volume of a fluid at the critical point is $1/n$ of the volume it would have if the perfect gas law were obeyed.

If pressures, volumes, and temperatures are expressed in terms of the critical constants a new system of units, called the reduced units, is obtained. These units are expressed as

Reduced pressure $= P = \dfrac{p}{p_c}$

Reduced volume $= V = \dfrac{v}{v_c}$

Reduced temperature $= T = \dfrac{t}{t_c}$

When the perfect gas law for one mole of gas, $pv = Rt$, is divided by $p_c v_c = \dfrac{Rt_c}{n}$, one obtains the equation $PV = nT$.

This can be called the equation of an ideal gas. That is, it is the equation of a real gas, in terms of its

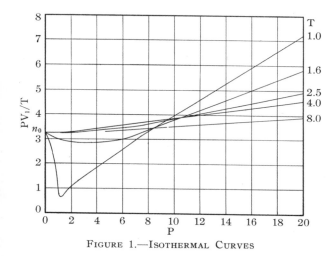

FIGURE 1.—ISOTHERMAL CURVES

critical constants, at pressures sufficiently low for the perfect gas law to be followed.

### GENERAL PROPERTIES OF REAL FLUIDS

Before starting a discussion of equations of state it is desirable to outline something of the picture of pressure-volume-temperature relationships of fluids as they are at present known from the many experimental studies of many different substances. These relationships can best be elucidated by first discussing various methods used to plot them.

A much used method is to plot $p$ against $v$ values along various isothermal lines. This method is very useful for finding the work done in changing from one condition to another by obtaining the value of $\int p\,dv$ from the initial to the final state along the particular path of the change. However, it is of little value for indicating the departure of a substance from perfect gas conditions.

A second method, due to Amagat, is to plot values of $pv$ against $p$. This method has been improved by plotting $pv/t$ values against $p$. On such a graph all of

the values satisfying the perfect gas law fall on the single horizontal line whose equation is $pv/t = R$, and the departure from perfect gas conditions is directly indicated by the distance of any point, indicating a given set of conditions, from that line. On this graph, however, the critical point for each substance will fall at a different point.

When it is desired to compare one substance with others on the same graph in terms of reduced units a similar plot is used but the units are changed so that $PV/T$ is plotted against $P$ (6). On such a graph the critical point is represented by the point (1,1) and ideal gas conditions by the line $PV/T = n$.

On this graph each substance will have a different ideal gas line. In order to compare different substances, then, it will be necessary to stretch the graphs of the different substances so that the space from $\dfrac{PV}{T} = 0$ to $\dfrac{PV}{T} = 1$ is undisturbed and so that all of the $\dfrac{PV}{T} = n$ lines will coincide at some arbitrary line, $\dfrac{PV_1}{T} = n_0$. The equation for converting $\dfrac{PV}{T}$ values on the unstretched graph to $\dfrac{PV_1}{T}$ values on the stretched graph is

$$\frac{PV_1}{T} = \frac{PV}{T}\frac{n_0 - 1}{n - 1} + \frac{n - n_0}{n - 1}, \text{ in which } n_0 = 3.25$$

Such graphs are shown in Figures 1 and 2, and a discussion of these figures will show what general statements can be made about fluids which will be useful in formulating equations of state.

In Figure 1 the critical points of all substances fall at the point (1,1), and ideal gas values fall on the line $\dfrac{PV_1}{T} = n_0$. This, of course, is true because the figure was constructed in order to produce this particular effect. The interesting thing is that many other regularities, accurate to within but a few per cent., become evident in studying data plotted in this way.

The critical isotherms of all substances start at (0, 3.25) and pass in order through the points (0.5, 2.6), (1,1), (2, 1.1), (10, 4) and (20, 7.2). Above a temperature of about 2.5 the isotherms all lie above the ideal gas line. Mathematically, this is expressed by the relationship, $\left(\dfrac{\partial \dfrac{PV}{T}}{\partial P}\right)_T = 0$ when $P = 0$ at $T = 2.5$.

This temperature is known as the Boyle temperature (7). All isotherms between $T = 1.5$ and $T = 3.5$ pass through or very close to the point (11, 4). This point is called the unique point (8). No gas occupies less than the ideal gas value above $P = 8$.* The isotherms for $T = 4$ pass through the points (10, 3.85) and (20, 4.55). The isotherms for $T = 8$ pass through the points (10, 3.5) and (20, 3.9).

The orthobaric curves, the curves for gases and liquids

* For ammonia this point may be as high as $P = 11$.

133

in equilibrium, all pass through the points (0, 3.25), (1, 1), and (0, 0) (see Figure 2). However, these curves do not all follow quite the same paths between $P = 0$ and $P = 1$. The particular path followed seems to be a function of the critical coefficient, $n$. At $P = 0.4$, for instance, the curves for $n = 3.4$ ($n_0 = 3.25$) pass through the points (0.4, 2.43) and (0.4, 0.229) and for $n = 4$ they pass through the points (0.4, 2.37) and (0.4, 0.216).

Two recent studies confirm the idea that the orthobaric curve is a function of $n$. Fales and Shapiro (9) show that $ln \dfrac{V_g}{V_l} = K \dfrac{(1 - T^2)^m}{T^q}$ where $V_g$ and $V_l$ are the reduced volumes of gas and liquid, respectively, in equilibrium at the reduced temperature, $T$. The constant, $m$, varies for different substances from 0.347 to 0.420 and $q$ from 0.821 to 1.558. $K$ is almost identical with the critical coefficient, $n$, and varies from 3.2 to 4.9 for the thirty substances they studied. They conclude that there is no basis for dividing liquids into associated and non-associated groups. Bauer, Magat, and Surdin (10) have shown that liquids in equilibrium with their vapor act alike with reference to a derived function of critical and triple point temperatures. They let $\Theta = \dfrac{t - t_f}{t_c - t_f}$ where $t_f$ is the triple point temperature and $t_c$ is the critical temperature. Plotting $\Theta$ against $\dfrac{v}{v_f}$ ($v_f$ = triple point volume) gives a single curve for all substances investigated, the equation of which may be written $\log \left( 4.36 - \dfrac{v_t}{v_f} \right) = \dfrac{1}{10} \log (1 - \Theta)$. Compressibility, $\beta$, and surface tension, $\sigma$, in terms of $\Theta$ are found to be $\dfrac{\beta_t}{\beta_f} = \dfrac{1 - \Theta^4}{(1 - \Theta)^2}$ and $\dfrac{\sigma_t}{\sigma_f} = \left( \dfrac{V_t}{V_f} \right)^{2/3} (1 - \Theta)$.

A study of Figures 1 and 2 shows, then, that fluids do have general properties which can serve as a basis for the formulation, not only of equations of state for each separate substance, but also for the formulation of a general equation of state which should represent, with a fair degree of accuracy, the behavior of all normally acting substances.

### VAN DER WAALS' EQUATION

As is well known, the first somewhat theoretically satisfactory equation of state is that of van der Waals. Writing his equation in the reduced form it becomes $(P + \dfrac{A}{V^2})(V - B) = nT$. The constant, $B$, is a corrective term to allow for the volume actually occupied by molecules of finite size and it is usually considered, according to Clausius, to be equal to four times the actual volume of the molecules. $A/V^2$ is a corrective term applied to the pressure to allow for the backward force on molecules about to hit the confining surface and thereby reduce the pressure below what it would be if there was no attraction between molecules. According to van der Waals this backward force on each mole-

cule is proportional to the density, and the number of molecules about to strike the surface is also proportional to the density. Therefore the corrective force should be directly proportional to the square of the density or inversely proportional to the square of the volume. This reasoning seems to be correct as far as

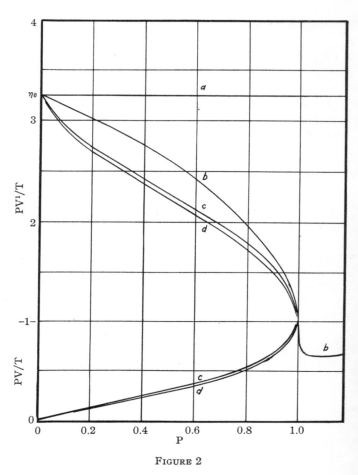

FIGURE 2

a. Isothermal Curve $T = 2.5$   c. Orthobaric Curve $n = 3.4$ $n_0 = 3.25$
b. Isothermal Curve $T = 1.0$   d. Orthobaric Curve $n = 4.0$ $n_0 = 3.25$

it goes, but it does not quite tell the whole story. According to Clausius, the pressure exerted by a gas is due to the change of momentum of the molecules colliding with the container. Therefore the corrective term should be proportional to the loss of momentum due to the attractive forces rather than to the attractive forces themselves. That is, the corrective term should be proportional to $\int f dx$ for the time the force acts, where $f$ is the force and $x$ is the time. Since the time is inversely proportional to the velocity or to the square root of the temperature, it now seems that the pressure corrective term should be written $A/T^{1/2}V^2$. Another effect for which van der Waals did not allow at all is the surface tension effect. That is, for an increased density at the surface due to molecular attractions.

The constants of this equation are evaluated by considering the fact that on the $(P, V)$ graph the critical isotherm has a point of flexion at the critical point. This means that the equation is a perfect cubic in $V$ for $P = T = 1$. Equating coefficients in the expanded form, $V^3 - (B + n) V^2 + AV - AB = 0$ to those of $V^3 - 3V^2 + 3V - 1 = 0$, the values of the constants are found to be $A = 3$, $B = 1/3$, and $n = 8/3$.

The value of $n$ found in this manner brings to light the greatest difficulty of van der Waals' equation. It makes no allowance for the variation in $n$ for different real gases and gives a value to $n$ lower than its actual value for any real gas.

The obvious method for correcting this difficulty would be to introduce the experimental value of $n$ for any substance studied and at the same time to introduce an additional constant into the equation so that the condition that the equation be a perfect cubic at the critical point could still be satisfied. This point does not seem to have been clear to many of the investigators following van der Waals, for a great amount of effort seems to have been expended in the hope of changing the form of the equation so as to obtain a better value of $n$. This was due, of course, to the limited number of critical constants available. And most of the substances whose critical constants had been measured have a value of $n$ of about 3.7.

### EQUATIONS TO OBTAIN A BETTER VALUE OF THE CRITICAL COEFFICIENT

A few of the attempts to find an equation giving a better value of $n$ than does van der Waals' will be discussed.

In 1881 Lorentz (11) suggested an equation which, in the reduced form, is $\left(P + \dfrac{A}{V^2}\right) V = nT \left(1 + \dfrac{B}{V}\right)$. Expressed as a cubic in $V$ this becomes $PV^3 - nTV^2 + V(A - nTB) = 0$. Since this equation contains no constant term it cannot be a perfect cubic at the critical point.

In 1898 Dieterici (12) proposed an equation which in the reduced form is $P(V - B) = nTe^{\frac{-C}{NTV}}$.

Since this is an exponential form its constants cannot be evaluated by making it a perfect cubic at the critical point. However, the condition from the calculus for a point of flexion, namely, that the first and second derivatives of $P$ with $V$ be equal to zero, $T$ being constant, can be used. That is $\left[\left(\dfrac{\partial P}{\partial V}\right)_T\right]_{Cr} = 0$ and $\left[\left(\dfrac{\partial^2 P}{\partial V^2}\right)_T\right]_{Cr} = 0$. The constants valuated in this way are $B = 1/2$, $C = e^2$ and $n = \dfrac{e^2}{2} = 3.6945$ and the equation may be written very simply $P = \dfrac{Te^2}{2V - 1}$. This value of $n$ is better than van der Waals' for some substances.

In the following year, 1899, Dieterici (13) proposed

another equation $\left(P + \dfrac{A}{V^{5/3}}\right)(V - B) = nT$. Determining these constants by differentiation $A = 4$, $B = 1/4$ and $n = 3.75$.

In 1900 Berthelot (14) proposed the equation $\left(P + \dfrac{A}{TV^2}\right)(V - B) = nT$ which is just the same as van der Waals' except that the pressure correction term is made an inverse function of $T$ as is the case in Rankine's equation. The constants for this equation are the same as for van der Waals', namely $A = 3$, $B = 1/3$, and $n = 8/3$.

In the year 1908 Planck (15) suggested $P = \dfrac{-KT}{B \ln\left(1 - \dfrac{B}{V}\right)} - \dfrac{A}{V^2}$. Evaluating the constants by differentiation, $A = K = 2.58$ and $B = 1/2$.

Even as late as 1918 Shaha and Basu (16) proposed the equation $P = \dfrac{-nT}{2B} \ln \dfrac{(V - 2B)}{V}$. The first derivative of this equation leads to the unusable result that $n = 0$.

In 1919 Kam (17) proposed the equation $P = \dfrac{nT}{V} - \dfrac{2A}{(V + B)^2}$ where $A = \dfrac{27}{8}$, $B = 1/2$ and $n = 4$.

The foregoing examples are sufficient to give some idea of the immense amount of work which has been done on equations of state which do not allow the experimental values of $n$ to be used.

### EQUATIONS USING EXPERIMENTAL VALUES OF THE CRITICAL COEFFICIENT

Turning now to equations which allow the experimental values of $n$ to be used, Clausius (18) in 1880 proposed an equation which in the reduced form is $\left(P + \dfrac{A}{T(V + C)^2}\right)(V - B) = nT$ where $A = \dfrac{27n^2}{64}$, $B = 1 - \dfrac{n}{4}$, and $C = \dfrac{3n}{8} - 1$. This equation cannot be used for substances for which $n = 4$ or more because $B$ becomes zero or negative for these values. Moreover, when $n = 3.25$, $T = 1$ and $V = 0.4$ the value of $P$ is 3.7 according to this equation, but the experimental value of $P$ for these conditions is 10.

The equation of Kammerlingh Onnes (19) (1902), $pv = A_v + \dfrac{B_v}{v} + \dfrac{C_v}{v^2} + \dfrac{D_v}{v^4} + \dfrac{E_v}{v^6} + \dfrac{F_v}{v^8}$ with $A_v$, $B_v$, and so forth each a function of $t$ is completely empirical and too complex for easy computation.

In 1914 Wohl (20) introduced the equation which in the reduced form is $\left(P + \dfrac{A}{TV(V - B)} - \dfrac{C}{T^2V^3}\right)(V - B) = nT$. The constants of this equation are rather involved functions of $n$. They are

$$\dfrac{2n - 3 + 6B - 3nB - 3B^2}{1 - 2B} = \dfrac{5n - 6 + 18B - 12nB - 18B^2 + 6nB^2 + 6B^3}{3 - 9B + 5B^2}$$

$$A = \dfrac{2n - 3 + 6B - 3nB - 3B^2}{1 - 2B} \qquad C = \dfrac{A + 1 - n - B}{1 - B}$$

135

For $n = 3.25$ this equation becomes

$$\left(P + \frac{4.3196}{TV(V - .1897)} - \frac{2.32}{T^2 V^3}\right)(V - .1897) = 3.25T$$

Complex as this equation is, it does not fit experimental data well. One example will suffice to show this. When $n = 3.25$, $T = 1$, and $V = .4$ the value of $P$ computed by this equation is 15.2 but the experimental value is 10.

The Beattie-Bridgeman equation (21) $P = \dfrac{Rt(1 - \epsilon)}{v^2}$ $(v + B) - \dfrac{A}{v^2}$ where $A = A_0\left(1 - \dfrac{a}{v}\right)$, $B = B_0\left(1 - \dfrac{b}{v}\right)$, and $\epsilon = \dfrac{c}{vt^3}$ can be made to fit the experimental values of many fluids over wide ranges. However, as pointed out by the authors, this equation is not adapted for use in regions near the critical point.

Keyes (22) has done much work on equations of state, recently in connection with the preparation of steam tables. His equation for steam is $p = \dfrac{Rt}{v - B}$ where $B$ is a complex function of $p$ and $t$. However, his interest lies in very accurate representation of the data available rather than in satisfying general properties over the widest possible ranges.*

## BOYLE TEMPERATURE

An additional criterion for testing equations of state is furnished by consideration of the Boyle temperature. The Boyle temperature has been defined as the temperature above which the gas never occupies a space less than would be occupied by a perfect gas, no matter what the pressure. As has been stated, this temperature has been found to be very close to two and one-half times the critical temperature for all substances which have been measured. Applying this criterion to some of the equations discussed above, the Boyle temperature is found to be 3.375 times the critical for van der Waals' equation, 1.839 for that of Berthelot, and 4 for that of Dieterici. According to the equation of Clausius, the Boyle temperature changes rapidly with $n$, being 1.839 for $n = \dfrac{8}{3}$, 2.705 for $n = 3.25$, infinity for $n = 4$ and imaginary for values of $n$ greater than 4. According to Wohl's equation $T_B = 2.65$ for $n = 3.25$. And according to the Beattie-Bridgeman equation $T_B = 4.58$ for helium and 2 for carbon dioxide.

## GENERAL EQUATIONS OF STATE

The realization that fluids have general properties naturally leads to attempts to formulate these relationships in a general equation of state. Two courses seem to be open for doing this. One is to set up an equation in which $P$ is an odd power function of $V$. This form is necessary so that the equation may have a point of flexion at the critical point on the $(p, v)$ plot.

* KEYES, F. G., "Note on a corresponding-states equation of practical interest for general physico-chemical computations," *J. Am. Chem. Soc.*, **60**, 1761–4 (1938). In this paper he deduces a reduced equation of state.

This can be done, of course, by making all roots equal at this point. Plank (23) does this and represents conditions quite accurately up to $P = 3$.

The author (6) adopted the second course, that of starting with van der Waals' equation, keeping the pressure a cubic function in $V$, but adding additional terms for increased flexibility. His equation $\left(P + \dfrac{A}{T^{1/2}V^2 + CT^y V + DT^z}\right)(V - B) = nT + KP + q \log\left(\dfrac{P}{T} + 1\right)$ represents conditions quite well up to $P = 86$ except in the region of liquids in equilibrium with the vapor. $A$, $B$, $C$, $D$, $n$, $K$, $q$, $y$, and $z$ are constants. For the particular value of the critical coefficient, $n = n_0 = 3.25$, $B$ is equal to 0, a fact which makes the evaluation of the constants considerably simpler than it would be otherwise. Above $P = 86$ the $KP$ term has to be modified to $\left(K - \dfrac{\alpha P^{1/3}}{T^x}\right)P$ (24) to fit the high pressure data of Bridgman (25). The terms $\alpha$ and $x$ are constants.

## FUTURE DEVELOPMENTS

Since the recognition that there are general properties of fluids is comparatively recent and since no present equation of state satisfactorily represents them all, it is natural to expect future developments in this subject. Though no one can predict just what form these developments will take, it may not be amiss to indicate one or two possibilities.

Since Bauer, *et al.* (10), were so successful in formulating a general equation for liquids in equilibrium with their vapors, it may be expected that this work will be extended to include liquids at all conditions.

The author's pressure correction term $\dfrac{A}{T^{1/2}V^2}$ is believed to have some theoretical foundation, but the $C$ and $D$ terms were added empirically to allow for surface tension effects. It now seems that the surface tension equation of Ramsay and Shields may be utilized to give a theoretical expression for this effect, possibly of the form $\dfrac{A - ET}{T^{1/2}V^2}$. This involves the idea of a negative surface tension effect for gases above the critical temperature. Or it may be that this expression can be kept in its present form but that in evaluating $y$ from the expression $\left[\left(\dfrac{\partial^2 P}{\partial T^2}\right)_V\right]_{Cr} = 0$ (24) the negative root of the quadratic equation in $y$ will fit the liquid region better than has the positive root which has been used.

Though it has been well stated that the task of finding suitable forms for equations of state and of evaluating their constants is an endless one, it would seem that progress is being made as long as results which more closely approximate experimental data are being obtained.

(1) "Encyclopedia Britannica," Encyclopedia Britannica Co., Ltd., London, 14th ed., **1937**. Articles on
"Boyle, Robert," **3**, 994.
"Charles, Jacques Alexandre César," **5**, 290.
"Gay-Lussac, Joseph Louis," **10**, 81.
"Heat," **11**, 313–43.
"Liquefaction of gases," **14**, 172–90.
"Lorentz, Hendrik Antoon," **14**, 393.
"Vaporization," **22**, 979–85.
"Waals, Johannes Diderik van der," **23**, 263.

(2) CLAUSIUS, R., "Die kinetische Theorie der Gase," F. Vieweg und Sohn, Braunschweig, **1889**, Chap. II.

(3) RANKINE, from JOULE, J. P. AND W. THOMSON, "On the thermal effects of fluids in motion. Part II," *Phil. Trans.*, **144**, 336–7 (1854).

(4) VAN DER WAALS, J. D., "Over de Continuiteit van den Gas en Vloeistoftoestand," Leyden, **1873**; tr. THRELFALL AND ADAIR, **1890**; *cf.*, JÜPTNER, H. v., "Verdampfungsstudien. II," *Z. physik. Chem.*, **63**, 579–618 (Heft 5, 1908) and "Verdampfungsstudien. V," *Z. physik. Chem.*, **73**, 343–82 (Heft 3, 1910).

(5) LOEB, L. B., "Kinetic theory of gases," 2nd ed., McGraw-Hill Book Co., Inc., New York City, **1934**, pp. 18–9.

(6) WOOLSEY, G., "A general equation of state," *J. Am. Chem. Soc.*, **58**, 984–7 (June, 1936).

(7) WOOLSEY, G., "The Boyle temperature and a general equation of state," *ibid.*, **58**, 2229–31 (Nov., 1936).

(8) BARTLETT, E. P., H. C. HETHERINGTON, H. M. KVALNES, AND T. H. TREMEARNE, "Compressibility isotherms of hydrogen, nitrogen and a 3:1 mixture of these gases at temperatures of −70, −50, −25 and 20 degrees and at pressures to 1000 atmospheres," *ibid.*, **52**, 1363–82 (Apr., 1930).

(9) FALES, H. A. AND C. S. SHAPIRO, "Orthobaric densities of substances as a function of reduced temperatures," *ibid.*, **58**, 2418–28 (Dec., 1936); "Thermodynamic properties of substances as a function of reduced temperature. I—Latent heat. Vapor volume and vapor pressure of water; II—Vapor pressures of liquids and the principle of corresponding states," *ibid.*, **60**, 784–805 (1938).

(10) BAUER, E., M. MAGAT, AND M. SURDIN, "Reduced temperature and general properties of pure liquids," *Trans. Faraday Soc.*, **33**, 81–6 (Jan., 1937).

(11) LORENTZ, H. A., "Ueber die Anwendung des Satzes von Virial in der kinetischen Theorie der Gase," *Ann. Phys.*, **12**, 127–36 (Heft 1, 1881); *ibid.*, **12**, 660–1 (Heft 4, 1881).

(12) DIETERICI, C., "Kinetische Theorie der Flüssigkeiten," *ibid.*, **66**, 826–58 (Heft 13, 1898).

(13) DIETERICI, C., "Ueber den kritischen Zustand," *ibid.*, **69**, 685–705 (Heft 11, 1899).

(14) BERTHELOT, D., "Quelques remarques sur l'equation caractéristique des fluides," *Arch. Néerl.*, **5**, Series 2, 417–46 (1900).

(15) PLANCK, M., "Über die kanonische Zustandsgleichung einatomiger Gase," "Königlich Preussischen Akademie der Wissenschaften," pp. 633–47 (June, 1908).

(16) SHAHA, M. N. AND S. N. BASU, "On the influence of the finite volume of molecules on the equation of state," *Phil. Mag.*, **36**, 199–202 (Aug., 1918); APPLEBEY, M. P. AND D. S. CHAPMAN, "On the equation of state," *ibid.*, **40**, 197–200 (Aug., 1920.)

(17) KAM, J., "Molecular attraction and attraction of mass, and some new gas equations," *ibid.*, **37**, 65–97 (Jan., 1919).

(18) CLAUSIUS, R., "Ueber das Verhalten der Kohlensäure in Bezug auf Druck, Volumen und Temperatur," *Ann. Phys.*, **9**, 337–57 (Heft 3, 1880); *Cf.* SARRAU, M. E., "Sur la compressibilité des fluides," *Compt. Rend.*, **101**, 941–4 (1885); "Sur la tension des vapeurs saturées," *ibid.*, **101**, 994–7; "Sur l'equation caractéristique de l'acide carbonique," *ibid.*, **101**, 1145–8.

(19) ONNES, H. KAMMERLINGH, AND C. A. CROMMELIN, "Isotherms of monatomic substances and of their binary mixtures. XIII. The empircal reduced equation of state for argon," *Proc. Akad. Wetenschappen Amsterdam*, **14**, 273–80 (1912); *Cf.*, JEANS, J. H., "The dynamical theory of gases," 2nd ed., Cambridge University Press, Cambridge, England, **1916**, p. 164.

(20) WOHL, A., "Untersuchungen über die Zustandsgleichung," *Z. Physik. Chem.*, **87**, 1–39 (Heft 1, 1914).

(21) BEATTIE, J. A. AND O. C. BRIDGEMAN, "A new equation of state for fluids," *Proc. Am. Acad. Arts Sci.*, **63**, 229–308 (Dec., 1928).

(22) KEYES, F. G. AND R. S. TAYLOR, "The adequacy of the assumption of molecular aggregation in accounting for certain of the physical properties of gaseous nitrogen," *J. Am. Chem. Soc.*, **49**, 896–911 (Apr., 1927); KEYES, F. G., L. B. SMITH, AND H. T. GERRY, "The specific volume of steam in the saturated and superheated condition together with derived values of the enthalpy, entropy, heat capacity and Joule Thomson coefficients," *Proc. Am. Acad. Arts Sci.*, **70**, 319–64 (Feb., 1936); KEENAN, J. H. AND F. G. KEYES, "Thermodynamic properties of steam," John Wiley and Sons, Inc., New York City, **1936**, 89 pp.

(23) PLANK, R., "Betrachtungen über den kritischen Zustand an Hand einer neuen allgemeinen Zustandsgleichung," *Forsch. Gebiete Ingenieurw.*, **7**, 161–73 (Juli/August, 1936).

(24) WOOLSEY, G., "A simplified general equation of state," *J. Am. Chem. Soc.*, **59**, 2743–4 (Dec., 1937).

(25) BRIDGMAN, P. W., "The physics of high pressure," The Macmillan Company, New York City, **1931**, pp. 108–11.

---◆---

## CHEMIKER ANEKDOTEN

VERLAG Chemie, Weinheim, Germany, has published a little volume with this intriguing title. Its 71 pages contain glimpses into the lighter side of the lives of 66 famous chemists. Many whimsical drawings add to the attractiveness of this compilation by JOSEF HAUSEN under the auspices of the Gesellschaft Deutscher Chemiker. For a price of 4.80 Deutschmark, this book should provide many a chuckle to enliven a student's struggle with the language examination.

The editors of THIS JOURNAL have received permission to reproduce selections. It is hoped that readers will try their best on their own before turning to page 147 where Professor JULIAN A. SMITH of Lenoir Rhyne College, Hickory, North Carolina, has supplied a translation.

Nach seiner Emeritierung hatte Nernst sich auf seinem Ruhesitz eine Karpfenzucht angelegt. Als ein Kollege ihn fragte, weshalb er es nicht lieber mit der Hühnerzucht versucht habe, antwortete er; "Man muss Tiere zuchten, die im thermodynamischen Gleichgewicht mit ihrer Umgebung sind. Warum soll ich mit meinem Geld den Weltraum heizen?"

# HENRY LE CHATELIER:  1850 *to* 1936[*]

## ALEXANDER SILVERMAN

University of Pittsburgh, Pittsburgh, Pennsylvania

HENRY LE CHATELIER was born in Paris, France, October 8, 1850. He was the son of Louis Le Chatelier (1815–1873) who was inspector General of Mines for France. The father was one of the engineers who created the French National Railways in whose interests he worked from 1855 to 1868. He was consulting engineer to bankers who financed the railway systems, not only of France, but also of Spain, Austria, and Russia. He was an associate of H. de Sainte-Claire Deville in the establishing of the first aluminum industry of France, and of Sir William Siemens with whom he constructed the first open hearth steel furnace.

The mother, Elisabeth Durand, came from a family of artists and scientists which included sculptors, engravers, geographers, etc. She was an ardent Catholic and through her own early environment and her love of poetry fostered in her son that appreciation of art and letters which was evident throughout his life. The mother was a rigid disciplinarian and so directed the lives of her children that they would not only prove conscientious as students, but appreciate physical well-being and rest, as well. Henry arose early each morning and prepared his lessons. Later, on entering the École Polytechnique (1869), he would go to his father's study each morning at 7:30 and review his lessons for the day. He learned to respect law and order, and he enjoyed the almost military attitude in the École Polytechnique.

Even his grandfather was a factor in determining Henry's career. He operated lime kilns, and during his vacations Henry would visit the grandfather's plants where he acquired his first interest in mortars and cements.

While Henry was at the École Polytechnique he assisted his father and, as the latter received visitors who were interested in the fields of agriculture, medicine, chemistry, and metallurgy, the son gained valuable experience. To observe the analytical mind of his father and the manner in which he solved problems was helpful. Not only would the father teach him mathematics, but he would provide him with essays on chemistry which had been written by Sainte-Claire Deville, Debray, Dumas, Chevreul, and others of his associates. The boy read the reports of the French Academy of Sciences. He was permitted to assist his father while the latter helped to create the aluminum industry, and

HENRY LE CHATELIER

thus gained much first-hand information about this new metal. Sainte-Claire Deville permitted the lad to work in his laboratory and coöperated with the father in guiding the son's efforts. Henry Le Chatelier stated many years later that the influence of his father and the contacts with his father's associates were important influences in "shaping his career and establishing that reputation which he held as a chemist."

* Contribution No. 350 from the Department of Chemistry, University of Pittsburgh. Presented before the Division of the History of Chemistry of the American Chemical Society, Rochester, New York, September 6, 1937.

While we are considering the father, the mother, the grandfather, and others who influenced Henry's career, it might be interesting to note that his own brothers and sister were likewise interested in science. His brother Louis was a bridge and railway engineer, and constructed steel plants. Alfred was an army officer and had much to do with the development of the French colonial empire. This brother worked on high temperature enamels. His brother George was an architect.

Henry Le Chatelier as a Student in the École Polytechnique (1869–1871)

A fourth brother, André, the oldest of the children, worked with Henry in creating the autogenous welding industry and devised methods for the safe storing of liquid acetylene. He not only made studies on the resistance of metals to high temperatures, but devised metal lath, which is still in use. This substitute for wood possessed a much greater strength and was fireproof. The sister, Marie, married a Dr. Leroux who was a pediatrician.

Henry's early education was obtained in Paris where he attended a military academy for a short time and then entered the Collège Rollin, receiving the Bachelor of Letters in 1867 and Bachelor of Science in 1868. He entered the École Polytechnique in 1869 where his work was interrupted by the war of 1870. His studies were completed in 1872, and he registered as a mining engineer. In 1874 he was licensed to practice physical science. In 1877 he became Professor in the École des Mines. In 1882 he was lecturer in the École Polytechnique. In 1883 he became Professor in the Collège de France and later Professor at the Sorbonne. The degree of Doctor of Physical and Chemical Science was conferred upon him in 1887, when he became Professor of Industrial Chemistry and Metallurgy in the École des Mines. Until 1897 he devoted himself to the mechanics of chemical reactions, establishing the laws of chemical equilibrium and the displacement of equilibrium. He studied solutions. Applying thermodynamic values he was able to anticipate possibilities, instead of depending on trial and error methods and performing costly experiments which might result negatively. In 1889 he won the title of Chief Engineer and that year returned to the Collège de France as Professor of Inorganic Chemistry, remaining until 1908. Already in 1907 he had been appointed Professor of General Chemistry of the Faculty of Science of Paris. This title he retained until he became Honorary Professor in 1925. During the period 1908 to 1922 he directed the researches of more than one hundred graduate students, of whom twenty-four obtained the doctorate as his majors.

Le Chatelier was a reformer. He was not content with providing the descriptive material and facts which his colleagues presented, but constantly introduced theory and the newer ideas, presenting his own interpretation of fundamental principles and laws.

In the research field Henry Le Chatelier possessed great versatility. He is recognized chiefly for his contributions to thermodynamics and chemical theory. We are familiar with his principle on stress and strain which is coupled with that on heat advanced by van't Hoff. It is not strange that he should have accomplished the synthesis of ammonia from the elements in 1901, anticipating Fritz Haber, who is usually the only one mentioned in connection with the process. Henry Le Chatelier was interested in allotropy, especially in carbon, silica, and certain metals. He made extensive solubility studies, including dissociation. He studied the dissociation of gases at high temperatures and the combustion of gas mixtures, and applied the results to the utilization of fuels and the economics of furnace operation. Later he entered the field of explosives and indicated their use in mining operations. While generally interested in metallurgy, he devoted himself more particularly to the production and properties of iron and steel. He applied the phase rule of Willard Gibbs for which he devised simple proofs, and it is said that without Le Chatelier's principle of mobile equilibrium the phase rule and phase law diagrams might have waited long for their practical applications. While working in the field of metallurgy he devised a metallurographic microscope with which he could study and photograph crystals in alloys. This device divulged the formation of compounds between iron and carbon, and proved the value of heat treatment in steel. His dilatometer enabled him to measure the expansion rate of metals. Le Chatelier experienced difficulty in the

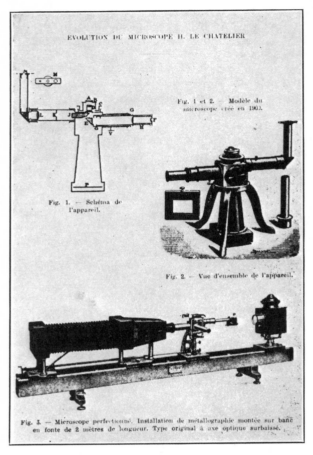

METALLURGICAL MICROSCOPE OF HENRY LE CHATELIER

measuring of the higher temperatures in his studies. Instruments were in existence which would measure up to 500°C., but beyond that results were inaccurate. He adopted the platinum platinum-rhodium thermocouple, for gas thermometers were unreliable.

In the field of ceramics Le Chatelier was interested in mortars and cements, clay, silica, and the silicates, glass. He determined the coefficient of expansion and electrical conductivity of some of these materials.

Henry Le Chatelier published over five hundred journal articles and books.* They not only included chemistry and ceramics, but numerous biographies, and, toward the end of his life, articles on social welfare.

Le Chatelier's books included a volume on the measurement of high temperatures which appeared in 1900 under the joint authorship of O. Boudouard. This volume underwent numerous revisions and translations, and is known in the United States under the title, "The Measurement of High Temperatures," by

* "Henry Le Chatelier: His Publications," *Ceram. Abs.*, **16**, 316–22 (Oct., 1937).

Burgess and Le Chatelier. In 1903 a volume appeared on "Hydraulic Materials." This dealt with lime, mortars, and cement. Again, the volume was revised and translated. In 1908 he published his "Lessons on Carbon." This volume had its beginning in his early lectures on the subject. 1912 brought his "Introduction to the Study of Metallurgy" which included industrial heating. In 1914 his volume on "Silica and the Silicates" appeared, and in 1925 his book on "Science and

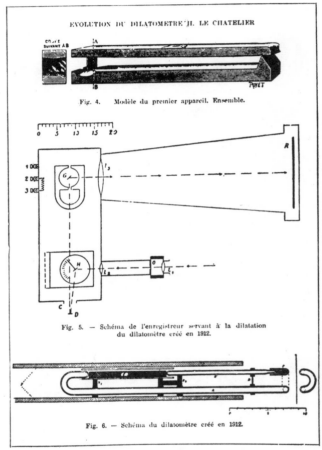

HENRY LE CHATELIER'S DILATOMETER

Industry." In the last named volume he particularly stressed the Taylor system of organized management and production which originated in England and which he greatly admired.

In his books and journal articles Le Chatelier's exact scientific trend of mind is in constant evidence. He provides illustrations, but sparingly, and never superfluously. His translators were more generous in this regard than the author himself.

Le Chatelier was a great national figure. His linking of science with industry and especially with national defense was important to France, for not only the nation but the Academy of Sciences had neglected this. His frequent appeals to the French Academy of Sciences, in which he referred to the utilization of science in industry and national affairs in Germany, Great

Britain, and the United States finally won national support for research, and his favorable reference to our own nation undoubtedly prompted Woodrow Wilson to consult him in an advisory capacity when our National Research Council was established in 1916.

The reward of Le Chatelier's appeal to the National Academy of Sciences and the French nation came through his numerous appointments. He was on the French Commission on Explosives in 1902, the National Science Bureau in 1913, the Commission on Weights and Measures from 1913 to 1917, and the Commission

HENRY LE CHATELIER (ENLARGEMENT FROM 16-MM. MOTION PICTURE TAKEN BY A. S.), APRIL, 1934

for the Standardization of Metallic Products. Upon him was placed the responsibility for specifying standards, for materials of construction other than wood, and his committee finally determined the standards for all products. In 1919 France made him a member of the Commission on Inventions, and in 1922 he was placed on the Committee for the Control of the French Monetary Circulation. Le Chatelier represented France at numerous international meetings.

Henry Le Chatelier was the recipient of many honors. These included the Jerome Ponti Prize of the French Academy of Sciences (1892), and the Lacaze Prize (1895). In 1907 he was made a member of the French Academy of Sciences. It may seem strange that the Academy should have waited so long, but one has only to think of the case of Louis Pasteur to realize that election to this body requires time. He had been a Chevalier of the Legion of Honor of France since 1886. In 1908 he became an officer, in 1919 a Commander, and in 1927 Grand Officer. In 1906 he was made a knight of the Order of St. Anne of Russia, and in 1928 a Chevalier of the Order of the New Republic of Poland.

His applications of science to industry brought him recognition which scientists rarely receive. Thus, in 1900 he received the Grand Prize of the Paris Exposi-

tion; in 1908 the Medal of Honor of the Society of Mineral Industry of France; in 1928, the Gold Medal of the Commission on Bridges and Highways of France. In 1904 he received the Grand Prize of the St. Louis Exposition (U. S. A.); in 1905 the Diploma of Honor of the International Exposition in Liege, Belgium; in 1906 the Grand Prize of the International Exposition in Milan, Italy. During 1910 he received the Grand Prize of the International Exposition in Brussels, Belgium; the Grand Prize of the Franco-British Exposition; and the Bessemer Gold Medal of the Iron and Steel Institute of London. In 1911 the International Exposition of Industries and Manufactures of Turin, Italy, awarded him the Grand Prize. In 1916 he received the Davy Medal of the Royal Society of London. In 1932 he was awarded the medal of the Association of Engineers of Liege, Belgium. Henry Le Chatelier was not only a member and officer in many national and foreign societies, but was made an honorary member of innumerable organizations.

Le Chatelier's honorary degrees included that of Doctor of Engineering from Aix la Chapelle, Germany (1910); Doctor of Science from the University of Manchester, England (1920); Doctor of Technical Science from the Polytechnique Institute of Copenhagen, Denmark (1921); Doctor of Science, University of Louvain, Belgium (1927); Doctor of Science, University of Madrid, Spain (1934).

It would hardly seem right to present this article without saying something of Le Chatelier's family life. On May 29, 1876, he married Genevieve Nicolas, the daughter of a former chum of his father at the École Polytechnique. There were seven children by this marriage, three sons and four daughters. The influence which Henry Le Chatelier enjoyed through his grandfather, his father, and mother, and their families is repeated through his influence and that of Mme. Le Chatelier on their children and grandchildren. The oldest son, Charles, became a mining engineer. The oldest daughter married an engineer. The next daughter also married an engineer and after her marriage coöperated with her father in establishing the *Revue de métallurgie*. The third daughter married an agricultural engineer. The son, Louis, is an engineer. The fourth daughter married an engineer, and the youngest child, a son François, is a mining engineer. It is to this son that the writer is particularly obligated for much of the valuable information contained in the present article.

In June, 1936, Professor and Mme. Le Chatelier celebrated their sixtieth wedding anniversary surrounded by their children, thirty-four grandchildren, and six great-grandchildren. Le Chatelier devoted all of his spare time to his family. The tall, slender, serious, but pleasant, father played with the children and would take them on numerous excursions. He interested himself in their studies and in the studies of his grandchildren. It is said that in the spring of 1936 he went to Miribel-les-échelles with his grandchildren to give them a review in chemistry and physics, and that on the eve of his death, disregarding his fatigue, he dictated to one of his children advice concerning the study of descriptive geometry to help a grandchild who was experiencing difficulty with the subject.

We must pay tribute to Mme. Le Chatelier. Her self-abnegation as the wife of a professor with a limited income, and her devotion to the education of her children to lighten the burdens of her husband as much as possible proved an important factor in helping to establish his brilliant career.

Le Chatelier traveled extensively in the interests of his studies and through invitation of foreign societies; also during his vacations, when Mme. Le Chatelier invariably accompanied him.

Finally, like most scientists who reach a ripe old age, he indulged in philosophy. On January 22, 1922, the French Academy of Sciences celebrated the fiftieth anniversary of Le Chatelier's graduation from the École Polytechnique and presented him with a bronze medal. Copies of this medal by an eminent sculptor had been distributed in return for subscriptions which resulted in a fund of 100,000 francs. This fund was presented to the Academy of Sciences in Le Chatelier's honor and utilized for researches under his direction. There were many addresses in which he was given high praise and commendation. When his friends and associates had finished Le Chatelier thanked them and closed by stressing some of his own ideals. He emphasized the necessity for clear thinking verified by exact experimentation, and illustrated the importance of this procedure by citing the failures of a number of eminent men whose carelessness resulted in embarrassment following their published accounts of faulty researches. He told how his pleasure in life had come through studying the laws of the universe, observing their application and discovering new consequences. He warned against the tendency to invalidate or question natural laws and said that one should aim to confirm those laws which predecessors had disclosed. He felt that this attitude was an advantage which led to his own supplementary contributions and which accounted for that measure of his success which the Academy was celebrating. He could not destroy the edifices of the past, for he considered science "a collection of contributions made by many workers, which might be supplemented or modified by duly authenticated new discoveries." He stressed the importance of discipline which his parents had imposed upon him and which was practiced at the École Polytechnique while he was a student. He deplored the decreasing seriousness of study and increasing tendency toward pleasure and even license in modern colleges and universities. He likened the irresponsible student to a bold individual who dodges vehicles in crossing a street and risks being crushed, to say nothing of the fact that he seriously ties up traffic. To the young chemist he recommended modesty with a reluctance to overthrow the findings of the past until he has positive proof. "One makes discoveries if he can and not merely through the wish to make them. The sensational is detestable." Of himself Le Chatelier

said, "... throughout my scientific career I strove without any desire for the sensational, contenting myself each day with the conscientious pursuit of the task of the day. In the end I was amply rewarded."

Le Chatelier was a lover of liberty and cherished the privileges which men enjoyed in the French Republic. He differentiated between discipline and liberty. To him discipline meant the voluntary respect of the law, whether natural or social. He characterized civilized man through recognition and respect of the law. To him liberty consisted not in the breaking of laws, but, on the contrary, in the prevention of law violation. Liberty refuses to tolerate injustice and should modify laws instead of revolting against them.

Le Chatelier placed integrity above everything. At one time after he had received an honor, a statesman approached him for a favor to a particular political faction. Le Chatelier replied, "I have never sought an honor, and I, therefore, assume that when it was con-

HENRY LE CHATELIER AND MME. LE CHATELIER. (ENLARGED FROM 16-MM. MOTION PICTURE TAKEN BY A. S.) APRIL, 1934

ferred it was mine without obligation." He might have enjoyed many favors and promotions had it not been for this ideal. In fact, he lost his chair in the École Polytechnique through his conscientious adherence to his principles.

After his retirement and during the last years of his life, he became interested in numerous problems of a general nature. He campaigned for the return of the classical studies to college and university curricula, stressing the importance of literature and Latin as a part of a general education. As already intimated, he advocated scientific management according to the Taylor System, and others, for increasing the efficiency of workmen in French factories. He advocated political economy, recommending a more liberal status for the workman and a greater restraint on political expenditures. Shortly before his death, as President of the inaugural International Congress of Mines and Metallurgy and of Applied Geology, at which delegates from forty nations were present, Le Chatelier took occasion to indicate that much attention was being given to the development of industrial technic which was based on the collaboration of science and industry. He admitted that at one time he had supported this policy and that it was still desirable, but lamented the fact that not enough attention was being paid to social progress. Wishing to leave this thought as an indelible impression, he prepared an article entitled "Morals and Human Affairs." So anxious was he that the manuscript should be exactly right, that he corrected it on his death bed, and insisted repeatedly that it be sent to a journal where the ideals expressed would make a sympathetic appeal, namely, the *Bulletin of the Social Union of Catholic Engineers of France*. It appeared in this *Bulletin* as a posthumous article in December, 1936.

After 1935 Le Chatelier suffered occasionally from angina pectoris. Several days before his death a particularly violent attack affected his heart, and he succumbed. His death was a peaceful one, on September 17, 1936, at his country estate, Miribel-les-échelles (Isère), France, in his eighty-sixth year.

HENRY LE CHATELIER AND MME. LE CHATELIER WITH CHILDREN, GRANDCHILDREN, AND GREAT GRANDCHILDREN CELEBRATING DIAMOND WEDDING ANNIVERSARY, JUNE, 1936

Illustrations which accompany this article are presented through the courtesy of the *Revue de Métallurgie*, Paris, which issued a special memorial number in January, 1937. The other photographs are enlargements from motion pictures which the writer had the privilege of taking in Professor Le Chatelier's residence in Paris during April of 1934.

---

**David Kritchevsky**
The Wistar Institute
Philadelphia 4, Pennsylvania

# Friedrich Goppelsroeder, Pioneer of Paper Chromatography

The beginnings of paper partition chromatography stem from the experiments of Runge, Schoenbein, and Goppelsroeder, who studied capillary analysis during the last half of the nineteenth century. The technique of capillary analysis resembles paper chromatography; a strip of filter paper is dipped into a solution of a dye or salt and the extent of rise of the liquid is noted as well as the appearance of the material under investigation. Zones appear colored or may be detected by some specific reagent.

Of the three men mentioned above, Friederich Goppelsroeder (1837–1919) devoted his career to experiments involving capillary analysis. He was a student of Schoenbein's and began working in this field in 1861. Although his work must be judged crude by present standards he suggested a number of techniques which are in current vogue.

Goppelsroeder was able to separate mixtures of dyes and to determine the components of pure dyes by this method. Thus, he was able to separate picric acid from curcuruma dye and from indigo.[1] He showed that commercial fuchsin contained one more component than did pure fuchsin. When textile merchants complained that azulene dyes gave a purplish cast to their material Goppelsroeder showed that capillary analysis of an alcoholic solution of azulene yielded blue, violet, and rose colored zones. Elution of the blue zone with alcohol yielded cleaner blue dyes. Thus the technique had applications as a preparative method.

In a book published in 1904[2] Goppelsroeder discussed capillary analysis of urine samples obtained from patients at the Basel Bürgerspital where he did most of his work. In searching for compounds which might be present in the urine, Goppelsroeder developed tests for identifying these materials. A comparison of his tests with those in use today is tabulated below:

| Compound | Goppelsroeder's test | Present test |
|---|---|---|
| Arabinose | Fehling's solution | Aniline oxalate |
| Taurocholic acid | Furfural—$H_2SO_4$ | $SbCl_3$ |
| Leucine | Quinone powder—NaOH | Ninhydrin |
| Urea | $CuSO_4$—NaOH | Hypochlorite |
| Creatine | Alk. picric acid | Alk. picric acid |
| Uric acid | $AgNO_3$ | $Hg(NO_3)_2$ |

To test the strips a section was cut out for the color reaction and rematched for possible elution and reanalysis.

Although he recognized the possibility of using aqueous solvents, his work usually entailed the use of pure liquids or aqueous solutions. Goppelsroeder did

---

[1] GOPPELSROEDER, F., *Verhandl. naturforsch. Ges. Basel*, part 3, 268 (1863).

[2] GOPPELSROEDER, F., "Studien uber die Anwendung der Capillaranalyse," E. Birkhaüser, Basel, **1904**.

(*Concluded on page 158*)

# PROUT'S HYPOTHESIS[1]

## O. T. BENFEY
### Haverford College, Haverford, Pennsylvania

It is the purpose of this paper to focus on some of the less well-known aspects of the work of William Prout (1785–1850) and of the hypothesis that bears his name.[2]

## THE ORIGINS OF PROUT'S HYPOTHESIS

When in 1816 Prout put forward the suggestion that all atomic weights were integral multiples of that of hydrogen, and that hydrogen may be considered the "protyle" of the ancients, the substance from which other elements are made, he remarked that the idea was "not altogether new."[3] In the literature of the history of chemistry there has been considerable discussion as to what Prout might have meant by this comment. Certainly Thomas Thomson was approaching the idea of integral atomic weights when in a paper in 1813 he noted that eight elements had atomic weights that were integral multiples of that of oxygen.[4] However it is probable that Prout was thinking of Sir Humphry Davy who, though not considering the question of relative atomic weights, had come very close to suggesting hydrogen as the primary matter. J. C. Gregory[5] and J. R. Partington[6] have briefly set out Davy's ideas but in the knowledge of this author Davy's views have never been quoted in detail.[7] They appear near the end of his "Elements of Chemical Philosophy"[8] published in 1812 both in London and in this country. The page numbers refer to the Philadelphia edition of 1812:

We know nothing of the true elements belonging to nature; but as far as we can reason from the relations of the properties of matter, hydrogene is the substance which approaches nearest to what the elements may be supposed to be. It has energetic powers of combination, its parts are highly repulsive as to each other, and attractive of the particles of other matter; . . . [pp. 274–5].

His studies on ammonium amalgam suggested to him the composite nature of metals:

On the most probable view of the nature of the amalgam from ammonia, as I have mentioned, it must be supposed to be composed of hydrogene, azote, and quicksilver; and it may be regarded as a kind of type of the composition of the metals; and by supposing them and the inflammable bodies different combinations of hydrogene with another principle as yet unknown in the separate form; all the phenomena may be easily accounted for, and will be found in harmony with the theory of definite proportions [p. 275].

Even if it should be ultimately found that oxygene and hydrogene are the same matter in different states of electricity, or that two or three elements in different proportions constitute all bodies, the great doctrines of chemistry, the theory of definite proportions, . . . must remain immutable; . . . the numbers representing [the substances now considered as primary elements] . . . would probably be all found to be produced by the additions of multiples of some simple numbers or fractional parts [pp. 278–9].

The last part of this section must have suggested strongly to chemists that they analyze the characteristic weights of the elements to see whether simple mathematical relations could be found among them. It may well have been the stimulus that led Prout to his hypothesis of integral atomic weights. The passage is the more remarkable since Davy was only interested in combining weights, for he was doubtful, as we have seen, whether chemists had discovered as yet any true elements.

It is interesting that Prout himself doubted the validity of the whole atomic theory. In his Gulstonian lectures on the "Application of chemistry to physiology, pathology and practice" in 1831 he had suggested that the atomic theory was a "conventional artifice, exceedingly convenient for many purposes but [one] which does not represent nature."[9] He believed that the so-called "atomic weights" may merely be members of series of the type 3, 6, 9, 12, 15 and that other members of the series may be found in other chemical combinations of the substance. This view is criticized by Daubeny[10] who shows that Prout's view has the same consequences as Dalton's law of multiple proportions and is therefore an unnecessary complication. Prout defends himself in a communication at the end of Daubeny's book. It is here that Prout states his view that

[1] Presented before the Division of the History of Chemistry at the 119th Meeting of the American Chemical Society, Boston, April, 1951.

[2] (a) An excellent paper by S. Glasstone, elucidating Prout's original papers and discussing Prout's hypothesis in its relation to the history of chemistry, appeared in J. CHEM. EDUC., 24, 478–81 (1947). (b) Alembic Club Reprint 20, "Prout's Hypothesis," Alembic Club, Edinburgh, 1932, contains not only the important papers by Prout, Stas, and Marignac but also a valuable historical introduction.

[3] Ann. Phil. 7, 111 (1816). The paper is entitled "Correction of a Mistake in the Essay on the Relation between the Specific Gravities of Bodies in their Gaseous State and the Weights of their Atoms." The original "Essay" appeared the previous year, ibid., 6, 321 (1815).

[4] Ibid., 2, 114 (1813); see also ref. (2a).

[5] GREGORY, J. C., "A Short History of Atomism," A. & C. Black, Ltd., London, 1931, pp. 142–3.

[6] Chymia, 1, 120 (1948).

[7] Glasstone (ref. 2a) suggests that the views were never published, probably from reading Gregory. But it is clear from the agreement of Gregory's material with Davy's words that Gregory knew the original writings.

[8] DAVY, SIR H., "Elements of Chemical Philosophy," Bradford and Inskeep, Philadelphia, 1812, Part 1, Vol. 1.

[9] DAUBENY, C., "An Introduction to the Atomic Theory," J. Murray, Oxford, 1831, p. 62.

[10] Ibid., p. 44.

perhaps the ultimate unit of matter is not hydrogen but some still smaller particle.[11]

Davy was intrigued by the possibility of a single primary matter manifesting itself in so many different forms:

There is, however, no impossibility in the supposition that the same ponderable matter in different electrical states, or in different arrangements, may constitute substances chemically different [p. 278].

[The idea of elements being] different arrangements of the same particles of matter . . . [has been] sanctioned by the authority of Hooke, Newton, and Boscovich. . . [p. 279].

Probably the greatest controversy has centered on the claim made by Professor J. L. G. Meinecke of Halle in 1816 that Dalton himself had anticipated Prout.[12] The question is discussed in detail in Alembic Club Reprint No. 20 (ref. 2b) in which the authors of the Introductory Section[13] come to the conclusion that Meinecke's claim had no basis in fact. Now Meinecke never explicitly suggested that the elements were constituted of hydrogen as the primary matter, nor did he claim that Dalton held this belief. He claimed that there was no need to refer to Prout when suggesting that atomic weights (called "Antheile" by him) were integral multiples of that of hydrogen since "according to Dalton, all stoichiometric magnitudes are multiples by whole numbers of the value of hydrogen."

Dalton believed that atoms were indivisible and he therefore could not conceive of hydrogen as the primary matter. But this does not dispose of the problem, for a type of Pythagorean number mysticism has often appeared in science and has at times received considerable confirmation from the strikingly simple mathematical laws that describe many natural phenomena. Considering the simplicity of the atomic theory and its power in correlating divers chemical phenomena, it would not have been difficult to believe that the numbers representing the relative weights of the atoms also obeyed simple laws.

Meinecke's claim receives strong confirmation from passages in Thomas Thomson's "History of Chemistry."[14] After quoting from his notes taken at a discussion with Dalton in 1804 that "the ultimate particles of all simple bodies are atoms incapable of further subdivision" he proceeds to discuss Dalton's atomic weight table of 1804 containing integral and half-integral values. A few pages later he comes to the 1808 table appearing in Dalton's "New System of Chemical Philosophy"[15] on which he comments:

The following table shows the atomic weight of the simple bodies, as he at that time had determined them from the best analytical experiments that had been made. . . . He had made choice of hydrogen for unity, because it is the lightest of all bodies. *He was of opinion that the atomic weights of all other bodies are multiples of hydrogen;* and, accordingly, they are *all* expressed in whole numbers. He had raised the atomic weight of oxygen from 6.5 to 7, from a more careful examination of the experiments on the component parts of water. [Italics mine.]

It is almost inconceivable that this was an error of memory on Thomson's part. Thomson had published one of the earliest printed accounts of Dalton's atomic theory in the third edition of his "System of Chemistry."[16] As editor of the *Annals of Philosophy* he kept in close touch with chemical developments and wrote frequent reviews on the progress of chemistry. He was an ardent supporter of Prout's hypothesis and devoted much time to analytical studies which proved to his satisfaction the validity of Prout's view.[17]

It is strange that Thomson does not even mention Prout's hypothesis in his "History of Chemistry." He mentions the papers that led to the hypothesis only in connection with their significance in correlating volume relations and the atomic theory.[18] The reason for his silence is probably Berzelius' attack on Thomson's analytical work as being valueless.[19] In Berzelius' eyes Prout's hypothesis had no reliable evidence to support it. Thomson ends his "History" with a short explanation of his own work, admitting that some of it had not been too accurate. He continues to have the highest respect for Berzelius: "It is to his labours chiefly that the great progress which the atomic theory has made is owing."[20]

If Dalton did believe in integral atomic weights he did not believe in them for long, for in 1810 his table again contained some nonintegral values.[21] Taking Thomson's account as accurate, one must explain Dalton's references in 1808 to certain combining weights as being "nearly" whole numbers as a recognition of current experimental results being in disagreement with the whole-number theory. Thus: "Water is a binary compound of hydrogen and oxygen, and the relative weights of the two elementary atoms are as 1:7, nearly."[22] This would agree with Meinecke's statement that Dalton believed in integral atomic weights "without, however, calculating these values accurately by the aid of available analyses."[23] Meinecke flattered himself as having found integral atomic weights by the most careful investigation of all available analyses. This would exonerate Meinecke somewhat for making

[11] *Ibid.*, p. 129; this passage is quoted in ref. (2a).

[12] *Ann. Physik*, new series, **24**, 162 (1816).

[13] KENDALL, J., *Proc. Roy. Soc. Edinburgh*, **A, 63**, 1 (1949–50), reveals that he and L. Dobbin were the authors of this section.

[14] THOMSON, T., "History of Chemistry," H. Coburn and R. Bentley, London, **1831**, Vol. 2, pp. 289–94. Also *ibid.*, 2nd ed., **1833**.

[15] DALTON, J., "New System of Chemical Philosophy," R. Bickerstaff, London, **1808**, Vol. 1, Part 1, p. 219.

[16] THOMSON, T., "System of Chemistry," 3rd ed., G. Bell and Sons, Edinburgh, **1807**, pp. 424–9, 451–2. The section is reprinted in Alembic Club Reprint No. 2, "Foundations of the Atomic Theory," University of Chicago Press, Chicago, **1911**, p. 42.

[17] THOMSON, T., "An Attempt to Establish the First Principles of Chemistry by Experiment," Baldwin, Cradock and Joy, London, **1825**.

[18] Ref. (14), Vol. 2, p. 300.

[19] *Jahresber.*, **6**, 77 (1827); quoted in ref. (2a).

[20] Ref. (14), Vol. 2, p. 305.

[21] DALTON, J., *op. cit.*, **1810**, Vol. 1, Part 2, p. 560.

[22] *Ibid.*, **1808**, Vol. 1, Part 1, p. 215.

[23] *J. Chem. Physik*, **27**, 46 (1819). Translated in ref. (2b), p. 11.

use of Prout's and Thomson's values without mentioning them, since he clearly states that he used all available data.

## PROUT AS EXPERIMENTER

Since Prout's hypothesis was enunciated on the basis of very incomplete data, and since later analyses showed the idea of integral atomic weights to be untenable as first formulated, it is common to think of Prout as a man of great speculative ability but of little experimental skill. Prout may have helped to foster this prejudice by prefacing his first paper (ref. 3) with a disclaimer as to his experimental ability (ref. 2a).

This view of Prout can be partly countered by pointing to his scientific achievements, including the discovery of hydrochloric acid in the stomach,[24] of uric acid in boa constrictor excrement (1815) and of murexide (1818), and his development of urine analysis and organic combustion analysis (1815–27).[25]

Perhaps even greater confirmation of his scientific ability can be obtained from the references to Prout's work in the writings of other scientists of his time.

When F. Wöhler performed his classical synthesis of urea he required the most authoritative analysis of natural urea in order to prove the identity of the two products. Of the available reports of analyses he chose Prout's as probably the most accurate.[26] When in 1830 Berzelius reported on Wöhler's synthesis he too used Prout's data in discussing the results.[27]

Edward Turner, who in 1829 was delegated by the British Association for the Advancement of Science to inquire into and report on the question of Prout's hypothesis, mentions that Prout had remarked to him the evolution of hydrogen chloride when fusing even the most carefully purified silver chloride. This was confirmed by Turner.[28]

But perhaps the most decisive testimony comes from Berzelius in a rather amusing connection. In his annual report on chemical progress for 1834 he states that Prout had reported at a recent Oxford Scientific Conference a difference in the specific gravity of air before and during the cholera outbreak in London. Then follows the significant comment: "From a less able observer than Prout, I would not have considered it worth while even to mention this result here."[29] This is high praise indeed when compared with his scathing attack on Thomas Thomson some years earlier as an investigator from whom science can derive no advantage whatever (ref. 19).

[24] *Ann. Phil.*, **24**, 117 (1824).
[25] Ref. 2a, and PARTINGTON, J. R., "A Short History of Chemistry," The Macmillan Co., New York, 1937, p. 213.
[26] *Ann. Physik Chem.*, [2], **12**, 88 (1828). The passage appears in translation in WHETHAM, W. C. DAMPIER, "Cambridge Readings in the Literature of Science," Cambridge University Press, Cambridge, 1924, p. 215.
[27] *Jahresber.*, **9**, 266 (1830).
[28] *Rept. Brit. Assoc. Advance. Sci.*, 1833, 400.
[29] *Jahresber.*, **13**, 52 (1834). "Von einem weniger guten Beobachter als Prout, würde ich es nicht für die Mühe werth gehalten haben dieses Resultat hier nur zu nennen."

## MODIFICATIONS TO FIT NONINTEGRAL ATOMIC WEIGHTS

The growing weight of evidence throughout the nineteenth century that atomic weights relative to hydrogen were not integral by no means saw the end of Prout's hypothesis as a fertile source for speculation.

I shall by-pass in this account the better known suggestions that the fundamental mass unit may be a particle smaller than hydrogen, and also Crookes' brilliant anticipation of isotopes. It was C. Marignac in 1860 who first tried to account for deviations from integral or half-integral values by suggesting a modification of the law of gravitation.[30] He saw Prout's hypothesis as a limiting law similar to the ideal gas laws, with deviations caused by complicating factors. His suggestion was that the cause that determined particular groupings of the primordial matter to form our atoms, also "exercised an influence on the manner according to which these groups of primordial atoms would obey the law of universal attraction, in such wise that the weight of each group might not be exactly the sum of the weights of the primordial atoms composing it."

A suggestion for the reason for expecting such a modification appears in a book by George Rudorf, a student of Sir William Ramsay, entitled "The Periodic System, Its History and Significance for Chemical Theory."[31]

We know that the atoms mutually attract each other in the molecule; if an atom is a complex of "protyles," then we must assume that the protyles also attract each other in the atom. The force of cohesion between the protyles is very large compared with their weight; therefore it may—and probably does—influence the weight of a system of protyles. With molar quantities this attraction is extremely small; therefore, considering our ignorance of the nature of gravitation we have no right to assume that the weight, as we measure it, of $n$ protyles is $n$ times as great as that of one protyle. For it is likely that the Newtonian laws, which apply to molar quantities, do not hold rigidly when we deal with molecules; this has been pointed out by Pearson.

These speculations found their fulfillment in the discovery of the packing effect.

Lothar Meyer put forward a different solution. Commenting on Marignac's speculations he suggests the admixture of a ponderable ether to the primordial matter:[32]

It is conceivable that the atoms of all or of many elements are essentially composed of smaller elementary particles of one primordial matter, perhaps of hydrogen, but that their weights do not appear as rational multiples of each other because in addition to the primordial particles, greater or smaller amounts of . . . luminiferous ether, which may not be devoid of all weight, may enter into the composition of atoms.

[30] *Bibliothèque Universelle* (Archives), **9**, 97 (1860). For the relevant portions of Marignac's paper see ref. (2b).
[31] RUDORF, G., "Das periodische System, seine Geschichte und Bedeutung für die chemische Systematik," translated from the English. L. Voss, Hamburg and Leipzig, 1904, p. 271.
[32] Translated from MEYER, LOTHAR, "Die modernen Theorien der Chemie," 6th ed., Maruschke and Berendt, Breslau, 1896, Book 1, p. 124.

(*Concluded on page 157*)

**Robert K. Fitzgerel**[1]
Ohio Wesleyan University
Delaware, Ohio
**Frank H. Verhoek**
The Ohio State University
Columbus

# The Law of Dulong and Petit

In 1819, Dulong and Petit found that when the atomic weight of an element was multiplied by its specific heat, the number obtained was approximately the same for all elements.[2] This fact was expressed by them as follows:

"Les atomes de tous les corps simples ont eactement la même capacité pour la chaleur," which translates to read: "The atoms of all simple substances [that is, elements] have exactly the same capacity for heat."

It is interesting to note that there is confusion among chemistry teachers today over the use of a variety of numbers for the so-called Dulong and Petit constant. Generally the values given in various sources range from 5.9–6.5. Actually there is no number approximating this value in the original paper (Fig. 1) since Dulong and Petit used a scheme of atomic weights in which oxygen was assigned a value of 1. Thus the numbers given in the various textbooks merely indicate that different data were used in determining an average value and that modern atomic weight units were used as a basis. Of much greater significance and a genuine cause for alarm is the fact that textbooks generally avoid assigning units to the value selected for use. It seems far more appropriate to point out the atomic, thermal, and "molar" characteristics of the phenomenon, rather than to place emphasis on a numerical value for the constant.

The Law of Dulong and Petit was initially used as an empirical rule, along with other empirical rules, in determining approximate atomic weights of the elements. Dalton's original atomic weights in the "New System of Chemical Philosophy" were quickly followed by the results calculated from Berzelius' careful determinations of combining weights. In some cases Berzelius was in error; for example, he deduced that the relationship between silver and oxygen was $AgO_2$, a formula which required an atomic weight four times the actual value for silver. Slowly, errors of this nature were corrected by the application of the rule of Dulong and Petit coupled with the empirical rules of Gay-Lussac's Law of Combining Volumes and Mitscherlich's Law of Isomorphism, although it is not always possible to tell which rule most influenced different investigators in making their deductions. However, it is of interest to note that Berzelius

discredited the validity of the rule of Dulong and Petit because it did not function satisfactorily for several elements, of which carbon was one.

By 1831 Neumann extended the generalization of Dulong and Petit to include compounds and formulated a law for them: "Stoichiometrical quantities of bodies of analogous chemical composition have the same capacity for heat."[3]

( 403 )

| CHALEURS spécifiques (1). | | POIDS RELATIFS des atomes (2). | PRODUITS du poids de chaque atome par la capacité correspondante. |
|---|---|---|---|
| Bismuth, | 0,0288 | 13,30 | 0,3830 |
| Plomb, | 0,0293 | 12,95 | 0,3794 |
| Or, | 0,0298 | 12,43 | 0,3704 |
| Platine, | 0,0314 | 11,16 | 0,3749 |
| Etain, | 0,0514 | 7,35 | 0,3779 |
| Argent, | 0,0557 | 6,75 | 0,3759 |
| Zinc, | 0,0927 | 4,03 | 0,3736 |
| Tellure, | 0,0912 | 4,03 | 0,3675 |
| Cuivre, | 0,0949 | 3,957 | 0,3755 |
| Nickel, | 0,1035 | 3,69 | 0,3819 |
| Fer, | 0,1100 | 3,392 | 0,3731 |
| Cobalt, | 0,1498 | 2,46 | 0,3685 |
| Soufre, | 0,1880 | 2,011 | 0,3780 |

(1) La chaleur spécifique de l'eau est prise pour unité.

(2) Le poids de l'atome d'oxigène est supposé égal à un.

Figure 1. Photograph of a portion of page 403 of Ann. chim. et phys., **10** (1819), showing the table published by Dulong and Petit in their paper "Recherches sur quelques points important de la théorie de la chaleur."

Many other investigators extended the rules and methods for ascertaining atomic weights, but always on an empirical basis. Nevertheless, great confusion existed in this area during the entire first half of the nineteenth century. At the middle of the century the most noteworthy chemist working on atomic weights was Cannizzaro, who brought the work of Avogadro out of obscurity and refined the methods for establishing correct atomic weights and for determining the proper formulas of compounds. Cannizzaro, for example, was

[1] Present address: R. B. Worthy High School, Saltville, Virginia.

[2] DULONG P. L., AND PETIT, A. T., *Ann. chim. et phys.*, **10**, 395 (1819).

[3] NEUMANN, F., *Ann. Physik und Chem.*, **23**, 1 (1831): "Die stöchiometrischen Quantitäten bei chemisch ähnlich zusammengesetzten Stoffen besitzen gleiche specifische Wärme-Quantität."

## CHEMIKER ANEKDOTEN—WALTHER NERNST

PROFESSOR NERNST in retirement raised carp. When asked why not chickens, he said he preferred animals in thermodynamic equilibrium with their environment; why spend money to heat world space?

(See page 137)

convinced, from his work on vapor densities, that the atomic weight of mercury was 200, and not 100 as had been assumed. He found corroboration for the higher value in the heat capacity of calomel. If the formula were HgCl, corresponding to an atomic weight of 200 for mercury, the heat capacity of mercury should be one-third less than would be observed for the formula $Hg_2Cl$ appropriate to an atomic weight of 100. Thus application of the Law of Dulong and Petit and its corollary, Neumann's Law, was established as an important aid in determining the relation between the atomic weight and the experimental combining weight.

What is the significance of the empirical constant in the Law of Dulong and Petit? Except for methods using mass spectrometry, the fundamental requirement for the determination of atomic or molecular weights is that one be able to count the atoms or molecules, or at least that one be able to measure equal numbers of atoms or molecules for comparison. This is the principle involved in the measurement of the gram molecular volume for gases and of the freezing point depression for soluble non-ionizing liquids and solids. The Law of Dulong and Petit must also involve a counting of atoms. How does it do this?

To explain, we first need some definitions. Nearly everyone is familiar with the term "specific heat" but the related term "heat capacity" may not be so well known. The specific heat of a substance is the quantity of heat absorbed by a unit mass of the substance when its temperature is raised by one degree. The heat capacity of a system is the quantity of heat absorbed by the entire system when its temperature is raised by one degree. If we go further and define our system to be $6.023 \times 10^{23}$ atoms of a solid element (1 gram atom, or 1 "mole") the quantity of heat required to raise its temperature one degree is called the molar heat capacity and is given the symbol $C$. If we assume, as we do with specific heat, that heat capacity is the same for a one-degree interval anywhere in the range of convenient temperatures, we may calculate that the energy absorbed in heating a gram atom from $T_0$ to $T$ is $C(T - T_0)$.

## Heat Capacity of a Perfect Gas

Although the law stated by Dulong and Petit applies only to solid elements, there is nothing in the above definitions that restricts us to such a system. Suppose instead that we discuss a mole of a perfect monatomic gas. The reason for choosing a substance like this is the fact that we may now neglect any energy involving the electrons and the nucleus, and can presume that all the energy of the system is kinetic energy. We know something about kinetic energy. The kinetic energy of a molecule of mass $m$ moving with speed $v$ is $1/2mv^2$, and the kinetic energy of $N$ molecules will be $1/2Nmv^2$. If $N$ is Avogadro's number, this is the energy of a mole of gas. Since we assume that a perfect gas has no kinetic energy at absolute zero, the total energy (all kinetic) at temperature $T$ is given by our heat capacity equation as $E = C(T - 0) = CT$. The experimental value for the heat capacity of a monatomic gas (at constant volume) is 3 calories per mole per degree centigrade, so the total energy at temperature $T$ can be calculated to be $3T$ calories.

It is easy to show that this must be the case. From the experimental gas laws we know that for a mole of gas, $PV = RT$, where $R$ is a constant. From the kinetic theory of gases, as derived in textbooks of college physics or physical chemistry, we know further that for a mole of gas, $PV = 1/3 \, Nm\overline{v^2}$. Here $\overline{v^2}$ is the average of the square of the speed of the gas molecules. Equating the two expressions, we get $1/3 \, Nm\overline{v^2} = RT$. But the energy of a mole of gas, $E$, is $1/2 \, Nm\overline{v^2}$ and substitution gives $E = 3/2 \, RT$. Because the value of $R$ in calories per degree per mole is 2, the molar heat capacity $E/T$ is found to be $3/2 \, R$, or 3 calories per degree per mole, in agreement with experiment.

It is also pertinent to discuss the average energy per molecule. This is obtained by dividing $E$ by $N$

$$\epsilon = \frac{E}{N} = \frac{3}{2} \frac{RT}{N} = \frac{3}{2} kT$$

where $k$ is known as Boltzmann's constant and may be considered to be the gas constant per molecule.

The speed of a molecule may be expressed in terms of the components of velocity in three perpendicular directions as $v^2 = u^2 + y^2 + w^2$. The average values of these four quantities are similarly related, $\overline{v^2} = \overline{u^2} + \overline{y^2} = \overline{w^2}$. Since the molecules have an equal probability of moving in any direction, the average of the square for any one component will be the same as that for the other two, or $\overline{u^2} = \overline{y^2} = \overline{w^2}$, and $\overline{v^2} = 3\overline{u^2}$. Hence the total average kinetic energy of a molecule, $1/2 \, m\overline{v^2}$, is equal to three times the average kinetic energy of motion in one direction:

$$\epsilon = \frac{3}{2} kT = \frac{1}{2}m\overline{v^2} = 3 \times \frac{1}{2} \, m\overline{u^2}$$

and $1/2 \, m\overline{u^2} = 1/2 \, kT$. What we have shown, then, is that the average kinetic energy associated with motion in one direction is $1/2 \, kT$.

The equating of $\overline{u^2}$ to $\overline{y^2}$ and to $\overline{w^2}$, and, hence of $\overline{v^2}$ to $3\overline{u^2}$, is really an application of the principle of equipartition of energy. This principle states that when energies may be described by giving appropriate values to the squares of certain fundamental variables, the average energy associated with each such variable is the same. In the perfect gas case just discussed, the fundamental variables are the three perpendicular components of velocity $u$, $y$, and $w$; the energy is described in terms of the squares of these as

$$\epsilon = \frac{1}{2}mu^2 + \frac{1}{2}my^2 + \frac{1}{2}mw^2$$

and the average energy associated with each such variable is $1/2 \, m\overline{u^2}$, $1/2 \, m\overline{y^2}$ and $1/2 \, m\overline{w^2}$. The principle of equipartition of energy states that these three average energies must be the same: $1/2 \, m\overline{u^2} = 1/2 \, m\overline{v^2} = 1/2 \, m\overline{w^2}$, and we have just calculated the value of each of the averages as $1/2 \, kT$. The equipartition principle says that these results are of general application, and calculation of the average energy value shows it always to be $1/2 \, kT$, just as it was in the special case of the perfect monatomic gas.

There are many places in physics and chemistry in which the energy is expressed in terms of the square of a variable. In translational motion we are concerned

with the square of the velocity components, $u^2$, $y^2$, and $w^2$, giving the corresponding energies $\frac{1}{2}mu^2$, $\frac{1}{2}my^2$, and $\frac{1}{2}mw^2$. In rotational motion the energy is expressed by $\frac{1}{2}I\omega^2$, where $I$ is the moment of inertia and $\omega$ the angular velocity, again a variable appearing as a square. In simple harmonic motion we describe the kinetic energy of a particle vibrating at the end of a spring as $\frac{1}{2}mv^2$, where $m$ and $v$ are its mass and velocity, and the potential energy of the stretched spring by $\frac{1}{2}Kd^2$, where $K$ is the Hooke's Law constant and $d$ the displacement from the rest position. Each of these quantities, needed to describe the energy of a system, is called a squared term, and the equipartition principle tells us that the energy $\frac{1}{2}kT$ is, on the average, associated with each squared term. If $n$ such squared terms are needed to describe the energy, then the total energy will be $n/2kT$.

A molecule of a monatomic gas needs three squared terms, corresponding to its possibility of motion in three directions, and its energy is $\frac{3}{2}kT$. A molecule of a diatomic gas has the same possibilities of translational motion as a monatomic gas and needs three squared terms to describe its translational energy. In addition, however, the diatomic molecule can undergo rotation (end over end, like a dumbbell) about either of two axes perpendicular to each other and to a line joining the two atoms, and thus requires two more squared terms to describe the energy associated with this rotational motion. Two further squared terms are needed to describe the kinetic and potential energies arising from the harmonic vibratory motion as the atoms stretch and compress the valence bond between them. On the basis of the principle of equipartition of energy, we would predict that the average energy of a diatomic molecule should be $(3 + 2 + 2) \times (\frac{1}{2}kT) = \frac{7}{2}kT$, for the seven squared terms needed to describe its motion. If this prediction is correct, the energy of a mole of a diatomic gas should be $\frac{7}{2}NkT = \frac{7}{2}RT$, and the heat capacity should be $1/T(\frac{7}{2}RT) = \frac{7}{2}R$.

Unfortunately, our prediction is found to be more often incorrect than correct. The heat capacity per mole is close to $\frac{7}{2}R$ for the diatomic molecule $I_2$, but for the lighter molecules such as oxygen or nitrogen it is only $\frac{5}{2}R$ (Table 1). The explanation formerly given for this was that in these lighter elements, in contrast to iodine, the vibratory motion was somehow "frozen," so that heat energy which was fed to the molecule did not increase the displacement $d$ and velocity $v$, or at least not as much as one might have expected. Hence the energy associated with these modes of motion was not proportional to $kT$, as required by the equipartition principle, and the heat capacity was less than $\frac{7}{2}R$ in consequence. Acceptance of this explanation thus demands—correctly, as it turns out—that we admit the principle of equipartition to be not exact, but only an approximation.

## Application of Equipartition to Solids

What has all this discussion of gases to do with the Law of Dulong and Petit, which is concerned only with the specific heat of solid elements? The answer is that the atoms in a solid are in motion, just as are the molecules in a gas and the atoms within those molecules. In a solid, however, the atoms do not move from one

### Table I.   Heat Capacities of Gases at Constant Volume

| Gas | $H_2$ | $N_2$ | $O_2$ | $F_2$ | $Cl_2$ | $Br_2$ | $I_2$ |
|---|---|---|---|---|---|---|---|
| Heat capacity (cal/mole at 25°) | 4.9 | 5.0 | 5.0 | 5.5 | 6.1 | 6.6 | 6.8 |

place to another, but execute only a vibratory motion about their equilibrium positions in the crystal lattice.

Let us assume that the energy of the crystal is divided into two parts. One part, which we can denote by $E_0$, fixes the atoms in their equilibrium positions; this part is a definite characteristic of the crystal, and cannot be changed without destroying the crystal. The second part of the energy, $E$, will allow for the motion of the atoms away from and back to their equilibrium positions. While the first part is fixed and hence independent of the temperature, the second part can be changed by increasing the displacements of the atoms from equilibrium, and will so change as the temperature increases. It is this second part which will be observed in measurements of heat capacity, for if at temperature $T'$ the energy is $E_o + E'$ and at $T$ it is $E_o + E$, the energy input in going from $T$ to $T'$ is $(E_o + E') - (E_o + E) = E' - E$ and the heat capacity is $(E' - E)/(T' - T)$. Thus for our purposes we need consider only the second, temperature-dependent, part of the energy.

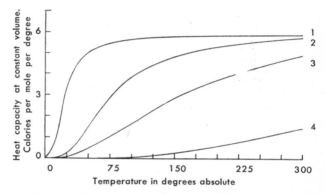

Figure 2. Molar heat capacities as a function of temperature: curve 1 lead; curve 2, copper; curve 3, silicon; curve 4, carbon (diamond).

Let us imagine that the atoms are held to their equilibrium positions by little springs which obey Hooke's Law. The atoms will then undergo simple harmonic motion and will have kinetic energy $\frac{1}{2}mv^2$ and potential energy $\frac{1}{2}Kd^2$. The motion of the atoms can be described in terms of the components of the motion in three perpendicular directions in space. With two squared terms ($\frac{1}{2}mv^2$ and $\frac{1}{2}Kd^2$) needed for each direction there will be a total of $3 \times 2 = 6$ squared terms in all. If the principle of equipartition of energy is applicable, the average energy in these 6 squared terms will be $6 \times \frac{1}{2}kT = 3kT$. Then the total energy for $N$ atoms will be $N \times 3kT$, and the total energy serves to measure the number of atoms. Each atom brings a package of energy $3kT$ to the total energy of the solid. This, the essence of the Law of Dulong and Petit, was first pointed out by Boltzmann[4] in 1871.

We do not measure the energy directly, but rather its change with temperature. Again at temperatures

[4] BOLTZMANN, L., *Sitzber. kgl. Akad. Wiss.*, Wien, **63**, 2, 679 (1871).

$T'$ and $T$ it is $E_o + 3NkT'$ and $E_o + 3NkT$, so that the heat capacity is

$$C = \frac{(E_o + 3NkT') - (E_o + 3NkT)}{T' - T} = \frac{3Nk(T' - T)}{T' - T} = 3Nk$$

If $N$ is Avogadro's number, $3Nk = 3R$, and the heat capacity for a mole of atoms in a solid should be 6 calories per degree.[5] The heat capacity for a mole is equal to the mass of $N$ atoms (that is, the gram atomic weight) times the specific heat, and we arrive at the usual equation of the Law of Dulong and Petit,

(gram atomic weight) $\times$ (specific heat) = 6 calories/degree

The heat capacities and specific heats to be used in the above calculations are those at constant volume. The quantity usually measured is the heat capacity at constant (atmospheric) pressure. For a solid substance the heat capacity at constant volume is almost the same as the heat capacity at constant pressure, and the last equation, above, is nearly correct when the measured specific heats are used. This difference between $C_V$ and $C_P$, however, would prevent the "constant" of the Dulong and Petit equation from being the same for all substances, even if there were no other reasons why it should not be constant.[6]

## How Constant Is the "Constant"?

But there are other reasons why it should not be constant. Dulong and Petit were fortunate in that the common substances, and in particular the ones listed in Figure 1, do have their energies divided among the squared terms with the value of $1/2 kT$ for each, in accord with the principle of equipartition of energy. The cases studied by Dulong and Petit occupy a position comparable to that of iodine molecules in the diatomic gas case. Had they worked with some of the lighter elements (or even with those they did examine, but at much lower temperatures) their data would have been much more difficult to interpret. This is evident from the curves of Figure 2, which show the change of the heat capacity per mole with change in temperature for different elements. It is evident that the heat capacity decreases from the equipartition value, $3R$, as the temperature decreases, and more rapidly for light elements than for heavy ones. Again we try an explanation that the vibrations are partly frozen, so that their energies are less than $1/2 kT$ and change in some manner other than in direct proportion to the temperature. Another way of saying this is to say that the principle of equipartition of energy is a good approximation only at high temperatures.

If the principle of equipartition of energy is only an approximation to the truth, what is the correct description of the vibrational energy of a solid? The answer is that the vibrational energies are quantized, as all energies are. For a simple harmonic oscillator of fundamental frequency $\nu$, the quantum theory tells us that the energy is given by $E = 1/2 h\nu + vh\nu$, where $h$ is Planck's constant and $v$ is the vibrational quantum

number. From this we can show that for $3N$ such oscillators independent of each other and all with the same fundamental frequency,[7] the energy is

$$E - E_o = \frac{3Nh\nu}{(e^{h\nu/kT} - 1)}$$

Thus the variation with temperature is not the direct proportion given by the equipartition principle. When $T$ is small, the term on the right-hand side is very small, and the heat capacity is correspondingly small. As $T$ becomes larger, however, $e^{h\nu/kT}$ becomes smaller and the energy (and the heat capacity) increases. This is in accord with the curves of Figure 2. When $h\nu/kT$ is small enough, we may represent $e^{h\nu/kT}$ by the first two terms of the infinite mathematical series

$$1 + \left(\frac{h\nu}{kT}\right) + \frac{1}{2}\left(\frac{h\nu}{kT}\right)^2 + \frac{1}{6}\left(\frac{h\nu}{kT}\right)^3 + \frac{1}{24}\left(\frac{h\nu}{kT}\right)^4 + \cdots$$

and approximately

$$E - E_0 = \frac{3Nh\nu}{1 + h\nu/kT - 1} = 3NkT = 3RT$$

We thus obtain the same result at high temperatures as is obtained from the equipartition principle. The substitution of $1 + h\nu/kT$ as an approximation for $e^{h\nu/kT}$ is satisfactory only when $h\nu/kT$ is small; hence a substance whose oscillators have a high frequency will require a higher temperature to approach the equipartition value $3NkT$ than will be needed for a substance with a smaller value of $\nu$. This accounts for the difference between diamond and lead in Figure 2. Diamond has a vibration frequency more than 10 times that of lead; in terms of the spring model above, the springs holding the carbon atoms in place are much stiffer (their force constants are greater) than those for the lead atoms.

There are still two difficulties. The equation derived by Einstein predicts that the specific heats at constant volume which are calculated from it will be equal to $3R$ at high temperatures and will drop off at low temperatures, and this is an agreement with experiment; however, the shape of the curve obtained on plotting the calculated $C_V$ against $T$ is different from that found experimentally. Hence there is something wrong with the theory. The trouble is that we assumed the oscillators to be independent of each other and to have the same frequency. Actually the atoms are tied together and vibrate in unison with a great many different frequencies. To specify exactly what the energy was, these frequencies would have to be related to the elastic constants of the crystal, which determine, for example, the transmission of sound through it. An approximation due to Debye[8] presumes that the frequencies have values between zero and a maximum value and that the number of oscillators having a particular frequency increases with the frequency in the same way that the volume of a spherical shell increases with the radius of the shell. The result of using this approximation is to obtain a heat capacity-temperature curve, Figure 2, which agrees closely with experiment. It predicts a maximum value of $3R$ at high temperatures and a change proportional to $T^3$ at low temperatures.

---

[5] Strictly speaking it should be $3NkT - (6 \times 1/2 kT) = (3N - 3)kT$ since 6 squared terms determine the translational and rotational motion of the solid as a whole. However $(3N - 3)kT$ is indistinguishable from $3NkT$ if $N$ is very large, as it is when it is Avogadro's number.

[6] Lewis, G. N., *J. Am. Chem. Soc.*, **29**, 1165, 1516 (1907).

[7] Einstein, A., *Ann. Physik*, **22**, 180, 800 (1907).

[8] Debye, P., *Ann. Physik*, **13**, 789 (1912).

The other difficulty with the equation is that it predicts a maximum of $3R$ for the heat capacity at constant volume. Actually the experimental data show values higher than this, particularly for the metals, as shown by the following values for platinum:

| Temp. (°C) | $C_V$(cal/mole/degree) |
|---|---|
| 20 | 5.95 |
| 500 | 6.4 |
| 1600 | 6.65 |

For non-metallic solid elements the increase is very slight in the range where they are still solid. The reason for the increase is that in metals the valence electrons are more or less free to move, and at high temperatures the absorption of energy in their motion contributes to the heat capacity. This effect is not great near room temperature, but it too helps to make the observed value of the "constant" of the Law of Dulong and Petit not quite constant.

From what has been said above it is evident that a complete study of the Law of Dulong and Petit could include a broad field of physical chemistry. Far from being the empirical law of 1819 recorded in the textbooks, it leads through statistical mechanics and quantum theory to the whole modern study of the physics of the solid state. It is a tribute to the astuteness of the investigators of 140 years ago that their bold generalization from the data of Figure 1 stands today as a limiting case reached under appropriate conditions by the complex apparatus of modern theories.

## Bibliography

*Historical Information*

Alembic Club Reprints, University of Chicago Press: No. 2, "Foundations of the Atomic Theory" (comprising Papers and Extracts by John Dalton, William Hyde Wollaston, M.D., and Thomas Thomson, M.D.), 1802–08, 44 pp.; No. 4, "Foundation of the Molecular Theory" (comprising Papers and Extracts by John Dalton, Joseph Louis Gay-Lussac, Amedeo Avogadro), 1808–11, 52 pp.; No. 18, "Sketch of a Course of Chemical Philosophy" by Stanislao Cannizzaro, 1958, 55 pp.

CONANT, J. B., AND NASH, L. K., eds., "Harvard Case Histories in Experimental Science," vol. 1, case no. 4, in "The Atomic-Molecular Theory," Harvard Univ. Press, Cambridge, Massachusetts, 1957, 115 pp.

LEICESTER, H. M., AND KLICKSTEIN, H. S., "A Source Book in Chemistry (1400–1900)," McGraw-Hill Book Co., Inc., New York, 1952, pp. 208–20, 231–38, 258–65, 272–75, 292–308, and 406–17.

*Discussions of Theory*

MOORE, WALTER, "Physical Chemistry," 2nd ed., Longmans, Green & Co., Inc., New York, 1957, pp. 163–66, 188–93, and 406–10:

MAYER, J. R., AND MAYER, M. G., "Statistical Mechanics," John Wiley & Sons, Inc., 1948, chap. 11.

# FRIEDRICH ROCHLEDER (1819-74)

## MORITZ KOHN
New York, New York
*Translated by Henry M. Leicester*

THE Chemical Institute of the University of Vienna was built according to the plans of Josef Redtenbacher.[1] When Redtenbacher died (1870) Friedrich Rochleder, until then professor in the University of Prague, was chosen as his successor. Rochleder was born in Vienna (1819), studied medicine in the University of Vienna, and became Doctor of Medicine in 1842. He obtained his chemical training in Liebig's laboratory in Giessen (1842 and 1843). In 1845 he became professor in the newly founded Technical Academy in Lemberg, in 1849 he was called to the University of Prague as successor when Redtenbacher was called to Vienna, and in 1870 he became Redtenbacher's successor in Vienna. Rochleder was a full member of the Imperial Vienna Academy of Sciences from its establishment (1848). The new building of the Chemical Institute was not completed when Rochleder was called to Vienna and he occupied the building first in 1873.

Rochleder and his pupil Heinrich Hlasiwetz[2] (1825–75) founded the study of plant chemistry (phytochemistry) in Austria. Rochleder was especially interested in the study of substances in plants which were closely related botanically. In his activities in Prague he found in Hlasiwetz an excellent collaborator. Hlasiwetz, in his later independent work, continued under the influences which he had felt in Rochleder's laboratory. Rochleder worked on the constituents of the coffee bean, the horse chestnut, reactions of tannins, caffeine, and different glucosides. He also carried on work with Theodor Wertheim (1820–64) who from 1861 to 1864 was professor in the University of Graz. Rochleder and Wertheim reported in 1845 and 1849 on a volatile base which resulted from treating piperin from pepper with alkali. In 1853 Cahours characterized this base, piperidine, more carefully. The discovery of the amines led to the recognition that various plant substances contained methyl groups united to the nitrogen. Rochleder obtained a base from caffeine which he called "formylin." Shortly afterward (1849) Wurtz showed that Rochleder's formylin was methyl amine. In 1851 Rochleder isolated from madder root the glucoside of alizarin which he called ruberythric

[1] KOHN, M., J. CHEM. EDUC., **24**, 366 (1947).
[2] KOHN, M., *ibid.*, **22**, 55 (1945).

*(Concluded on page 221)*

# J. A. R. NEWLANDS: A PIONEER IN ATOMIC NUMBERS

**WENDELL H. TAYLOR**
The Lawrenceville School, Lawrenceville, New Jersey

A HALF-CENTURY has elapsed since the death of John Newlands and a reappraisal of his work is long overdue. For Newlands has suffered something worse than neglect: he is widely remembered for but a portion of his work which has been misrepresented and misunderstood by many of his warmest partisans.

John Alexander Reina Newlands

As the author of the Law of Octaves—a pioneering generalization which preceded those of Mendeleeff and Meyer by nearly five years—the name of Newlands finds a place in every history of 19th century chemistry, nor do we lack sympathetic accounts of the ridicule which met the English chemist when he presented his ideas on the periodicity of the elements to the London Chemical Society in 1866. Newlands was belatedly honored by his fellow countrymen in 1887 by the presentation of the Davy Medal of the Royal Society, five years after Mendeleeff and Meyer had been similarly recognized. But the recording of these facts in most of the histories is a poor substitute for a comprehensive account of Newlands' work. The final, improved version of Newlands' table of the elements has not been reprinted by any of his commentators, several of whom have grossly distorted the earlier tables which they discuss. Newlands' very original work of 1872-78 on atomic numbers has also been much neglected, thereby helping to create the picture of an ill-starred minor genius who collapsed completely after the cold reception accorded his prophetic proposal of 1866. Actually, Newlands published no fewer than sixteen papers at fairly regular intervals between 1863 and 1890, all dealing with the classification of the elements and with his claim to be recognized as the discoverer of the Periodic Law.

Since most of the critical summaries of Newlands' work were written prior to the elucidation of atomic numbers by Moseley in 1913–14 it is not surprising that the earlier Englishman's speculations in this field aroused little interest. But today Newlands' constant emphasis upon the ordinal numbers of the elements is one of the most interesting features of his work, to an account of which we may now turn.

John Alexander Reina Newlands was born in 1837, only a short walk from Faraday's birthplace in Southwark, London (1). He was educated privately by his father, the Rev. William Newlands, a minister of the Established Church of Scotland and a graduate of Glasgow University. From his mother, who was of Italian descent, young Newlands very likely inherited the taste for music which at a later date showed itself even in his chemical theorizing. Doubtless this Italian strain was also partly responsible for his joining the insurrectionary movement under Garibaldi which attracted so many English volunteers to Italy in May, 1860. Only in November of that year did Newlands return to England to resume his work with Professor Way, chemist to the Royal Agricultural Society, whose assistant he had become in 1857 after a year at the Royal College of Chemistry. After 1864 Newlands set up in analytical practice on his own account and at this time and for some years afterward was a teacher of chemistry at the Grammar School of St. Saviour, Southwark, at the School of Medicine for Women, and at the City of London College. For most of his professional life Newlands was an expert in sugar chemistry. He became chief chemist at the refinery of J. Duncan in 1868 and developed several improvements in processing, including the alum process for purification of beet molasses. A treatise on sugar, written in collaboration with his brother (2), and various technical articles including those on "Sugar" in Thorpe's Dictionary are evidence of his stature in his field. After 1886, when he retired from the sugar refinery, Newlands returned to his consulting practice in partnership with his brother, B. E. R. Newlands. He died of influenza in July, 1898, leaving a widow, as well as a son who took his father's place in the firm. He was remembered by one of his most illustrious contemporaries (3) as a kindly, courteous man, and this is borne out by the prevailingly even and modest tone of the numerous printed claims of priority in the matter of the Periodic Law which a sense of justice and self-respect led him to issue from time to time until his death.

Enough has been said to show that Newlands was far from a chemical nobody, quite apart from his work on the classification of the elements. But in the latter he showed from the start a quite unusual grasp of a difficult contemporary problem. Before 1860 Gmelin (4), Pettenkofer (5), and Dumas (6) had developed the triad concept of Döbereiner (7) to a considerable degree, and Gladstone (8), Cooke (9), and Odling (10) had published elaborate tables of elements which accomplished little save to stress the existence of family resemblences; the highly inaccurate atomic weights then in use prevented the emergence of any relationship between all known elements. Only after the Karlsruhe Conference of 1860, at which Cannizzaro distributed his famous pamphlet (11) clarifying the problem of atomic and molecular weights, did the way lie open for the adoption of consistent atomic weight values. Young and enthusiastic, Newlands was among the first to accept the new atomic weights based upon the hypothesis of Avogadro. An early paper (12), mainly a re-working of Dumas' ideas of 1857, classified the elements in eleven families and sought to discover simple arithmetical relationships among their equivalents (on the old basis) but really presented nothing new. A year later Newlands, at the early age of 27 and only four years after Cannizzaro's revelation, had adopted the new atomic weights, using those published by Willliamson (13) and was already in possession of the great secret of periodicity among the elements.

Gladstone's list of 1853 had arranged the 56 known

Mr. JOHN A. R. NEWLANDS read a paper entitled " *The Law of Octaves, and the Causes of Numerical Relations among the Atomic Weights.*" The author claims the discovery of a law according to which the elements analogous in their properties exhibit peculiar relationships, similar to those subsisting in music between a note and its octave. Starting from the atomic weights on Cannizzaro's system, the author arranges the known elements in order of succession, beginning with the lowest atomic weight (hydrogen) and ending with thorium (= 231·5); placing, however, nickel and cobalt, platinum and iridium, cerium and lanthanum, &c., in positions of absolute equality or in the same line. The fifty-six elements so arranged are said to form the compass of eight octaves, and the author finds that chlorine, bromine, iodine, and fluorine are thus brought into the same line, or occupy corresponding places in his scale. Nitrogen and phosphorus, oxygen and sulphur, &c., are also considered as forming true octaves. The author's supposition will be exemplified in Table II., shown to the meeting, and here subjoined :—

*Table II.—Elements arranged in Octaves.*

| No. | | No. | | No. | | No. | | No. | | No. | | No. | | No. | |
|---|---|---|---|---|---|---|---|---|---|---|---|---|---|---|---|
| H | 1 | F | 8 | Cl | 15 | Co & Ni | 22 | Br | 29 | Pd | 36 | I | 42 | Pt & Ir | 50 |
| Li | 2 | Na | 9 | K | 16 | Cu | 23 | Rb | 30 | Ag | 37 | Cs | 44 | Os | 51 |
| G | 3 | Mg | 10 | Ca | 17 | Zn | 24 | Sr | 31 | Cd | 38 | Ba & V | 45 | Hg | 52 |
| Bo | 4 | Al | 11 | Cr | 19 | Y | 25 | Ce & La | 33 | U | 40 | Ta | 46 | Tl | 53 |
| C | 5 | Si | 12 | Ti | 18 | In | 26 | Zr | 32 | Sn | 39 | W | 47 | Pb | 54 |
| N | 6 | P | 13 | Mn | 20 | As | 27 | Di & Mo | 34 | Sb | 41 | Nb | 48 | Bi | 55 |
| O | 7 | S | 14 | Fe | 21 | Se | 28 | Ro & Ru | 35 | Te | 43 | Au | 49 | Th | 56 |

Figure 1

elements in order of increasing atomic weight, but since the values he used were erroneous in three-quarters of the cases, owing to incorrect ideas of valency, the sequence of elements was meaningless. Newlands therefore must take the credit for publishing the first list of elements correctly arranged in order of increasing atomic weight. He was led to do this in refutation of a suggestion that the atomic weights are multiples of eight, made by an anonymous contemporary. But in the same communication (14) he shows that he had already sensed the division into repeating families which such an arrangement of elements gives. Acknowledging its incompleteness and referring to other tables he had prepared "of a more complete character," Newlands presented a table of 37 elements arranged in ten horizontal families (three of them fragmentary) which was a considerable advance on those current at the time. It is scarcely necessary to reprint this, but it is important to note that in this early table Newlands was quite aware of the need for leaving blanks for uncertain or undiscovered elements. His failure to do so later was a principal cause of mistrust of the Law of Octaves and the tables which illustrated it. In this early table of 1864 Newlands left many blanks, including those appropriate for aluminum (which for some reason he did not include) and those for the unknown scandium, yttrium, indium, and germanium, for the last of which he correctly predicted the atomic weight.

Within a month of this Newlands published (15) a portion of another table in which he had assigned to the elements, arranged as before, a series of consecutive atomic numbers. He was quite explicit about this, "calling hydrogen 1, lithium 2, glucinum 3, boron 4, and so on . . ." and was able to observe that "elements having consecutive numbers frequently occupy similar positions in different groups." From this time henceforth the concept of the ordinal numbers of the elements was to play a central part in all of Newlands' speculations.

In the busy year between August, 1864 and August, 1865, Newlands tried several schemes for arranging the elements so as to bring out the parallel family relationships to good advantage, and came back again and again to that based upon the atomic numbers. We have his word for it that he "had tried several other schemes before arriving at that now proposed. One founded upon the specific gravity of the elements had altogether failed, and no relation could be worked out of the atomic weights under any other system than that of Cannizzaro." The system "now proposed" was first given to the public in August, 1865 (16). The table of 62 elements arranged in eight vertical columns according to increasing atomic weight and forming seven horizontal families has often been reprinted correctly. A portion of the memorable announcement which accompanied it must, however, be quoted.

If the elements are arranged in the order of their equivalents with a few slight transpositions, as in the accompanying table, it will be observed that elements belonging to the same group usually appear on the same horizontal line. It will also be seen that the numbers of analogous elements generally differ either by 7 or by some multiple of seven; in other words, members of the same group stand to each other in the same relation as the extremities of one or more octaves in music.... The eighth element starting from a given one is a kind of repetition of the first. This peculiar relationship I propose to provisionally term the *Law of Octaves*.

A week later Newlands, full of his new scheme, published another short article (*17*) in which he endeavored to show "that all the numerical relationships among the equivalents, pointed out by M. Dumas and others, including the well-known triads, are merely arithmetical results flowing from the existence of the *Law of Octaves*." There is no record that the sweeping generalizations thus brought before the chemical world excited much interest nor, in fact, that they were really understood. A few months earlier Odling, one of the most astute students of the elements, had published another attempt at classification (*18*) in which he made use of the new atomic weights, but came to no valuable conclusion save that "among the members of every well-defined group the sequence of properties and the sequence of atomic weights are strictly parallel to each other" and

| | | | | | | H 1<br>1 |
|---|---|---|---|---|---|---|
| Li 2<br>7 | Be 3<br>9 | B 4<br>11 | C 5<br>12 | N 6<br>14 | O 7<br>16 | F 8<br>19 |
| Na 9<br>23 | Mg 10<br>24 | Al 11<br>27.5 | Si 12<br>28 | P 13<br>31 | S 14<br>32 | Cl 15<br>35.5 |
| K 16<br>39 | Ca 17<br>40 | Cr 19<br>52.5 | Ti 18<br>(50) | Mn 20<br>55 | Fe 21<br>56 | Co, Ni 22<br>58.5 |
| Cu 23<br>63.5 | Zn 25<br>65 | Y 24<br>(64) | In 26<br>(72) | As 27<br>75 | Se 28<br>79.5 | Br 29<br>80 |
| Rb 30<br>85 | Sr 31<br>87.5 | Ce, La 33<br>(92) | Zr 32<br>89.5 | Di, Mo 34<br>(96) | Rh, Ru 35<br>104 | Pd 36<br>106.5 |
| Ag 37<br>108 | Cd 38<br>112 | U 40<br>(120) | Sn 39<br>118 | Sb 41<br>122 | Te 43<br>129 | I 42<br>127 |
| Cs 44<br>133 | Ba, V 45<br>(137) | Ta 46<br>(138) | W 47<br>184 | Nb 48<br>(195) | Au 49<br>(196) | Pt, Ir 50<br>(197) |
| Os 51<br>(199) | Hg 52<br>200 | Tl 53<br>203 | Pb 54<br>207 | Bi 55<br>210 | Th 56<br>238 | |

**Figure 2.  Newlands' 1866 Table Rearranged in Vertical Families**

*Note:* The atomic numbers follow the symbols and are those of Newlands.  Beneath each symbol is the atomic weight used by Newlands; where grossly inaccurate it is enclosed in parentheses.

after detailed examination of the numerical differences between the atomic weights of analogous elements decided that these relations, though possibly in part accidental, were "too numerous and decided not to depend upon some hitherto unrecognized law." The law dimly discerned by Odling was of course the Periodic Law, already clearly detected by Newlands though awkwardly named and poorly developed by him.

During the winter of 1865–66 Newlands worked on his new law and made substantial improvements in the table which illustrated it, guided throughout by the atomic numbers and not hesitating to place together in the same family elements then otherwise classified, if the sequence of atomic numbers demanded it. At last all was ready for the presentation of his ideas before the Chemical Society, of which Newlands had been a Fellow since 1860 and to whose Journal he had been an occasional contributor. Doubtless the young man hoped for helpful criticism from his senior colleagues, perhaps for encouragement and recognition, most certainly for their serious attention. He received but little.

The date was March 1, 1866, and the place Burlington House. The Vice-President, Professor A. W. Williamson, Ph.D., was in the chair—an eminent organic chemist who owed his fame to his discovery of the nature of the ether linkage, made when he was a young man of exactly Newlands' age. For the details of what occurred at this meeting we must depend upon its reporting in the *Chemical News* a week later (19). Routine business was transacted. Four papers were read and discussed, Newlands' being the second. The contributions of Church on new Cornish minerals, of Wanklyn on organo-metallic bodies, and of Wright on photographic papers all appeared duly in the *Journal of the Chemical Society*. Newlands' paper was returned to him later as "not adapted for publication in the Society's Journal." The only reason vouchsafed Newlands for this refusal was given him seven years later on the occasion of his attempting to secure publication in the same Journal of a brief note establishing priority in the matter of the discovery of the Periodic Law. Dr. Odling, then President, stated that the 1866 paper had not been published because they "had made it a rule not to publish papers of a purely theoretical nature, since it was likely to lead to correspondence of a controversial character." This suave rejoinder scarcely explains, however, why Newland's priority note of 1873 was not published either.

We must turn, then, to contemporary accounts and to Newlands' later reminiscences to learn just what was presented to the distinguished audience under the title: "The Law of Octaves and the Causes of Numerical Relations Among the Atomic Weights." Newlands' statement of the law was presumably the same as that given above. The table (see Fig. 1) which is here reprinted for the first time in 83 years, was a considerable improvement on the one of 1865, which is the one usually given.

The revised table resembles the one of 1865 in its failure to leave blank spaces for unknown elements, in its ill-judged location of the recently discovered indium, and in the assigning of the same atomic numbers to six pairs of elements whose atomic weights were nearly identical. But it has reduced from ten to four the cases of discontinuity in the series of atomic numbers. By following his new law nearly to the letter Newlands had placed Tl with B and Al instead of with the alkali metals as was then customary; he had also placed Pb with C, Si and Sn instead of with the alkaline earths, and had put Hg with Zn and Cd instead of with the ill-matched carbon family. Te and I he continued to place in reverse order of atomic weight, sensing as did Mendeleeff after him an exception from the general law which had to be left for a later generation to explain.

The new locations for some of these heavier elements came in for criticism almost as severe as that which was leveled at the lack of blanks in the table. Dr. Gladstone found the elements in the last vertical column to resemble each other more than they did the families in which Newlands had placed them. Another critic condemned an arrangement which placed such elements as Mn and Cr far apart, also the separation of Fe, Co, and Ni. But it is easy to see that what the meeting lacked was the necessary background for the appreciation of a scheme which proposed to trace a relationship among the atomic weights of all the elements. At that time, as Mendeleeff himself later remarked (20), only analogous elements were seriously compared, so that Newlands' proposals doubtless appeared grandiose. Even so, the laughter provoked in Burlington House by the Fellow who "humorously inquired" whether Newlands had thought of examining the elements in the order of their initial letters has a hollow sound today, and may serve forever as a warning to too-hasty critics.

Newlands replied soberly to his colleagues' objections, but most of his remarks are not of record. Two weeks later (21) he endeavored to make clear the provisional nature of his "octaves" and his belief that his new law would not be upset by the discovery of other elements. "For, although the difference in the numbers of analogous elements might in that case be altered from 7, or a multiple of 7, to 8, 9, 10, 20, or any conceivable figure, the existence of a simple relation among the numbers of analogous elements would be none the less evident." The discovery of the group of inert gases could clearly have been no blow to Newlands, and it is pleasant to think that he lived to witness a part of it.[1]

But, as H. S. Taylor has observed (22), if only these elements had been known in 1865, Newlands' unfortunate octave would never have been mentioned and his detractors would have had less to ridicule.

The independent discovery of the Periodic Law by

[1] Sir William Ramsay's book, "The Gases of the Atmosphere," dealing in part with helium and argon, was published in 1896 and contemporary chemical journals were full of the new elements. Newlands' last publication, a brief note in the *Chemical News* for June 26, 1896, bears witness that he had read carefully a page in the issue of the previous week on which appears an account of Ramsay's Boyle Lecture at Oxford on helium and argon.

Mendeleeff and Lothar Meyer in 1869–70 and its great development in the hands of both men soon left Newlands' table a little-known curio, but its author did not abandon his speculations. He welcomed the newly named law and adopted it as his own. He hailed Roscoe's new atomic weight for vanadium which made it possible for him to divorce that element from its uneasy location with barium and place it with nitrogen. He published two elaborate papers (23) in which, assuming a fairly constant ratio between atomic weight and atomic number, he endeavored to evaluate this constant and by division obtain a complete series of atomic numbers, including those of undiscovered elements. His final effort gave him 101 elements from hydrogen to uranium, with 37 intermediate blank spaces. In 1878, after the discovery of gallium had awakened the chemical world to the significance of Mendeleeff's work, Newlands summarized (24) his claims as discoverer of the Periodic Law, and six years later published a small book (25) containing a reprint of all his papers on the subject. He also sent a full account of his work to the German Chemical Society (26). These, together with the recommendations of Professor Frankland, brought him the Davy Medal in 1887. Fame, such as it was, did not dull his interest, and as late as 1890 Newlands published a keen rejoinder (27) to several inaccurate observations on his work made by Mendeleeff in his Faraday Lecture of 1889.

Trying finally to evaluate Newlands' achievement, we may consider the claims made by himself in 1878. These were:

(1) That he was the first to publish a list of the elements in the order of their atomic weights and also the first to describe the periodic law showing the existence of a simple relation between them when so arranged.
(2) That he applied this period law to the following among other subjects:

(a) Prediction of the atomic weights of missing elements, e. g., Ge = 73.
(b) Prediction of the probable atomic weights of elements whose atomic weights were unknown, e. g., In.
(c) Selection of Cannizzaro's atomic weights instead of the old system of equivalents.
(d) Prediction that the revision of atomic weights or the discovery of new elements would not upset the harmony of the law, since illustrated by the case of vanadium.
(e) Explaining the existence of numerical relationships between the atomic weights.
(f) Selecting that of two atomic weights assigned to an element which was more in accord with the periodic law, e. g., Be = 9.4 instead of 14.
(g) Grouping certain elements so as to conform to the periodic law instead of adopting the ordinary groups, e. g., Hg with the Mg group, Tl with the Al group, Pb with the C group, Te above I.
(h) Recognition of certain diagonal relationships, e. g., Li and Mg.

Without attempting, for the moment, to decide the justice of Newlands' first and major claim, we may readily admit the correctness of all the items in claim (2) since these are verifiable by reference to Newlands' published papers, all of those concerned being of earlier date than any by Mendeleeff or Meyer. To what ex-

tent Newlands was "applying" his Law of Octaves in some of these cases is nevertheless doubtful. One suspects that the imposing mass of deductive material assembled by Mendeleeff in his paper of 1871 (28) led the ill-treated Newlands to systematize his claims along the very lines in which the Russian was so impressive. But in the prediction of the undiscovered germanium, and of the atomic weights for beryllium and indium, it is worth noting that Newlands was correct in the first two cases and that in the third he made an alternate (correct) prediction which unfortunately was not the one he selected for his own use.

Finally, Newlands' chief claim: The discovery of the Periodic Law. If, as the present author believes, Newlands is to be credited with this, there are two matters to be settled. First, what of the speculations of de Chancourtois in 1862–63, and second, to what extent did the best table of elements produced by Newlands bear out his rather fancifully named generalization of 1865?

The work of de Chancourtois (29), with its three-dimensional helix and his terse statement that "the properties of bodies are the properties of numbers" has yet to receive thorough evaluation by the chemical historian. It was utterly unknown to the chemical world until 1889, and when presented then in the most favorable light by the Frenchman's compatriots still seemed a mathematical tangle to most chemists. In it are to be discerned things which we may now regard as a forecast of the Periodic Law, but one is tempted to agree with Sir William Crookes (30) that there is "...no sufficient evidence that the author disentangled such matter from accompanying speculations."

Newlands, on the other hand, was clear and explicit in his statement of the Law of Octaves, and careful to the point of infinitive splitting in the matter of the provisional nature of the octaves themselves. What he undoubtedly discovered and repeatedly urged upon a reluctant public was the repetition of similar properties after a regular interval, to be observed when the chemical elements are arranged in order of increasing atomic weight. This is the Periodic Law. If Newlands' table, given above, is rearranged so as to present the vertical families with which we are familiar (Fig. 2) and is then compared with Mendeleeff's table of 1871 the following correspondence[2] is to be noted:

(1) Disregarding the location of the three groups of transition elements (Fe, Co, Ni) (Ru, Rh, Pd) (Os, Ir, Pt) which Newlands bunched properly but did not attempt to place in an eighth column, and of hydrogen which is exceptional, there are 14 elements improperly placed by Newlands out of 62.
(2) Of these 14 elements, nine were assigned grossly incorrect atomic weights in 1864–65, but reasonably correct values for these were available to Mendeleeff by 1870. These nine elements were In, Ce, La, Di,[3] U, V, Ta, Au, and Os.
(3) Cr, Mn, Mo, Th, and W were misplaced by Newlands

---

[2] Garrett, A. E., "The Periodic Law," Appleton, New York, 1909, makes such a comparison but his use of the imperfect table of 1865 affords scant justice to Newlands.

[3] The rare earth "didymium" which, in 1885, von Welsbach showed to be a mixture of neodymium and praseodymium.

although their atomic weights were substantially correct. Of these, Cr was used to fill the space that should have been left blank for Sc. (Similarly, Newlands used In, with a misjudged atomic weight, to fill the space appropriate for Ge, which he had himself predicted.) Mn, although certainly not belonging in the nitrogen family, was properly placed with respect to Fe, Co, and Ni so that if these had been assigned to a column by themselves Mn would have fallen correctly among the halogens. The other three must be counted as unredeemed mistakes.

Viewed even in this most favorable light, it is easy to find fault with Newlands' table. It would truly be but a poor substitute for those we employ today, yet it points inescapably at the great generalization of the Periodic Law. Today we can scarcely deny the truth of the dictum with which Newlands sought to emphasize his claims as discoverer:[4]

## ACKNOWLEDGMENTS

The author wishes to acknowledge his indebtedness to the standard works by Freund (31), Garrett (32), Lowry (33), Rudorf (34), and Venable (35), and to express his appreciation of the help rendered by his former colleagues and the library staff of the Frick Chemical Laboratory, Princeton University. Thanks are also due Miss Elizabeth G. C. Menzies, who very painstakingly photographed the 1866 table.

## LITERATURE CITED

(1) Cameron, J. A., *Chem. Age*, **000**, 354 (1948). (Much of the biographical material in this paper is drawn from reference (3), *q. v.*)
(2) Lock, C. G. W., Newlands, B. E. R., and Newlands, J. A. R., "Sugar, A Handbook for Planters and Refiners," E. and F. N. Spon, London, **1888**.
(3) Tilden, Sir W. A., *Nature*, **58**, 395 (1898). (An obituary.)
(4) Gmelin, L., "Handbuch der Chemie," 4th ed., **1843**.
(5) Pettenkofer, M., *Ann.*, **105**, 187 (1858).
(6) Dumas, J. B., *Ann. chim. phys.*, **55** (3), 129 (1859).
(7) Döbereiner, J. W., *Pogg. Ann.*, **15**, 301 (1829).
(8) Gladstone, J. H., *Phil. Mag.*, **5** (IV), 313 (1853).
(9) Cooke, J. P., *Am. J. Sci.*, **17** (II), 387 (1854).
(10) Odling, W., *Phil. Mag.*, **13** (IV), 423, 480 (1857).
(11) Cannizzaro, S., "Sketch of a Course of Theoretical Chemistry Held at the University of Genoa," **1858**. German translation in Ostwald's *Klassiker der Exacten Wissenschaften*, No. 30.

[4] In his *Berichte* article of 1884 (*loc. cit.*). The German is Newlands' own:
So lange die Kernidee unverändert bleibt, kann die spätere Entwickelung einer Theorie an der Urheberschaft derselben nichts ändern.

(12) Newlands, J. A. R., *Chem. News*, **7**, 70 (1863). (Not Newlands' first chemical publication, however. A year earlier he had published in *J. Chem. Soc.*, **15**, 36 (1862) an ambitious paper on the construction of tables exhibiting the relations among organic substances.)
(13) Williamson, A. W., *J. Chem. Soc.*, **17**, 211 (1864).
(14) Newlands, J. A. R., *Chem. News*, **10**, 59 (1864).
(15) Newlands, J. A. R., *ibid.*, **10**, 94 (1864).
(16) Newlands, J. A. R., *ibid.*, **12**, 83 (1865).
(17) Newlands, J. A. R., *ibid.*, **12**, 94 (1865).
(18) Odling, W., *Quart. J. Sci.*, **1**, 642 (1864).
(19) Newlands, J. A. R., *Chem. News*, **13**, 113 (1866).
(20) Mendeleeff, D., "Faraday Lecture of June 4, 1889," *J. Chem. Soc.*, **55**, 634 (1889).
(21) Newlands, J. A. R., *Chem. News*, **13**, 130 (1866).
(22) Taylor, H. S., "Treatise on Physical Chemistry," 2nd ed., D. Van Nostrand Co., New York, **1931**, Vol. 1, p. 6.
(23) Newlands, J. A. R., *Chem. News*, **32**, 21 (1875) and **37**, 255 (1878).
(24) Newlands, J. A. R., *ibid.*, **38**, 106 (1878).
(25) Newlands, J. A. R., "On the Discovery of the Periodic Law and On Relations Among the Atomic Weights," E. and F. N. Spon, London, **1884**.
(26) Newlands, J. A. R., "Zur Geschichte des Periodischen Gesetzes," *Ber.*, **17**, 1145 (1884).
(27) Newlands, J. A. R., *Chem. News*, **61**, 136 (1890).
(28) Mendeleeff, D., *Ann.* (Supplement), **8**, 133–229 (1872). An English translation appeared in *Chem. News*, **40** and **41** (1879–80).
(29) Chancourtois, B. de, *Compt. rend.*, **55**, 757, 840, 967 (1862). These and later papers in *Compt. rend.* were reprinted by de Chancourtois' in a pamphlet issued by Mallet-Bachelier, Paris, **1863**.
Hartog, P., *Nature*, **41**, 186 (1889) gives English translation of de Chancourtois first paper, and de Boisbaudran and de Lapparent present a review of his work in *Compt. rend.*, **112**, 77 (1891).
(30) Crookes, Sir W., *Chem. News*, **63**, 51 (1891).
(31) Freund, I., "The Study of Chemical Composition," Cambridge University Press, **1904**. Prints the 1865 table only, correctly.
(32) Garrett, A. E., "The Periodic Law," Appleton, New York, **1909**. Gives the 1864 (triad) table and the 1865 table, both correctly.
(33) Lowry, T. M., "Historical Introduction to Chemistry," Macmillan, London, **1936**. Gives a rearranged version of the triad table and a badly confused table purporting to be of later date, but not corresponding to any of Newlands'.
(34) Rudorf, G., "Das Periodische System," Voss, Hamburg & Leipzig, **1904**. A fair critical study, unfortunately with serious errors in both the early tables presented.
(35) Venable, F., "The Development of the Periodic Law," Chemical Publishing Co., Easton, Pa., **1896**. An inappreciative treatment of Newlands' work, coupled with a table which is a composite of the 1866 and 1865 tables, badly confused.

—————— ✦ ——————

## Prout's Hypothesis    *Continued from page 146*

Meyer's idea was incorporated into W. Preyer's "Genetic System of the Chemical Elements." In the introduction he states his hope that:[33]

. . . the hypothesis of the derivation of the elements of high atomic weight from those of lower atomic weight and finally from one extremely finely divided primordial matter, or from

[33] Translated from Preyer, W., "Das genetische System der chemischen Elemente," R. Friedländer und Sohn, Berlin, **1893**, p. iv.

hydrogen, or from hydrogen and the universally distributed ether . . . may soon . . . claim the rank of a theory.

This theory died with the modern recasting of physics which has discarded the ether concept, but the foregoing suggestions show the tenacity with which an idea is held even when disproved in its original form. Since Prout's hypothesis has been resurrected in the form of our knowledge of isotopes, it looks as though one should be as cautious about discarding a plausible theory as in putting forward a new one.

not have the concept of $R_f$ but always recorded the height of rise of solvent and of the colored zone. He tried to relate these distances to the concentrations of materials being studied. With smaller quantities of compound and with greater sophistication in choice of solvent he might have obtained discrete spots rather than zones.

In another work published in 1901[3] Goppelsroeder reviewed the history of capillary analysis and detailed his own work between 1861 and 1901. He used wood, wool, linen, silk, and parchment as well as filter paper in his experiments. He also used filter paper impregnated with albumin and suggested conversion of the cellulose to oxycellulose to give greater definition.

During his career Goppelsroeder investigated dyes, alkaloids, fats, and oils, petroleum products, beverages, and inorganic ions. In his later dye experiments he attempted separation of mixtures containing as many as ten components.

In his work with natural oils, Goppelsroeder studied the rise of pure oils over periods as long as thirty days. The height of rise was characteristic for each oil and the results were reproducible.

Little of Goppelsroeder's work is of immediate value today, but many of his innovations such as elution and re-analysis, impregnation of paper, and use of adsorption media other than paper are being applied and rediscovered.

(I am indebted to Dr. Max Feurer for supplying the few biographical facts presented above.)

[3] GOPPELSROEDER, F., *Verhandl. naturforsch. Ges. Basel,* **14,** 1–545 (1901).

---

# TYPES *of* GRAPHIC CLASSIFICATIONS *of the* ELEMENTS[*]

## I. *Introduction and Short Tables*

### G. N. QUAM

Long Island University, Brooklyn, New York

### AND MARY BATTELL QUAM

New York Public Library, New York City

*A bibliography of periodic tables, beginning with the work of Mendeléeff and Meyer, is presented. The tables are classified into five definite types and each type is treated chronologically with illustrations and descriptions.*

+ + + + + +

### INTRODUCTION

THE average student of chemistry does not obtain a comprehensive view of the various systems of classification of the elements from his reading of textbooks and books of reference. Even a perusal of the literature may not result in an orderly picture of the developments of types of classifications. Since the publication of the excellent treatise on the periodic law by Venable (*1*) a number of books (*2, 3, 4, 5, 6, 7, 8*) with similar titles have appeared. Among textbooks, the one by Caven and Lander (*9*) no doubt is still unique in its thorough treatment of "Systematic Inorganic Chemistry from the Standpoint of the Periodic Law."

The authors of this paper do not pretend to supply a need for an up-to-date comprehensive treatment; they believe, however, that the classification of systems as to type is unique and will prove to be a means to a better understanding of systems of classification of the elements. No claim is made that such a classification is the only, or even the best method of approach. The attempts to classify the elements up to the time of the pronouncement of the periodic law seem to lend themselves readily only to the chronological treatment.

Every text or reference book devoting one or more chapters to the classification of elements makes the student familiar with the notable contributions of Dalton (Table of Atomic Weights—1803), Prout (Hypothesis—1815), Döbereiner (Triads—1829), and Newlands (Law of Octaves—1865). Among the less familiar may be mentioned Cooke for his unique table of classification (1854); Odling for his extension of the work on triads resulting in a "Natural Grouping of the Elements" (1857); Williamson for a "Classification of the Elements in Relation to their Atomicities" (1864), which made application of the excellent contribution by

---

[*] This study was begun as a bibliography prepared by the second author for a course in "Subject Bibliography," taught by Dr. Harriet D. MacPherson, School of Library Service, Columbia University.

| Series. | Group I R₂O | Group II RO | Group III R₂O₃ | Group IV RH₄ RO₂ | Group V RH₃ R₂O₅ | Group VI RH₂ RO₃ | Group VII RH R₂O₇ | Group VIII RO₄ |
|---|---|---|---|---|---|---|---|---|
| 1 ....... | H=1 | | | | | | | |
| 2 ....... | Li=7 | Be=9.4 | B=11 | C=12 | N=14 | O=16 | F=19 | |
| 3 ....... | Na=23 | Mg=24 | Al=27.3 | Si=28 | P=31 | S=32 | Cl=35.5 | |
| 4 ....... | K=39 | Ca=40 | —=44 | Ti=48 | V=51 | Cr=52 | Mn=55 | Fe=56, Co=59 Ni=59, Cu=63 |
| 5 ....... | (Cu=63) | Zn=65 | —=68 | —=72 | As=75 | Se=78 | Br=80 | |
| 6 ....... | Rb=85 | Sr=87 | ?Y=88 | Zr=90 | Nb=94 | Mo=96 | —=100 | Ru=104, Rh=104 Pd=106, Ag=108 |
| 7 ....... | (Ag=108) | Cd=112 | In=113 | Sn=118 | Sb=122 | Te=125 | I=127 | |
| 8 ....... | Cs=133 | Ba=137 | ?Di=138 | ?Ce=140 | | | .... | .... |
| 9 ....... | .... | .... | | | .... | | | |
| 10 ....... | .... | | ?Er=178 | ?La=180 | Ta=182 | W=184 | .... | Os=195, Ir=197 Pt=198, Au=199 |
| 11 ....... | (Au=199) | Hg=200 | Tl=204 | Pb=207 | Bi=208 | .... | .... | .... |
| 12 ....... | .... | | .... | Th=231 | .... | U=240 | .... | .... |

FIGURE 1.—MENDELÉEFF'S TABLE

Cannizzaro; and lastly, Hinrichs, whose "Chart of the Elements" (1867) may very well be considered the first of the spiral systems of classification in much the same way that we think of the telluric screw of de Chancourtois as the first of the helical systems. Although Hinrichs was a devoted proponent of the Proutian hypothesis and a vigorous critic of the periodic law, he concluded his "Programm der Atomechanik, oder die Chemie eine Mechanik der Panatome" (10) with the remarkable statement, "The properties of the chemical elements are functions of their atomic weights."

## CLASSIFICATIONS BASED ON THE PERIODIC LAW

Since the announcement of the periodic law by Mendeléeff (1869), a larger and more varied array of systems of classification has appeared. Each new effort has arisen from the author's attempt to overcome objectionable features of systems then in the literature, and to produce a more useful instrument. The average student of chemistry cannot hope to acquire a mental picture of each individual system in its chronological order, but through an orderly arrangement of types, a fairly comprehensive view can be obtained. It was with the hope of attaining this latter objective that the authors entered upon this study. Through the study of books, articles, and photostatic copies or tracings of the various types of classifications, five or six distinct types of systems, based on graphic arrangement primarily, have been discovered. Only those systems for which copies of tables could be obtained are included in the bibliography. Each type of classification is indicated by naming one notable example; thus, I, Short Chart (Mendeléeff type); II, Long Chart (Werner type); III, Long Chart (Bayley type); IV, Spiral Arrangement (Baumhauer type); V, Helical Arrangement (Harkins type); VI, Miscellaneous (distinctly individual classifications).

## I. SHORT CHARTS (MENDELÉEFF TYPE)

Although short charts had been presented at earlier dates, those of Mendeléeff and Meyer are the first syste-

matic classifications based on the periodic law. Charts of this division are all arranged in columns (groups), not to exceed nine, and the long periods consist of two or more series.

MENDELÉEFF—1872 (11): His first scheme, 1869, commonly called the vertical table, can best be classified with the long charts. The chart announced in 1872 (Figure 1) is the model commonly associated with the name of the great Russian chemist. The boldness and success of his classic work in prophesying the properties of missing elements are familiar to every student of chemistry.

MEYER—1870 (12): Although vertical, Meyer's table, produced independently and practically simultaneously, bears a marked resemblance to the horizontal short table of Mendeléeff. A mirror image of the latter's table, cut between the second and third groups, and the left strip placed along the right edge, would make a fairly accurate reproduction of Meyer's table. In his "Modern Theories of Chemistry" (13) he produced a much improved table of the "Mendeléeff type," and suggested the possibility of rolling it on a vertical cylinder in such a way that Ni is joined to Cu, Pd to Ag, and Pt to Au, thus showing the continuity of a spiral. His atomic volumes curve, which demonstrates graphically the periodic law, is, however, the contribution with which we associate the name of Lothar Meyer most generally.

GRETSCHEL and BORNEMANN—1883 (14): An arrangement based on the horizontal tables by Meyer and Mendeléeff is described. Cu, Ag, and Au are not listed in group VIII. The groups are called families, and the subgroups are listed as groups "A" and "B." The eighth group elements are all listed in "group B." The few rare-earth elements then known are consolidated in their "family III, group A."

DEELEY—1893 (15): This author claimed to have arranged the elements more in accord with their properties than preceding investigators had done. There are nine columns or groups. The Li and Na periods read from right to left; Na, however, is shifted to the left end of its period. All other periods read from left to right, and then right to left, ending with the halogens in the third column from the left side. The so-called alkali, alkaline earth, halogen, sulfur, phosphorus, carbon, aluminum, magnesium, and copper (headed by Li) families appear in order from left to right. Fe, Ru, and Os form family A in the seventh column; Mn, Rh, Ir, in the eighth; and Ni, Co, Pd, Pt, in the ninth (each in order of atomic weight in its respective series).

VENABLE—1895 (16): Venable suggested that "the idea of periodicity be subordinated at least until it can be fully proved" (1). The table presented is similar to the Mendeléeff short table except that Cu, Ag, and Au are definitely placed in group I. The seven "bridge elements" of the first period, are centered at the top of each column, and directly under them are placed those of the second period, "typical elements." The elements of each long period are in one series, thus those in the two families of the same period are on the same horizontal line and form a double column at each side of the "bridge" and "typical" elements. Venable observed that "from the typical element of each group diverge two subgroups, generally triads" (1). The emphasis appears to be placed on the regularity of increments in atomic weights and properties.

ARMSTRONG—1902 (17): This table consists of sixteen columns, and the elements are arranged in series from left to right beginning with H in the first column and first series, and ending with U in the sixteenth column and last series. Each element is given a whole number regardless of its exact atomic weight. The author regarded argon and similar elements as polyatomic, like nitrogen. Since the elements of the argon family are considered diatomic, their positions are unusual. The first complete horizontal series is: 1 H, 2 He, 3, 4, 5, 6, 7 Li, 8, 9 Be, 10 Ne, 11 B, 12 C, 13, 14 N, 15, 16 O. The "dominant principle on which the arrangement is based is that of maintaining elements which belong to the same family in the appropriate column."

BRAUNER—1902 (18): This table (Figure 2) is practically identical with the Mendeléeff short table,

| Reihe | Gruppe 0 | Gruppe I | Gruppe II | Gruppe III | Gruppe IV RH₄ | Gruppe V RH₃ | Gruppe VI RH₂ | Gruppe VII RH | Gruppe VIII | | | |
|---|---|---|---|---|---|---|---|---|---|---|---|---|
| | R | R₂O | RO | R₂O₃ | RO₂ | R₂O₅ | RO₃ | R₂O₇ | RO₄ | | | |
| 1 | | 1 H | | | | | | | | | | |
| 2 | He 4 | Li 7 | Be 9 | B 11 | C 12 | N 14 | O 16 | F 19 | | | | |
| 3 | 20 Ne | 23 Na | 24 Mg | 27 Al | 28 Si | 31 P | 32 S | 35.5 Cl | | | | |
| 4 | A 40 | K 39 | Ca 40 | Sc 44 | Ti 48 | V 51 | Cr 52 | Mn 55 | Fe 56 | Co 59 | Ni 59 | Cu 63 |
| 5 | | 63 Cu | 65 Zn | 70 Ga | 72 Ge | 75 As | 79 Se | 80 Br | | | | |
| 6 | Kr 82 | Rb 85 | Sr 87 | Y 89 | Zr 90 | Nb 94 | Mo 96 | -100 | Ru 102 | Rh 103 | Pd 106 | Ag 106 |
| 7 | | 108 Ag | 112 Cd | 114 In | 119 Sn | 120 Sb | 128 Te | 127 J | | | | |
| 8 | Xe 128 | Cs 133 | Ba 137 | La 139 | Ce 140 Pr 141 Nd 144 -145 | | | | | | | |
| | | | | | -147 Sm 148 Eu 151 -152 | | | | | | | |
| | | | | | -155 Gd 156 -159 -160 | | | | | | | |
| | | | | | Tb 163 Ho 165 Er 166 -167 | | | | | | | |
| | | | | | Tm 171 Yb 173 -176 | | | | | | | |
| | | | | | -178 | Ta 182 | W 184 | -190 | Os 191 | Ir 193 | Pt 195 | Au 197 |
| 9 | | 197 Au | 200 Hg | 204 Tl | 207 Pb | 209 Bi | 212— | 214— | | | | |
| 10 | -218 | -220 | Rd 225? | -230 | Th 233 | -235 | U 239 | | | | | |

FIGURE 2.—BRAUNER'S TABLE

except that new elements, atomic numbers, group zero, and more exact atomic weights are introduced. Through a thorough study of the rare-earth elements, Brauner concluded that all should be placed in a miniature table following La and preceding the space now occupied by Hf.

BILTZ—1902 (19): To simplify the classification, the author eliminated the eighth group and the detailed list of rare earths, and represented each of these aggregations of elements by the symbol of a representative preceded by a summation sign. The eighth group elements are indicated as family A of group VII.

ZENGHELIS—1906 (20): This attempt to improve the table resembles that of Biltz, except that Zenghelis gave in brackets the complete list of elements in place of abbreviating with a summation sign.

BAUER—1911 (21): The eighth group is reinstated, giving place to the groups of elements consolidated in the seventh group by Biltz and Zenghelis. Bauer separated the complete table on a line between the fourth and fifth groups, permitting a rectangular space between Sn and Ce on the left, and Sb and Ta on the right for the remainder of the rare-earth elements.

RYDBERG—1913 (22): A chart (Figure 3) is developed from a consideration of the theories of atomic structure and valence. The first period starts with He and extends to the right to C, and then doubles back, causing F to fall in the same column with Li; likewise, Cl falls in line with Na in the next period. The first long period establishes the extreme right column with Co, thus placing Br under K. The rare earths cause their period to occupy four lines across the chart, two to the right and two to the left. The most

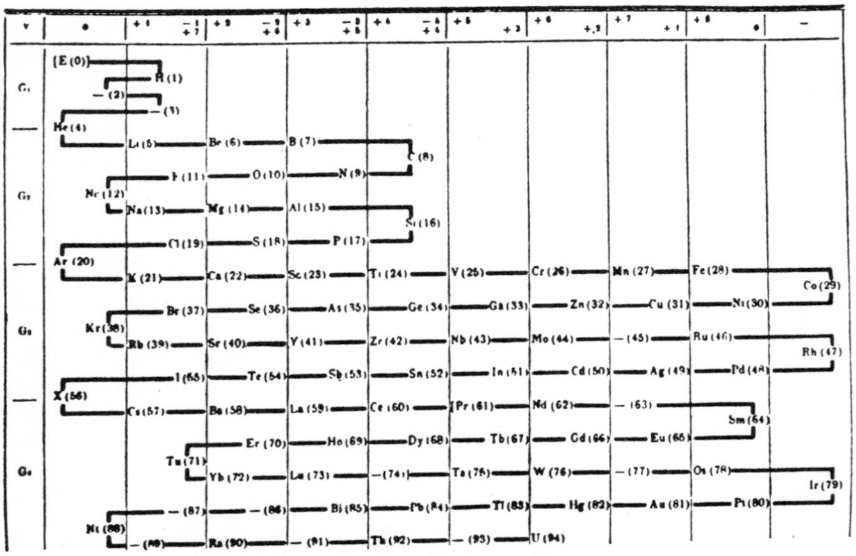

FIGURE 3.—THE RYDBERG TABLE

electropositive and electronegative elements appear in group I. On the basis of atomic structure, the arrangement shows elements other than H preceding He, as well as beyond U.

DUSHMAN—1915 (23): The Mendeléeff table is brought up-to-date to include the zero group elements at the left, the body of rare-earth elements as an enlargement of the position we could expect to be occupied by a single element in group III, and the isotopes of the radioactive elements.

DAUVILLIER—1922 (24): A new table is proposed in which modern theories of atomic structure determine the positions of the elements. It differs from the ordinary table mainly in the sixth group, which contains in the potassium series, Mn, Fe, Co, Ni, in addition to Cr, as members of family A, and the corresponding elements of the rubidium and cesium series hold analogous positions; the sulfur family elements constitute family B, as usual. Group VII contains the halogen family only, and group VIII, the helium family. The remainder of the rare-earth elements are indicated with Ce in group IV; these fourteen elements which follow cerium, are listed below the table in two horizontal lines.

RENZ—1922 (25): A suggested improvement in Mendeléeff's table, by vertical elongation, gives space to a single vertical column of all the rare-earth elements in group III, family A.

SEARS—1924 (26): This table has been constructed to emphasize, by lines, the distinctions between families. An attempt has been made to show the relationships of the elements of the lithium and sodium periods to those of the long periods. A second table (27) has been designed to show group and family relationships by a third dimension, and by arrows, to indicate the order of increasing activity and basicity.

GEAUQUE—1925 (28): Geauque has retained the eight groups of the Mendeléeff table and has utilized the Rydberg arrangement. Group VIII is usual, but the elements from La to Hf, inclusive, form a miniature Rydberg table within the limits of groups I and IV. These latter elements and Sc and Y are inclosed by a heavy line.

ROLLA—1928 (29): A typical Mendeléeff table is presented, but H is placed before He without group designation. Although families "a" and "b" are indicated in the group headings, the elements are arranged in straight vertical lines. The rare-earth elements are

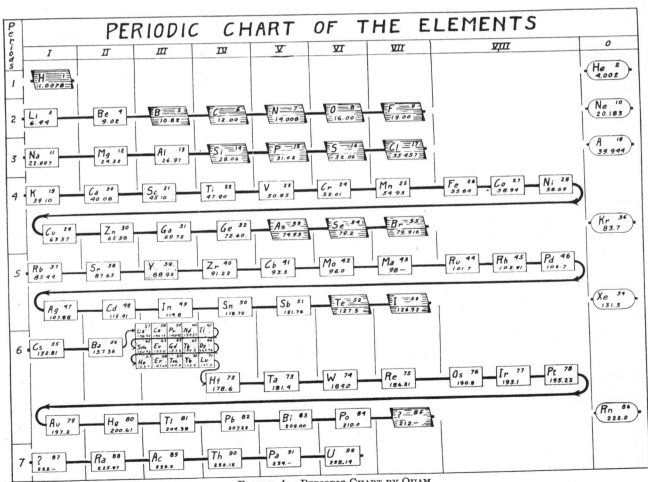

FIGURE 4.—PERIODIC CHART BY QUAM

listed in two horizontal rows, from Ce to Tb, and Dy to Hf. The enclosure may lead the student to think that the rare-earth elements are Ce to Hf, or atomic numbers 58 to 72, inclusive.

SILVERMAN—1928 (30): This table is, as the compiler states, "Mendeléeff's Periodic System of the Elements." In modernizing the table, group 0, atomic numbers, periods, and many new elements have been added. The rare-earth elements are enumerated at the bottom of the table and blank spaces are indicated as in the original. The period containing the rare-earth elements is numbered 5 and 6.

HUBBARD—1928 (31): This is a typical short table in which the helium family appears both in group zero and in group eight; the rare-earth elements are indicated by inclusive atomic numbers in group III, and are named at the bottom of the table in two horizontal lines. The table is crowded with much physical data usually sought in handbooks.

CENTRAL SCIENTIFIC COMPANY—1930 (32): This table appears to be a slightly modified Brauner table (Figure 2) brought up to date. The elements Pr to Hf, inclusive, are listed as the rare-earth elements in an enclosure in groups III and IV under La and Ce, and preceding Ta.

MITRA—1931 (33): The author claims to have combined the periodic chemical chart and the electron configuration chart. The groups read horizontally from left to right; group I starts at the top with H and Li, while VIII, at the bottom, includes the helium family, in addition to the usual group VIII elements.

The table is designed to show electron levels and quantum values of orbits. The elements Ce to Lu are placed in an enclosed series extending from group III to group VII, inclusive.

SHEMYAKIN—1932 (34): The helium family is placed in group VIII in this typical "Mendeléeff" table. The rare-earth elements, however, are distributed across the table in three series from group III to VII1, inclusive. The author has very definitely placed the elements of the lithium and sodium periods in families; Li and Na are in family A, and all others, including the inert elements, in B families.

QUAM—1933 (35): The chart (Figure 4) is a modification of the Brauner table. The heavy black lines maintain the continuity of each period. An effort has been made to indicate families by alignment in each group. Thus the positions of Be and Mg indicate a closer relation to Zn and Cd than to the alkaline-earth elements. The non-metals, other than the zero group elements, are indicated by shading, and the rare-earth elements by the dotted rectangles in group III. The so-called inert elements are placed in group 0 at the right to show the completion of the stable atomic arrangement, and also to show the transition from the extreme electronegative elements of one period to the extreme electropositive of the next.

CONCLUSION

Several of the short tables cited may appear to be unlike the Mendeléeff table in minor details as to form, but the authors in all cases have been guided by the principles of the periodic law.

LITERATURE CITED

(1) F. P. VENABLE, "The development of the periodic law," Chemical Publishing Co., Easton, Pa., 1896, 321 pp.
(2) E. HUTH, "Das periodische Gesetz der Atomgewichte und das natürliche System der Elemente," R. Friedländer und Sohn, Berlin, 1887, 16 pp.
(3) G. RUDORF, "The periodic classification and the problems of chemical evolution," Whittaker & Co., New York City, 1900, 1–154 pp.
(4) A. E. GARRETT, "The periodic law," Paul, Trench Trübner & Co., London, 1909, 294 pp.
(5) K. MAHLER, "Atombau und periodische System der Elemente," Otto Salle, Berlin, 1927, 123 pp.
(6) I. KOPPEL, "Der Bau der Atome und das periodische System," Leopold Voss, Leipzig, 1927, 174 pp.
(7) D. O. LYON, "Das periodische System in neuer Anordnung," Franz Deuticke, Leipzig, 1928, 40 pp.
(8) E. RABINOWITSCH AND E. THILO, "Periodische System, Geschichte und Theorie," F. Enke, Stuttgart, 1930, 302 pp.
(9) R. M. CAVEN AND G. D. LANDER, "Systematic inorganic chemistry from the standpoint of the periodic law," Blackie & Son, London, 1930, 502 pp.
(10) G. HINRICHS, "Programm der Atomechanik, oder die Chemie eine Mechanik der Panatome," Iowa City, author, 1867, 44 pp.
(11) D. I. MENDELÉEFF, "Die periodische Gesetzmassigkeit der chemischen Elemente," Ann., Supplementband, VIII, 1872, pp. 133–229.
(12) L. MEYER, "Die natur der chemischen Elemente als Function ihrer Atomgewichte," Ann., Supplementband, VII, 1870, pp. 354–64 (Heft 3).
(13) L. MEYER, "Modern theories of chemistry" (translated from the German, 5th ed., by P. P. BEDSON and W. C.

WILLIAMS), Longmans, Green & Co., London & New York City, 1888, pp. 109–70.
(14) H. GRETSCHEL AND G. BORNEMANN, "Das natürliche System der Elemente," Jahrbuch der Erfindungen, 19th Jahrgang, pp. 241–306 (Oct., 1883).
(15) R. M. DEELEY, "A new diagram and periodic table of the elements," J. Chem. Soc., 63, 852–67 (1893).
(16) F. P. VENABLE, "A modified arrangement of the elements under the natural law," J. Am. Chem. Soc., 17, 75–84 (Feb., 1895).
(17) H. E. ARMSTRONG, "Classification of the elements," Proc. Roy. Soc., 70, 86–94 (Mar., 1902).
(18) B. BRAUNER, "Uber die Stellung der Elemente der seltenen Erden im periodischen System nach Mendelejeff," Z. anorg. Chem., 33, 1–30 (Aug., 1902).
(19) H. BILTZ, "Zur Kenntniss des Perioden-Systems der Elemente," Ber., 35, 562–8 (Jan., 1902).
(20) C. ZENGHELIS, "System und die methodische Einteilung der Elemente," Chem.-Ztg., 30, 294–5 (Apr., 1906).
(21) E. BAUER, "Uber das periodische System der Elemente," Z. physik. Chem., 76, 569–83 (May, 1911).
(22) J. R. RYDBERG, "Untersuchungen über das System der Grundstoffe," Harrassowitz, Leipzig, 1913, 41 pp. (Lunds Universitets årsskrift, n.f. afd. 2, bd. 9, nr. 18. K. Fysiografiska sällskapets handlingar, n.f. bd. 24, nr. 18.)
(23) S. DUSHMAN, "The periodic law," Gen. Elec. Rev., 18, 614–21 (July, 1915).
(24) A. DAUVILLIER, "Analyse de la structure électronique des élèments," J. phys. radium, 3, 154–77 (May, 1922).
(25) C. RENZ, "Die seltenen Erden im periodischen System," Z. anorg. allgem. Chem., 122, 135–45 (Jan., 1922).
(26) G. W. SEARS, "A new form of periodic table as a practical

means of correlating the facts of chemistry," J. Chem. Educ., **1**, 173–7 (Oct., 1924).

(27) G. W. Sears, "A theoretical point of view in the teaching of inorganic chemistry," *ibid.*, **10**, 431 (July, 1933).

(28) H. A. Geauque, "A classification of the elements with respect to their properties," *ibid.*, **2**, 464–6 (June, 1925).

(29) L. Rolla, "The rare earths in the general classification of the chemical elements," *Scientia*, **43**, 159–68 (1928).

(30) A. Silverman, "Mendeléeff's periodic system of the elements," Wall Chart, Fisher Scientific Co., Pittsburgh, **1928**.

(31) H. D. Hubbard, "Periodic chart of the atoms," Wall Chart, W. M. Welch Scientific Co., Chicago, **1928**.

(32) Central Scientific Co., "Periodic classification of the elements," Wall Chart, Central Scientific Co., Chicago, **1930**.

(33) S. K. Mitra, "On the periodic classification of the elements," *Phil. Mag.* (Series VII), **11**, 1201–14 (June, 1931).

(34) F. M. Shemyakin, "Inclusion of rare earths in the periodic system," *J. Gen. Chem.* (U.S.S.R.), **2**, 63 (Jan., 1932).

(35) G. N. Quam, "Laboratory exercises in general chemistry," 4th ed., Edwards Bros., Ann Arbor, **1933**, p. 101.

# II.  Long Charts

### LONG CHARTS (WERNER TYPE)

THE CHARTS of this division are essentially those in which short charts have been elongated in such manner that the elements of each period are arranged in single series.

MENDELÉEFF—1869 (*36*): Mendeléeff's first table was a vertical arrangement in which the elements could be read in order of increasing atomic weight from the top down and in successive series from left to right. The first column consisted of H and Li; the second, of Be to Na; the third started with Mg. An improved form of this table appeared in 1872 (*37*) (Figure 5).

|  |  |  | K | Rb | Cs | ... | ... |
|--|--|--|---|----|----|-----|-----|
|  |  |  | Ca | Sr | Ba | ... | ... |
|  |  |  | ... | ? Yt | ? Di | Er | ... |
|  |  |  | Ti | Zr | Ce | ? La | Th |
|  |  |  | V | Nb | Mo | ... | ... |
|  |  |  | Cr | Mo | ... | W | U |
|  |  |  | Mn | ... | ... | ... | ... |
|  |  |  | Fe | Ru | ... | Os | ... |
|  |  |  | Co | Rh | ... | Ir | ... |
|  |  |  | Ni | Pd | ... | Pt | ... |
| Typical Elements |  | | Cu | Ag | ... | Au | .... |
| H | Li | Na | Zn | Cd | ... | Hg | ... |
|  | Be | Mg | ... | In | ... | Tl | ... |
|  | B | Al | ... | Sn | ... | Pb | ... |
|  | C | Si | As | Sb | ... | Bi | ... |
|  | N | P | Se | Te | ... | ... | ... |
|  | O | S | Br | J | ... | ... | ... |
|  | F | Cl |  |  |  |  |  |

FIGURE 5.—MENDELÉEFF'S VERTICAL TABLE

H occupied the first position separately; the vertical series in order were Li to F, Na to Cl, K to Br, etc., causing the halogens to appear in the same bottom series, while H, Li, Na, Cu, Ag, and Au constituted a midway series, and K, Rb, and Cs formed the topmost series.

WALKER—1891 (*38*): Walker's is similar to the Mendeléeff vertical table (*37*). He pointed to the objection to placing Li and Na in line with Cu, Ag, and Au, and to the unique position of the non-metals in the lower left triangular area. His use of the terms "odd and even series" seems reminiscent of the "short chart" type.

BASSETT—1892 (*39*): This table (Figure 6) also resembles Mendeléeff's later vertical arrangement (*37*). The Cs period, however, starts far above the horizontal line of K and Rb, thereby giving space to the known and predicted elements of that period. The alkali metals appear in three horizontal lines. Co and Ni are arranged in order of their atomic weights. Bassett suggested cutting out the table and rolling it onto a cylinder of such circumference that similar elements would fall in

| | |
|--|--|
| Cs | ? |
| Ba | ? |
| La | ? |
| Ce | Th |
| Nd | ? |
| Pd | U |
| ? | ? |
| Sm | ? |
| ? | ? |
| ? | ? |
| ? | ? |
| ? | ? |
| Tb | ? |
| Ho | ? |
| ? | ? |
| Er | ? |
| ? | ? |
| Tm | |
| ? | |
| Yb | |

| | | | |
|--|--|--|--|
| K | Rb | ? | |
| Ca | Sr | ? | |
| Sc | Y | ? | |
| Ti | Zr | ? | |
| V | Nb | Ta | |
| Cr | Mo | W | |
| Mn | ? | ? | |
| Fe | Ru | Os | |
| Ni | Rh | Ir | |
| Co | Pd | Pt | |

| Li | Na | Cu | Ag | Au |
|----|----|----|----|----|
| Be | Mg | Zn | Cd | Hg |
| B | Al | Ga | In | Tl |
| C | Si | Ge | Sn | Pb |
| N | P | As | Sb | Bi |
| O | S | Se | Te | ? |
| F | Cl | Br | I | ? |

FIGURE 6.—VERTICAL ARRANGEMENT BY BASSETT

line, forming what are now known as groups and families. For instance, Li, Na, K, Rb, and Cs would then fall on a line parallel to the axis of the cylinder.

RANG—1893 (*40*): The table (Figure 7) is arranged so that closely related elements are in the same vertical row. The four groups, A, B, C, D, classify elements of common properties; "A" contains the most electropositive elements, "D" the most electronegative. The position of H over Ga, In, and Tl is most unusual.

| Valence | I | II | III | IV | V | VI | VII | VIII | | | I | II | III | IV | V | VI | VII |
|---|---|---|---|---|---|---|---|---|---|---|---|---|---|---|---|---|---|
| Series | | | | | | | | | | | | | | | | | |
| 1 | " | " | " | " | " | " | " | " | " | " | " | " | H | " | " | " | " |
| 2 | Li | Be | B | C | " | " | " | " | " | " | " | " | " | " | N | O | F |
| 3 | Na | Mg | Al | Si | " | " | " | " | " | " | " | " | " | " | P | S | Cl |
| 4 | K | Ca | Sc | Ti | V | Cr | Mn | Fe | Ni | Co | Cu | Zn | Ga | Ge | As | Se | Br |
| 5 | Rb | Sr | Y | Zr | Nb | Mo | " | Ru | Rh | Pd | Ag | Cd | In | Sn | Sb | Te | I |
| 6 | Cs | Ba | Di | " | Ta | W | " | Os | Ir | Pt | Au | Hg | Tl | Pb | Bi | " | " |
| 7 | " | Ms | " | Th | " | U | " | " | " | " | " | " | " | " | " | " | " |
| Group | 1 | 2 | 3 | 4 | | | | | | | 5 | | | | | 6 | 7 |
| | A | | | B | | | | | | | C | | | | | D | |

"Di here represents all the triads that are between Ba and Ta. H may not be exactly in its true place, still it cannot be very far from it."

FIGURE 7.—RANG'S PERIODIC TABLE

The order of Co and Ni is the same as in the Bassett table (*39*).

HORSLEY—1900 (*41*): Horsley's chart appears in Rudorf's book (*41*) as one of four modifications of Mendeléeff's arrangement (*37*). This horizontal chart shows the usual families, including the zero group elements, which occupy the central position. The elements read from left to right, beginning with He and Li as the first series; Be to Na (Na under Li), as the second; Mg to Co (K under Na), third; Cu to Pd (Zn under Mg), fourth; Ag to Pt, etc. Horsley's chart appears to be the forerunner of the types in which the helium family occupies a central position adjacent to the halogen family on the left and the alkali family on the right.

STAIGMÜLLER—1901 (*42*): In this chart the arrangement by Rang (*40*) is modified to include the He family before the alkali metals. H is placed to the left of He, thus being the first member of the first period. Ru and Os appear in their respective periods under Mn, Rh and Ir under Fe, Pd and Pt under Ni, Au under Co, and Hg under Ag. The Cs period consists of two series, but the rare-earth elements receive little consideration. The author called attention to the location of the non-metals in an upper right enclosure, as did Walker (*38*).

WERNER—1905 (*43*): Werner avoided periods of two or more series by allowing the Cs period to determine the width of the table (Figure 8). Among the irregularities in order of atomic weights, he cited the case of Nd and Pr which are no longer so placed. The "inert elements" complete each period, and the distribution is made to show family relationships. Be and Mg are definitely classed with Zn and Cd.

SCHMIDT—1911 (*44*): Schmidt attempted to show by means of his table that elements form systems and sub-systems which stand in genetic relation to each other. In form it appears to be a modification of the charts of Staigmüller (*42*) and Werner (*43*), divided into several vertical areas consisting of from one to four families. A table similar to that of Schmidt would result if Staigmüller's chart were cut on a line between the N and Ge families, and the right segment fitted to the left, causing the elements to join in the usual order of atomic weight increase. This arrangement opened between the columns consisting of C-Si-Ti-Zr-Ce-Th and V-Nb-Ta, respectively, to allow space for the Werner rare-earth series, completes a Schmidt arrangement. Schmidt placed Pr before Nd, but did not leave spaces for missing rare-earth elements. The positions of the "eighth group" elements correspond to Werner's arrangement.

STACKELBERG—1911 (*45*): Stackelberg's first table is patterned after Staigmüller's (*42*) with slight modifications. H is placed in the Li family instead of in the Li period. C and Si are transferred to the right, over Ge. The "zero group" elements appear at the right edge as well as at the left in the table. The

| | | | | | | | | | | | | | | | | | | | | | | | | | | | | | | | |
|---|---|---|---|---|---|---|---|---|---|---|---|---|---|---|---|---|---|---|---|---|---|---|---|---|---|---|---|---|---|---|---|
| ... | | | | | | | | | | | | | | | | | | | | | | | | | | | | | | ... | ... |
| H | | | | | | | | | | | | | | | | | | | | | | | | | | | | | | ... | He |
| Li | | | | | | | | | | | | | | | | | | | | | | | | | Be | B | C | N | O | F | Ne |
| Na | | | | | | | | | | | | | | | | | | | | | | | | | Mg | Al | Si | P | S | Cl | A |
| K | Ca | | | | | | | | | | | | | | | Sc | Ti | V | Cr | Mn | Fe | Co | Ni | Cu | Zn | Ga | Ge | As | Se | Br | Kr |
| Rb | Sr | | | | | | | | | | | | | | | Y | Zr | Nb | Mo | ... | Ru | Rh | Pd | Ag | Cd | Jn | Sn | Sb | Te | J | Xn |
| Cs | Ba | La | Ce | Nd | Pr | ... | ... | Sa | Eu | Gd | Tb | Ho | Er | Tu | Y | ... | ... | Ta | W | ... | Os | Ir | Pt | Au | Hg | Tl | Pb | Bi | ... | ... | ... |
| ... | Ra | Laα | Th | ... | ... | ... | ... | ... | U | ... | ... | ... | ... | Ac | ... | ... | ... | ... | ... | ... | ... | ... | ... | ... | ... | ... | Pbα | Biα | Teα | ... | ... |

FIGURE 8.—WERNER'S PERIODIC TABLE

"platinum elements," Au and Hg, are restored to their logical places in the arrangement, as shown by Werner (43) and Schmidt (44), but the order of Ni and Co is according to their atomic weights. A second table was designed by cutting the first on a line between Co and Cu and fitting the segments together, causing the "zero group" elements to assume the central position as in the Horsley chart (41). The author described the formation of a cylindrical chart from the second arrangement, as an additional aid in the study of relationships between elements.

CÁCERES—1911 (46): The author claimed that his vertical table was not essentially different from Werner's (43). By starting the first period with H and He, he reduced the number of periods to six. Unlike Werner, he placed Be and Mg in line with the alkaline-earth elements, and made the Cs period of the same length as the K and Rb series by arranging that portion containing the rare-earth elements in four series, two descending and two ascending. Although the author regarded this irregular arrangement as an aid in classification, it is rather unusual to find Sm in the Mn family, and Nd, Eu, and Tm in the Cr family.

MEYER—1918 (47): The second of the author's two tables is a modification of the first, a Bayley type. Meyer's table differs from Schmidt's (44) in that Ni, Pd, and Pt constitute the right ends of their respective periods. The rare earths are arranged in order of increasing atomic number after Ba, and H is placed above Li, thereby occupying a central position. Valence numbers are placed at the tops of the groups, which are numbered at the bottom with Roman numerals.

CHAUVIERRE—1919 (48): Chauvierre's table probably resembles Stackelberg's (45) in form more than any other long chart of the "Werner Type." The first two periods are divided on a line between Gl and B; the "zero group" elements appear on the left side only; the additional rare-earth elements are extended across the table, causing Tb to appear in the Al family, "Tu" in the C family, and Yb in the P family. The middle section of the table is arranged to show the "famille du fer," which includes V and Cr also, the "famille du palladium," which includes Nb and Mo also, the "famille du didyme" (Pr and Sm), the "famille du platine," and the "metaux radioactifs" (Th and U). Seventeen empty spaces are shown representing places for missing elements, including one noble gas, but the chart as printed shows Cu and Hg in positions apparently not meant for them by the author, which may account for the excessive number of blank spaces.

STEINMETZ—1918 (49): The chart is a modification of the one by Staigmüller (42) in which H is placed over F, Co precedes Ni, many elements are added, and the "platinum metals" are treated in a more orderly manner.

PFEIFFER—1920 (50): Pfeiffer shortened the Werner chart (43) by indicating the position of the rare-earth elements following Ce and placing them below the last period in a single line.

ODDO—1920 (51): Oddo's arrangement appears to be a modification of Staigmüller's (42). H is placed over Li and the non-metals of the Staigmüller table are transferred as a unit to the left side, thus allowing the two major headings, "Metalloidi" and "Metalli." The rare earths are arranged in two series which, with Sc and Yt, are enclosed by a dotted line. An attempt has been made to place the isotopic forms of the radioactive elements. In a revision (52), Oddo placed Sb with the non-metals and B with the metals, and elaborated his treatment of the radioactive elements.

BURY—1921 (53): Bury's is a Werner table (43) brought up to date in connection with an extensive treatment of the atomic structure of the elements. The structures of the so-called transition elements and the rare earths are given especially detailed consideration.

NORRISH—1922 (54): This table, patterned after Stackelberg's arrangement (45), is derived from a consideration of colored ions, valency, and atomic structure. Many physical data are presented below each symbol.

LORING—1922 (55): The author claimed that his "Wedge Periodic Table" indicated where missing elements were of low concentration, if existent at all. In design, it appears to be a mirror image of a Bassett table (39) in which the periods are moved to place the alkali elements in line, rather than the halogens. The "zero group" and many other new elements are included. The sketch is designed to justify the unique title.

COURTINES—1925 (56): The unfolded tower arrangement (Figure 9) appears much like a modernized Chauvierre chart (48) cut on a line between Ni and Cu, with the right part fitted to the left in order of increasing atomic numbers. The rare-earth elements, however, are placed on a novel accordion-like folded strip with ends made secure just below Yt and between Ba and Hf. The author describes in detail the method of folding the chart into a tower-like cylindrical model. H is folded back to show its lack of relationship to other groups of elements. In the space for each symbol, electron arrangements and isotopes are also enumerated.

RODEBUSH—1925 (57): Rodebush has taken the Rang arrangement (40) and brought it up-to-date from the standpoint of Bohr's conception of the grouping of electron orbits, which are indicated by the shell structure of the inert gases at the end of each period. H is placed above F, and the list of rare-earth elements is shown occupying a position following La and preceding Hf.

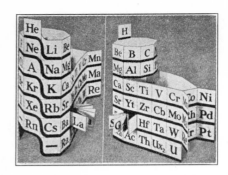

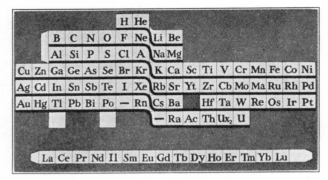

FIGURE 9.—COURTINES' PERIODIC CLASSIFICATION

LEROY—1931 (58): Although LeRoy referred to his chart as being a modification of Deming's periodic table (69), it seems more reasonable to consider it a modification of Werner's table (43). To construct a chart similar to LeRoy's, move Sc and Y of Werner's table (Figure 8) to a position above La, cut the table on a vertical line to the left of Ti and join the outside edges, draw a line from H to both Li and F and add the new elements not listed in Figure 8. The positions of Pa and U in LeRoy's chart were dictated by geometric form, apparently, rather than chemical relationships.

CONCLUSIONS

The majority of the charts of this division are arranged, like Werner's, with the most electropositive elements at one edge, and the most electronegative at the other. The arrangements of Schmidt, Meyer, Oddo, Courtines, and LeRoy appear to be efforts to bring the most active elements to a central position. With the exception of Schmidt's table, the "inert elements" divide the electronegative from the electropositive elements. The charts of Mendeléeff, Walker, Bassett and Loring fail to show the family relationships consistently because of their insistence on unbroken short periods. That there is great difference of opinion as to where the intermediate elements of the short periods should be placed is very apparent. The division between C and N is favored by Rang, Staigmüller, Schmidt, Meyer, Steinmetz, and Rodebush; between B and C, by Stackelberg and Norrish; between Be and B, by

Cáceres, Chauvierre, Oddo, and Courtines; and between Li and Be, by Werner, Pfeiffer, Bury, and LeRoy. The placing of the rare-earth elements has also been treated in a diversified manner.

LONG CHARTS (BAYLEY TYPE)

The arrangements in this division include those long charts which show the relationships within the short-chart groups without destroying the advantage of simplicity of the Werner type. By solid and dotted lines and shading, the authors have attempted to show family distinctions.

BAYLEY—1882 (59): The elements are arranged (Figure 10) in order of increasing atomic weight, and divided into cycles and series. Bayley observed the recurrence of the same groups of properties in sets of seven and emphasized, graphically, family relationships.

CARNELLEY—1886 (60): Carnelley's diagram is similar to Bayley's table (59). The Cs period is kept in line with those of K and Rb by dividing it into two series.

THOMSEN—1895 (61): This table, similar to Bayley's (59), was arranged to show genetic relationships of elements. The elements of the five periods of one series each, are arranged from electropositive to electronegative. H forms the head of the table, while the remaining elements are divided into two periods of 7 elements each, two of 17 each, and one of 31. Al-

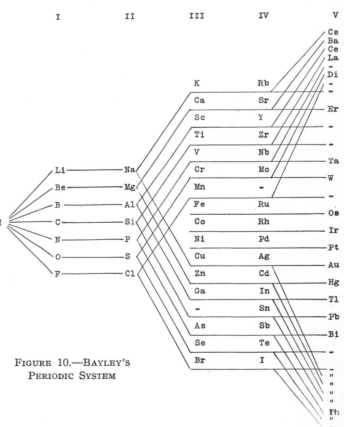

FIGURE 10.—BAYLEY'S PERIODIC SYSTEM

though the rare-earth elements are listed in the Cs period, the family relationships are maintained by connecting lines. Numerous modifications of Thomsen's table have appeared from time to time, notable among which should be mentioned the Thomsen-Bohr Table (62).

RICHARDS—1898 (63): Richards stated that his table was a modified form of the Thomsen arrange-

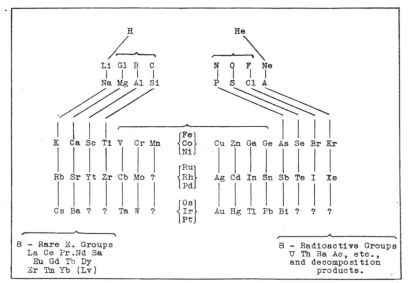

FIGURE 11.—ADAMS' PERIODIC TABLE

ment (61). His modification appears to be a Thomsen chart in which the last period is arranged in a manner similar to Carnelley's plan (60). Many blank spaces are introduced and the author listed as unclassified He, A, Pr, Ne, Sa, Gd, Tb, Er, Th, and Yt.

ADAMS—1911 (64): The table (Figure 11) is virtually a mirror image of Thomsen's chart (61), arranged in a horizontal position. He with H brings the number of periods up to six. The rare-earth elements are arranged in a compact group following Ba, thereby reducing the length of the Cs period. Adams attempted to remedy what he considered the principal defect of the Mendeléeff table (11), namely, the placing of dissimilar elements in the same family.

HOPKINS—1911 (65): In describing his arrangement, Hopkins stated "that Richards' table (63) is in all essentials identical with the one now proposed." Hopkins' chart, however, is a mirror image of Richards' chart, turned through ninety degrees in the clockwise direction, omitting H and He, and placing the "zero group" elements, Ne to Xe, on the right side. Ra and

several rare-earth elements are added. In place of showing the family relationships by lines as proposed by Carnelley (60) and Richards, Hopkins has attempted to show by figures at the heads of the columns, approximate specific gravities and position numbers; the latter are considered the fundamental properties of elements.

MEYER—1918 (47): The form of the first of two tables is practically identical with the Adams' chart (64). The "Mendeléeff" group numbers are used to identify the columns of both short and long periods. The Cs period is completed with U, but the rare-earth elements are indicated between Ba and Ta, and are enumerated in a horizontal row at the bottom of the table.

SCHALTENBRAND—1921 (66): This skeleton arrangement which appears like an expanding family tree, is an attempt to show the derivation of the periods of elements by an "extension" of the first, H-He, period. In the second period, Li, C, F, and He, only, are enumerated. The expansion for the rare earths appears to be in anticipation of Antropoff's arrangement (68) and Bohr's modification of Thomsen's chart (62).

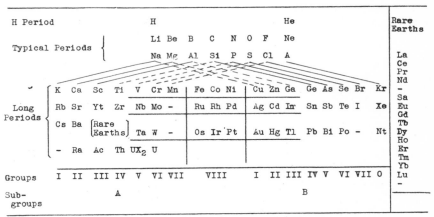

FIGURE 12.—MARGARY'S PERIODIC TABLE

MARGARY—1921 (67): Margary's table (Figure 12) was designed to show each period in an orderly complete form and all family relationships of the short-type chart. The "subgroups" are clearly indicated and the rare-earth elements are placed between Ba and Ta by giving the inclusive atomic numbers and enumerating the elements at the right side of the chart in a vertical column.

ANTROPOFF—1926 (68): Antropoff's chart in its final form is virtually a Margary table (67) in which the elements of the short periods are given enough

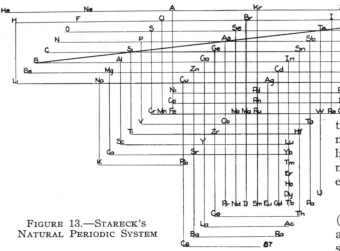

FIGURE 13.—STARECK'S
NATURAL PERIODIC SYSTEM

by lines much as in the Margary table; the rare-earth elements are treated as in the latter's table, except that the vertical column is replaced by a rectangular area in the lower central part; H is given an important central position as in Antropoff's arrangement. The electron orbits of the He family elements are effectively shown in a manner similar to that of Rodebush. By heavy black lines, the elements are clearly classified as inert gases, non-metals, heavy metals, light metals, and rare-earth elements.

STARECK—1932 (70): In Stareck's periodic table (Figure 13) the elements are grouped according to atomic numbers and arranged to indicate degree of similarity in physical properties. The non-metals are plainly segregated. The straight horizontal and zig-zag lines show relationships of groups and families. The rare-earth elements fit into a large V-shaped arrangement. The typical eighth-group elements develop a similar, but smaller, arrangement.

horizontal space to extend them in line with the long periods. In place of using lines, the columns are variously shaded. The He family appears at both sides of the chart, while in a central position above C, H appears as the element from which all others are derived. The rare-earth elements are enumerated in a horizontal arrangement at the lower edge instead of at the right side, as in Margary's table.

DEMING—1927 (69): In its general make-up, Deming's chart embodies many of the good features of the charts of Norrish (54), Margary (67), Antropoff (68), Rodebush (57), and others. It appears to be a Norrish chart with the He family on the left side only; the relation of the short periods to the long periods is shown

CONCLUSIONS

In the early tables of the "Bayley Type," the relationships of the subgroups were not indicated; the charts of Margary, Antropoff, and Deming, however, suggest the relations of families within a "Mendeléeff group" by full and broken lines, or by shaded areas. The rare-earth elements have received varied treatment.

LITERATURE CITED

(36) MOORE, F. J., "A history of chemistry," 1st ed., McGraw-Hill Book Co., New York City, **1918**, p. 184.

(37) MENDELÉEFF, D. I., "Die periodische Gesetzmassigkeit der chemischen Elemente," *Ann.*, Supplementband, **8**, 133–229 (1872).

(38) WALKER, J., "On the periodic tabulation of the elements," *Chem. News*, **63**, 251–3 (May, 1891).

(39) BASSETT, H., "A tabular expression of the periodic relations of the elements," *ibid.*, **65**, 3–4, 19 (Jan., 1892).

(40) RANG, P. J. F., "The periodic arrangement of the elements," *ibid.*, **67**, 178 (Apr., 1893).

(41) RUDORF, G., "The periodic classification and the problem of chemical evolution," Whittaker and Co., New York City, **1900**, p. 153.

(42) STAIGMÜLLER, H., "Das periodische System der Elemente," *Z. physik. Chem.*, **39**, 245–8 (Dec., 1901).

(43) WERNER, A., "Beitrag zum Ausbau des periodischen Systems," *Ber.*, **38**, 914–21 (Feb., 1905).

(44) SCHMIDT, C., "Studien über das periodische System," *Z. physik. Chem.*, **75**, 651–64 (Jan., 1911).

(45) VON STACKELBERG, E., "Versuch einer neuen tabellarischen Gruppierung der Elemente auf Grund des periodischen Systems," *ibid.*, **77**, 75–81 (June, 1911).

(46) CÁCERES, T., "Classification of the elements," *Chem. Abstr.*, **6**, 5 (Jan. 1912). [*Anales soc. españ. fís. quím.*, **9**, 121–4 (1911).]

(47) MEYER, S., "Periodische Systeme der Elemente," *Physik. Z.*, **19**, 178–9 (May, 1918).

(48) CHAUVIERRE, M., "Sur une nouvelle classification périodique des elements chimiques," *Bull. soc. chim.*, [4], **25**, 297–305 (Nov., 1919).

(49) STEINMETZ, C. P., "The periodic system of elements," *J. Am. Chem. Soc.*, **40**, 733–5 (May, 1918).

(50) PFEIFFER, P., "Die Befruchtung der Chemie durch die Röntgen-strahlenphysik," *Naturwissenschaften*, **8**, 991 (Dec., 1920).

(51) ODDO, G., "Nuova classificazione periodica degli elementi," *Gazz. chim. ital.*, **50**, II, 213–45 (Nov., 1920).

(52) ODDO, G., "La mia classificazione periodica degli elementi e la costituzione elettrica degli atomi e della valenza," *ibid.*, **55**, 149–74 (Mar., 1925).

(53) BURY, C. R., "Langmuir's theory of the arrangement of electrons in atoms and molecules," *J. Am. Chem. Soc.*, **43**, 1602–9 (July, 1921).

(54) NORRISH, R. G. W., "Transition elements and the octet theory," *Chem. News*, **124**, 16–22 (Jan., 1922).

(55) LORING, F. H., "Missing elements in the periodic table," *ibid.*, **125**, 386–8 (Dec., 1922).

(56) COURTINES, M., "A model of the periodic table," J. CHEM. EDUC., **2**, 107–9 (Feb., 1925).

(57) RODEBUSH, W. H., "A compact arrangement of the periodic table," *ibid.*, **2**, 381–3 (May, 1925).

(58) LEROY, R. H., "A modified periodic classification of elements adapted to the teaching of elementary chemistry," *ibid.*, **8**, 2052–6 (Oct., 1931).

(59) BAYLEY, T., "On the connexion between the atomic weights and the chemical and physical properties of elements," *Phil. Mag.*, [5], **13**, 26–37 (Jan., 1882).

(60) CARNELLEY, T., "Suggestions as to the cause of the periodic law and the nature of the chemical elements," *Chem. News*, **53**, 197–200 (Apr., 1886).

(61) THOMSEN, J., "Systematische Gruppierung der chemischen Elemente," *Z. anorg. Chem.*, **9**, 190–3 (Apr., 1895).

(62) LYON, D. O., "Das periodische System in neuer Anordnung," 2nd ed., Franz Deuticke, Leipzig, **1928**, p. 13.

(63) RICHARDS, T. W., "A table of atomic weights," *Chem. News*, **78**, 193–5 (Oct., 1898).

(64) ADAMS, E. Q., "A modification of the periodic table," *J. Am. Chem. Soc.*, **33**, 684–8 (May, 1911).

(65) HOPKINS, A. J., "The specific gravities of the elements considered in their relationship to the periodic system. Part II. The form of the periodic system," *ibid.*, **33**, 1019–27 (July, 1911).

(66) SCHALTENBRAND, G., "Die Gleiderung des periodischen Systems der Elemente," *Z. anorg. allgem. Chem.*, **115**, 127–30 (Jan., 1921).

(67) MARGARY, I. D., "The periodic table. A modification more in accord with atomic structure," *Phil. Mag.*, [6], **42**, 287–8 (Aug., 1921).

(68) VON ANTROPOFF, A., "Eine neue Form des periodischen Systems der Elemente," *Z. angew. Chem.*, **39**, 722–5 (June, 1926).

(69) DEMING, H. G., "Periodic table," Wall Chart, John Wiley & Sons, Inc., New York City, **1927**.

(70) STARECK, J. E., "A natural periodic system including the rare earths," *J. CHEM. EDUC.*, **9**, 1625–35 (Sept., 1932).

## III. *Spiral, Helical, and Miscellaneous Charts*

### SPIRAL ARRANGEMENT (BAUMHAUER TYPE)

THE ARRANGEMENTS classified in this division are all flat spirals. Although two or three tables do not strictly comply with the definition, the authors have considered their general character such that "spiral arrangement" best describes them. Were it not for the fact that Hinrichs did not recognize the periodicity among elements, his "Chart of the Elements" should surely have the honor of first place in the class of flat spiral arrangements.

BAUMHAUER—1870 (*71*): Baumhauer's spiral (Figure 14) shows the elements arranged in order of increasing atomic weight beginning with H at the center. Similar elements fall in line from the center to the periphery, causing the whole to be divided into seven segments. Many of the chemical families are clearly shown, and in the more difficult arrangements, Baumhauer has attempted to indicate relationships of elements by means of arrows.

* This study was begun as a bibliography prepared by the second author for a course in "Subject Bibliography," taught by Dr. Harriet Mac-Pherson, School of Library Service, Columbia University. Parts I and II appeared in J. CHEM. EDUC., **11**, 27–32 and 217–23 (1934).

VON HUTH—1884 (*72*): von Huth followed the plan of Baumhauer in developing a spiral in order of increasing atomic weights. From the center, seven radii diverge, each representing the location of a group of elements. Li is placed on the first radius, 7 mm. from the center; then Be on the second, at 9 mm. The intersection of a radius by the spiral gives the location of an element. In the case of the "eighth group elements," the clusters of elements are placed in a single position. The Mendeléeff families, or subgroups, are shown by listing the elements on each side of each radius, the "Iron-Platinum" and "Halogens" constituting the seventh radius. Von Huth also observed that his spiral could be divided into areas of "acid formers," "indifferent elements," and "base formers."

LOEW—1897 (*73*): Loew represented the positions of elements by points on an Archimedean spiral in which $V = \phi = \sqrt{W}$, where "$W$" is the atomic weight, "$V$" the radius vector, and $\phi$ the polar angle. If the spiral is cut by a line passing through the origin, the segments contain lists of elements of which corresponding members form related chemical groups, as P, As, and Sb, Bi. F and

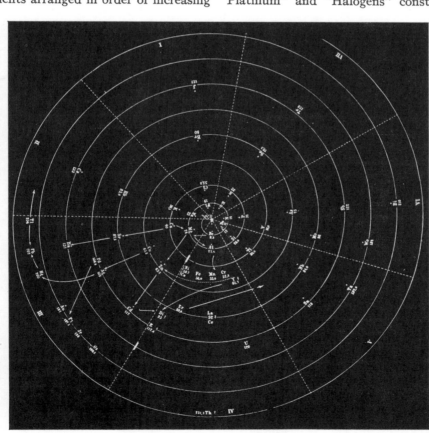

FIGURE 14.—BAUMHAUER'S SPIRAL

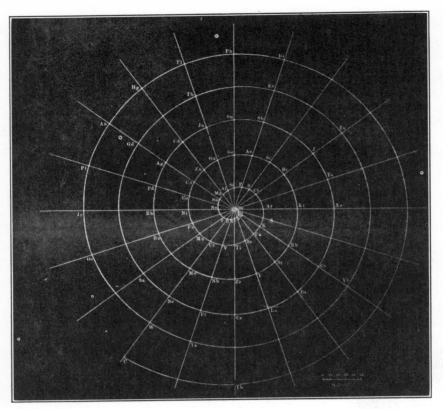

FIGURE 15.—ERDMANN'S SPIRAL TABLE

circles. The ratios of the radii are 1:4:9:16. The center is occupied by E, and H is the first point on the first circle. The second circle contains the elements of the two short periods; the third, the elements of the two long periods; and the outermost circle, which is incomplete, consists of the Cs and the "87" periods. On the X-axis are placed the "inert elements." Horizontal lines above and below the X-axis cut the circles at positions of elements of the same groups, as arranged in Rydberg's short-type table (22).

WELLS—1918 (77): The elements in Wells' spiral are arranged in the angular order of their atomic numbers, and the distances from the center are proportional to the atomic weights. The periodicity is of eight instead of sixteen, as in the Stoney spiral (74). Each group is radially arranged; the sub-groups are slightly displaced as in the Mendeléeff tables. The eighth group and "zero group" elements constitute a single group.

NODDER—1920 (78): Nodder claimed no essentially novel features for his spiral arrangement (Figure 16), which he stated "is practically the Harkins' spiral arrangement (92) adapted for a representation in one plane." Missing elements are indicated; dotted lines point out

A, however, are classified with the iron and platinum groups. The many exceptions make the usefulness of the system doubtful.

STONEY—1902 (74): Stoney designed a logarithmic spiral, in which the atomic weights were indicated by volumes of concentric spheres; the radii of these spheres were used as radii vectors of a polar diagram. The author claimed that the spiral afforded the same information as the Mendeléeff table and noted the absence of elements on a particular sesqui-radius, the positions on which have since been filled by the "inert elements." On the sixteen radii are shown a number of definite families, but a number of inconsistencies are very apparent; among these may be mentioned, F and Mn on the same radius; Na, Cu, Ag, Au; O, Cr, Mo, W, U. The quadrants are alternately labeled "electropositive" and "electronegative."

ERDMANN—1902 (75): Erdmann arranged the elements around hydrogen in the clockwise direction (Figure 15) making one turn for a long period and one for the two short periods, thereby causing Na to fall on a radial line with Cu, Ag, Au. Each of the twenty radial lines locates a family, the distance from the center representing the atomic weight of each element. In this arrangement Co follows Ni; and Te follows I, thus causing Te to occupy a special radial line and to lose its connection with the sulfur family.

RYDBERG—1914 (76): Rydberg's spiral is not a spiral in the true sense of the term, but a series of concentric

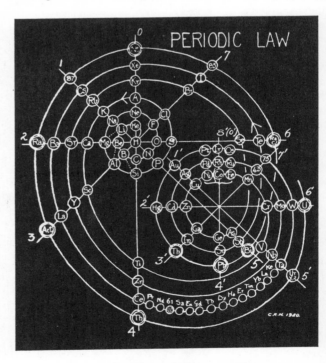

FIGURE 16.—NODDER'S PERIODIC TABLE

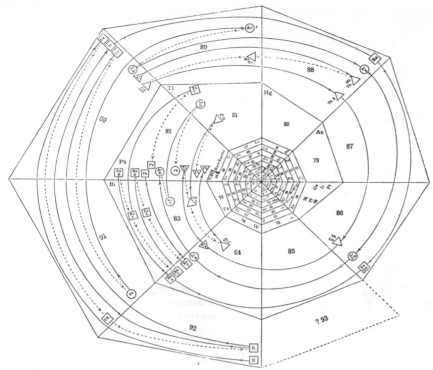

FIGURE 17.—PARTINGTON'S PERIODIC ARRANGEMENT OF THE ELEMENTS

The corresponding elements of the eighth group are given separate radii. The author concluded his discussion with, "A great amount of space is left for new elements."

STEWART—1928 (81): The elements are arranged in a clockwise direction in order of their atomic numbers, starting with H at the center. The spiral is divided into eight segments. About the pole of the spiral, and through each member of the zero group, appear broken-line circles which mark the position of "isoteric forms of many of the elements whose atoms change during ionization, so that they have an extra-nuclear electronic arrangement similar to that of the particular zero group element through which the circle passes." The rare-earth elements fail to fall into an orderly arrangement and the family relationships, generally, are very obscure.

HACKH—1929 (82): By means of a continuous clockwise curve, starting with H at the center, Hackh

interesting resemblances, such as Li and Mg; double circles represent pleiads of isotopes; and barbs are placed between elements out of order with respect to atomic weights.

PARTINGTON—1920 (79): The central portion of this spiral (Figure 17) is a simple arrangement with H at the center and the elements enumerated in a counter-clockwise direction. The arrangement is divided into eight segments by eight radial lines, along which are placed the elements of families in order of increasing atomic weight. The position of rare-earth elements is indicated. The outer part of the spiral displays the Soddy-Fajans relation between isotopes of radioactive elements in a unique diagrammatical manner.

TANSLEY—1921 (80): Tansley's spiral is divided by eighteen radii (subgroups), 20° each, giving each group equal importance. Unlike Stoney's arrangement (74), the elements are plotted, as they decrease in atomic weight, in a counter-clockwise direction. The spiral starts with U at the center and ends with H at the end of the halogen radius.

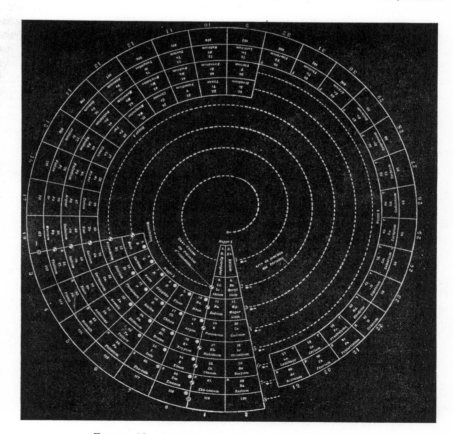

FIGURE 18.—JANET'S "HELICOIDAL CLASSIFICATION"

171

has caused seven major families to radiate into the upper half of the table in regular order. The long periods cause the elements in the middle zone to droop, forming two parallel lines for the K and Rb periods, while the rare earths cause the Cs period to droop still lower. By this arbitrary arrangement, the strong electronegative elements are found in the upper left region, while the weak negatives are in the lower left; the strong electropositive in the upper right, and the weak in the lower right. The amphoteric elements are in the lower part of the so-called spiral. The orbital arrangement of electrons is shown with the "inert elements" on the upper central radius. The tabular arrangement of Hackh's table will be discussed under "Miscellaneous."

JANET—1929 (83): This spiral-like chart (Figure 18) appears to be a long chart shaped into a disc-like arrangement much as Courtines shaped his flat chart into a cylindrical arrangement (56). The "spiral," separated on a line between F and Ne, instead of Ba and La, would appear like an improved Chauvièrre chart in which the rare-earth elements are arranged "Werner-like." Helium, of course, would be placed above Ne as usual. The author states that his arrangement is in harmony with modern theories of atomic structures, and it accounts for the position of the metalloids.

CASWELL—1929 (84): The elements are represented on a spiral by points 20° apart. The inert gases lie on one radial line at 0°, alkali metals at 20°, Be, Mg, and alkali-earth metals at 40°, the rare earths together at 60°, B and Al at 260°, and, finally, the halogens on the 340° line. Unlike Janet's chart, the rare earths occupy the position of one element and the division occurs between Be and B.

CLARK—1933 (85): Clark's chart appears to be a modification of the Hackh spiral (82). The cesium period has been shortened by merely writing the words "rare earths" between La and Hf, thus clearly restoring the other elements to their proper places in sub-groups. The "main groups" and "subgroups" are given the typical Mendeléeff group numbers at the outer edge of the spiral, and an attempt has been made to show the degrees of relationship by lengths of dotted and solid lines. Unfortunately, the latter effort has been hampered by insistence on symmetry. Be and Mg are shown to be closely related to Ca, Sr, Ba, and very distantly related to Zn and Cd. Likewise, B and Al are shown to be far more closely related to Sc than to Ga. H is shown to be related to both Li and F, but more closely to the former by relative length of dotted line.

## CONCLUSIONS

The spiral arrangements may be classified in several ways. In the charts by Loew, Erdmann, Wells, Stewart, Hackh, and Clark, the elements are arranged in the clockwise direction, while the counter-clockwise arrangement was used by Baumhauer, von Huth, Stoney, Rydberg, Nodder, Tansley, Partington, and Janet.

Of those having radial lines, two have seven radii, two have eight radii, and one each has sixteen, eighteen, and twenty radii. Five of the charts cited do not use radial lines to assist in showing the positions and relationships of elements.

The resultant symmetry of the arrangements has in several instances placed some of the members of the first two periods in unusual positions with respect to groups, and the pairs of elements Be–Mg and B–Al in many instances have been placed in positions not in accord with the facts.

### HELICAL ARRANGEMENT (HARKINS TYPE)

The "Harkins arrangement" is typical of the cylindrical systems, but this division also includes three helical systems which are screwlike in character. In all cases the authors have endeavored to show physical, as well as chemical relationship more clearly by extending the spiral into a third dimension.

DE CHANCOURTOIS—1863 (86): On the assumption that the difference between atomic weights of adjacent members of an orderly series must be constant, de Chancourtois arranged the elements in order of atomic weights along the generatrix of a vertical cylinder, the circumference of whose base he divided into sixteen equal parts. Figure 19 is a portion of the cylinder, "telluric screw," unfolded. When the atomic weights failed to conform to prime numbers, he imagined new varieties of simple bodies which he called "secondary characteristics." Although led to many mistaken analogies by enthusiasm and an active imagination, de Chancourtois deserves the credit for producing the first helical arrangement based on the fundamental idea of periodicity.

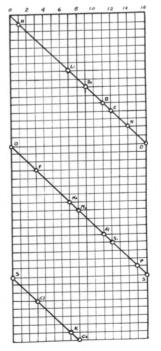

FIGURE 19.—THE TELLURIC SCREW

CROOKES—1898 (87): The elements are arranged in order of atomic weights on a line which traces out a figure-eight spiral (Figure 20). Each of the successive loops is divided into eight equal parts and an element, or a cluster of elements (eighth group elements), is placed at each point of division. Analogous elements are found on the same vertical rod at distances proportional to their atomic weights. The blank spaces following Ce and preceding Ta are reminiscent of Mendeléeff's short horizontal chart (11). The arrangement has space for the "inert elements."

SCHIRMEISEN—1900 (88): Schirmeisen represented the

elements in a system of circles, defining a cylinder, the angular displacement in a clockwise direction from the highest point being proportional to the excess of

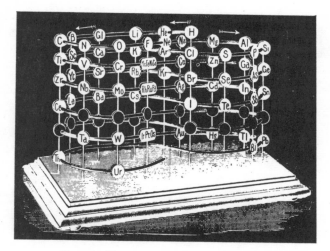

atomic weight above the initial value. The first circle consists of He to F, Li at 68.8° and F at 337.7°; in the second circle are Ne to Cl; the angular displacement of Na is 64.4° and of Cl, 325.3°; the third and fourth circles form a figure-eight arrangement, K—32.7°, Co—337.8°, Cu—45.7°, Br—269.7°. The succeeding circles can be constructed similarly from the angular displacements given in degrees.

EMERSON—1911 (89): This helical arrangement (Figure 21), which, according to the author, is based on Crookes' spiral (87), involves two symmetrical groups of eight elements each (octaves) in two circles, four groups of sixteen elements each (double octaves) in four circles, and, finally, the first quadrant of a larger circle of thirty-two elements. Preceding the first octave circle is shown a group of four elements, hydrogen to helium, in a full circle and a first group of two, ether and coronium, in a half circle. The elements are placed in order of increasing atomic weights on successive coils; the distances between elements on the helix, the interspaces, are proportional to the successive increments in atomic weight. The average increment is two units for the octaves, three for the double octaves, and four for the quadruple octaves. A slightly modified helix by the same author appeared seventeen years later (90).

SODDY—1914 (91): Soddy's helix is a modified Crookes' figure-eight arrangement (87) brought up to date. H and He are treated independently

and the first two periods are arranged around the same helical core. The "inert elements" are located at the sharp turns of one helix while the eighth-group elements are arranged along slow turns of the other, showing the "differences in the rate of change of properties in the passage from one place to the next." The rare-earth elements are arranged along the surface in the position occupied by Group III.

HARKINS AND HALL—1916 (92): Unlike Crookes (87) and Soddy (91) who used the figure-eight arrangement, Harkins and Hall developed two concentric helices (Figure 22), the central helix being formed by the long periods. The rare earths and the isotopes of the radioactive elements are arranged vertically in positions determined by the atomic-weight scale, reading from the top to the base. Each vertical rod of the model represents a group, and the relation of subgroups is indicated by a bridge near the top.

STINTZING—1916 (93): Instead of constructing double cylinders as did Crookes (87), Soddy (91), and Harkins and Hall (92), Stintzing increased the radius of a single spiral as the periods lengthened. This screw-like figure represents the elements on axes radiating from a center point. Certain unsymmetrical periodic insertions correspond to the peculiar relations of the rare earths, the radioactive elements, and the eighth group.

VOGEL—1918 (94): Vogel's contribution was fragmentary in that his proposal dealt with more justifiable arrangements of the rare-earth elements, and eighth-group triads in the periodic system. He proposed a subsidiary loop for the rare earths by causing the spiral to change its course after passing Ba, to form a loop of rare-earth elements, rejoining the larger spiral at Ta. Similar subsidiary loops were suggested for each of the eighth-group triads.

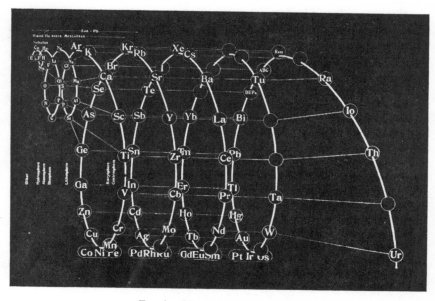

FIGURE 21.—EMERSON'S HELIX

SCHALTENBRAND—1920 (95): In this unusual table (Figure 23) the elements are arranged in order of atomic weights on an eccentric spiral. The four sets of curves include positions of similar elements. The first small turn carries H and He; the remainder of the "inert elements" and the halogens are on successive center to the outer edge. The two central rods support the elements of the helium and alkaline-earth families, headed by H; the rods of the second loop are headed by Be, B, C, N, O, and F; the rods of the third by Sc, Ti, U, Cr, Mn, Fe, Co, Ni, Cu, and Zn; and the rods of the fourth by Ce, Pr, Nd, and eleven single rare-earth elements.

STEWART—1928 (81): Stewart designed a three-dimensional screw-like arrangement from his flat

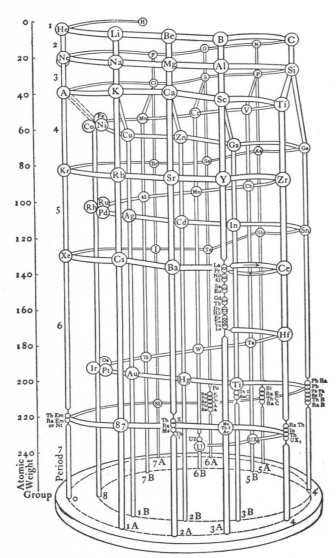

FIGURE 22.—PERIODIC TABLE BY HARKINS AND HALL

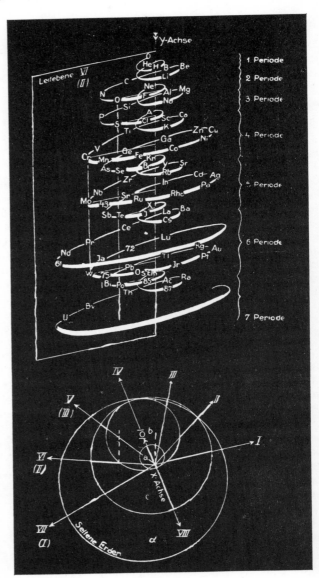

FIGURE 23.—SCHALTENBRAND'S PERIODIC TABLE

small turns in analogous positions. On the next larger turn are found the alkali, alkaline-earth, and aluminum family elements. The long periods require larger turns and the period containing the rare-earth elements requires the longest turn of all. Elements of the same group are found in the same plane passing through the axis of the spiral.

MONROE AND TURNER—1926 (96): The principle of this arrangement is quite similar to that of Schaltenbrand (95). Four sets of concentric loops are supported by 2, 6, 10, and 14 rods, respectively, from the

spiral, in which isotopes were represented by clusters of lead shot.

RIXON—1933 (97): The Rixon spiral (Figure 24) has a horizontal axis and combines in a simple graphic manner the advantages of the Thomsen table (61), the Soddy helix (91), and the Harkins cylinder (92). The author has attempted to develop the idea of periodicity

174

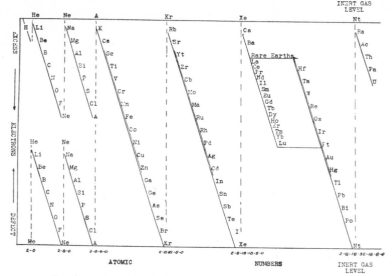

FIGURE 24.—RIXON'S DIAGRAM OF THE PERIODIC TABLE

of elements in the light of their atomic structure. The two short periods and the two long periods seem to be patterned after the Emerson helix (89). The great or Cs period gives the effect of a double period by an offset caused by the rare-earth elements. The attempt to place in line, parallel to the axis, elements having similar outer electronic arrangements has been quite successful. Transition elements are indicated by a thin secondary line running parallel to the spiral.

CONCLUSIONS

The helical arrangements cited above may be reclassified into five subdivisions: the plain spirals (cylindrical and screw-like), the double cylinders (placed end to end), the figure-eight arrangement, the concentric cylinders, and the helices consisting of several sets of curves per period.

MISCELLANEOUS (INDIVIDUAL CLASSIFICATION)

The arrangements of this division might lend themselves to classification into distinct types, but the authors are content to consider them in their chronological order. In some instances they show marks of resemblance to one or more of the preceding five types and are deserving of serious consideration; the uniqueness of some may mark the beginning of new approaches to the study of graphical arrangements based on the periodic law.

GIBBES—1875 (98): L. R. Gibbes developed a crude table and spiral representing most of the important principles of the periodic law. The vertical table reading from top to bottom in "series," was made into a spiral by rolling it in much the same manner as that suggested by Lothar Meyer in his "Modern Theories of Chemistry" (13).

SPRING—1881 (99): W. Spring of the University of Liége prepared the diagram (Figure 25) without ac-

companying notes. It was the precursor of similar tables by Reynolds (100) and Crookes (101).

REYNOLDS—1886 (100): Reynolds' expanding curve vibrated to either side of a central line cutting what we now know as the positions of the inert gases. Three of the ten nodal positions are held by the eighth-group elements which the author called "interperiodic bodies." The bends in the curve take place along lines equally distant from and parallel with the axis, instead of along lines approaching a common point at the top, as in Spring's diagram (99). Reynolds excluded Mendeléeff's twelfth series. The atomic weights are indicated on the central line, starting with zero at the bottom. The first two periods constitute the first wave; the third and fourth periods occupy one wave each; and the Cs period, almost one and one-half waves because of the long vacant line from Di to Ta.

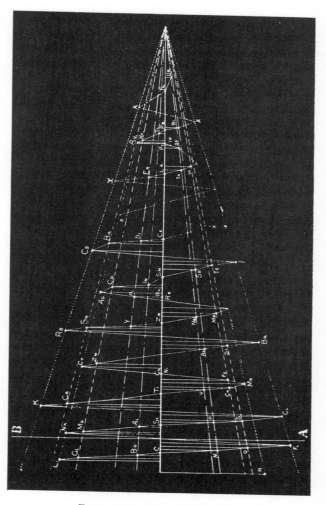

FIGURE 25.—SPRING'S DIAGRAM

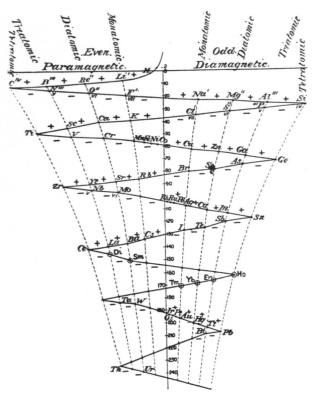

FIGURE 26.—CROOKES' PERIODIC TABLE

This author arranged the elements in order of increasing atomic weight in a rectangular parallelopiped, five spaces deep, three wide, and eight long. The top surface consists of three rows, He to F, Ne to Cl, and A to Mn. The next lower layer consists of Fe to Zn (three blank spaces), "blank space" to Br (three blank spaces), and Kr to Ru; the next three layers are similarly arranged. The table provides for 120 spaces. Van den Broek pointed out that spaces are provided for rare earths, radioactive elements and their decomposition products, and that Na, Cu, Ag, and Au are not placed in the same vertical column.

LORING—1915 (104): Loring has attempted to illustrate by means of an irregular spiral-like arrangement his theory that elements may be "possibly evolved out of whirls of energy" and are formed "when there are time breaks in the continuity of the flow of energy."

HACKH—1918 (105): The table (Figure 28) was derived from a spiral previously described in this paper (82). The upper half contains elements possessing high electropotential, simple spectra, and colorless ions, while the lower has low electropotential, complex spectra, and colored ions. On the left side are the electropositive, on the right, the electronegative, elements. The central lower half contains the amphoteric elements. Similar elements are found in the upper half in the vertical direction, while similarity is

CROOKES—1886 (101): The arrangement by Crookes (Figure 26) is quite similar to the one by Reynolds (100), turned through ninety degrees and extended to include Th and U. H is placed between the axis and Li (Reynolds placed these elements on opposite sides of the axis), and several additional elements are shown. While Reynolds' diagram was rectangular in character, Crookes' is fan-shaped and he likened it to a pendulum swing declining in amplitude.

FLAVITZKY—1887 (102): Flavitzky stated that the arrangements of Bayley (59), von Huth (72), Spring (99), and Reynolds (100) could not be represented by single mathematical equations and sought to show that the periodic law must be represented by some function of tangent or cotangent. Figure 27 illustrates Flavitzky's idea in a schematic manner. The function fails with the eighth group and the lack of conformity in the higher periods he assumed to be caused by the greater complexity of the molecules of the elements.

VAN DEN BROEK—1911 (103):

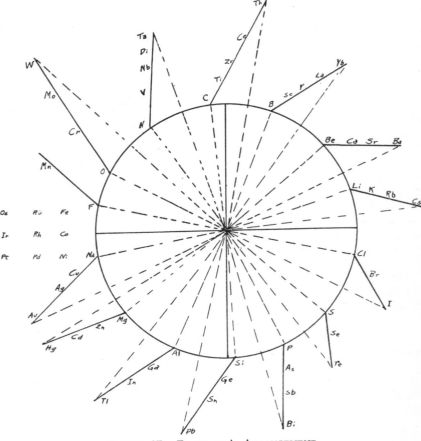

FIGURE 27.—FLAVITZKY'S ARRANGEMENT

176

on the horizontal, in the lower half. A modification of the table brought up to date appeared in 1929 (106).

| | 4 | 5A | 6A | 7A | 0 | 1A | 2A | 3A | 4 | |
|---|---|---|---|---|---|---|---|---|---|---|
| Vb | Pb | Bi | Po | 85 | Nt | 87 | Ra | Ac | Th | VIa |
| IVb | Sn | Sb | Te | I | Xe | Cs | Ba | La | Ce | Va |
| IIIb | Ge | As | Se | Br | Kr | Rb | Sr | Y | Zr | IVa |
| IIb | Si | P | S | Cl | Ar | K | Ca | Sc | Ti | IIIa |
| Ib | C | N | O | F | Ne | Na | Mg | Al | Si | IIa |
| | | | | H | He | Li | Be | B | C | Ia |
| III' | Ti | V | Cr | Mn | Fe Co Ni | Cu | Zn | Ga | Ge | III' |
| IV' | Zr | Cb | Mo | 43 | Ru Rh Pd | Ag | Cd | In | Sn | IV' |
| V'' | Ce Pr Nd 61 Eu Gd Tb Dy Ho Er Ad Cp Yb Lu | | | | | | | | | V'' |
| V' | La | Ta | W | 75 | Os Ir Pt | Au | Hg | Tl | Pb | V' |
| VI | Th | Bv | U | | | | | | | |
| | 4 | 5B | 6B | 7B | 8 | 1B | 2B | 3B | 4 | |

FIGURE 28.—HACKH'S CLASSIFICATION OF THE ELEMENTS

FRIEND—1925 (107): In an attempt to include the rare earths without unduly destroying symmetry,

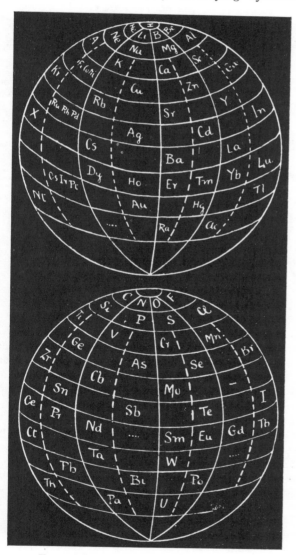

FIGURE 29.—FRIEND'S PERIODIC SYSTEM

Friend arranged the elements around the surface of a sphere (Figure 29). The periods are arranged much like those in a Mendeléeff chart. The rare-earth elements are closely packed into a belt in the lower "torrid zone." Below the equatorial belt, the elements tend to show greater instability. The order of B and Be is obviously an error in copy.

STEPHENSON—1929 (108): The elements are here arranged in order of their atomic numbers and the "percentage increase of atomic weight of each element over its predecessor" is calculated. Negative values for A − K, Co − Ni, and Te − I are accepted and used in the statistical series. H is left out, as it has no predecessor. When arranged in columns of six (Figure 30) some chemical relationships are shown. The author states that "each column begins and ends with related elements," and "contains two sets of triads."

| I | II | III | IV | V | VI |
|---|---|---|---|---|---|
| H → He | Li | Be | B | C | N |
| O | F | Ne | Na | Mg | Al |
| Si | P | S | Cl | A | K |
| Ca | Se | Ti | V | Cr | Mn |
| Fe | Co | Ni | Cu | Zn | Ga |
| Ge | As | Se | Br | Kr | Rb |
| Sr | Yt | Zr | Nb | Mo | (43) |
| Ru | Rh | Pd | Ag | Cd | In |
| Sn | Sb | Te | I | Xe | Cs |
| Ba | La | Ce | Pr | Nd | (61) |
| Sm | Eu | Gd | Tb | Dy | Ho |
| Er | Tm | Yb | Lu | Hf | Ta |
| W | (75) | Os | Ir | Pt | Au |
| Hg | Tl | Pb | Bi | (84) | (85) |
| Rn | (87) | Ra | (89) | Th | (91) → U |

FIGURE 30.—STEPHENSON'S STATISTICAL PERIODIC TABLE

## CONCLUSIONS

The contributions by Gibbes, Spring, Reynolds, and Crookes, cited in this section may be considered the forerunners of the modern helical arrangements. The other tables included seem to hold unique places among systems of classification and apparently have not been subjected to numerous modifications as is true of the tables by Bayley, Thomsen, Werner, and others which have appeared in textbooks in grossly modified forms without being so designated.

## LITERATURE CITED

(71) H. BAUMHAUER, "Die Beziehungen zwischen dem Atomgewichte und der Natur der chemischen Elemente," Braunschweig, 1870, 23 pp.
(72) E. VON HUTH, "Das periodische Gesetz der Atomgewichte und das natürliche System der Elemente," 2. Aufl., R. Friedländer u. Sohn, Berlin, 1887, 16 pp. (Sammlung Naturwissenschaftlicher Vorträge, No. 1.)
(73) E. LOEW, "Versuch einer graphischen Darstellung fur das periodische System der Elemente," Z. physik. Chem., 23, 1–12 (June, 1897).
(74) G. J. STONEY, "On the law of atomic weights," Phil. Mag., [6], 4, 411–6 (Sept., 1902).
(75) H. ERDMANN, "Lehrbuch der anorganischen Chemie," 3. Aufl., Braunschweig, Druck u. Verlag von Friedrich Vieweg u. Sohn, 1902.
(76) J. R. RYDBERG, "Recherches sur le système des éléments," J. chim. phys., 12, 585–639 (Dec., 1914).
(77) P. V. WELLS, "Note on the periodic system of the elements," J. Wash. Acad. Sci., 8, 232–4 (Apr., 1918).
(78) C. R. NODDER, "A convenient form of the periodic classification of the elements," Chem. News, 121, 269 (Dec., 1920).

(79) J. R. Partington, "Periodic classification of the elements," *ibid.*, **121**, 304 (Dec., 1920).

(80) L. B. Tansley, "Spiral classification of the elements," *ibid.*, **122**, 121–2 (Mar., 1921).

(81) O. J. Stewart, "Another attempt to base a classification of the elements on atomic structure," J. Chem. Educ., **5**, 57–63 (Jan., 1928).

(82) I. W. D. Hackh, "Chemical dictionary," P. Blakiston's Son and Co., Philadelphia, **1929**, p. 544.

(83) C. Janet, "The helicoidal classification of the elements," *Chem. News*, **138**, 372–4 (June, 1929).

(84) A. E. Caswell, "A new graphical arrangement of the periodic table," *Phys. Rev.*, [2], **34**, 543 (Aug., 1929).

(85) J. D. Clark, "A new periodic chart," J. Chem. Educ., **10**, 675–7 (Nov., 1933).

(86) A. E. B. de Chancourtois, "Vis tellurique, classement naturel des corps simples ou radicaux obtenu au moyen d'un système de classification helicoidal et numérique," Gauthier-Villars, Paris, **1863**, 21 pp.

(87) W. Crookes, "On the position of helium, argon, and krypton in the scheme of elements," *Proc. Roy. Soc.* (London), **63**, 408–11 (June, 1898), and *Chem. News*, **78**, 25–6 (July, 1898).

(88) K. Schirmeisen, "Zur Ausgestaltung des periodischen Systems der chemischen Elemente," *Z. physik. Chem.*, **33**, 223–36 (Apr., 1900).

(89) B. K. Emerson, "Helix chemica—a study of the periodic relations of the elements and their graphic representation," *Am. Chem. J.*, **45**, 160–210 (Feb., 1911).

(90) B. K. Emerson, "The helix chemica," *Chem. Reviews*, **5**, 215–29 (June, 1928).

(91) F. Soddy, "The chemistry of the radio-elements. Part II. The radio-elements and the periodic law," Longmans, Green & Co., London, **1914**, 9–12 pp.

(92) W. D. Harkins and R. E. Hall, "Atomic structure. V. The periodic system and the properties of the elements," *J. Am. Chem. Soc.*, **38**, 169–221 (Feb., 1916).

(93) H. Stintzing, "Eine neue Anordnung des periodischen Systems der Elemente," *Z. physik. Chem.*, **91**, 500–7 (May, 1916).

(94) R. Vogel, "Über die Beziehungen der seltenen Erden zum periodischen System," *Z. anorg. allgem. Chem.*, **102**, 177–200 (Apr., 1918).

(95) G. Schaltenbrand, "Darstellung des periodischen Systems der Elemente durch eine räumliche Spirale," *ibid.*, **112**, 221–4 (Sept., 1920).

(96) C. J. Monroe and W. D. Turner, "A new periodic table of the elements," J. Chem. Educ., **3**, 1058–65 (Sept., 1926).

(97) F. W. Rixon, "A new diagram of the periodic table," *Chem. & Ind.*, **52**, 260–1 (Mar., 1933).

(98) F. R. Venable, "The development of the periodic law," Chemical Publishing Co., Easton, Pa., **1896**, pp. 126–32.

(99) *Ibid.*, pp. 177–9.

(100) J. E. Reynolds, "Note on a method of illustrating the periodic law," *Chem. News*, **54**, 1–4 (July, 1886).

(101) W. Crookes, "Address to the chemical section of the British Association," *ibid.*, **54**, 115–26 (Sept., 1886).

(102) F. R. Venable, *loc. cit.*, pp. 210–3.

(103) A. Van den Broek, "Das Mendelejeffsche 'kubische' periodische System der Elemente und die Einordnung der Radioelemente in dieses System," *Physik. Z.*, **12**, 490–7 (June, 1911).

(104) F. H. Loring, "The cyclic evolution of the chemical elements. Part I," *Chem. News*, **111**, 157–9 (Apr., 1915).

(105) I. W. D. Hackh, "A new table of the periodic system," *J. Am. Chem. Soc.*, **40**, 1023–6 (July, 1918).

(106) I. W. D. Hackh, "The new periodic table and atomic structure," *Chem. News*, **139**, 275–8 (Nov., 1929).

(107) J. A. N. Friend, "The periodic sphere and the position of the rare earth metals," *ibid.*, **130**, 196–7 (Mar., 1925).

(108) H. H. Stephenson, "A statistical periodic table," *ibid.*, **138**, 129–30 (Mar., 1929).

**Robert Siegfried**
University of Illinois
Urbana

# Humphry Davy and the Elementary Nature of Chlorine

It is commonly stated in beginning chemistry texts and in histories of chemistry that Humphry Davy was the first to demonstrate the elementary nature of chlorine. However, these sources usually omit two points essential to the understanding of the historical significance of Davy's work: first, the conceptual and experimental difficulties associated at that time with the establishment of any substance as an element, and second, the effect that the establishment of chlorine as an element had on contemporary chemical theory. It is the purpose of this paper to give a brief account of this episode in the development of chemical thought, not only because it is inadequately treated in most available sources, but also because it illustrates certain philosophical problems of scientific knowledge which are still present in modern science.

The significance of Davy's work on chlorine lies in its relationship to certain views established by Lavoisier and his contemporaries of the late eighteenth century chemical revolution. By the first decade of the nineteenth century, it was becoming increasingly clear that Lavoisier's most significant contribution was his insistence on the quantitative measurements which would allow the development of chemistry into a more nearly exact science. Though Lavoisier can hardly be credited with originating quantitative procedure, his successful use of it in clarifying the nature of combustion accelerated its general acceptance as standard chemical practice. The particular aspect of this quantitative experimental view which interests us here is his definition of the chemical element. To Lavoisier a chemical element was any substance which had not yet been decomposed. The application of such a definition must involve quantitative analytical procedures circumscribed by the law of conservation of mass. But even so, the results were tentative and Lavoisier's list of elements was subject to deletions and additions. If a substance failed to yield to determined efforts to decompose it, it was assigned to the list of elements. But no amount of experimental evidence could prove that a substance could not be decomposed. The conditional nature of the list of elements was widely recognized and felt to be philosophically unsatisfying. As a result, chemists of the early nineteenth century frequently raised the question as to the elementary nature, not only of new substances, but of some of the old ones as well. Charcoal, sulfur, and phosphorus among the old, and palladium, sodium, and potassium among the new, were some of the elements which were seriously considered by respectable chemists to be compound.

In addition to the general philosophical difficulties associated with all the elements at this time, the study of chlorine involved two others which stem from the central role given to oxygen in the generally accepted chemical theory. Beginning with the writings of Lavoisier, oxygen was considered the sole agent responsible for the support of combustion, and it was regarded as the essential ingredient of all acids, as the etymology of its name implies. Other substances which supported combustion were believed to do so because they contained oxygen, for example, nitrous oxide and oxy-muriatic acid gas (chlorine).

Acids were formed by the combustion of certain acidifiable substances, the most important of which were sulfur and phosphorus. Though acids were commonly used in water solution, the water was considered only as a solvent and no significant interaction between the acid (anhydride) and the water was postulated. Acids, either dry or in solution, reacted with bases or earths (metallic oxides) to form salts. According to this scheme, all salts contained oxygen and such a thing as a binary salt was inconceivable.

Consistent with the oxygen theory, muriatic acid (HCl) was thought to be composed of oxygen and some as yet unisolated substance, presumably an element. Muratic acid reacted with pyrolusite ($MnO_2$), which was known to contain an excess of oxygen, to produce a gas thought to be a combination of the excess oxygen with the muriatic acid. This gas was accordingly known as oxy-muriatic acid gas (chlorine). Since this gas presumably contained more oxygen than muriatic acid, it should have possessed stronger acid properties than muriatic acid, but the facts were just the reverse. Because of this inconsistency between fact and theory, Lavoisier expressed some uncertainty about the composition of oxy-muriatic acid gas. None the less, the composition implied by the name remained the generally accepted one up to 1810.

Prior to Davy's work on chlorine in 1810, a number of workers had attempted to confirm the presence of oxygen in muriatic acid and in oxy-muriatic acid gas, but without success. The failure of these two substances to conform to the oxygen theory of acids constituted the most obvious weak point of that theory, but it was also widely known that hydrogen cyanide and hydrogen sulfide were weakly acidic though containing no oxygen. Though generally accepted, the oxygen theory of acids was very much an open question in the early nineteenth century.

Davy reasoned that if oxy-muratic acid gas (chlorine) were composed of muriatic acid and oxygen, charcoal would be expected to react with the oxygen and liberate the muriatic acid. Previous attempts by a number of workers to carry out this reaction had given ambiguous results, largely because of the organic materials normally present in the charcoal. Davy heated his charcoal electrically to drive off all volatile matter and then exposed it at a white heat to a stream of dry oxy-muriatic acid gas, but there was no reaction. This result led him "to doubt of the existence of oxygen in that substance, which had been supposed to contain it above all others in a loose and active state."

Davy then carried out several additional experiments, each designed to separate the oxygen from the muriatic acid. When phosphorus was treated with chlorine, he obtained a mixture of phosphorus and phosphoric chlorides. Separating the phosphoric chloride, which according to the current interpretation was a compound of phosphoric acid ($P_2O_5$) and mu iatic acid, he added to it some dry ammonia gas. It was intended for the ammonia to react with the muriatic acid to form ammonium muriate ($NH_4Cl$) and leave the phosphoric acid, but the resulting product possessed none of the properties of either expected compound. The product was a solid white mass, unaffected by any reagent except hot concentrated alkali. (This was probably a phospham polymer, and Davy was much puzzled that its properties were so different from those of its ingredients.)

Metallic potassium plus oxy-muriatic acid gas gave a dry salt (KCl). ' When the gas was added to potassium oxide, the same salt was produced and oxygen liberated. Though he admitted that the oxygen might have come from the oxy-muriatic acid gas, he pointed out that "It is contrary to sound logic to say, that this exact quantity of oxygen is given off from a body not known to be compound, when we are certain of its existence in another."

In another experiment, he was unable to detect any change in dry oxy-muriatic acid gas after passing electric sparks through it with "strong explosions" for several hours.

As a result of these and many other unsuccessful attempts to detect oxygen in oxy-muriatic acid gas, Davy pointed out that the behavior of this substance could more easily be explained by assuming it to be one of the elements, or as Davy cautiously called them, the undecompounded bodies. He also suggested that the name be changed to chlorine, basing the choice only on the color of the gas. "Should it hereafter be discovered to be compound, and even to contain oxygen, this name can imply no error, and cannot necessarily require change."

Davy's subsequent discovery of chlorine dioxide provided further evidence which was most easily explained by assuming chlorine to be an element. "If the power of bodies to burn in oxy-muriatic gas depended upon the presence of oxygen, they all ought to burn with much more energy in the new compound. . . ." This was not the case.

His final argument was based on the fact that phosphorus oxymuriate (PCl₅) reacted with oxygen at a red heat to form phosphoric oxide and liberated the oxymuriatic acid gas. "Now if oxygen existed in the oxy-muriate of phosphorus, there is no reason why this change should take place. On the idea of oxy-muriatic gas being undecompounded, it is easily explained. Oxygen is known to have a stronger attraction for phosphorus than oxy-muriatic gas has, and consequently ought to expel it from this combination."

In retrospect, it seems just to give Davy credit for

establishing the elementary nature of chlorine, but Davy himself made no such claim. By his own standards, he had shown only that he had been unable to detect any oxygen in the substance, and that its properties were most easily explained by assuming it to be simple. "As yet we have no right to say that it has been decompounded; and as its tendency of combination is with pure inflammable matters, it may possibly belong to the same class of bodies as oxygen." Davy here for the first time suggests that oxygen is not unique in its chemical properties, as had been assumed, and that chlorine is to be regarded as an analogous substance. He marshalled considerable evidence to support this idea. The fact that chlorine supported combustion Davy explained by giving a broader definition to that process, stating that the emission of heat and light, so characteristic of combustion is ". . . merely the result of the intense agency of combination," and is not confined to those reactions involving oxygen. He cited as examples the combinations of sulfur with certain metals which also produce heat and light, and ". . . such an effect might be expected in an operation so rapid, as that of oxy-muriatic acid upon metals and inflammable bodies."

In regard to the fact that chlorine, though containing no oxygen, formed a strong acid when combined with hydrogen, Davy said, "May it not in fact be a peculiar acidifying and dissolving principle, forming compounds with combustible bodies, analogous to acids containing oxygen. . . On this idea muriatic acid may be considered as having hydrogen for its basis and oxymuriatic acid for its acidifying principle."

The unique role of oxygen in chemical theory had forced chemists to consider chlorine as containing oxygen. That is, chlorine was similar to oxygen because it contained oxygen. The experimental evidence provided by Davy made this view difficult to accept and in its place he suggested that chlorine should take its place beside oxygen as another substance capable of supporting combustion and of forming acids. Davy also emphasized that chlorine like oxygen was strongly electronegative and that these two elements were the only ones known to be liberated by

electrolysis at the positive wire. If all this destroyed the oxygen theory, so much the worse for the theory, for to Davy, chemistry was too young a science to be developing theories which at this stage could only lead to rigidly established error.

Other chemists, however, were justifiably reluctant to give up the advantages of a unifying theory on the strength of the negative evidence derived from only one substance. They could and did reserve judgment about chlorine while still using the oxygen theory in many of its other applications.

The discovery of iodine in 1811 and the subsequent investigation of its properties (by Gay-Lussac and by Davy) provided another substance so similar to chlorine that it had to be classed with chlorine and oxygen among the electronegative elements. Davy's investigation of the compounds of fluorine furnished still another member of this class. As a result of this accumulation of evidence, Davy's views ultimately prevailed.

Davy succeeded not only in establishing chlorine as an element, but also in undermining Lavoisier's oxygen theory. In recognizing the inconsistency between the properties of chlorine and the requirements of that theory, he characteristically attacked the problem by gathering new experimental evidence and further demonstrated the inadequacies of the theory. Though Davy's satisfaction lay in this re-affirmation of the primacy of experiment over speculation, he had also cleared the ground for the later development of the hydrogen theory of acids and still broader concepts of oxidation.

### Bibliographic Note

Those who wish to read the original literature on which this paper was based will find most of the pertinent material collected in two Alembic Club Reprints (University of Chicago Press, 1906). Reprint Number 13, "The Early History of Chlorine," contains translations of selected passages from the writings of C. W. Scheele, who in 1774 first prepared chlorine and described it as dephlogisticated marine acid air; and from C. L. Berthollet (1785) and L. B. Guyton de Morveau (1787), who developed the concept that the new gas was oxy-muriatic acid gas, in conformity with Lavoisier's oxygen theory of acids. The final section in this Reprint is from later (1809) writings of J. L. Gay-Lussac and L. J. Thenard who, after extensive investigation of the properties of chlorine just prior to Davy's work, decided that the interpretation of Berthollet was still to be preferred. They did mention, however, that the gas might be considered an element, though they rejected this interpretation for themselves.

Reprint Number 9, "The Elementary Nature of Chlorine," contains nearly all of Davy's writings which deal with chlorine, including some which antedate his conviction that chlorine contained no oxygen. Thus the transformation of Davy's views regarding the nature of chlorine, and the experimental evidence supporting it, are clearly and chronologically given in his own words.

The conscientious reader of these Reprints will find his time rewarded by an increased respect for those chemists who faced the tremendous difficulties of a time when the list of elements had no independent confirmation from the periodic table or from Moseley's law, and when the systematic use of quantitatively based arguments had hardly been established.

# THE RENAISSANCE OF INORGANIC CHEMISTRY[1]

**RONALD S. NYHOLM**
University College London,
London, England

THOSE of us who were familiar with the state of inorganic chemistry in universities twenty to thirty years ago will recall that at that time it was widely regarded as a dull and uninteresting part of the undergraduate course. Usually, it was taught almost entirely in the early years of the course and then chiefly as a collection of largely unconnected facts. On the whole, students concluded that, apart from some relationships dependent upon the periodic table, there was no system in inorganic chemistry comparable with that to be found in organic chemistry, and none of the rigor and logic which characterized physical chemistry. It was widely believed that the opportunities for research in inorganic chemistry were few, and that in any case the problems were dull and uninspiring; as a result, relatively few people specialized in this subject. The effect of this neglect, incidentally, became apparent during the last war and in the post-war years, when chemists with a sound knowledge of inorganic chemistry were required for the development of atomic energy projects. So long as inorganic chemistry is regarded, as in years gone by, as consisting simply of the preparation and analysis of elements and compounds, its lack of appeal is only to be expected. This state is now past and for the purposes of our discussion we shall define inorganic chemistry today as the integrated study of the formation, composition, structure, and reactions of the chemical elements and their compounds, excepting most of those of carbon. Many will regard this as an all-embracing definition and may suggest that I have defined not inorganic chemistry alone, but chemistry itself. I offer no defense; indeed, I accept this criticism as largely correct for it emphasizes one of our major themes—that the earlier divisions of chemistry are disappearing and the subject is once more becoming an integrated whole. The modern inorganic chemist has scant regard for the distinctions between inorganic, organic, and physical chemistry. Thus, he has no hesitation in attaching *organic* groups to a metal atom if the properties of the resulting compound make it more convenient for investigation; similarly, he is prepared to use any of the available techniques of *physical* chemistry as may be necessary to solve his problem.

The factors primarily responsible for the modern forward-looking spirit in inorganic chemistry are two external developments, which give it, first, a new sense of purpose, and, second, new tools with which to achieve this purpose. The first of these developments is the growth of the theoretical techniques of quantum mechanics to an extent permitting widespread chemical application. This has already proceeded far enough to show the unity of inorganic chemistry even though quantitative experimental investigations are required to reveal it fully. The second external development consists of those new optical electrical and magnetic techniques of physical measurement by which structure can be investigated in the physical terms demanded by the electromagnetic nature of matter. For a full appreciation of the way in which these advances have affected the development of inorganic chemistry a brief survey of the history of the subject over the past century is essential.

## HISTORY

We might well start with 1828, the year in which Wohler's paper appeared dealing with the conversion of ammonium cyanate into urea. This paper was the first move toward the rejection of the vitalistic theory and the launching of organic chemistry as a distinct branch of the subject.[2]

Ammonium cyanate, $NH_4NCO$, is an example of that class of elements and compounds which includes metals, minerals, and rocks, and which were regarded as *non-living*. Urea, however, was believed to be formed only in *living* organisms. Compounds of this latter type thus came to be called "organic" while those in the former category were known as "inorganic." Wohler's syntheses of urea showed the interrelationship between inorganic and organic chemistry. Thus the essential unity of chemistry is illustrated in one reaction

$$[NH_4]^+ \, [N{=}C{=}O]^- \xrightarrow[\text{Transition occurs}]{\text{Action of heat}} O{=}C\begin{smallmatrix} NH_2 \\ NH_2 \end{smallmatrix}$$

Ammonium cyanate                              Urea
INORGANIC             PHYSICAL           ORGANIC

For the next fifty or so years inorganic and organic chemistry progressed side by side. The main work carried out in inorganic chemistry was concerned with the preparation of new compounds and the development of methods of analysis. Vast numbers of new compounds were described and important work was carried out on the determination of atomic weights. The year 1887 may be accepted as the date of emergence of physical chemistry as yet another branch of the subject; in that year the *Zeitschrift für physikalische Chemie* was founded. Many research workers were

---

[1] Based on an Inaugural Address given at University College London on March 1, 1956. The original address was published by the College and is available from H. K. Lewis & Co. Ltd., London.

[2] Dr. D. McKie has discussed the significance of this paper in his excellent article, Wohler's "Synthetic" Urea and the Rejection of Vitalism: a Chemical Legend, in *Nature*, Lond., **153**, 608 (1944).

now attracted to physical chemistry because it offered an exactness which was lacking in inorganic chemistry. In the meantime, armed with the postulate of the four-covalent, tetrahedral carbon atom developed simultaneously by van't Hoff and le Bel in 1874, organic chemistry developed into a system in which structure could be determined. Denied the technique needed for such stereochemical investigation, inorganic chemistry lagged behind. Thus we find that by this time organic chemistry, because of its system, and physical chemistry, because of its exactness, were steadily attracting workers from the more empirical and much less integrated field of inorganic chemistry. It has been said by others that facts give a science subjects its substance, but it is the integrating theory which provides its strength. There was no lack of substance in inorganic chemistry in the late nineteenth century, but it was sadly lacking in cohesion. It is primarily owing to the development of this integrating theory that inorganic chemistry has before it such exciting prospects at the present time.

## ALFRED WERNER

At the turn of the century the work of that great chemist, Alfred Werner, did much to put order into inorganic chemistry. Werner is specially remembered for his studies on the apparently anomalous inorganic addition compounds, many of which had been described during the preceding half-century. Werner put forward the first satisfying theory for the structure of these compounds. His theory involved the idea of a definite coordination number for a metal with ligands arranged about it according to definite geometrical patterns, of which the octahedral, the tetrahedral, and the square planar arrangements are the most important. This theory enabled much of the conflicting mass of data to be tied together for the first time. Paradoxically, however, Werner answered so many questions that he left many people with the impression that in inorganic chemistry there were but few advances to be made. However, no satisfactory explanation of the nature of chemical combination, or of valency, had been advanced and our knowledge of the stereochemistry was still limited to two or three common shapes.

## VALENCE THEORY

After the first world war, however, ideas on valency were gradually beginning to take firm shape. It is important to stress the need for developments in valency theory and stereochemistry, because without an advance in these, any hope for an understanding of much of the factual matter of inorganic chemistry itself could not be expected. The fundamental ideas of the ionic and covalent bonds were crystallized in 1916 in papers by W. Kossel in Germany and G. N. Lewis in America. Without attempting to mention the names of all who contributed one can say fairly that a great step forward occurred in 1927 with the publication of Sidgwick's outstanding monograph, *The Electronic Theory of Valency*. Shortly after this we saw the application of quantum mechanics to problems of chemical combination. Of special importance to inorganic chemistry was the work of Linus Pauling. By the time we reached the middle thirties the new valency theory was being applied to a wide variety of compounds. Quantum mechanics not only provided an explanation of how atoms joined together, but it also led on to some understanding of the strength of bonds and offered an explanation of their orientation in space. Equally important was the fact that quantum mechanics gave a sense of purpose to many physical measurements which previously were of much more limited value in deciding the structure of chemical compounds. Furthermore, these physical measurements provided quantum mechanists with many of the parameters which they needed for the development of their theories. Thus, in a sense, quantum mechanics and physical methods of attack on structure are complementary. For example, the determination of a magnetic susceptibility is easy; measurements having been carried out since the days of Faraday in 1850. But until quantum mechanics provided a theory which related the magnetic susceptibility with the number of unpaired electrons, it was not possible to draw conclusions of any significance about molecular structure.

It is my essential thesis that the impact of quantum mechanics and of modern physical methods of attack are the main reasons for the renaissance of inorganic chemistry, leading to the present period of rapid growth. Some have maintained that quantum mechanics has provided little that could not have been obtained by other methods of attack. This view is unacceptable; but at the same time it should be remembered that the discussions which arose from Pauling's enunciation of his theories led chemists to the study of a wide variety of phenomena aimed at proving or disproving these theories. This, of itself, was a good thing for inorganic chemistry. The main effect of the new development was not evident, however, until after the second world war.

It has been frequently pointed out that many of the early hopes of quantum mechanics have not been realized. Sir Harold Hartley quotes Lord Rutherford as saying in 1919, "What's the use of going back to chemistry when Bohr will soon be able to calculate anything you can find out?"[3] Similar optimism prevailed in 1929 when the new quantum mechanics was applied to valency; but it soon became apparent that in real molecules great mathematical difficulties are involved in obtaining a rigorous solution. As a result, various methods of approximation, some of which are unrealistic, have to be adopted. The most fruitful results have accrued from quantum mechanics when the theoretical workers are allied with the more experimental investigators. Inorganic chemistry, in particular, benefits most effectively from this kind of cooperation.

## TRENDS OF MODERN INORGANIC RESEARCH

Before discussing the present position and the likely direction of progress in research it is useful to have in mind the following table as a genealogy of the usual course of an inorganic chemical investigation.

Once the preparation and the chemical analysis of a compound has been achieved one may study its properties from two different angles. On the one hand we are concerned with the structure of the compound in its widest sense, as embracing all bond properties and the

[3] HARTLEY, H., *J. Chem. Soc.*, 1947, 1282.

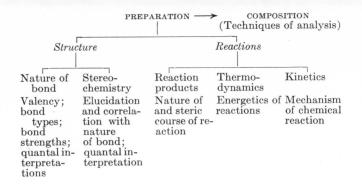

PREPARATION $\longrightarrow$ COMPOSITION (Techniques of analysis)

| Structure | | Reactions | | |
|---|---|---|---|---|
| Nature of bond | Stereo-chemistry | Reaction products | Thermo-dynamics | Kinetics |
| Valency; bond types; bond strengths; quantal interpretations | Elucidation and correlation with nature of bond; quantal interpretation | Nature of and steric course of reaction | Energetics of reactions | Mechanism of chemical reaction |

shape of the molecule—the latter a function of the type of bonds present. On the other hand the chemical behavior of the substance leads us to investigations of its chemical reactions. The first interest is, naturally, reaction products and the steric course of the reaction. But we are also interested in the energy changes which occur in reaching equilibrium and in the rate at which the reaction proceeds. Indeed, this table illustrates the fusion of the various branches of chemistry. The preparation commonly involves the attachment of *organic* groups after which we proceed to study the product by classical *inorganic* methods and with the whole armory of *physical chemistry*. The latter rests on the three pillars of the kinetic theory, thermodynamics, and quantum mechanics as reflected in the table.

Looking at the current scene in the light of the table, one is struck at once by the fact that the large amount of preparative work now in progress has a new sense of purpose which was absent from much of the older work. The driving force behind most of this modern preparative work arises from the predictions which follow from our studies of the structure and reactivity of known compounds. This preparative work includes, on the one hand, the chemistry of *new elements* (e.g., the actinides) and, on the other, the stabilization of formerly *uncommon or unknown valency states* of well-known elements—using the appropriate ligands. Today we know much more than formerly about the selection or synthesis of ligands which will stabilize unusual valency states; as a result univalent and zerovalent compounds of the transition elements are now quite common. Similarly the use of fluorine has led to the isolation of high valency states such as NiIV which were previously considered very doubtful. Ligands, other than the customary halide ions, ammonia and water, are being used extensively. Knowing something of why carbon monoxide stabilizes the zerovalent state, we are now able to use many other ligands, such as the phosphorous halides, to achieve this purpose. A new chapter has been opened with the use of various unsaturated ligands, such as ethylene, cyclopentadienyl, and benzene, for the formation of metal complexes. The intriguing sandwich-like structure of the cyclopentadienyl compounds is of special interest for theories of valency.

The study of the shape of molecules is today of major interest to the inorganic chemist. Although we recognize the X-ray technique as of supreme importance in arriving at the arrangement of atoms, the time and difficulty involved in carrying out a complete structure determination leaves much scope for the application of other techniques. In particular, by making use of appropriate ligands one can prepare complexes whose solubility in organic solvents enables one to study their properties with a wide variety of physical techniques. Now that we are able fairly readily to prepare compounds in which the metal is not at the center of the usual octahedrom or tetrahedrom, the stereochemistry of less common coordination numbers has become of major interest. We may expect from now on to see much more work on shapes such as the square pyramid and seven- and eight-coordinated complexes of the heavier metals. Allied with such purely stereochemical problems are the studies of valency theory and the elucidation of bond type and bond order.

A brief reference only may be made to thermodynamics, where much work is in progress. In particular, the equilibria in solution between metal complexes and their constitutive metal ions and ligands are being extensively studied. The stability of a complex is, of course, of intrinsic interest to the chemist, but other reasons for the great interest in this field are the importance of stability constants in analytical chemistry, in biochemistry, and in the more applied processes involving metal-ion separation and metal-ion inactivation.

One may confidently predict that there will be major advances in the borderline field of inorganic chemistry and biology from now on. The role of metal complexes of iron in human and animal life processes, and of magnesium in plants, has long been recognized, but more recently many other metals, such as copper and cobalt, have been shown to be very important in processes involving enzymes and vitamins. It is only in recent times, when our knowledge of the metal-ligand bond has reached a reasonable stage of development, that speculations as to structure and mechanism have proved very fruitful. Indeed, it can fairly be said that much of the research needed in the biological field is in fact fundamental research in inorganic chemistry.

This brief outline of some fields of inorganic research omits many of major importance including the study of the chemistry of the lighter elements (boron, nitrogen, and sulfur, for example) and the chemistry of the solid state. In the latter field inorganic chemistry overlaps physics itself.

The wide application of physical techniques for studying inorganic problems has brought with it the necessity of acquiring much expensive apparatus. Modern inorganic chemistry uses as its tools all the usual branches of spectroscopy—visible, ultraviolet, and infrared—as well as the more recently developed fields like microwave and nuclear quadrupole spectra. Paramagnetic and nuclear magnetic resonance measurements are finding an ever increasing application in inorganic chemistry. Other techniques include the use of radioactive and heavy isotopes, while magnetic and electrical properties also provide valuable information concerning structure.

## INORGANIC CHEMISTRY IN THE CURRICULUM

The rapid strides made in research in this field, and the consequent systemization of the subject have profound implications for undergraduate courses in inorganic chemistry. I have already referred to the undergraduate's lack of interest in inorganic chemistry in earlier years, and suggested the reason for this. But there is another factor. Most inorganic chemistry in universities has, until recently, been taught mainly in the first two undergraduate years, whereas during those years students have not been taught sufficient physical chemistry to provide an explanation of the experimental data. To illustrate this, we may consider the chemistry of the metal carbonyls. If this topic is dealt with relatively early in the course, it is not possible to discuss with students the way in which stretching frequencies, double bonding, orbital hybridization, magnetic and electric dipole moment provide an understanding of the general chemistry of these compounds and of their structure. The value of magnetic moments, in particular, in discussing problems of valency and bond type in the lanthanide and actinide series needs no emphasis. This does not mean, of course, that one studies the whole of physical chemistry before tackling the basic chemistry of the periodic table. We do not wish to train students in chemistry who can calculate with the molecular obital theory of valency without knowing the solubility or color of silver chloride! I do plead, however, for a better arrangement and interweaving of inorganic and physical chemistry in undergraduate courses. It is suggested that the center of gravity of the inorganic chemistry course be placed later in the curriculum than it is in many universities today. Topics such as metal carbonyls, actinides, the chemistry of the solid state, inorganic reaction mechanisms, and nuclear and isotopic chemistry should be treated later in the course; but, before, or while, discussing the compounds of the periodic table earlier in the course students should have been given enough physical theory to enable observed structures and properties to be explained. Thus, an introductory qualitative treatment of modern valency theory, stereochemistry, crystal chemistry, and introductory thermodynamics should come before the main treatment of the periodic table and not after it. A further example of this is the study of complex or coordination compounds. It should be emphasized to students from the outset that "complex chemistry" is an *approach* to the whole inorganic chemistry and not a *topic* to be dealt with alone or a separate course of lectures.

It is when we look at practical courses, however, that we have more cause for concern. Most students sum up their inorganic practical courses as consisting of scores of unknown salts to be qualitatively analyzed, a succession of uninteresting analyses, and a few preparations if time permits. The aims of the practical course should be to familiarize students with the appearance of chemical substances, their methods of analysis, their physical and chemical properties, and with the basic techniques of inorganic chemistry. How is it then that qualitative analysis has come to occupy such a disproportionately large amount of time for inorganic practical work? The answer lies, I believe, in the historical development of inorganic chemistry. One hundred years ago the subject was closely allied with metallurgy and one of the main tasks of the chemist was the qualitative identification of elements in rocks and minerals and their quantitative determination. Having been originally an important part of the inorganic practical course, qualitative analysis of a particular number of metal ions has acquired a hallowed position ever since. Thus, in the "classical" separation tables cobalt has a position of honor whereas titanium is omitted, despite the fact that at the present time compounds of the latter are more widely used in industry. There is no doubt whatever that the subject can also be a suitable means of teaching much inorganic chemistry —simple laboratory techniques, the colors and solubilities of compounds, and some important principles of physical chemistry. But let us stop at this point and recognize that by forcing students to analyze more difficult mixtures, bearing little or no relation to commonly occurring chemical systems, we achieve little beyond enabling them to acquire skill in the automatic use of—and often a disgust for—separation tables. The distinctly separate objectives of a qualitative analysis as a vehicle for the transport of simple ideas of chemistry on the one hand, and as a utilitarian advanced analytical course in identification on the other, have become hopelessly mixed up at the expense of the students' interest in inorganic chemistry.

The important subject of quantitative analysis occupies its rightful place in the undergraduate course, but there needs to be a wide recognition that the main aim should be to teach the principles of the various unit operations. Substances for analysis should be chosen for the *technique* which they teach, rather than as illustrations of *types* of compounds. In the inorganic field analytical methods are standard, except in rare cases. For the investigator of inorganic compounds, however, a new compound or a mixture of substances usually results in a minor investigation to find a reliable method of analysis. Often he will find his particular problem has not been investigated before. Hence, wide experience of the analysis of different standard substances is of less value than good technique at separating elements in a quantitative manner and estimating each in turn.

I believe that we should find more time to enable students to acquire these techniques of inorganic chemistry, as for instance, the handling of substances in the absence of air or of moisture, the manipulation of gaseous substances, and reactions involving low or high temperatures. Finally, I am convinced that, in keeping with the new sense of purpose in inorganic chemistry, the maximum opportunity should be provided for the undergraduate to prepare a compound, to establish its purity by analysis, and to investigate as many of its properties by chemical and physical techniques as he is able to do. This means that we effectively illustrate the wholeness of modern chemistry, and I believe that we can thereby develop a genuine enthusiasm for this subject at the undergraduate level. It is essential for us to stimulate students at the undergraduate level, otherwise we shall not be able to attract research students into this exciting field in which there are so many opportunities and, relatively, so few trained people available to explore them.

**George B. Kauffman**
Fresno State College
Fresno 26, California

# Sophus Mads Jorgensen (1837–1914)

## A chapter in coordination chemistry history

Today most chemists, regardless of their field of specialization, are acquainted with the nature and importance of the work of Alfred Werner. Indeed, practically every freshman chemistry student is now introduced to at least the essentials of his coordination theory. Yet, except for those who have had occasion to delve into the study of complex compounds, the name of Sophus Mads Jørgensen remains entirely unknown.

Few realize that Werner's new and revolutionary theory was based upon experimental data carefully and painstakingly accumulated over a number of years by Sophus Mads Jørgensen, professor of Chemistry at the University in Copenhagen (1871–1908). It is perhaps not an exaggeration to say that Werner's theory might never have been propounded had not Jørgensen's work provided the observations requiring explanation.

Except for some early isolated research, Jørgensen devoted himself exclusively to investigating the coordination compounds of cobalt, chromium, rhodium, and platinum, and this work, upon which his fame rests, forms an interconnected and continuous chain from 1878 to 1906. His interpretations of the luteo, purpureo, roseo, praseo, violeo, croceo, flavo, and other series of complex salts were made in the light of his extensions and modifications of the famous chain theory (1, 2) proposed by the Swedish chemist, Christian Wilhelm Blomstrand (1826–1897).

Jørgensen's views remained essentially unchallenged until 1891 when the twenty-six-year-old Werner published his "Beiträge zur Theorie der Affinität und Valenz." The subsequent controversy between the two men forms an exciting chapter in the history of chemistry and still serves today as a fine example of an ideal scientific discussion.

Yet, despite the obvious importance of Jørgensen's work, no biographical data are available in English with the exception of a short eulogy by one of his most distinguished students, Niels Bjerrum (3). It is with a view to filling this gap in the literature of the history of chemistry that this paper is written. The biographical details are taken largely from three Danish articles (4, 5, 6).

Presented in part before the Division of the History of Chemistry of the American Chemical Society at the 133rd National Meeting, San Francisco, California, April, 1958.

## Biography

Sophus Mads Jørgensen was born in Slagelse, Denmark, on July 4, 1837. His early schooling was obtained at Slagelse and later at the *Sorø Velvillie*. At this academy, his interest in chemistry was awakened by F. Johnstrup. This dedicated teacher allowed the older students to work in his own private laboratory on Sundays, and Jørgensen eagerly availed himself of the opportunity.

After his graduation in 1857, Jørgensen entered the University at Copenhagen and in 1869 received his doctorate with the dissertation "Overjodider af Alkaloiderne" (Polyiodides of Alkaloids). In 1871 he became *Lektor* at the University and in 1887, Professor of Chemistry, a position which he held until 1908, the year of his retirement. He died on April 1, 1914.

During his 41 years of teaching, Jørgensen exerted a profound influence on a whole generation of Danish chemists and may even be said to have founded a school. Such outstanding men as O. T. Christensen, E. Koefoed, Niels Bjerrum, and S. P. L. Sørensen initiated their research careers under his direction.

Jørgensen always preferred facts to bold hypotheses, and his controversy with Werner clearly reflects this attitude. Niels Bjerrum (3) relates how Jørgensen reminded advanced students that although the atomic theory was a useful concept for correlating and explaining a large number of experimental facts, they ought not to think of atoms as actual objects.

Although not actually eloquent, Jørgensen could completely absorb his audience's attention when a subject caught his interest. For example, his lectures on Lavoisier's life and work made a profound impression on his students. In his teaching, he consistently managed to convey to them not only a clear understanding of chemistry, but also a love and respect for the science.

Through his textbooks, Jørgensen was able to extend his teaching influence far beyond the select circle of his own students. These works reflect the same characteristic thoroughness that he expended in his laboratory investigations. Probably his most famous text is "Kemiens Grundbegreben" (Fundamentals of Chemistry), published in 1902. In less than 200 pages, Jørgensen gives not only a summary of the basic concepts of chemistry, but also a survey of its historical development. This little classic has been translated

Sophus Mads Jorgensen (1837–1914), professor of chemistry in Copenhagen (1871–1908). ("*Proceedings of the Symposium on Co-ordination Chemistry, Copenhagen, Aug. 9–13, 1953*," Danish Chemical Society, Copenhagen, **1954**, p. 14.)

into several languages, among them German (1903), Italian (1904), Greek (1904), and English (1908).

As a research worker, Jørgensen was methodical, deliberate, and careful. Although he could have delegated much routine work to assistants, he insisted on personally performing all his analyses. In view of his passion for perfection, his output was tremendous, and we are indebted to him for many of the basic experimental facts of coordination chemistry.

In contrast, Werner was a rapid worker who preferred qualitative tests using porcelain plates and watch glasses to more conventional quantitative methods. Niels Bjerrum recalls the following incident typical of Werner's impulsive temperament. When Arthur Hantzsch, Werner's professor, asked him, on short notice, for a paper describing the coordination theory, Werner entered a room with a box full of cigars and did not leave until the paper was written and the cigar box empty (*3*).

Like many famous chemists, Jørgensen was not content merely to make original contributions in the laboratory, but was also keenly interested in the historical development of chemistry, especially in Denmark. His studies in this field are characterized by the same enthusiasm and thorough workmanship shown in his laboratory investigations. Unfortunately, few of these studies have been published.

Jørgensen's strong sense of history caused him to view Werner's new theory as an unwarranted break in the development of the theories of chemical structure. He regarded it as an *ad hoc* explanation insufficiently supported by experimental evidence.

Although unjustly neglected today, Jørgensen's work aroused great interest among his contemporaries. In 1906 the French *Académie des sciences* presented him with its Lavoisier medal. Early in 1907 Henri

Moissan, the Nobel prize laureate in chemistry for that year, drafted a proposition to the Nobel committee nominating Jørgensen for the next prize in chemistry. Unfortunately, Moissan died later that year, and the proposition was never submitted.

## Nineteenth Century Chemical Confusion

In order to appreciate adequately the magnitude of both Jørgensen's and Werner's achievements, we must take into account the confused state of affairs in which chemistry floundered during most of the nineteenth century. Various rival systems of chemistry flourished. The dualistic theory of Berzelius, which hitherto had been quite successful in the formulation of inorganic compounds, was falling into disrepute as a result of the inroads of the new organic chemistry. No clear distinction was made between equivalent, atomic, and molecular weights. It was only in 1858 that Cannizzaro's revival of Avogadro's hypothesis marked the beginnings of a consistent atomic weight scale. When Cannizzaro spoke at Karlsruhe, Svante Arrhenius had not yet been born. Indeed, years of proselytizing by Arrhenius, van't Hoff, and Ostwald were to be necessary before the electrolytic dissociation theory was finally accepted by the scientific world. Thus, Werner's view of the two types of linkage, ionizable and non-ionizable, did much to clarify ideas of chemical bonding a generation before the views of Kossel and Lewis (1916) led to our present concepts of ionic and covalent bonding.

Today any chemist familiar with modern orbital theory knows that nitrogen can form at most only four bonds. Armed with such knowledge, he might scoff at the apparent naïveté of Blomstrand and Jørgensen whose structural formulas involved chains of ammonia molecules containing quinquevalent nitrogen. Our hindsight is always much better than our foresight. To view the works of great men of the past in the light of modern knowledge is perhaps to belittle their achievements. Thus, in evaluating the work of Jørgensen and Werner, we must preserve a sense of historical perspective.

Werner's coordination theory is familiar to most chemists and need not be elaborated here. However, since Jørgensen's interpretations were all based on the now obsolete Blomstrand chain theory (*1, 2*), a few remarks about this presently little known theory seem in order.

Odling (*7*) had proposed that the hydrogen atoms in ammonia could be replaced by metal atoms just as they were replaced by organic radicals in forming amines. As an extension of this idea, Blomstrand suggested that these ammonia molecules could link together as —$NH_3$— chains, analogous to —$CH_2$— chains in hydrocarbons.

The number of ammonia molecules associated with the metal, i.e., the length of the chain, depended upon the metal and its valence. This point was later accounted for more adequately by Werner's concept of the coordination number. Blomstrand also made provision for different reactivities of various atoms and groups. Thus, halogen which could be precipitated by silver nitrate was called "farther," while that which could not was called "nearer," a close approximation of Werner's later concept of outer and inner spheres.

Although Jørgensen created no new structural theory of his own, he logically and consistently extended and modified Blomstrand's chain theory to interpret the many new series of complex compounds which he had succeeded in preparing for the first time. Just as astronomers tried to force an explanation for the motion of the planets in terms of the Ptolemaic theory by postulating more and more complicated epicycles, so Jørgensen, in his attempts to account for his newly prepared compounds from a unified theoretical point of view, strained the theory of his mentor Blomstrand to the breaking point. In 1891 the Copernican figure of Alfred Werner appeared on the scene to challenge the old system with a radically new theory based, by Werner's own admission, upon the sturdy foundation of Jørgensen's painstaking experimental investigations. Indeed, Jørgensen's work bore the seeds of the Blomstrand-Jørgensen theory's destruction, for many of the compounds first prepared by him later proved instrumental in demonstrating the validity of Werner's views. One is tempted to compare this situation with Priestley's discovery of oxygen, which led to Lavoisier's classic experiments on the nature of combustion and to the subsequent collapse of the Phlogiston theory. However, unlike Priestley, who staunchly defended this theory until his death, Jørgensen finally became convinced of the correctness of Werner's theory and graciously acknowledged its worth.

Jørgensen's research can be divided into seven groups. The first (1866–1878) includes a few isolated papers and his work on alkaloid polyiodides, while the other six (1878–1906) constitute the work for which he was famous—his investigations of metal-ammine complexes. These studies, entitled "Beiträge zur Chemie der Kobaltammoniakverbindungen" (eight papers), "Beiträge zur Chemie der Chromammoniakverbindungen" (ten papers), "Beiträge zur Chemie der Rhodiumammoniakverbindungen" (nine papers), "Über Metalldiaminverbindungen" (seven papers), "Zur Konstitution der Platinbasen" (four papers), and "Zur Konstitution der Kobalt-, Chrom-, und Rhodiumbasen" (eleven papers) appeared in various publications of the *Videnskabernes Selskab*, then in the *Journal für praktische Chemie*, and after 1892 in the newly founded *Zeitschrift für anorganische Chemie*. Indeed, the fortunate subscriber to this new periodical had a ringside seat for the battle between Jørgensen and Werner.

In the following comparison between Jørgensen's work and that of Werner, we shall concentrate on octahedral hexacovalent ammines of cobalt(III).[1] The survey is organized on the basis of compound type, rather than in strict chronological sequence. First to be considered is type $MA_6$ in which the coordination number of the central metal atom is satisfied by six ammonia molecules. We shall then proceed to replace the ammonia molecules one at a time with other groups, giving one example from each type.[2]

---

[1] Chapter 2 of J. C. Bailar's "The Chemistry of the Coordination Compounds," Reinhold Publishing Corp., New York, **1956**, has been a valuable source of information in the preparation of this discussion.

[2] For a fuller discussion of Jørgensen's life and work, see KAUFFMAN, G. B., *Chymia*, 6 (1960).

**Type $MA_6$—Hexammines (Luteo Salts), $[M(NH_3)_6]X_3$.** During the first half of the nineteenth century, measurement of vapor density was the only method for determination of molecular weights. Until the classical studies of Raoult and van't Hoff about 1882 on colligative properties of solutions, no reliable method existed for the determination of molecular weights of non-volatile compounds. Thus, cobalt(III) chloride was thought to have the composition $Co_2Cl_6$ (by analogy with volatile $Fe_2Cl_6$), and hence cobalt ammines were considered dimers. Jørgensen (8) in 1890 and Petersen (9) in 1892 deduced evidence for monomeric molecular weights by freezing point and conductivity measurements of such solutions, and Blomstrand's original formulas were halved. Thus, luteo cobaltic chloride, originally written $Co_2Cl_6 \cdot 12NH_3$, was henceforth written $CoCl_3 \cdot 6NH_3$. The concept of octahedral configuration based on coordination number six was a fundamental postulate of Werner's theory from its inception. It is possible that without Jørgensen's halving of Blomstrand's formulas, this theory might never have been conceived.

Luteo cobaltic chloride was found to be a stable yellow-orange compound (10). In solution, all the chlorine is immediately precipitated by silver nitrate. Although ammonia is a base, treatment of luteo cobaltic chloride with hydrochloric acid at 100°C does not remove any ammonia. Furthermore, treatment of the solid with sulfuric acid does not remove any ammonia, but yields the compound $Co_2(SO_4)_3 \cdot 12NH_3$, i.e., the chlorine atoms are replaced by sulfate groups. Clearly, some sort of very stable metal-ammonia, but much less stable metal-chlorine bonding is indicated in luteo cobaltic chloride. Blomstrand proposed the symmetrical formula

$$Co_2 \begin{cases} NH_3\text{—}NH_3\text{—}Cl \\ NH_3\text{—}NH_3\text{—}Cl \\ NH_3\text{—}NH_3\text{—}Cl \\ NH_3\text{—}NH_3\text{—}Cl \\ NH_3\text{—}NH_3\text{—}Cl \\ NH_3\text{—}NH_3\text{—}Cl \end{cases}$$

On heating, however, one-sixth of the ammonia is lost, and only two-thirds of the chlorine in the resulting purpureo cobaltic chloride can now be precipitated by silver nitrate:

$$[Co(NH_3)_6]Cl_3 \xrightarrow{\Delta} [Co(NH_3)_5Cl]Cl_2 + \overline{NH_3}$$

Removal of two ammonia molecules from Blomstrand's formula for the luteo salt results in a structure which does not sufficiently account for the great difference between the two types of chlorine atoms in the purpureo salt. Therefore, Jørgensen proposed the following symmetrical formula for the luteo salt

$$Co_2 \begin{cases} NH_3\text{—}Cl \\ NH_3\text{—}NH_3\text{—}Cl \\ NH_3\text{—}NH_3\text{—}NH_3\text{—}Cl \\ NH_3\text{—}NH_3\text{—}NH_3\text{—}Cl \\ NH_3\text{—}NH_3\text{—}Cl \\ NH_3\text{—}Cl \end{cases}$$

postulating that halogen atoms which are bound to the metal atom through other groups such as ammonia can be precipitated by silver nitrate, while those bound directly to the metal atom cannot (11). Since he later regarded four as the maximum number of ammonia molecules that could enter into a chain and since he regarded such a chain as a particularly stable arrangement, Jørgensen (12) subsequently modified this formula to

$$Co_2 \begin{cases} NH_3—Cl \\ NH_3—Cl \\ NH_3—NH_3—NH_3—NH_3—Cl \\ NH_3—NH_3—NH_3—NH_3—Cl \\ NH_3—Cl \\ NH_3—Cl \end{cases}$$

Henceforth, all his structural formulas will show this four–ammonia chain although his original proposals were slightly different. Both Jørgensen's[3] and Wer-

$$Co\begin{smallmatrix} \diagup NH_3—Cl \\ —NH_3—NH_3—NH_3—NH_3—Cl \\ \diagdown NH_3—Cl \end{smallmatrix}$$

Jørgensen

Werner

ner's structures are compatible with the experimental observations but differ in that Jørgensen regarded the chlorine atoms as attached to the metal atom through ammonia molecules, while Werner regarded them as ionic—"at large," so to speak—a concept considered quite revolutionary at that time. Werner also regarded the central metal atom and the ammonia molecules as comprising a discrete unit, a complex cation. Such a structure should yield four ions in solution, and this was later confirmed by the conductivity studies of Werner and Miolati (13).

*Type MA₅B—Pentammines (Purpureo Salts)*, $[M(NH_3)_5X^{-n}]Y_{3-n}$. The term purpureo (purple) is derived from the color of purpureo cobaltic chloride, $[Co(NH_8)_5Cl]Cl_2$, the substance with which Jørgensen began his research on complexes. This compound is formed by heating luteo cobaltic chloride,

$$[Co(NH_3)_6]Cl_3 \xrightarrow[>100°C]{\Delta} [Co(NH_3)_5Cl]Cl_2 + \overline{NH}_3 \; (10)$$

and thus purpureo salts were regarded by Jørgensen as luteo salts in which one-sixth of the ammonia had been replaced by halogen. The ammonia molecules are quite strongly bound to the cobalt atom in the purpureo salt as shown by the fact that ammonia is not evolved even on heating to 100°C. Furthermore, Jørgensen showed that cold concentrated sulfuric acid did not react with the ammonia in the salt but yielded the compound $[Co(NH_3)_5Cl]SO_4$, which, although it contained chlorine, gave no immediate precipitate with silver nitrate. He also found that only two-thirds of the chlorine in the original salt could be immediately precipitated by silver nitrate, while the remaining third was precipitated only on long boiling (14).

To account for this difference in reactivity, Jørgensen suggested, as did Werner after him, that the "unreactive" or "masked" chlorine was bound directly

³ For simplicity, monomeric formulas will be used for the remainder of this discussion although they were not used by Jørgensen until 1890.

to the metal atom. The structures proposed by these two investigators,

$$Co\begin{smallmatrix} \diagup Cl \\ —NH_3—NH_3—NH_3—NH_3—Cl \\ \diagdown NH_3—Cl \end{smallmatrix}$$

Jørgensen

Werner

are both compatible with the experimental facts but differ again in the mode of attachment of the "reactive" chlorine atoms. Jørgensen regarded these atoms as linked to the metal atom through ammonia molecules, while Werner considered them as not linked to any particular atom, but attracted to the complex cation as a whole by electrostatic forces.

Werner explained the formation of the purpureo salt from the luteo salt by evolution of ammonia as a conversion of one of the three chlorine atoms from a primary (ionic) to a secondary (non-ionic) valency. The entrance of the negative chlorine into the complex cation lowers the charge of the latter by one, and the charge of the resulting complex cation is now two, rather than three. Jørgensen criticized this interpretation, arguing that if a given negative group is coordinated to the central metal atom, it cannot simultaneously satisfy one of the primary valencies of the metal (15), a point which Werner (16) later clarified. Werner's structure requires that a solution of purpureo cobaltic chloride furnish three ions, a fact confirmed by the conductivity studies of Werner and Miolati (13).

*Type MA₄B₂—Tetrammines.* These compounds may be regarded as luteo salts in which one-third of the ammonia has been replaced by other groups. It is among such compounds that we first encounter the possibility of stereoisomerism.

*Cis- and trans- Dichlorobis(ethylenediamine) Salts (Violeo and Praseo Salts)*, $[M\{C_2H_4(NH_2)_2\}_2Cl_2]X$. The best known example of *cis–trans* isomerism among inorganic complexes was first observed by Jørgensen not among simple tetrammines, but among salts in which the four ammonia molecules have been replaced by two molecules of the bidentate organic base, ethylenediamine (17). He evaporated an aqueous solution of the green compound, praseo cobaltic chloride $[Co\{C_2H_4(NH_2)_2\}_2Cl_2]Cl$, and obtained an isomeric violet compound which he called violeo cobaltic chloride. Treatment of the violeo compound with hydrochloric acid regenerates the original praseo compound. Two-thirds of the chlorine in these compounds is "masked" but becomes ionic in solution as a result of aquation (18).

Jørgensen also prepared other members of the praseo (green) and violeo (violet) series as well as many ethylenediamine derivatives of platinum. He regarded the difference in color as due to structural isomerism connected with the linking of the two ethylenediamine molecules. Werner, on the other hand, believed these compounds to be stereoisomers, i.e., compounds with the same atoms and bonds but differing only in the orientation of these atoms and bonds in space:

Cl   C₂H₄

Co—NH₂—NH₂—NH₂—NH₂—Cl

Cl                    C₂H₄

Violeo

Cl        C₂H₄

Co—NH₂—NH₂—NH₂—NH₂—Cl

Cl                    C₂H₄

Praseo

Jørgensen

$$[Co(NH_2)... ]^+ \; Cl^-$$

Violeo (cis; 1, 2)

Praseo (trans; 1, 6)

Werner

According to Werner, this isomerism was merely a geometric consequence of the octahedral structure and should be observed in compounds of type $MA_4B_2$ which do not contain ethylenediamine. Thus, his theory would predict the existence of a series of violeo (cis-dichlorotetramminecobalt(III)) salts, $[Co(NH_3)_4Cl_2]Cl$, isomeric with the corresponding praseo (trans) compounds. However, replacement of both nitro groups in flavo (cis-dinitrotetramminecobalt(III)) salts with chlorine using dilute hydrochloric acid always resulted in formation of the praseo (trans) compounds. Naturally, Jørgensen, being a confirmed empiricist, criticized Werner's theory on the ground that it implied the existence of such unknown series of compounds. The apparent non-existence of a violeo (cis-dichlorotetramminecobalt(III)) series, however, represented only a temporary victory for Jørgensen since this series was finally discovered by Werner (19), who also subsequently explained the formation of trans compounds from cis compounds by a theory of rearrangements (20). Werner further predicted that as a consequence of its asymmetric octahedral structure, the violeo salt should exist in enantiomorphic forms. Cis-dichlorobis(ethylenediamine)cobalt(III) chloride was finally resolved into its optical antipodes by Werner (21) in 1911 and later by Bailar and Auten (22).

*Type MA₃B₃—Triammines,* $[M(NH_3)_3X_3]°$. These compounds may be regarded as luteo salts in which one-half of the ammonia has been replaced by other groups. This type of compound played a most prominent role in the supersession of the Blomstrand-Jørgensen chain theory by the Werner coordination theory.

So far we have seen how Jørgensen's and Werner's formulations for metal-hexammines, pentammines, and tetrammines, both systems reasonably compatible with experimental facts, permitted two rival hypotheses to exist side by side for a limited time. However, the scientific mind feels uneasy at accepting two alternative explanations for a given group of phenomena, the coexistence of the wave and corpuscular theories of light notwithstanding. As more experimental evidence accumulated, the scales began to tip in favor of Werner's theory.

When successive ammonia molecules in a hexammine are replaced by negative groups such as chlorine atoms, these enter the coordination sphere and thus become non-ionic or "masked." With the replacement of the first two ammonia molecules, the ionic character of the compounds as predicted by the two theories is in complete agreement, but with that of the third ammonia molecule, the ionic character of the resulting compounds differs radically according to the two theories:

Four Ions   $[Co(NH_3)_6]Cl_3$

—NH₃

Three ions   $[Co(NH_3)_5Cl]Cl_2$

—NH₃

Two Ions   $[Co(NH_3)_4Cl_2]Cl$

—NH₃

Non-Electrolyte $[Co(NH_3)_3Cl_3]°$

Two Ions

Jørgensen                    Werner

Jørgensen predicted that the chain of four ammonia molecules would merely be shortened by one and the resulting compound would be similar to the preceding one in forming two ions in solution, one of the chlorine atoms still remaining ionic. On the other hand, Werner (23) predicted an abrupt change in properties. The resulting compound should be a non-electrolyte soluble in non-polar solvents, and such solutions should not conduct an electric current. Werner pointed out that the properties of such compounds agreed with his theoretical predictions. Jørgensen (12) protested that the very few triammine complexes of trivalent metals then known were too poorly characterized to allow any conclusions to be drawn.

The classical conductivity studies of Werner and Miolati (13) on a wide variety of metal-ammine complexes agreed very well with Werner's theory. The conductivities of compounds such as $[Co(NH_3)_3(NO_2)_3]$ were found to be extremely low, an indication of non-electrolytic character. Petersen (24) verified Werner and Miolati's experiments but objected to their conclusions in those cases where the conductivities corresponded to a greater number of ions than that predicted by the coordination theory. Werner explained these apparent discrepancies by aquation reactions such as

$$[Co(NH_3)_3(NO_2)_2Cl]° + H_2O \longrightarrow$$
$$[Co(NH_3)_3(NO_2)_2(H_2O)]^+ + Cl^-.$$

However, measurements of compounds not containing as ligands groups readily displaced by water agreed completely with the theory. Petersen also tried to verify his conductivity measurements by cryoscopic studies, but he encountered some discrepancies. Jørgensen (15) seized upon these in an attempt to discredit the entire conductivity method and hence all of Werner and Miolati's results. Actually, Petersen's results did not support Jørgensen's view any better than they did Werner's theory.

## Conclusion

It was only natural that Werner's views, marking a sharp break in the classical theory of valency and structure, should have seemed too radical to Jørgensen. When Werner first proposed his theory, the octahedral configuration for cobalt(III) was a mere guess without adequate experimental verification. At this time, on the other hand, the older man had already devoted many years to thorough investigations of metal-ammine complexes and had accounted for his findings by a consistent application of Blomstrand's chain theory, which he modified, but only when absolutely necessary. However, when Werner (19) in 1907 finally succeeded in preparing the missing violeo (cis) series of dichlorotetramminecobalt(III) salts whose existence was a necessary consequence of his theory, but not of Blomstrand's, Jørgensen promptly acknowledged the validity of Werner's views.

Another necessary consequence of the octahedral configuration was the fact that compounds of type $M(AA)_3$, i.e., compounds in which the coordination number of the central metal ion is fulfilled by three symmetrical chelate groups (which can only span cis positions), should be optically active. When Werner in 1912 succeeded in resolving into optical antipodes compounds of type $[M\{C_2H_4(NH_2)_2\}_3]X_3$ of cobalt(III) (25), chromium(III) (26), and rhodium(III) (27), the correctness of Werner's views became all the more apparent to Jørgensen. Yet because of the prevalent view that optical activity was connected with carbon atoms, a number of Werner's contemporaries objected that the optical activity was due to the ethylenediamine molecules, even though these are optically inactive. Finally, in 1914, when Werner (28) succeeded in resolving the completely inorganic compound dodecammine-μ-hexol-tetracobalt(III) bromide

$$[Co\{{OH \atop OH} \diamond Co(NH_3)_4\}_3]Br_6,$$

using silver dextro-α-bromocamphor-π-sulfonate, even his most sceptical opponents were silenced, and the octahedral configuration of cobalt(III) was unequivocally established. Ironically, this compound, which forged a crucial link in the proof of Werner's coordination theory, was first prepared by Jørgensen (29), the foremost exponent of the rival Blomstrand chain theory.

The controversy between Jørgensen and Werner over the constitution of metal-ammine complexes provides us with an excellent illustration of the synergism so often encountered in the history of science. During the course of this competition, conducted without any trace of jealousy or rancor, each chemist did his utmost to prove his views, and in the process a tremendous amount of fine experimental work was performed

by both. Although not all Jørgensen's criticisms were valid, Werner, in many cases, was forced to modify various aspects of his theory. However, the basic postulates were verified in virtually every particular.

Although Werner's ideas eventually triumphed, Jørgensen's experimental observations are thereby in no way invalidated. On the contrary, his experiments, performed with extreme care, have proven completely reliable and form the foundation not only of the Blomstrand-Jørgensen theory, but of Werner's as well. From the very beginning of the controversy, Werner continually acknowledged his great debt to the older man. For example, in 1913, on his return to Zurich from Stockholm where he had received the Nobel prize, Werner addressed the *Kemisk Forening* in Copenhagen, acknowledging the important role that Jørgensen's experimental contributions had played in the development of the coordination theory. Unfortunately, Jørgensen's grave and final illness prevented the meeting of the two great adversaries.

Eduard Farber, on the occasion of the hundredth anniversary of Wilhelm Ostwald's birth, discusses Ostwald's twofold division of scientific genius (30). This dichotomy seems particularly applicable to Jørgensen and Werner. In Jørgensen, the conservative, we have the classic type, the slow and deep-digging completer who produces with long deliberation and slowly develops a traditional theory to new consequences. In Werner, the liberal, we have the romantic type, the impulsive and brilliant initiator who produces prolifically and easily at an early age. Each needs the other. Science has need of both.

## Acknowledgment

The author wishes to acknowledge the assistance of Professor Niels Bjerrum of the *Kgl. Veterinaer-og Landbohøjskoles kemiske Laboratorium*, København, in locating the Danish biographical articles. He is also indebted to Finn Inge Grønberg of Fresno State College for help in translating these.

## Literature Cited

(1) BLOMSTRAND, C. W., "Die Chemie der Jetztzeit von Standpunkte der elektrochemischen Auffassung aus Berzelius Lehre entwickelt," Heidelberg, 1869.
(2) BLOMSTRAND, C. W., *Ber.*, 4, 40 (1871).
(3) BJERRUM, N., "Proceedings of the Symposium on Coordination Chemistry, Copenhagen, August 9–13, 1953," Danish Chemical Society, Copenhagen, 1954, p. 12.
(4) VEIBEL, S., in "Dansk Biografisk Leksikon," Vol. 12, Schultz Forlag, Copenhagen, 1937, p. 251.
(5) SØRENSEN, S. P. L., *Fysisk Tids.*, 12, 217 (1913–14).
(6) SØRENSEN, S. P. L., *Oversigt over Videnskabernes Selskabs Forhandlinger*, 46 (1914).
(7) ODLING, W., *Chem. News*, 21, 289 (1870).
(8) JØRGENSEN, S. M., *J. prakt. Chem.*, [2] 41, 429 (1890).
(9) PETERSEN, E., *Z. physik. Chem.*, 10, 580 (1892).
(10) JØRGENSEN, S. M., *Z. anorg. Chem.*, 19, 78 (1899).
(11) JØRGENSEN, S. M., *J. prakt. Chem.*, [2] 35, 417 (1887).
(12) JØRGENSEN, S. M., *Z. anorg. Chem.*, 5, 147 (1894).
(13) WERNER, A. AND MIOLATI, A., *Z. physik. Chem.*, 12, 35 (1893); 14, 506 (1894); 21, 225 (1896).
(14) JØRGENSEN, S. M., *J. prakt. Chem.*, [2] 18, 209 (1878).
(15) JØRGENSEN, S. M., *Z. anorg. Chem.*, 19, 109 (1899).
(16) WERNER, A., *Ber.*, 46, 3674 (1913); 47, 1964, 1978 (1914).
(17) JØRGENSEN, S. M., *J. prakt. Chem.*, [2] 39, 1 (1889); [2] 41, 440 (1890).

(18) JØRGENSEN, S. M., *ibid.*, [2] **27**, 433 (1883).
(19) WERNER, A., *Ber.*, **40**, 4817 (1907).
(20) WERNER, A., *Ann.*, **386**, 1 (1912).
(21) WERNER, A., *Ber.*, **44**, 3279 (1911).
(22) BAILAR, J. C., AND AUTEN, R. W., *J. Am. Chem. Soc.*, **56**, 774 (1934); BAILAR, J. C., *Inorg. Syntheses*, **2**, 222 (1946).
(23) WERNER, A., *Z. anorg. Chem.*, **3**, 267 (1893).

(24) PETERSEN, E., *Z. physik. Chem.*, **22**, 410 (1897).
(25) WERNER, A., *Ber.*, **45**, 121 (1912).
(26) *Ibid.*, p. 865.
(27) *Ibid.*, p. 1228.
(28) WERNER, A., *Ber.*, **47**, 3087 (1914).
(29) JØRGENSEN, S. M., *Z. anorg. Chem.*, **16**, 184 (1898).
(30) FARBER, E., *J. Chem. Educ.*, **30**, 600 (1953).

**George B. Kauffman**
Fresno State College
Fresno, California
and **Alexander Beck**
University of California
Berkeley

# Nikolaĭ Semenovich Kurnakov

For more than six decades, Nikolaĭ Semenovich Kurnakov, one of Russia's most distinguished and versatile chemists, was an active force in the development of science and technology both in his homeland and abroad. He is regarded as the founder of a new chemical discipline, physicochemical analysis, probably the largest contemporary school of Soviet chemistry with applications in numerous branches of technology.

*Courtesy, I. I. Chernyaev*

Nikolaĭ Semenovich Kurnakov (1860–1941),
Academician, Academy of Sciences of the U.S.S.R.

A beloved teacher as well as a creative theorist and experimentalist of the first rank, Kurnakov organized and served as director of a number of laboratories, research institutes, and national and international commissions. He was largely responsible for the construction of several new chemical, mining, and metallurgical plants and was a pioneer in the systematic exploitation of Russian mineral resources, especially platinum, potassium, and magnesium. His more than 200 published articles and texts testify to his immense productivity in the widely-scattered fields of mineralogy, metallurgy, metallography, and halurgy (salt technology), and inorganic, analytical, organic, and physical chemistry. Through his active participation in scientific, public, and governmental affairs, he became a well-known public figure and a recipient of numerous honors.

Although many articles describing Kurnakov's achievements have appeared in Russian journals (*1–21*),[1] some even before his untimely death in 1941, no account of his life and work has yet been published in English. In their attempt to fill this gap, the present authors have made extensive use of these extremely informative articles, some of which are general and some highly specialized. The latter type often describe in minute detail the various aspects of his highly-diversified career.

## Life

Nikolaĭ Semenovich Kurnakov was born in Nolinsk, Vyatka province, on December 6 (November 24, O.S.), 1860, but spent his childhood in the village of Zhedrin, Nizhegorodskaĭa province. His father, an army officer, died in 1868, leaving him with his mother (Varvara Aleksevna Kurnakova, nee Mezentseva) and brother. From 1871 to 1877 he received the equivalent of our high school education at the military gymnasium at Nizhni Novgorod (now Gorki). Distantly related to the great organic chemist Markovnikov, he made an early choice of a career, setting up a home laboratory at the age of fourteen. Immediately after graduation, he entered the Saint Petersburg *Gornyĭ Institut* (Mining Institute) where independent research under chemists Sushin and Lisenko and mineralogist Yeremyev resulted in his first publication, a crystallographic study of alum and Schlippe's salt ($Na_3SbS_4 \cdot 9H_2O$) (*22*). After graduation from the *Zavodskoe Otdelenie* (Factory Section) in 1882 with the degree of *Gornyĭ Inzhener* (Mining Engineer), he was retained by the chemical laboratory of the institute.

Kurnakov's interest in chemical industry would not permit him to remain exclusively a laboratory worker,

Presented before the Division of the History of Chemistry at the 140th Meeting of the ACS, Chicago, September, 1961.

[1] Recent centennial articles include MAKAROV, S. Z., *Izvest. Akad. Nauk S.S.S.R., Otdel. Khim. Nauk*, 2073 (1960); BEREZHNOĬ, A. S., *Ukrain. Khim. Zhur.*, **26**, 684 (1960); ZVYAGINTSEV, O. E., *Zhur. Priklad. Khim.*, **33**, 2285 (1960); KLOCHKO, M. A., *Zhur. Obshchei Khim.*, **30**, 3509 (1960); and "Nikolaĭ Semenovich Kurnakov v vospominaniyakh savremennikov i uchenikov," *Akad. Nauk S.S.S.R.*, Moskva, 1961.

and he now began the first of his many trips to plants and factories. In the summer of 1882, together with Prof. N. A. Iossa, he investigated the smelting operations at the Altai (Siberia) refineries. The following year during a trip abroad, he toured the laboratories of the *Freiburg Akademie* where he attended the lectures of Winkler and Richter. A detailed study of salt manufacturing in Prussia, Lorraine, Würtemberg, Baden, Bavaria, and the Austrian Tyrol made during the summer of 1884 resulted the following year in his dissertation for the position of *Adiunkt* (Assistant) in metallurgy, halurgy, and assaying, a post which he held for eight years. This work, "Isparitel'nye Sistemy Solîanykh Varnits" (Evaporative Systems of Salt Boilers), containing the germs of Kurnakov's subsequent studies of salt equilibria, appeared long before van't Hoff's research on the Stassfurt salt beds. The eighties were years of great developments in physical chemistry; Kurnakov's work was in keeping with this trend.

Further scientifically-fruitful summer travels included: a chemical study of therapeutic mineral muds in the Crimean salt lakes (1894), which resulted in Kurnakov's introduction of the coefficient of metamorphization, a new and important unit for the characterization of natural salt solutions; a study of firedamp (methane) in the Donets Basin anthracite mines (1895) (*23*); work as an expert at the All-Russian Industrial and Artistic Exhibition at Nizhni Novgorod (1896); a visit to Germany and France to study methods for the investigation of detonating (oxyhydrogen) gas (1898); a trip as delegate to the International Congress on Chemical and Mining Industries and member of the Commission of Experts at the World's Fair, both in Paris (1900).

In 1893, Kurnakov was appointed Professor of Inorganic Chemistry following the successful defense of his dissertation "O Slozhnykh Metallicheskikh Osnovaniakh" (On Complex Metallic Bases) in which he described the reaction of Pt(II) and Pd(II) isomers with thiourea, now known as Kurnakov's reaction (*24*). In 1899, he was appointed Professor of Analytical Chemistry at the *Gornyĭ Institut* and organized the teaching of physical chemistry at the Saint Petersburg *Elektrotekhnicheskiĭ Institut* (Electrotechnical Institute). In 1902, he was appointed Professor of General Chemistry at the St. Petersburg *Politekhnicheskiĭ Institut* (Polytechnic Institute), which he had organized together with Mendeleev and Menschutkin; he held this post until 1930.

During the first decade of the 20th century, Kurnakov was concerned with the solution of industrial problems such as platinum refining, metallic alloys, metallography, and salt manufacturing. During the same period, he played a vital role in the planning and construction of new laboratories at the three institutes. The general chemistry laboratory of the *Politekhnicheskiĭ Institut*, one of the largest of its kind, was a milestone in the building of laboratories in Russia. The accumulated pressure of his many duties forced Kurnakov to abandon teaching at the *Elektrotekhnicheskiĭ Institut* in 1908.

In 1909, Kurnakov was awarded the degree of Doctor of Chemical Sciences *honoris causa* by Moscow University, became a contributing editor of the *Zeitschrift für*

*anorganische Chemie*, and was appointed a member of the *Gornyĭ i Nauchnyĭ Komitet* (Mining and Scientific Committee). In 1910, he directed studies of the Russian Council on Platinum Refining, and the following year he went abroad to study methods of transporting warm sulfur waters. In connection with his work on the Russian Commission for the Study of Toxic Properties of Commercial Ferrosilicon, he carried out chemical-metallographic studies of alloys of iron with aluminum, phosphorus, and silicon (*25*).

Official recognition abroad followed recognition at home. In 1912, Kurnakov was elected a council member in the *Société chimique* and became a member of the Russian Department of the International Commission on the Nomenclature of Inorganic Compounds. As a delegate of the *Russkoe Fiziko-Khimicheskoe Obshchestvo* (Russian Physical-Chemical Society), he participated in the meetings of the International Association of Chemical Societies held at Berlin (1912) and Brussels (1913). In 1913, he was elected vice-president of the Russian Metallurgical Society and became *Ordinarnyi Akademik* (Ordinary Academician) in chemistry at the *Akademiîa Nauk* (Academy of Sciences). The laboratory of the academy had been inactive for a number of years, but it experienced a rebirth as a result of Kurnakov's extraordinary organizational talent.

World War I brought new tasks for Kurnakov. He was instrumental in the creation of a number of new institutes and commissions. In 1915, together with fellow academicians V. I. Vernadskiĭ and A. E. Fersman, he organized and became assistant chairman of *Komissiîa po Izucheniîu Estestvenno Proizvodstvennykh Sil Rossii*, KEPS (Commission for the Study of Russian Natural Productive Sources), at the Academy. At KEPS, he established a Salt Commission, and the study of salt solutions and related problems occupied much of his time for the next few years.

Upon mobilization, Kurnakov became chairman of the newly-created Artillery Commission for the Study of Asphyxiating Gases where he conducted research both in the field and laboratory on the physiological action of war gases. From 1916 to 1918, he participated in the work of the chemical plant of the Military Industrial Committee in Petrograd. During the Civil War following the October (1917) Revolution, a trying period of frost, famine, and other disasters, when all organized life was completely disrupted, research continued in Kurnakov's laboratories. He even organized an expedition to investigate the formation of Glauber's salt ($Na_2SO_4 \cdot 10H_2O$) at Kara-Bogaz (*26*).

In 1919, he organized and became director (a position held until 1927) of the *Gosudarstvennyĭ Institut Prikladnoĭ Khimii*, GIPKh (State Institute of Applied Chemistry) with facilities located at Vasil'yevskiĭ Island on the Neva at Petrograd, which had grown out of the first Russian laboratory founded by Mikhail Vasil'yevich Lomonosov (1711–65). Here scientific workers from the provinces gathered, especially during the summers, to work under Kurnakov's guidance. In the fall, they returned home with ideas and projects for the next few years. In this manner, Kurnakov disseminated his ideas and expanded his rapidly-growing school.

In 1918 at KEPS, Kurnakov founded and became director of the initially-small *Institut Fiziko-Khimi-*

*cheskogo Analiza* (Institute of Physicochemical Analysis), and the following year he became editor of its *Izvestiia Instituta Fiziko-Khimicheskoyo Analiza* (now *Izvestiia Sektora Fiziko-Khimicheskogo Analiza*); he held both positions until his death. The first volume of this journal contained a classic in halurgy, *viz.*, Kurnakov and Zhemchuzhnyĭ's study of natural salt deposits of marine origin (*27*). The year 1922 saw Kurnakov become director of the General Chemistry Laboratory of the Academy, director of the *Institut po Izucheniiu Platiny i Drugikh Blagorodnykh Metallov* (Institute for Study of Platinum and Other Noble Metals) at KEPS upon L. A. Chugaev's death, and a member of the *Göttingen Akademie*.

In 1934, the Institute of Physicochemical Analysis, the Platinum Institute, and the General Chemistry Laboratory of the Academy merged into the *Institut Obshcheĭ i Neorganicheskoĭ Khimii*, IONKh (Institute of General and Inorganic Chemistry) with headquarters in Moscow and with Kurnakov as its director. IONKh rapidly became one of the leading scientific research institutes in the USSR and a center for physicochemical investigations of metallurgy, halurgy, precious metals, organic substances, and other economically-significant problems (*28*). Following Kurnakov's death in 1941, it was renamed the N. S. Kurnakov Institute, and under its present director, Academician I. I. Chernyaev, it has continued in the tradition of its founder.

From 1920 to the end of his life there were few chemical or metallurgical conferences in which Kurnakov failed to participate as chairman, lecturer, or delegate. Prominent in his career were the Berthelot Centennial and the congress on the organization of the International Chemical Association (Paris, 1928) and the International Congress on Applied Chemistry (Barcelona, 1930).

Kurnakov was chairman of the Chemical Association of the Academy of Sciences of the USSR (1930–38), vice-president of the D. I. Mendeleev All-Union Society, and in 1939–40 chairman of the society's All-Union Competition Jury for the selection of the best scientific research works. In addition to his industrial consulting, in which he gave technical advice to plants and factories throughout the USSR, Kurnakov was extremely active in public affairs.

Kurnakov's contributions were recognized on numerous occasions by the Soviet government. In 1936, he received the First Mendeleev Prize. In 1939, he was awarded the Order of the Red Banner for Toil, and in 1940, he received the title of Meritorious Worker of Science of the Russian Socialist Federated Union Republic. In 1941, the USSR Council of Ministers awarded him the Stalin Prize, First Class, for the fourth edition of his "Vvedenie v Fiziko-Khimicheskiĭ Analiz" (Introduction to Physicochemical Analysis) (*29*), a book dedicated to the memory of his closest friend, his wife Anna Mikhailovna, who for more than half a century had accompanied him everywhere and supported him in all his endeavors. In 1951, Kurnakov's portrait appeared on a postage stamp, part of a commemorative issue honoring Mendeleev, Butlerov, Lobachevski, Kalinnikov, and other outstanding figures of Russian art and science.

His wife's death in 1940 had serious effects on Kur-nakov's health. Ignoring the cancer which was soon to claim his life, he continued his full work schedule almost to the very end, and when his colleagues inquired as to the state of his health, which was visibly deteriorating, he quickly shifted the conversation to scientific topics. At the beginning of March, 1941, he entered the sanitarium at Barvikha where he died on March 19th. Although a scientist of international reputation, he remained a modest and considerate person, approachable to colleagues and students alike. He is survived not only by his son Nikolaĭ Nikolaevich, a chemist presently working at the Baĭkov Metallurgical Institute, but by an extensive school of scientists armed with new research methods, new apparatus, new theories, and new applications which he himself had created.

## Kurnakov's Work

The large volume of Kurnakov's research in a number of widely-diversified fields prohibits the authors from doing more than considering briefly his most representative and important studies.

*Coordination Chemistry (1, 16, 17, 19).* The mention of Kurnakov's name immediately brings to mind his later work on physicochemical analysis. However, his studies of complex compounds, carried out largely during the years 1891–1902 and following closely upon his early works on halurgy, constitute his first mature research. Two factors attracted Kurnakov to the field of platinum complexes—his interest in Russian natural resources and the then current controversy between the widely-accepted Blomstrand-Jørgensen chain theory and the revolutionary Werner coordination theory (*30*). While not completely accepting or rejecting either theory, Kurnakov regarded complexes as intermediate between chemical compounds of fixed composition and phases of varying composition (*31*), a harbinger of his later (1914) "berthollide-daltonide" dichotomy.

Kurnakov did not limit himself to the synthesis of new complexes, but he investigated and sought relationships between a number of their physical and chemical properties, a search which eventually led him to the development of physicochemical analysis. His analogy between complex ions and simple metallic ions was subsequently developed by L. A. Chugaev and his school, while Kurnakov's investigation of the relationship between acid-base properties of complexes and their solubilities (*32*) opened an area later explored more fully by A. A. Grinberg and co-workers. Kurnakov's study of refractive indexes is still of importance in connection with dipoles. His use of color as a means of investigating complex species in solution (*33*) was later continued by Niels Bjerrum in his elucidation of the composition of chromium complexes.

Chemical reactions permitting a distinction between inorganic geometric isomers are unfortunately all too rare, and Kurnakov's discovery of a reaction still used to differentiate *cis* from *trans* isomers of divalent platinum or palladium undoubtedly represents his most widely-known contribution to coordination chemistry (*24*). While investigating the substitution of ligands by thiourea and thioacetamide, Kurnakov found that replacement occurred with all the ligands of the *cis* compound, but only with acid radicals of the *trans* compound:

$$(cis) \begin{bmatrix} A & X \\ & Pt \\ A & X \end{bmatrix} + 4tu \longrightarrow \begin{bmatrix} tu & tu \\ & Pt \\ tu & tu \end{bmatrix} X_2 + 2A$$

$$(trans) \begin{bmatrix} A & X \\ & Pt \\ X & A \end{bmatrix} + 2tu \longrightarrow \begin{bmatrix} A & tu \\ & Pt \\ tu & A \end{bmatrix} X_2$$

(A = $NH_3$ or an amine, X = halogen or acid radical, tu = thiourea)

Kurnakov's classic reaction later played a crucial role in Werner's proof of the square planar configuration of Pt(II) and in the formulation of Chernyaev's *trans* effect.

Kurnakov is regarded as one of the principal founders of the platinum industry in the USSR. While directing IONKh, he did much to facilitate the development of coordination theory and the application of complexes to the refining of the platinum metals. The Sverdlovsk Refinery, utilizing methods developed by his co-workers N. I. Podkopaev and N. N. Baraboshkin, made Russia independent of other nations for its platinum refining (34).

*Halurgy* (2, 7, 10, 11). Contemporary halurgy is based largely on Kurnakov's research on salts, which began when he was still a student and continued throughout his lengthy scientific career. While studying a number of Crimean salt lakes during the period 1893–98, Kurnakov developed a general approach which made possible the correlation of hitherto unrelated facts into a significant and meaningful whole. He regarded salt deposits not as static systems but as dynamic laboratories in which extremely complex chemical reactions were occurring. It is difficult to select the most valuable of the numerous salt equilibria which he studied, but worthy of special mention is his detailed investigation of the reversible reaction, $MgCl_2 + Na_2SO_4 \rightleftharpoons MgSO_4 + 2NaCl$, an equilibrium of fundamental importance in the formation of salt lakes and in the production of table salt and Glauber's salt (27).

Kurnakov's profound understanding of natural processes, his refined scientific intuition, and his ability to relate industrial and economic needs to chemical theory played a vital part in the solution of one of the USSR's thorniest technological problems. As early as 1912, on the basis of studies of solid salts and solutions, Kurnakov predicted that someday the Northern Urals would become an economically-profitable source of potassium salts. His prophecy has been fulfilled by the construction of the huge salt combines at Solikamsk (35).

*Metallography* (5, 9, 10, 17, 20). Kurnakov was a pioneer in the creation of scientific metallography, along with Le Châtelier, Roozeboom, Roberts-Austen, and Heycock and Neville, and one of the founders of a theory of alloys. Following closely upon his research on halurgy and inorganic complexes, Kurnakov, in the period 1900–1910, began physicochemical studies of alloys (36), intermetallic compounds, heterogeneous equilibria, alkali metal amalgams (37), phases of constant and varying composition (38), solid solutions, and other topics of both theoretical and technological value. A small but active metallurgical research group quickly developed at the *Politekhnicheskiĭ Institut* and engaged in friendly competition with G. A. Tammann's similar group at the Göttingen Institute. Despite the marked superiority of the German group in facilities and number of personnel, victories in this scientific rivalry were won by Kurnakov's laboratory. During this period, in addition to his laboratory work, Kurnakov made use of his organizational talents in collecting, editing, classifying, and publishing fragmentary metallographic data.

The problem of the composition of intermetallic compounds presented a number of difficulties to early metallographers. In one of his first works in this field (39), Kurnakov examined the situation in which varying amounts of components A and B dissolve in the compound $AB_x$, a study which eventually led him to a formulation of the concept of a chemical compound. Kurnakov's modification of the Eschenhagen-Toepfer pyrometer in 1904 (40), now universally used in metallographic and physical chemistry laboratories, provided a means of studying equilibria not only of alloys but also of any system and, incidentally, gave impetus to his own metallographic research. It was almost immediately adopted by industrial laboratories where it facilitated the rapid and accurate determination of critical points in steels and other alloys. Kurnakov repeatedly investigated the relationship between alloy composition and mechanical and chemical properties, a topic of tremendous practical significance (41). Probably the first to recognize the importance of the vapor phase in eutectic fusion were Kurnakov and Efremov (42).

At the beginning of the nineteenth century, the composition of pure compounds constituted a major chemical problem. In one of the most famous controversies in the history of chemistry, Claude Louis Berthollet (1748–1822) affirmed that the composition of a chemical compound could vary, while his opponent, Joseph Louis Proust (1754–1826) maintained that it was constant. Proust's view prevailed, and the Law of Definite Proportions furnished one of the empirical cornerstones of Dalton's Atomic Theory (1808). A century later, Kurnakov realized that Berthollet's ideas contained some truth, and he suggested that alloys and other substances of indefinite composition be called "chemical compounds" or "berthollides" and ordinary compounds of fixed composition, "chemical individua" or "daltonides" (43, 44). "Berthollides" or Kurnakov phases, a major concern of solid state chemistry, are extremely common both in nature and in industrial products (45).

*Physicochemical Analysis* (1–4, 6, 8–11, 14, 18–20). This area of chemistry, a logical outgrowth of van't Hoff's earlier research on phase equilibria, developed (to quote Kurnakov) "from the needs of practical metallography" (29). The relationship between composition and properties of equilibrium systems, usually expressed graphically in the chemical diagram, "*sostav-svoĭstvo*" (composition-property), constituted the heart of the new approach. Originally applied to alloys, this general method, being independent of the system under investigation, was soon transferred to other systems such as silicates, glasses, molten salts, aqueous salt solutions, and organic substances. The complex approach to a given single system from different viewpoints found almost instantaneous technological applications.

From 1899, the year in which he published "Compounds of Metals with Themselves" (46), a study which formed the basis of physicochemical analysis, Kurnakov increasingly abandoned preparative methods in favor of the new method. During the period 1908–1910, physicochemical analysis, a term first used by Kurnakov in 1916, assumed its basic form. Investigations were made of previously-neglected physical properties such as electroconductivity (47), hardness (48), pressure of flow (49), and internal friction (50).

Thermal analysis, one of the characteristic experimental methods of the new school, was applied to natural formations (51) such as bauxite (52), hydrated oxides and silicates of iron (53), clay soils, pyrophyllite, and talc (54); these are materials which, because of their highly dispersed state, cannot be studied by the usual mineralogical and petrographic procedures. The foundations of physicochemical analysis were first systematically presented in Kurnakov's "Vvedenie v Fiziko-Khimicheskiĭ Analiz" (1925) (29).

Kurnakov's graphical expression of the results of physicochemical analysis formed a bridge between chemistry and mathematics, two sciences which had hitherto grown along separate paths. Many terms of physicochemical analysis (transformation, system, number of factors of equilibrium, etc.) correspond to basic concepts of algebraic theory (transformation, group, number of symbols, etc.). Chemical transformations and changes of state occur in a manner analogous to uninterrupted geometric transformations of space. Apparent breaks in continuity which are found in the formation of certain chemical compounds ("daltonides") represent merely invariable points ("singular points," "knot points," or "Dalton points") in these transformations. Kurnakov thus demonstrated that earlier concepts of integral stoichiometry and constancy of composition only represented rather special situations, that compounds of varying composition ("berthollides") are of importance equal to compounds of constant composition ("daltonides"), and that the use of topology permits a ready interpretation of phase transformations (55).

*Teaching* (10). It is not surprising that the man who organized the largest school of Russian chemists should have been an excellent teacher who stimulated and inspired beginning students and seasoned scientists alike. Starting in 1898, Kurnakov began to attract an ever-increasing number of followers, many of whom are now prominent scientists or industrial leaders and some even founders of their own schools. Throughout his long career, Kurnakov's personal and painstaking attention to the education of young scientists was an invariable concomitant of his research. He repeatedly declined a number of extremely attractive offers in order to continue his teaching and research.

Kurnakov was one of the first (1899) to introduce the teaching of physical chemistry in Russia. In his popular lectures at the *Politekhnicheskiĭ Institut* he made extensive use of well-integrated and thought-provoking demonstrations, even to the extent of presenting complete miniature factories to illustrate industrial processes. He never allowed the demands of his research to interfere with his teaching; despite his phenomenal memory and encyclopedic erudition, he always insisted on writing out his lectures, and he scrupulously studied these notes before every lecture.

Kurnakov, whose patience and empathy were proverbial, also devoted considerable time to questioning and instructing students in the laboratory. He readily admitted the younger students to research, a practice which at that time was not only uncommon but which met with hostile criticism from the more conservative faculty, a situation difficult for us to conceive today when undergraduate and even freshman research is becoming commonplace. Many research works of Kurnakov's young students were awarded prizes by the *Russkoe Fiziko-Khimicheskoe Obshchestvo.*

Today, in our efforts to promote basic research, we take great pains to differentiate science from technology. No such dichotomy existed for Kurnakov, for whom the two were inextricably linked. This extremely versatile teacher always warned his students that technology could not develop without a theoretical basis. At the same time, he cautioned them against isolating themselves and their science from everyday life and recommended that they visit factories, mines, and industrial plants, a practice which he himself followed throughout his life. Kurnakov's technological application of his theoretical results did not lower the standards of his investigations, but on the contrary, increased their value and led to ideas for further work.

The two-volume "Collection of the Selected Works of N. S. Kurnakov" (56), issued in 1938–39, contains a complete list of his research published up to that time. Although one must allow for the inevitable overvaluation found in the Russian articles which were an important source of information for this paper, the majority of Kurnakov's works, even those published as much as a half century ago, are still of great theoretical and practical interest.

## Acknowledgments

The authors wish to acknowledge the assistance of *Akademik* Ilya I. Chernyaev, *Direktor* of the *Institut Obshcheĭ i Neorganicheskoĭ Khimii imeni N. S. Kurnakova Akademii Nauk S.S.S.R.*, Moscow, who graciously provided information, reprints, and the photograph which appears in this article. The present study resulted from interest in Kurnakov aroused by a research project on the separation of inorganic geometric isomers sponsored by the Research Corporation and the National Science Foundation (NSF-G-11241).

## Literature Cited

(1) Urazov, G. G., and Nikolaeva, V., *Uspekhi Khim.*, **8,** 785 (1939).
(2) Vol'fkovich, S. I., *Uspekhi Khim.*, **10,** 757 (1941).
(3) Urazov, G. G., *Uspekhi Khim.*, **21,** 1019 (1952).
(4) Pogodin, S. A., *Usepkhi Khim.*, **21,** 1034 (1952).
(5) Kornilov, I. I., *Uspekhi Khim.*, **21,** 1045 (1952).
(6) Semenchenko, V. K., *Uspekhi Khim.*, **21,** 1068 (1952).
(7) Lepeshkov, I. N., *Uspekhi Khim.*, **21,** 1079 (1952).
(8) Voskresenskaya, N. K., *Uspekhi Khim.*, **21,** 1086 (1952).
(9) Dlugach, L. S., *Zavodskaya Lab.*, **10,** 109 (1941).
(10) Efremov, N. N., *Bull. acad. sci., U.R.S.S., Classe sci. chim.*, 449 (1941).
(11) Voskresenskaya, N. K., *Zhur. Priklad. Khim.*, **14,** 711 (1941).
(12) *J. Chem. Ind. (U.S.S.R.)*, **18,** 1 (1941).
(13) *J. Chem. Ind. (U.S.S.R.)*, **18,** 58 (1941).
(14) Kapustinskiĭ, A. F., *Zhur. Fiz. Khim.*, **15,** 417 (1941).
(15) Voskresenskaya, N. K., *Zhur. Fiz. Khim.*, **34,** 2625 (1960).

(16) Chernyaev, I. I., *Izvest. Sektora Platiny i Drugikh Blagorodnykh Metal., Inst. Obshchei i Neorg. Khim., Akad. Nauk S.S.S.R.*, **21**, 7 (1948).

(17) Zvyagintsev, O. E., *Izvest. Sektora Platiny i Drugikh Blagorodnykh Metal., Inst. Obshchei i Neorg. Khim., Akad. Nauk S.S.S.R.*, **28**, 133 (1954).

(18) Anosov, V. Ya., *Izvest. Sektora Fiz.-Khim. Anal., Inst. Obshchei i Neorg. Khim., Akad. Nauk S.S.S.R.*, **14**, 38 (1946).

(19) Efremov, N. N., *Izvest. Sektora Fiz.-Khim. Anal., Inst. Obshchei i Neorg. Khim., Akad. Nauk S.S.S.R.*, **14**, 63 (1946).

(20) Urazov, G. G., *Izvest. Sektora Fiz.-Khim. Anal., Inst. Obshchei i Neorg. Khim., Akad. Nauk S.S.S.R.*, **16**, 5 (1948).

(21) Zvyagintsev, O. E., *Zhur. Neorg. Khim.*, **2**, 2281 (1957).

(22) Kurnakov, N. S., *Zapiski Min. Obshch.*, **16**, 210, 331 (1880).

(23) Kurnakov, N. S., *J. Russ. Phys. Chem. Soc.*, **34**, 654 (1902).

(24) Kurnakov, N. S., *J. Russ. Phys. Chem. Soc.*, **25**, 565, 693 (1893); *J. prakt. Chem.*, **50**, 481 (1894).

(25) Kurnakov, N. S., Urazov, G. G., and Elin, G. S., *J. Russ. Phys. Chem. Soc.*, **45**, 676 (1913); Kurnakov, N. S., and Urazov, G. G., *Ministère du commerce et de l'industrie russe, 1915; Z. anorg. allgem. Chem.*, **123**, 89 (1922); *Rev. métal.*, **20**, 451 (1923); Kurnakov, N. S., Urazov, G. G., and Grigoriev, A., *Z. anorg. allgem. Chem.*, **125**, 207 (1922); *Rev. métal.*, **20**, 66 (1923).

(26) Kurnakov, N. S., and Zhemchuzhnyi, S. F., *Material, Akad. Nauk S.S.S.R.*, **73**, 339 (1930).

(27) Kurnakov, N. S., and Zhemchuzhnyi, S. F., *J. Russ. Phys. Chem. Soc.*, **48**, 634 (1916); **51**, 1 (1919); *Bull. acad. sci. russ.*, 1855 (1918); *Ann. inst. anal. phys.-chim. (U.S.S.R.)*, **1**, 185 (1919); **2**, 514 (1924); *Z. anorg. allgem. Chem.*, **140**, 149 (1924).

(28) Kurnakov, N. S., *Uspekhi Khim.*, **5**, 957 (1936).

(29) Kurnakov, N. S., "Vvedenie v Fiziko-Khimicheskii Analiz," 4-e izd., Akademiia Nauk S.S.S.R., Moskva, 1940.

(30) Kauffman, G. B., *J. Chem. Educ.*, **36**, 521 (1959); *Chymia*, **6**, 180 (1960).

(31) Kurnakov, N. S., *J. prakt. Chem.*, **52**, 177, 490 (1895).

(32) Kurnakov, N. S., *J. Russ. Phys. Chem. Soc.*, **24**, 629 (1892).

(33) Kurnakov, N. S., *Z. anorg. Chem.*, **17**, 207 (1898).

(34) Kurnakov, N. S., et al., *Ann. inst. platine*, **9**, 113 (1932).

(35) Kurnakov, N. S., *Bull. acad. sci. Petrograd*, 1411 (1916); Kurnakov, N. S., Byeloglazov, K. F., and Shmat'ko, M. K., *Bull. acad. sci. Petrograd*, 467 (1917); *J. Russ. Phys. Chem. Soc.*, **50**, 122 (1918); Kurnakov, N. S., *Bull. acad. sci. U.R.S.S., Classe sci. math. nat., Sér. Chim.*, 973 (977 in English) (**1937**).

(36) Kurnakov, N. S., and Pushin, N. A., *J. Russ. Phys. Chem. Soc.*, **33**, 565, 588 (1901); **38**, 1146 (1906); Kurnakov, N. S., and Stepanov, N. I., *Z. anorg. Chem.*, **46**, 177 (1905); Kurnakov, N. S., and Kusnetsov, A. N., *Z. anorg. Chem.*, **52**, 173 (1907).

(37) Kurnakov, N. S., and Zhukovski, G. U., *J. Russ. Phys. Chem. Soc.*, **38**, 1216 (1906); *Z. anorg. Chem.*, **52**, 416 (1907).

(38) Kurnakov, N. S., and Konstantinov, N. S., *J. Russ. Phys. Chem. Soc.*, **40**, 227 (1908); *Z. anorg. Chem.*, **58**, 1 (1908).

(39) Kurnakov, N. S., *Zapiski Russk. Tekh. Obshch.*, **35**, 7 (1901).

(40) Kurnakov, N. S., *Z. anorg. Chem.*, **42**, 184 (1904).

(41) Kurnakov, N. S., and Zhemchuzhnyi, S. F., *Izvestia St. Petersburg Politekhn. Inst.*, **19**, 323 (1913).

(42) Kurnakov, N. S., and Efremov, N. N., *J. Russ. Phys. Chem. Soc.*, **44**, 1992 (1913).

(43) Leicester, H. M., "The Historical Background of Chemistry," John Wiley and Sons, Inc., New York, **1956**, pp. 150–3.

(44) Kurnakov, N. S., *Bull. acad. sci. St. Petersburg*, 321 (1914).

(45) Ageev, N. V., *Ann. sect. anal. phys.-chim., Inst. chim. gén. (U.S.S.R.)*, **16**, 119 (1943).

(46) Kurnakov, N. S., *J. Russ. Phys. Chem. Soc.*, **31**, 927 (1899).

(47) Kurnakov, N. S., and Zhemchuzhnyi, S. F., *J. Russ. Phys. Chem. Soc.*, **39**, 211 (1907).

(48) Kurnakov, N. S., and Zhemchuzhnyi, S. F., *J. Russ. Phys. Chem. Soc.*, **39**, 1148 (1907); **40**, 1067 (1908); *Z. anorg. Chem.*, **60**, 1 (1908).

(49) Kurnakov, N. S., and Zhemchuzhnyi, S. F., *Z. anorg. Chem.*, **64**, 149 (1909).

(50) Kurnakov, N. S., and Zhemchuzhnyi, S. F., *J. Russ. Phys. Chem. Soc.*, **44**, 1964 (1912).

(*Concluded on page 204*)

---

# *The* BEGINNING *of* LIQUID AMMONIA RESEARCH *in the* UNITED STATES*

## ROBERT TAFT

### The University of Kansas, Lawrence, Kansas

THE properties of liquid ammonia as a solvent and the ammonia systems of compounds are now quite familiar to the chemists of the present day. On the other hand, the events leading up to the initiation of the experimental work in this country, upon which most of our knowledge of this subject is based, are not so well known. The conditions under which ideas are formed, put into execution, and developed into a well-defined branch of science are usually of interest and never without instructive value. For

this reason, as well as to make the historical record while the principals in the events here recorded are still with us in the flesh, the present paper has been written. The principals just mentioned are three well-known American chemists, Professors H. P. Cady, E. C. Franklin, and C. A. Kraus.

As the work to be described was begun at The University of Kansas in the middle nineties, a brief setting of the historic stage, with respect to both local conditions and the development of chemical theory, may enable the reader to obtain a truer perspective of the events to be noted.

* This paper has been read and approved by Dr. Franklin, Dr. Kraus, and Dr. Cady.

By 1895 theoretical chemistry had been in existence as a well-recognized and separate branch of the science for relatively few years. Indeed, H. C. Jones, in his book "A New Era in Chemistry," dates the beginning of this era from the establishment by Ostwald, van't Hoff, and others, of the *Zeitschrift für physikalische Chemie* in 1887. 1895 would find us then in the eighth year of the new era.

Few textbooks of physical chemistry were available, especially in this country. Nernst's "Theoretical Chemistry" had appeared, however, in an English translation in this year (1895). The books of Ostwald, which were to have such a marked influence on the development of physical chemistry in this country, appeared during this decade, especially toward the latter end.

The American journals of the period, *The American Chemical Journal* and the *Journal of the American Chemical Society*, published scarcely anything of a physico-chemical nature until somewhat later. For example, in the year 1895 only one paper of a definite physico-chemical character was published in both journals. To meet the growing interest in physical chemistry of this day, Professor Bancroft of Cornell, recently returned from Nernst's laboratory in Berlin, founded the *Journal of Physical Chemistry*. The first issue of this journal, however, did not appear until October, 1896.

The beginning student in an American university of this period was in a measure, then, dependent upon his own resources if the field of physical chemistry were of interest to him. Textbooks, such as Remsen's "Advanced Inorganic Chemistry," were available and were, as we shall see, capable of stimulating productive thought.

By 1895 The University of Kansas was twenty-nine years old, possessing at this time a faculty of some fifty members and a student body of approximately seven hundred of collegiate rank. The department of chemistry had a staff of three members and was housed in its own laboratory building. Laboratory and library facilities were, however, when compared to those of the present day, decidedly meager. Standard treatises on the chemistry of that day were available, but journal literature was scarce. Of course, one should remember that the total volume of chemical literature in that period was very considerably less than at the present day.

In the fall of 1893 there appeared at this University, from the plains of central Kansas, a nineteen-year-old boy who was already much engrossed with chemistry. This boy, Hamilton P. Cady, was so much interested in chemistry that by the time he was seventeen he had purchased with his own earnings Remsen's "Inorganic Chemistry," a supply of chemicals, some test tubes, and several evaporating dishes. Of necessity these were soon handled with respect and care, for when this supply was gone, time and money were required to replace the stock, and money was scarce. A balance and a barometer were constructed by this

HAMILTON P. CADY AS A SENIOR IN THE UNIVERSITY OF KANSAS

From a photograph taken in 1897. Cady had made considerable progress in his researches on liquid ammonia as an electrolytic solvent when this photograph was taken.

ingenious youth, and with this equipment many of the experiments described in Remsen's book were carried out. Cady, then, when he appeared at The University of Kansas, already had a working knowledge of chemistry. The chemistry staff in 1893–94 consisted of Dr. E. H. S. Bailey, the chairman of the department, Mr. F. B. Dains, assistant in chemistry (who was taking the place of Mr. E. C. Franklin, absent on leave at The Johns Hopkins University), and Mr. E. C. Case, assistant in chemistry. After consulting with Dr. Bailey, Cady enrolled as a freshman, but his knowledge of chemistry was judged sufficient to warrant his being enrolled in organic chemistry, a course which was then given in the junior year.

By the end of his sophomore year Cady had made such progress that he was made an assistant in chemistry and the following year had charge of the laboratory of qualitative analysis.

During the fall of 1895, Cady, then a sophomore, became interested in the water of hydration of salts, a topic of never-failing interest apparently to many generations of chemists. He prepared many such hydrates, especially those containing several metals. In attempts to establish the constitution of these hydrates, Cady reviewed the literature available, including his ever-ready Remsen. In Remsen's book[1] he ran across this statement,

It is a curious and interesting, though at present inexplicable, fact that anhydrous copper sulphate combines with five molecules of ammonia just as it does with five molecules of water, and that by lying in moist air the molecules of ammonia in the compound are successively replaced by water, so that the following series of compounds is formed:

$$CuSO_4 \cdot 5NH_3$$
$$CuSO_4 \cdot 4NH_3 \cdot H_2O$$
$$CuSO_4 \cdot 3NH_3 \cdot 2H_2O$$
$$CuSO_4 \cdot 2NH_3 \cdot 3H_2O$$
$$CuSO_4 \cdot NH_3 \cdot 4H_2O$$
$$CuSO_4 \cdot 5H_2O$$

From this it would appear that the ammonia in these compounds plays a part analogous to that played by the "water of crystallization."

_____

[1] REMSEN, "Inorganic Chemistry," 2nd ed., revised, Henry Holt & Co., New York City, **1890**, pp. 593–4.

This set Cady to work, looking up other possibilities, to see if the replacement of water by ammonia in hydrates was a general phenomenon. As a result of this study he reported before the chemical seminary of the University on March 18, 1896, upon "Ammonia Compounds Analogous to Salt Hydrates."*

Early in this study the possibility of using liquid ammonia as an electrolytic solvent occurred to Cady. Cady reasoned in this way: Water forms hydrates with certain salts. This indicates a certain unsaturatedness of water. These same salts form analogous compounds with ammonia. Water dissolves these hydrates—not only dissolves them—but in dissolving them produces a system which is an electrolytic conductor. Possibly *liquid* ammonia would dissolve these salts, the solution of which might likewise conduct electrolytically. After reasoning in this fashion, Cady undertook to look up the meager literature available in the library at his disposal. Weyl,[2] Seely,[3] and Gore[4] had all published some work on solutions in liquid ammonia, but none of these publications was available to Cady. Fortunately, Gore's paper had been abstracted in Watts' "Chemical Dictionary," a set of which was available. This abstract confirmed Cady's conjecture about the solvent ability of liquid ammonia, but, as Gore had not tried the electrical conductivity of his solutions, Cady had no further information relative to his second hypothesis. The student of electrochemistry will recall that this was before the days when the Nernst-Thomson rule[5] had become sufficiently well known to be included in the textbooks available, so that there was no working principle to help Cady out.† The reader should also recall that this was before Walden[6] began publishing his fruitful work on the chemistry and electrochemistry of non-aqueous solvents.

As Cady could find no information upon the electrical conductances of salts in liquid ammonia, he considered the possibility of determining the matter for himself. But neither equipment nor liquid ammonia in quantity was available. He then took the project to Prof. E. C. Franklin* who encouraged him and told him that his problem appeared feasible. Franklin had developed into a very skilful glass blower and to help Cady along made for him a small Dewar vessel with a wide mouth. Dr. Bailey, the head of the department, was then consulted and he agreed to purchase for Cady's use a cylinder of liquid ammonia.†

These last events took place in the spring of '96 and, as the liquid ammonia was slow in arriving, no further work was accomplished until the fall of that year. When school commenced again in the fall, the cylinder of liquid ammonia had arrived and Cady** began his actual experiments with liquid ammonia. Dr. Franklin had been granted a year's leave of absence for the school year of '96-'97,†† so that Cady began his experiments without the aid or advice of the elder man.

Cady's original equipment was comparatively crude. It consisted of an old ammeter, the Dewar tube made by Franklin and fitted with a pair of electrodes, and a 110 d. c. circuit as his source of electrical power. His first experiment consisted in the measurement of current which would flow through liquid ammonia itself. He found, as far as he could tell by his ammeter, that it was a non-conductor. This was surprising, as Bleekrode[7] had recorded that liquid ammonia was a good conductor of electricity. As the result of his subsequent work, Cady showed that Bleekrode had undoubtedly been using a solution of an electrolyte (presumably a sodium salt) rather than pure liquid ammonia.

As soon as he found that liquid ammonia would not conduct a current, he added a quantity of potassium iodide, which Gore had recorded as being very soluble, to the liquid ammonia and found that the resulting solution was a very good conductor. He also observed

EDWARD CURTIS FRANKLIN AT THE BEGINNING OF HIS TEACHING CAREER AT THE UNIVERSITY OF KANSAS

From a photograph taken in 1889.

* From the secretary's book of The University of Kansas Chemical Seminary in the possession of Prof. E. H. S. Bailey, former chairman of the department.

[2] WEYL, *Ann. Physik*, **121**, 601 (1864).

[3] SEELY, *Chem. News*, **23**, 169 (1871).

[4] GORE, *Proc. Roy. Soc.*, **21**, 140 (1872).

[5] THOMSON, *Phil. Mag.*, **36**, 320 (1893); NERNST, *Z. physik. Chem.*, **13**, 531 (1894).

† For that matter, the dielectric constant of liquid ammonia had not yet been determined and, in fact, the first determination of the dielectric constant was suggested by the conductivity experiments of Cady described herewith. See GOODWIN AND THOMSON, *Phys. Rev.*, **8**, 38 (1899).

[6] The first of Walden's papers was published in *Z. anorg. Chem.*, **25**, 209 (1900). For a complete summary, see Walden's book, "Elektrochemie Nichtwässeriger Lösungen," Johann Ambrosius Barth, Leipzig, **1924**.

* In the fall of 1894, after receiving his doctorate from The Johns Hopkins University, Dr. Franklin had returned to The University of Kansas as associate professor of chemistry. He was still a young man and was Cady's senior only by some twelve years.

† By 1896, liquid ammonia was an article of commerce. Professor Linde had constructed the first ammonia refrigerating system at Munich in 1873. After that time the refrigeration industry grew very rapidly, with the resultant increase in the production of liquid ammonia. The Kansas investigators had a considerable advantage over Gore, who had to prepare his liquid ammonia by Faraday's process, *i. e.*, decomposition of $AgCl \cdot 2NH_3$ and condensation of the ammonia thus formed in sealed tubes.

** The reader will recall that this was the beginning of Cady's senior year in college.

†† Franklin took this year's leave to engage in chemical work for a mining company in Costa Rica.

[7] BLEEKRODE, *Phil. Mag.* [5], **5**, 384 (1878).

two facts in connection with the passage of electricity through the tube—one was that the solution became blue around the cathode, and the other that it became brown around the anode. The blue color he immediately recognized as metallic potassium, as Gore had stated that the alkali metals were soluble in liquid ammonia and gave blue solutions. Cady next turned his attention to solutions of these alkali metals in liquid ammonia. He soon found that sodium dissolved in liquid ammonia was an excellent conductor and this led him to speculate concerning the mechanism of the conduction. The idea soon occurred to him that here was the possibility of decomposing an element. As far as Cady knew there was no other case on record where an element dissolved and gave a conducting solution, and in all conducting solutions of which he had any knowledge, chemical changes resulted from electrolysis. It is not to be wondered then that it was with considerable interest, bordering on excitement, that he undertook a quantitative study of the passage of electricity through liquid ammonia solutions of sodium. He found to his surprise and disappointment, however, that no decomposition of sodium took place—even after passing as many as twenty Faradays per gram atom of sodium there was no decomposition apparent. The explanation of this phenomenon was really a more difficult task than the more logical "decomposition" of sodium would have been. Cady explained it satisfactorily, however, and the explanation has stood the test of many careful experiments in the years since that day. His reasoning and explanation were as follows: Apparently the conduction of electricity in this solution did not follow Faraday's law, but metallic conduction also did not follow Faraday's law. Possibly this was a conductor of the first class (i. e., a metallic conductor). Conductors of the first class are further characterized by the fact that no polarization occurs where the current enters and leaves such systems. If sodium in liquid ammonia is a conductor of the first class, then there should be no polarization at the electrodes. This was tested out by passing a current through the solution, interrupting the current momentarily and observing if any back e. m. f., or current in the reverse direction, was noted. None was observed and hence Cady concluded that the conduction was analogous to metallic conduction.

Cady also showed at this time, while working with sodium, that its solutions could be extracted of their sodium content by shaking with mercury, forming sodium amalgam, and that no mercury passed into the liquid ammonia to compensate for the sodium extracted. This was undertaken to show, as conclusively as possible, that sodium existed in these solutions as metallic sodium and not as a sodium compound, which might possibly have been formed as the result of chemical reaction between sodium and ammonia.

Upon the basis of his knowledge gained thus far, Cady presented a paper before the Kansas Academy of Science which met in Topeka on December 31, 1896. It appeared on the program as "Water of Crystallization and Experiments with Liquid Ammonia."[8] It recounted in a somewhat similar fashion to that presented in this paper the beginning of the work in liquid ammonia. Cady's first paper in this field of liquid ammonia research was published in April, 1897.[9] It was entitled "Action of Liquid $NH_3$ on Iodine," and apparently was suggested by the formation of the "brownish coloration" at the anode in his electrolysis of potassium iodide. His results showed that there was actual reaction between iodine and ammonia.

Cady's next efforts were directed toward obtaining a more exact knowledge of the conductance of salt solutions in liquid ammonia. The conductances were measured by the usual Wheatstone bridge arrangement, using the old familiar buzzer as the means of securing an alternating current of high frequency and pasting strips of paper on his Dewar tubes to calibrate their volume. This arrangement, while crude in the light of present-day equipment, served its purpose and the results which were obtained compare favorably with the data obtained later by Franklin and Kraus with more elaborate equipment and greater precautions. The results of these experiments were published by Cady in the fall of 1897 under the title "The Electrolysis and Electrolytic Conductivity of Certain Substances Dissolved in Liquid Ammonia."[10] His results indicated that many salts were better conductors at the same concentration when dissolved in liquid ammonia than when dissolved in water. He suggested that the most probable explanation of this increased conductance was a greater ionic mobility in the first solvent, a speculation which he and Franklin later verified.

In his studies upon salt hydrates Cady had prepared some of the hydrates of hydrogen chloride at low temperatures. $HCl\cdot3H_2O$ and $HCl\cdot2H_2O$ were known, but $HCl\cdot H_2O$ had not been isolated. The fact that HCl formed hydrates suggested to Cady that ammonium chloride was in effect $HCl\cdot NH_3$, i. e., hydrogen chloride with one mole of ammonia of crystallization. This in turn suggested the possibility that ammonium salts in general in liquid

PROFESSOR KRAUS

[8] Trans. Kans. Acad. Sci., 15, 38 (1898).
[9] CADY, Kans. Univ. Quarterly, Series A, 6, 71 (1897).
[10] CADY, J. Phys. Chem., 1, 707–13 (1897).

PROFESSOR CADY

ammonia would have acid properties. Cady soon tested this out and found that ammonium salts in liquid ammonia reacted with metallic magnesium, liberating a gas. The gas was collected and found to be hydrogen, *i. e.*, ammonium salts in liquid ammonia produce hydrogen when allowed to act upon magnesium. As is well known, this is one of the characteristics of acids in water solution, and hence Cady felt that he had confirmed his conjecture concerning the acid character of ammonium salts. This property, discovered by Cady, suggested other possibilities to Franklin and in later years aided him (Franklin) in the development of a comprehensive system of compounds in this solvent.

Cady also recognized at this time the possibility of using liquid ammonia solution of sodium as a powerful reducing agent. He found that many organic compounds, particularly halides, were reduced by the solution. Dains[11] and his students subsequently developed this procedure as an alternate method for the tedious Carius process of determining halogen in organic compounds, as the halide is converted into the sodium salt by the action of the metallic sodium in this solvent. The student in this field will also recall the extensive applications of this reducing agent in the hands of Kraus, White, and their co-workers.[12]

The years of 1895–97 were thus seen to be particularly fruitful in the development of this new field. These developments, it should be remembered, were initiated by a college youth in his junior and senior years in an institution but little past the frontier stage and hence without large library and laboratory facilities. Educators, if they compare the product of the modern college with the achievements of this senior, need not find in the comparison a sad commentary upon their efforts. Rather, such achievements reflect more credit upon the intellectual capacity of a student who is able to give birth to such ideas and who possessed the manual ability and tenacity of purpose to rear such ideas to the stature of a well-formed field of research.

Cady was graduated from The University of Kansas in the spring of 1897. Through the efforts of the chemistry department he was offered and accepted a scholarship in chemistry at Cornell for the school year 1897-98. At Cornell he worked under the direction of Professor Bancroft. Cady had hoped to continue his work on liquid ammonia at Cornell, but Bancroft had just finished his book on the phase rule and consequently was much interested in the field of heterogeneous equilibria. Cady was accordingly set to work in this field, became interested in it, and made such progress that the following year he was promoted to a fellowship. It was during his stay at Cornell that he published the paper "Electromotive Force between Amalgams"[13] which contains the equation known to workers in this field as "the Cady equation," an equation which was subsequently verified by Richards and his students.[14]

Franklin returned to Kansas the year that Cady left, in the capacity of professor of physical chemistry. He followed Cady's experiments with considerable interest and, when it became apparent that Cady was not able to continue the work in this field at Cornell, asked Cady if it would be permissible to continue some of Cady's experiments in liquid ammonia. The permission was readily granted and Franklin set to work examining solubilities of a number of compounds in liquid ammonia. His work soon attracted the attention of a student in the engineering school. This was Charles A. Kraus, who was at this time (school year 1897-98) a senior in electrical engineering. Although Kraus had elected to study in the field of applied science, he had soon become interested in pure science. In his junior year, for example, he, together with two instructors in the physics department, published an account of the Zeeman effect.[15] This was one of the earliest studies made of the Zeeman effect in this country, being antedated only by the work of Professor Michelson of Chicago.

In the fall of 1897 Franklin and Kraus joined forces and decided to undertake a comprehensive survey of the solubility of substances in liquid ammonia. As a result of their studies they were able by June of 1898 to submit a paper to the *American Chemical Journal*, containing the record of the qualitative and approximate quantitative solubilities of over five hundred substances in this solvent. Some of this work confirmed Gore's original observations, but much of it was a considerable extension over that of Gore's work. This paper was published in the December number of the *American Chemical Journal* for 1898 and has been exceedingly useful to all workers in this field. This joint paper was followed shortly by three others: "Determination of the Molecular Rise in the Boiling Point of Liquid Ammonia" (also in the December issue of the *American Chemical Journal*, 1898) "Metathetic Reactions between Certain Salts in Solution in Liquid Ammonia"; and "Some Properties o[f

[11] DAINS, *J. Am. Chem. Soc.*, **40**, 936 (1918).
[12] KRAUS, *ibid.*, **45**, 768 (1923); WHITE and his students, *ibid.*, for 1923 and 1924.

[13] CADY, *J. Phys. Chem.*, **2**, 551 (1898).
[14] *Carnegie Inst. Pub.* Nos. 56 and 118.
[15] DUNSTAN, RICE, AND KRAUS, "The Effect of Magnetism upon the Spectral Lines of Sodium," *Kans. Univ. Quarterly* Series A, **6**, 77 (1897).

Liquid Ammonia." These last two appeared in the January, 1899, number of the *American Chemical Journal*.

Kraus continued on at Kansas after his graduation for a year of graduate study and as a result still another joint study upon the conductivity of solutions in liquid ammonia was made. These measurements were carried out with more precision than Cady's original measurements, Cady having called attention to the fact that his values were only approximate and needed revision. The results of this study were published in 1900.[16]

Kraus left The University of Kansas in the spring of 1899 with a record of marked achievement in helping to open up this new field of research. The reader will again notice, if he has not already done so, that a very considerable proportion of the work done by Kraus was done while he, too, was in his senior year at Kansas. Kraus's interest in liquid ammonia after leaving Kansas was not lost and after 1907 the publications of this investigator in this field continue in an almost uninterrupted flow until the present day. His well-deserved place among the foremost chemists of the day needs no further mention here.*

In the spring of 1899, Cady, after a two-year stay at Cornell, was offered an assistant professorship at his alma mater and accepted, returning to The University of Kansas in the fall of 1899. By that time the studies of Franklin and Kraus were well under way and were giving promise of many interesting results. Cady was eager to renew his work with liquid ammonia. After talking with Franklin, they decided to study the velocity of ionic migration in this solvent. It will be recalled that Cady had suggested that the increased conductance of salts in liquid ammonia was possibly due to a greater mobility of ions. It was some time before actual work was begun, but finally Franklin and Cady started work together upon this investigation. Both Franklin and Cady regard this work as their most difficult experimental study in this solvent. The method which they adopted for their study was that of measuring the velocities of moving boundaries, the work requiring the placing of three solutions together in a tube in such a fashion that a sharp and distinct surface of separation occurred between the solutions. Only those who have had occasion to work with solvents of low boiling point can appreciate their difficulties. They worked for weeks

PROFESSOR FRANKLIN

without getting results, even putting in their noon hours upon the task that they had set for themselves, Mrs. Franklin bringing them their lunches. With such persistence, the required technic was at last gained and the measurements followed each other in rapid succession, their results showing that ionic velocities were considerably greater in liquid ammonia than in water.[17]

After the completion of this work, Cady started work upon his doctor's thesis. Under Franklin's direction this was finished in the spring of 1903 and was a study of concentration cells in liquid ammonia.[18]

The following year (1903–04) Professor Franklin was called to Stanford University, where he has remained until the present day. His subsequent researches, as well as those of his many students, in the field of liquid ammonia are well known. His election to the presidency of the American Chemical Society in 1923 and the awards of the Nichols medal in 1925 and of the Willard Gibbs medal in 1932 are recognition of the worth of these fundamental researches.

Cady became Franklin's successor at The University of Kansas and has remained there since. His work subsequent to the departure of Professor Franklin has been in several fields. His co-discovery, with McFarland, of the presence of helium in natural gases of Kansas has been one of the most outstanding of his achievements. In recent years he and his students have again turned their attention to the field of liquid ammonia research, attention having been paid chiefly to the electrochemistry of liquid ammonia solutions and to phase rule studies in this solvent.

From the foregoing pages it is hoped that the idea has been developed that due credit should be given to three men for the present position of liquid ammonia research in this country—to Cady as the initiator of this work; to Kraus as the skilled experimentalist and elaborator; and to Franklin as the organizer of this body of learning. To all three men credit should also be given for their ability as teachers. All of them have been able to attract large numbers of students to this field. As a result, many of the scientific "children," "grandchildren," and possibly even "great grandchildren" of these men are themselves making contributions to this field of learning.

In the last place it should be said that it would be difficult to find a group of three men who were so kindly in character, so upright in purpose, and so keen in insight as these three founders of this field of research. To this statement their many students will all agree.

[16] FRANKLIN AND KRAUS, *Am. Chem. J.*, **23**, 277 (1900).
* The contributions of Kraus and Franklin to this field have been well summarized in the reviews of Fernelius and Johnson appearing in the issues of the JOURNAL OF CHEMICAL EDUCATION during the period 1928–30.

[17] CADY AND FRANKLIN, *J. Am. Chem. Soc.*, **26**, 499 (1904).
[18] CADY, *J. Phys. Chem.*, **9**, 476 (1905).

# A HISTORY OF THE NEUTRON

**VASILIS LAVRAKAS**
Lowell Textile Institute, Lowell, Massachusetts

THE neutron has played such a remarkable role in the development of science in the last 20 years, and in the economic and political world, that it may be of interest to trace the history of the speculation as to its existence through the early part of this century until its discovery in 1932. Originally the neutron came to the minds of some men as a nebulous concept existing only in their creative imagination. After the passage of approximately 30 years it suddenly appeared in experimental science as a definite entity having an existence uniquely its own. The pursuit and the discovery of the neutron provide an absorbing picture of the human side of science, for here the prize went not to the experimenters who discovered the puzzle but to the one who deciphered it. And he, as it so happened, was one who had sought for it long and diligently.

It is always interesting to consider the beginnings of an idea prior to its unequivocal discovery, such as that of the neutron, and the actual thing itself. Scientists realized almost 30 years before the neutron was discovered that such a neutral particle might exist because of the atomic character of electricity. Nernst (1), in his book on theoretical chemistry, discussed negative and positive electrons. The former were known to exist at that time but the latter had a hypothetical existence. Consequently Nernst said, "It is a question of much importance whether a compound of the positive and negative electrons (neutron, an electrically neutral massless molecule) really exists; we shall assume that neutrons are everywhere present like the luminiferous ether, and may regard the space filled by these molecules as weightless, nonconducting, but electrically polarizable, that is, as possessing the properties which optics assumes for the luminiferous ether."

Again well in advance of the actual discovery Nernst considers the possibility that the positive electron may exist. But its isolation will be difficult, he says, because of its "greater affinity for ordinary atoms or radicals. There appears to me at the present time to be no reason to doubt that positive electrons might be isolated." This particle was not found until 1932.

The word neutron appears in two rival theories of X-rays in the earlier part of 1912 (2). One was a pulse theory by Stokes and the other a corpuscular theory due to Bragg. Bragg postulated that when an electron hit the anticathode in an X-ray tube the electron picked up sufficient positive electricity to neutralize itself. Thus it became a "neutron." This neutron was very small; no larger than an electron. Bragg believed that such an hypothesis was necessary to account for the ionization of gases by X-rays with the subsequent appearance of electrons again. These electrons had nearly the same speed as the original electrons, hence it appeared likely to Bragg that the electrons were those which originally struck the anticathode; except that they had become "neutrons" along the way.

In a still earlier attempt to understand the nature of X-rays and gamma rays and their great penetrating power Rutherford wrote (3), "It is also possible that gamma rays may consist of uncharged particles projected with great velocity" and, as a reasonable support for this suggestion, added, "a small particle moving through matter would probably not be absorbed as rapidly as a charged particle of the same mass and velocity." It is obvious that the great penetrating powers of the neutron were recognized at a very early stage.

Later the Joliot-Curies, from the results of their experiments, were to take the opposite point of view from Rutherford. The neutron was actually present but they thought it was a high-energy gamma ray!

When the work of Rutherford on the nuclear atom was published in 1911 a clearer picture of atomic structure came into existence. From 1911 to 1920 it became apparent to some that another particle, the neutron, must be present in the atom to account for the atomic weights of the elements. Rutherford (4), in his second Bakerian Lecture to the Royal Society on June 3, 1920, predicted with amazing accuracy the existence and the properties of the neutron as they are today. He said in this lecture:

In other cases, it involves the possible existence of an atom of mass one which has a zero nuclear charge. Such an atomic structure seems by no means impossible. On present views the neutral hydrogen atom is regarded as a nucleus of unit charge with an electron attached at a distance, and the spectrum of hydrogen is ascribed to the movements of this distant electron. Under some conditions, however, it may be possible for an electron to combine much more closely with the hydrogen nucleus, forming a kind of neutral doublet. Such an atom would have very novel properties. Its field would be practically zero, except very close to the nucleus, and in consequence it should be able to move freely through matter. Its presence would probably be difficult to detect by the spectroscope and it may be impossible to contain it in a closed vessel. [These slippery qualities of the neutron were later described by Rutherford (5) as "like an invisible man passing through Piccadilly Circus; his path can be traced only by the people he has pushed aside."] On the other hand, it should enter readily the structure of atoms, and may either unite with the nucleus or be disintegrated by its field, resulting possibly in the escape of a charged hydrogen atom, or an electron or both.

Rutherford then went on to consider the possibility that in discharge tubes electrons may unite with protons and stated that experiments were to be tried to determine if this were so. In this lecture he also said that neutral particles of larger mass, 2, 3, 4, or more, might exist. Here he seemed to have gone astray for he claimed "the existence of such atoms seems almost necessary to explain the building up of the nuclei of heavy elements." And so Rutherford finished by complaining of the inadequate knowledge concerning the forces binding a nucleus together. This is still a major problem of physics today and one yet to be satisfactorily solved.

In addition to Rutherford there were others at that time who put forth the concept of a neutral, sub-atomic particle. One of these was W. D. Harkins (6), who in 1921 stated in his "General Theory of Isotopes and Atomic Number" that "the difference of four isotopic numbers between the maxima corresponds to four neutrons or a helio group, which is an alpha particle plus two electrons." O. Masson (7), L. Meitner (8), and S. Ono (9), about this time also brought forth various theoretical particles of mass 1, 2, 3, and 4. Miss Meitner published her paper on the different ways of radioactive disintegration and their possible application to nuclear structure. In many cases, she wrote, an alpha-ray change is followed by two successive beta-ray changes. Therefore it was likely that a neutral particle existed independently in the nucleus, and that it was made up of four protons and four electrons.

Experiments were performed during the years 1921 and 1922 by Glasson (10) and Roberts (11), both pupils of Rutherford, to discover this neutral particle. Glasson performed discharge-tube and absorption experiments, but he was unsuccessful, for as we know now no free neutrons are present. Roberts in 1922 attempted to find the neutron on the simple assumption that in a discharge tube filled with hydrogen the electrons might combine with protons to form neutrons. If this happened, he reasoned, the energy which would be released on the coupling of the two particles might be detected by calorimetric methods. But he also was unsuccessful.

It would appear that this problem was still very much alive for Rutherford and his co-workers, even after these two failures. In 1924 J. Chadwick (12), who was to discover the neutron, wrote Rutherford from his vacation place at Inveroran: "I still think we shall have to make a real search for the neutron. I believe I have a scheme which may just work but I must consult Aston first." What this scheme was, whether it was ever attempted, and, if so, whether the results were published cannot be determined at the present time.

Rutherford and Chadwick (13), in 1921, were still patiently searching. In an experiment which they were conducting on the energy relations in artificial disintegration an attempt was made to locate the neutron among the protons which were released. But they had to conclude forlornly at the end of a description of the experiment that, "There is no reason to suppose that the particles observed in the previous experiment were not all protons."

Langer and Rosen (14), in 1931, stated on theoretical and mathematical grounds that the existence of the neutron was very likely but that there was as yet no definite proof of such a particle. It would seem that the theoretical concept of the neutron had been laid for its detection. To many of the leading physicists of that time it was clear that such a particle should be present in matter. It was finally to reveal itself to Chadwick who was fully prepared in his background to recognize the experimental facts and to draw the *proper* conclusion from them. In the years 1931 to 1932 the climax was approached rapidly. Bothe and Becker (15) in 1930 found that if alpha rays from polonium interacted with Be or B a highly penetrating radiation came forth. They assumed that these rays were gamma rays. Irene Curie (16), repeated this work in the latter part of 1931. She found that the "gamma radiation" from Be was about five times as intense as that from Po itself. In the next paper, published by Curie and Joliot (17), they announced that the so-called gamma radiation was little affected by being passed through a thin sheet of aluminum or lead. But if this radiation were passed through substances such as paraffin, which contains hydrogen, high-velocity protons are thrown out. They suggested this effect might be due to high-energy gamma rays from the nucleus of the Be. Webster (18), in England, proceeded to make a survey of this, but again the main chance was missed.

Shortly after Chadwick's famous letter to the editor of *Nature* announcing "the possible existence of the neutron" the Curie-Joliots published a paper in which they still maintained the gamma-ray hypothesis and that the total absorption was due to the photoelectric and Compton effects. Another paper was published (19) showing photographs of tracks of protons and helium nuclei, which proved that the agent which brought about the ejection of the particles did not cause ionization along its path—hence it is neutral. Finally on March 19, 1932, a paper was presented (20), approximately a month and a half after Chadwick's announcement, which admitted that the radiation from Be is complex. It consists, they said, partly of gamma radiation and partly of a radiation which they admitted might consist of neutrons, absorbed by the ejection of hydrogen nuclei. It may be noted here that this reluctance to accept the neutron contrasts strangely with a remark made to A. Eve, the biographer of Rutherford, by F. Joliot. Prof. Joliot told him that, though they both followed all publications with care and interest, they had not read Rutherford's second Bakerian Lecture "because in such lectures it is rare to find anything novel which has not been published elsewhere." Joliot stated that if he and his wife had read Rutherford's prophetic suggestion about the neutron in the Bakerian Lecture it is possible or probable that they would have identified the neutron in place of Chadwick. In the light of the evidence of the published papers of the Joliot-Curies, it is hard not to accept this remark of F. Joliot as an instance of scientific sour grapes. At last, on June 20, a paper was published by the Joliot-Curies and Savel (21), on the radiations excited in light atoms by alpha particles in which for the most part the discussion is only of neutrons.

In England, meanwhile, Chadwick was not willing to

accept the hypothesis of the Curie-Joliots that they had found a "new mode of interaction of radiation with matter." "To do so would have meant, as Rutherford said (22) that we must relinquish the laws of the conservation of energy and of momentum in the production of this radiation and its interaction with matter." For it did not seem reasonable to these investigators that a quantum of radiation could have such a powerful effect as to eject protons with speeds up to $3 \times 10^9$ cm./sec. from paraffin. It was preferable and more accurate, as it turned out, to accept the neutron hypothesis. Chadwick (23) therefore wrote a letter to the editor of *Nature* in which his experiments are described, and his tentative belief in the existence of the neutron is put forth. Not only did he use paraffin from which these radiations ejected protons, but also hydrogen, helium, lithium, beryllium, carbon, and air. In this letter Chadwick wrote:

If we ascribe the ejection of the proton to a Compton recoil from a quantum of $52 \times 10^6$ e. v., then the nitrogen recoil atom arising by a similar process should have an energy not greater than about 400,000 volts, should produce not more than 10,000 ions and have a range in air at N. T. P. of about 1.3 mm. Actually some of these recoil atoms in nitrogen produce about 30,000 ions. Their range seems to be about 3 mm.

These results and others I have obtained in the course of the work are very difficult to explain on the assumption the radiation from beryllium is a quantum radiation, if energy and momentum are to be conserved in the collision. The difficulties disappear, however, if it be assumed that the radiation consists of particle of mass 1 and charge of 0.

Chadwick with typical scientific caution ends his letter in the same tentative way which he had titled it. He said:

It is to be expected that many of the effects of a neutron in passing through matter should resemble those of a quantum of high energy, and it is not easy to reach the final decision between the two hypothesis. Up to the present, all the evidence is in favor of the neutron, while the quantum hypothesis can only be upheld if the conservation of energy and momentum be relinquished at this point.

On June 1, 1932, an article was published by Chadwick (24) confidently entitled, "The existence of the neutron." In this article he published observations on recoil atoms produced by the neutron radiation. Chadwick expressed the belief that the neutron is a combination of an electron and a proton (which is believed to be too simple a view today). From his calculations he was able to announce that the weight of the neutron is between 1.005 and 1.008.

## ACKNOWLEDGMENT

The author wishes to express his appreciation to Dr. John A. Timm of Simmons College for his advice in the writing of this paper.

## LITERATURE CITED

(1) NERNST, W., "Theoretical Chemistry," 4th ed., Macmillan & Co., Ltd., London, **1904**.
(2) JAUNCEY, G. E. M., "Modern Physics," D. Van Nostrand Co., Inc., New York, **1932**.
(3) RUTHERFORD, E., "Radioactivity," Macmillan & Co., Ltd., London, **1904**.
(4) RUTHERFORD, E., *Proc. Roy. Soc.*, **1920A**, 374.
(5) EVANS, I. B. N., "Man of Power," Stanley Paul & Co., Ltd., London, **1939**.
(6) HARKINS, W. D., *J. Am. Chem. Soc.*, **43**, 1038 (1921).
(7) GLASSTONE, S., "Sourcebook of Atomic Energy," D. Van Nostrand Co., Inc., New York, **1950**.
(8) MEITNER, L., *Z. Physik*, **4**,1, 146 (1921).
(9) ONO, S., *Proc. Phys.-Math. Soc. Japan*, **8**, 76 (1926).
(10) GLASSON, J. L., *Phil. Mag.*, **42**, 596 (1921).
(11) ROBERTS, J. K., *Proc. Roy. Soc.*, **102A**, 72 (1922).
(12) EVE, A., "Lord Rutherford of Nelson," Macmillan Co., New York.
(13) RUTHERFORD, E., AND J. CHADWICK, *Proc. Cambridge Phil. Soc.*, **25**, 186 (1929).
(14) LANGER, R. M., AND E. ROSEN, *Phys. Rev.*, **37**, 1579 (1931).
(15) BOTHE, W., AND H. BECKER, *Z. Physik*, **66**, 289 (1930).
(16) CURIE, I., *Compt. rend.*, **193**, 1412 (1931).
(17) CURIE, I., AND F. JOLIOT, *ibid.*, **194**, 273 (1932).
(18) WEBSTER, H., *Proc. Roy. Soc.*, **136A**, 428 (1932).
(19) CURIE, I., AND F. JOLIOT, *Compt. rend.*, **194**, 876 (1932).
(20) CURIE, I., AND F. JOLIOT, *ibid.*, 1229.
(21) JOLIOT-CURIE, I., F. JOLIOT-CURIE, AND P. SAVEL, *ibid.*,194.
(22) RUTHERFORD, E., *Nature*, **129**, 457 (1932).
(23) CHADWICK, J., *ibid.*, 312.
(24) CHADWICK, J., *Proc. Roy. Soc.*, **136A**, 692 (1932).

EDITORS' NOTE: "The Neutron," a review article by H. A. Shadduck in J. CHEM. EDUC., **13**, 303–8 (1936), has some historical content, pictures of J. Chadwick and the Joliot-Curies, and 64 literature citations.

---

## Nikolai Semenovich Kurnakov     *Continued from page 196*

(51) KURNAKOV, N. S., *Ann. inst. anal. phys.-chim.*, **2**, 473 (1924); KURNAKOV, N. S., AND URAZOV, G. G., *Zhur. Priklad. Khim.*,**1**, 13 (1924).
(52) KURNAKOV, N. S., AND URAZOV, G. G., *Ann. inst. anal. phys.-chim.*, **2**, 495, 496 (1924).
(53) KURNAKOV, N. S., AND RODE, E. YA., *Ann. inst. anal. phys.-chim.*, **3**, 305 (1926); *Z. anorg. allgem. Chem.* **169**, 57 (1928).
(54) KURNAKOV, N. S., AND CHERNIUKH, V. V., *Ann. inst. anal. phys.-chim.*, **3**, 485 (1926); *Mem. soc. russe min.*, **55**, 74, 118 (1926).
(55) KURNAKOV, N. S., *Z. anorg. allgem. Chem.*, **169**, 113 (1928); *Ann. secteur anal. phys.-chim., Inst. chim. gén. (U.S.S.R.)*, **8**, 15 (1936); *Uspekhi Khim.*, **5**, 161 (1936); *Trav. congr. jubilaire Mendeleev, Acad. sci. U.R.S.S.*, **1**, 535 (557 in French); KURNAKOV, N. S., AND RAVICH, M. I., *Ann. inst. anal. phys.-chim.*, **7**, 211 (1935); KURNAKOV, N. S., AND KLOCHKO, M. A., *Compt. rend. acad. sci. U.R.S.S.*, **25**, 383 (1939) (in English).
(56) "Sobranie Izbrannykh Rabot N. S. Kurnakova," 2 vols., Moskva, Leningrad, **1938–39**.

# THE SEARCH FOR TRITIUM—THE HYDROGEN ISOTOPE OF MASS THREE

**MAXWELL LEIGH EIDINOFF**

Queens College, Flushing, New York

## INTRODUCTION

It has become apparent, as a result of studies carried out during the past few years, that the hydrogen isotope of mass three can be considered a very useful tracer atom (1). This isotope, commonly called *tritium*, will serve the purposes of the chemist and biologist in a manner comparable to the role of deuterium, the stable isotope of mass two. The search for tritium in nature started almost as soon as deuterium was discovered and is still going on at this time. Experiments carried out recently by the author (2) and described later in this article show that there is less than one tritium atom in $10^{17}$ atoms of ordinary hydrogen. In 1939 and 1940 tritium was prepared by nuclear transmutation reactions and shown to be a radioactive isotope having a half life of $31 \pm 8$ years. It is an emitter of beta particles that have the unusually small energy of only about 15,000 electron volts.

The hunt for tritium has engaged the attention of leading scientists in this country and in England. A variety of important experimental tools was employed in these researches. In common with other notable discoveries—an observation that is occasionally ignored in chemical education—incorrect conclusions and blind alleys dotted the path leading to its ultimate discovery. A résumé of the search for tritium is given below. It may serve to demonstrate how the varied tools of science have been utilized in attacking an apparently simple and fundamental research problem.

## THE DISCOVERY AND CONCENTRATION OF DEUTERIUM

Since the approach to this problem was based in the main upon the methods that were used successfully in the discovery and concentration of deuterium, it may be well to review briefly some familiar ground dealing with this very useful isotope.

The hydrogen isotope of mass two, deuterium, was one of the relatively few isotopes that were first detected by a spectroscopic method. Urey, Brickwedde, and Murphy (3) in December, 1931, were able to detect two very faint lines close to the familiar Balmer lines of ordinary atomic hydrogen. It could be shown by the application of quantum mechanics to the hydrogen atom that there would be a small, yet measurable separation of corresponding lines in the spectrum of hydrogen isotopes. These investigators showed that the measured separations corresponded exactly with the calculated lines for a hydrogen atom of mass two. The

hydrogen sample that they used was obtained as the residue from a large amount of liquid hydrogen that had been allowed to evaporate down in order to concentrate the supposedly less volatile heavier isotope. It is interesting to note that these investigators looked for lines for the isotope of mass three at this time but positive evidence was not obtained.

An unusual and significant development took place when it was discovered that deuterium could be concentrated by the electrolysis of aqueous solutions. As early as 1923 Kendall and Crittenden (4) had suggested that isotopes might be separated by electrolysis. There appeared little evidence to confirm this until 1932. In July of that year, Washburn and Urey (5) found that when ordinary water is electrolyzed under certain conditions, the atoms of mass one are liberated about six times as readily as those of the heavier isotope. Thus, by continued electrolysis, the small residue can become highly concentrated in deuterium. Only about two atoms of deuterium are present in 10,000 atoms of hydrogen. Taylor, Eyring, and Frost (6) reported in 1933 that it is necessary to electrolyze ordinary water until it is reduced to about one one hundred-thousandth of its original volume in order to obtain water containing 99 per cent deuterium. The electrolytic separation factor, $s$, is defined:

$$s = \left(\frac{H}{D}\right)_{\text{gas}} \Big/ \left(\frac{H}{D}\right)_{\text{liquid}} \tag{1}$$

where $H$ and $D$ are the concentrations of the two isotopes in the phases indicated.

The change in isotopic abundance as a result of electrolysis can be calculated from the separation factor ($s$) and the initial and final volumes of solution $V_0$ and $V$, respectively, by the formula:

$$\left(\frac{H_0}{H}\right)\left(\frac{D}{D_0}\right)^s = \left(\frac{V_0}{V}\right)^{s-1} \tag{2}$$

where ($H_0$, $D_0$) and ($H$, $D$) refer to the concentrations of the isotopes before and after the electrolysis, respectively. Values of $s$ between six and eight have been observed for silver, nickel, and platinum electrodes at room temperature (7).

## THE SEARCH FOR TRITIUM

*Spectroscopic Method.* As described above, deuterium was first detected by observing faint lines in the Balmer spectrum that were separated from much more intense lines by an amount predicted by theory for a hydrogen atom of mass two. Since it was highly probable that any tritium present in ordinary hydrogen would be concentrated along with deuterium, Lewis and Spedding (8) early in 1933 examined a deuterium-enriched sample of hydrogen using the spectroscopic method. Their sample contained about 67 atom per cent of deuterium. It was possible, as in the case of deuterium, to predict from theory the displacement of the tritium lines from the main lines of light hydrogen. No tritium lines were observed within the sensitivity of their apparatus. As a result they concluded that less than one tritium atom is present in $6 \times 10^6$ atoms of ordinary hydrogen.

*Magneto-optic Method.* At about the same time the problem was attacked by the magneto-optic method first reported by Allison in 1927 (9). This method is concerned with the rotation of the plane of polarization of light by transparent substances when placed in a magnetic field. The latter is called the Faraday effect. The method attempted to measure the lag of the Faraday effect behind the magnetic field and to correlate the data with minute traces of substances present in the solution. In September, 1933, Latimer and Young claimed that tritium could be detected by this method in water containing two atom per cent of deuterium (10). It now appears generally recognized, however, that the evidence for tritium by this method is highly questionable.

*Mass Spectrometer Studies.* At this point a number of painstaking studies were carried out using the mass spectrometer. The starting material for the studies were hydrogen samples that were very rich in deuterium. Estimates could be made of the factor by which the tritium had become enriched in these samples as compared with normal abundance by using equations similar to equation (2) above. The currents of ions produced from these samples were analyzed in the mass spectrometer. The critical step in this work is the establishment of definite proof that molecular ions of mass five correspond to $(DT)^+$ instead of the triatomic molecule ion not containing tritium at all $(HDD)^+$. Attempts were made to distinguish between the two ions by studying the ion currents as a function of pressure inside the mass spectrometer tube. By combining these results and the tritium enrichment factor stated above, it would then be possible to state the abundance of tritium in ordinary hydrogen. Bleakney and Gould (11) were able to conclude in January, 1934, that there is less than one tritium atom in $5 \times 10^8$ atoms of ordinary hydrogen.

By using a more sensitive instrument and a sample of almost pure deuterium, Lozier, Smith, and Bleakney, working at Princeton, reported in April, 1934, positive evidence for the existence of tritium in nature (12). They plotted the ratio $(I/P)$ as a function of the pressure $P$ where $I$ is the ion current of mass five ions while the pressure $P$ is measured by the number of $D_2^+$ ions. They observed an appreciable intercept at the extrapolated $P$ equal to zero. They interpreted this intercept as a measure of the ratio $TD/D_2$. The data appeared to rule out the triatomic ion $(HDD)^+$ since it was assumed that the concentration of triatomic ions would become negligible in the low-pressure range. It appeared from their data that five atoms of tritium were present in about one million atoms of their deuterium sample. After calculating the enrichment that took place in the preparation of their deuterium sample, they concluded that about one atom of tritium is present in one billion atoms of ordinary hydrogen.

*Nuclear Physics Experiments.* At about this time, evidence for the presence of tritium was sought by the nuclear physicists. In May, 1934, Tuve, Hafstad, and Dahl (13) working in Washington, D. C., reported positive evidence for the existence of tritium atoms of numerical abundance roughly equal to that reported by the Princeton group. These investigators projected high-speed ions obtained from a deuterium sample through an accelerating potential ranging up to about one million volts. They plotted the ranges in air of the high-speed particles as a function of the accelerating potential and looked for a curve that would correspond to a hydrogen atom of mass three.

In the meantime a very significant communication was reported in the March 17, 1934, issue of *Nature* by Oliphant, Harteck, and Rutherford, working at Cambridge (14). High energy deuterons (ranging up to several hundred thousand electron volts) were used to bombard deuterium atoms in target compounds. A pronounced emission of protons as well as neutrons was observed as products of the reaction. Two possible nuclear reactions were postulated:

$$\underset{\text{deuteron}}{D_1^2} + \underset{}{D_1^2} \longrightarrow \underset{\text{tritium}}{H_1^3} + \underset{\text{proton}}{H_1^1} \qquad (3)$$

$$\underset{\text{deuteron}}{D_1^2} + \underset{}{D_1^2} \longrightarrow \underset{}{He_2^3} + \underset{\text{neutron}}{n_0^1} \qquad (4)$$

They concluded that "while the nuclei of $H^3$ and $He^3$ appear to be stable for the short time required for their detection, the question of their permanence requires further consideration."

*More Extensive Electrolysis—Mass Spectrometer Studies.* It still appeared desirable to check the mass spectrometer approach to this problem more thoroughly. In April, 1935, Selwood, Taylor, Lozier, and Bleakney, working at Princeton University (15), reported the results of such an experiment. In order to effect as large an enrichment of tritium as possible, 75 metric tons of ordinary water were electrolyzed down to 0.5 ml. of practically pure $D_2O$. This represents a reduction in volume by a factor of 150 million. The mass spectrometer data appeared to indicate the presence of an ion of mass five, interpreted as $(DT)^+$. On this basis, one atom of tritium was present in only $10^4$ atoms of the deuterium sample. On the basis of the exhaustive electrolysis mentioned above, they concluded that the abundance of tritium in ordinary hydrogen is about 7 atoms in ten billions.

In August, 1937, Lord Rutherford, eminent pioneer in nuclear studies, published a careful appraisal of the evidence for tritium to date (16). He reviewed the positive evidence for the formation of tritium from the deuterium bombardment reaction stated above (equation (4)). However, he reported *negative results* in the extensive electrolysis-mass spectrometer project that he had concluded. A large-scale electrolysis experiment had been set up at a hydroelectric plant at Oslo, Norway, for the purpose of producing pure heavy water. The starting material for the electrolysis was a 43.4-kg. batch of heavy water having a deuterium content of 99.2 atom per cent and prepared by the prior electrolysis of about 13,000 tons of ordinary water. The 43.4-kg. batch was then electrolyzed down to only 11 ml. Deuterium prepared from this final residue was sent to the laboratory of F. W. Aston, Nobel prize winner for work in the field of mass spectrometer analysis. Aston could not detect any positive evidence for the $(DT)^+$ ion and concluded that there was less than one atom of tritium in 100,000 atoms of the enriched sample. The Princeton group had reported that about one atom of tritium was present in 10,000 atoms of their enriched sample. Rutherford did point out, however, that the two experiments were not strictly comparable since the initial electrolysis of the Norwegian sample had not been carried out under ideally controlled conditions.

As a result of the above experiments the problem of the natural abundance of tritium was left in an unsatisfactory state. In order to resolve the problem, the Princeton group embarked on an even more thorough study. The heavy water sample used in the work described above (15) was decomposed on a hot tungsten filament and the deuterium allowed to flow through a system of 29 glass diffusion pumps in order to further concentrate any heavier molecules having the formula DT. After a careful mass spectrometer analysis, Sherr, Smith, and Bleakney (17) concluded *that they had found no evidence for tritium and that previous interpretations of similar data were in error.* In the light of their results they suggested that it would be of interest to repeat the work of Tuve, Hafstad, and Dahl, referred to above. Estimating the total tritium enrichment from electrolysis and diffusion, they could definitely assert that less than one atom of tritium is present in $10^{12}$ or one thousand billion atoms of ordinary hydrogen. This important negative result was reported in 1938.

## THE IDENTIFICATION OF TRITIUM AS AN ARTIFICIALLY RADIOACTIVE ISOTOPE

In September, 1939, Alvarez and Cornog, working at the University of California Radiation Laboratory, made a notable contribution to this subject (18). Following the pioneer experiments of Oliphant, Harteck, and Rutherford cited above, they bombarded deuterium gas with high-speed deuterons and passed the resulting gas mixture into an ionization chamber connected to an amplifier. Any radioactivity in the gas would initiate ionization in the chamber and be registered as an ionization current. *The gas showed a definite activity of long half life.* These investigators proved that the activity was associated with hydrogen molecules by circulating the gas through activated charcoal at liquid nitrogen temperatures and by allowing the gas to diffuse through hot palladium. They showed that the par-

ticles emitted by the radioactive atoms had a very short range and therefore low energy. They concluded that the radioactive tritium was formed according to equation (3) above.

Further information dealing with the production and properties of tritium was reported by the University of Illinois investigators, O'Neal and Goldhaber, at an April, 1940, meeting of the American Physical Society (19). They found that beta particles having an energy of $13,000 \pm 5000$ electron volts were emitted from an "aged" beryllium cyclotron beam target that had previously been bombarded with one million electron volt deuterons. It appeared plausible to ascribe the activity to tritium from the magnitude of the beta particle energy. These workers postulated that the tritium could have been formed by the reaction:

$$Be^9 + D^2 \longrightarrow Be^8 + H^3 \qquad (5)$$

They showed that a radioactive gas could be extracted from the beryllium target either by heating the latter or by dissolving it in sulfuric acid. In September, 1940, they showed that the half life of tritium was $31 \pm 8$ years (20). In the following year Brown found that the beta particles emitted by tritium can penetrate only $13 \pm 1$ mm. of helium gas at atmospheric pressure (21). Shortly thereafter, O'Neal's measurements confirmed this value and set a more reliable value for the beta particle energy at $15,000 \pm 3000$ electron volts (22).

## USE OF A MORE SENSITIVE METHOD FOR STUDYING TRITIUM ABUNDANCE

By the end of 1938 it had been concluded that less than one atom of tritium is present in $10^{12}$ atoms of ordinary hydrogen. The experiments leading to this conclusion have been described above. Recently the author has attempted to reduce this upper limit by using the radioactivity associated with tritium as a quantitative indication of the presence of tritium. This method is many million times more sensitive than the mass spectrometer technique described above for this particular isotope.

The method employed consists essentially in determining the number of beta particles emitted per unit time in a space containing a known number of hydrogen atoms. Let us assume that there are $\Delta n_T$ beta particles emitted in the time $\Delta t$ for a sample containing $n_T$ atoms of tritium in $N_H$ atoms of hydrogen. The half life of tritium is $t_{1/2}$. It is possible to solve for $n_T$ in terms of the measured counting rate and known half life using the familiar equation of radioactive decay:

$$-\left(\frac{\Delta n_T}{\Delta t}\right) = \frac{0.693 n_T}{t_{1/2}} \qquad (6)$$

The moles of hydrogen gas at pressure $P$ and temperature $T^\circ K$. occupying a volume $V$ is calculated using the familiar perfect gas law equation:

$$\text{Moles of hydrogen} = \frac{PV}{RT} \qquad (7)$$

and the number of hydrogen atoms is given by:

$$N_H = \frac{2N_A PV}{RT} \tag{8}$$

where $N_A$ is the Avogadro number. Then the atom fraction of tritium is given by the relationship $n_T/N_H$ using equations (6) and (8). In the event that the hydrogen sample used has become enriched in tritium relative to normal by a factor $(F)$, then:

$$\text{Atom fraction tritium in normal hydrogen} = \frac{n_T}{N_H F} \tag{9}$$

Tritium is conveniently counted by adding the hydrogen sample directly to the inside of the Geiger-Müller counter tube. Since hydrogen is a poor counting gas, an argon and ethyl alcohol vapor mixture is also added to the counter tube. The tube used in these experiments is shown in Figure 1. The normal background count (caused by cosmic radiation, radioactivity in surrounding material) was 2.85 counts per second. Deuterium gas at a pressure of 22 mm. was added to the counter tube. It was observed that the addition of the deuterium gas did not change the counting rate within the precision of the measurements. The average deviation (based on four independent experiments) was 0.03 count per second. This value was used in order to calculate a new upper limit to tritium abundance.

Using equations (6–8) above and the following numerical values $\Delta n_T/\Delta t = 0.03$ count per second (upper limit); $t_{1/2} = 31$ years; $P = 22$ mm.; $V = 200$ ml.; $T = 300°K$., it follows that the atom fraction of tritium in ordinary water or hydrogen is less than $1.5 \times 10^{-13}/F$, where $F$ is the factor by which the tritium was enriched in the electrolysis of normal water from 99.98 per cent H to the final 95 per cent D content. The enrichment factor $F$ was calculated using the separation factors (equation (1)) and an equation similar to equation (2). Some separation factors for H:T have recently been measured by the author (23). Taking the $s$ values for H:D and H:T as 5 and 10, respectively, $F$ equals $2.0 \times 10^4$. Taking the corresponding $s$ values to be 6.5 and 13, $F$ equals $1.3 \times 10^4$. If we use $1.5 \times 10^4$ as the probable $F$ value, then there is less than one tritium atom in $10^{17}$ atoms of ordinary hydrogen. It is clear from this value that the search for tritium by the less sensitive methods described above could not be successful. By exhaustive electrolysis and concentration of heavy water or hydrogen, it will be possible to decrease the magnitude of this upper limit. This value may be of interest, since tritium is a possible reaction product in nuclear processes taking place in the atmosphere of the earth (24).

## LITERATURE CITED

(1) Some references dealing with use of tritium as a Tracer Atom: (a) POWELL, T. M., AND E. B. REID, J. Am. Chem. Soc., 67, 1020 (1945). (b) FONTANA, B. J., ibid., 64, 2503 (1942). (c) ALLEN, M. B., AND S. RUBEN, ibid., 64, 948 (1942).
(2) EIDINOFF, M. L., J. Chem. Phys., 15, 416 (1947).
(3) UREY, H. C., F. G. BRICKWEDDE, AND G. M. MURPHY, Phys. Rev., 39, 164, 864 (1932).
(4) KENDALL, J., AND E. D. CRITTENDEN, Proc. Nat. Acad. Sci., 9, 75 (1923).

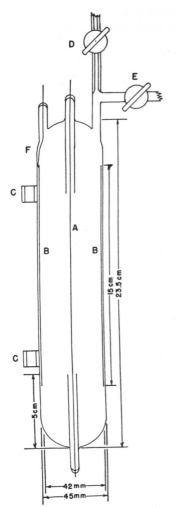

**Figure 1.  Geiger Counter Tube Used for Tritium Counting**

The copper gauze cathode (B) is made of 100-mesh gauze. The tungsten wire anode (A) has a diameter of 4 mil. The glass envelope (F) encloses the electrodes. Glass supports at C are used for the insertion of standard activity uranium solutions in order to check counter action. The capillary stopcock (D) goes to the gas filling line while the 6-mm. bore stopcock (E) goes to the high vacuum line.

(5) WASHBURN, E. W., AND H. C. UREY, ibid., 18, 496 (1932).
(6) TAYLOR, H. S., H. EYRING, AND A. A. FROST, J. Chem. Phys., 1, 823 (1933).
(7) TAYLOR, H. S. (Review of H:D Separation Factor), "Treatise on Physical Chemistry," D. Van Nostrand Co., New York, 1942. Vol. I, pp. 65–9.
(8) LEWIS, G. N., AND F. H. SPEDDING, Phys. Rev., 43, 964 (1933).
(9) ALLISON, F., ibid., 30, 66 (1927).
(10) LATIMER, W. M., AND H. A. YOUNG, ibid., 44, 690 (1933).
(11) BLEAKNEY, W., AND A. J. GOULD, ibid., 45, 281 (1934).
(12) LOZIER, W. W., P. T. SMITH, AND W. BLEAKNEY, ibid., 45, 655 (1934).
(13) TUVE, M. A., L. R. HAFSTAD, AND O. DAHL, ibid., 45, 746, 840 (1934).

(Continued on page 221)

**J. C. Wallmann**
Radiation Laboratory
University of California
Berkeley

# The First Isolations of the Transuranium Elements

## A historical survey

**A**ny discussion of the history of the isolation of the transuranium elements would not normally include any mention of their discovery. This is because for the transuranium elements the first evidence for unique chemical behavior—the criterion of discovery—has always been based on experiments in which the quantity of material is so small that it is detectable only because of its radioactive decay. This means that for the transuranium elements the discovery has not coincided with the isolation of the element—as it has for most of the other elements discovered in the past three centuries. When we speak here of the isolation we mean the purification of the element from contaminants and the measurement of a property of the element; tracer methods are excluded and the direct observation of a macroscopic property is implied. Among the transuranium elements this observation has generally been made on a compound of the element rather than the elemental matter itself because of the experimental difficulties inherent in producing reactive metals on a microgram scale.

The six transuranium elements and the years in which they were isolated are neptunium, 1944; plutonium, 1942; americium, 1945; curium, 1947; berkelium and californium, 1958. They will be discussed in the chronological order in which they were isolated.

## Plutonium

Plutonium was the first of the transuranium elements isolated. This was done in August and September of 1942 by B. B. Cunningham and L. B. Werner at the Metallurgical Laboratory of the University of Chicago, a unit of the wartime Manhattan District. Cunningham is now Professor of Chemistry at the University of California, Berkeley, and Werner is at the U. S. Naval Radiological Defense Laboratory in San Francisco. The isotope involved in the isolation was the familiar plutonium-239 with a half life for alpha decay of approximately 25,000 years. The isolation followed the discovery of the fissionable isotope by Kennedy, Seaborg, Segre, and Wahl by about 18 months, a period during which all of the investigations of plutonium chemistry had been carried out by tracer techniques.

The three principal objectives of the isolation work were (1) to determine the specific alpha disintegration rate of $Pu^{239}$, (2) to determine the chemical properties of pure plutonium compounds and the chemical behavior of plutonium solutions at ordinary chemical concentrations, and (3) to demonstrate a chemical process for the separation of plutonium from uranium and fission products. The establishment of a reliable value for the specific activity of $Pu^{239}$ by a direct weighing and alpha-counting method was a prime objective because this figure entered directly into the calculation of the thermal-neutron-fission cross section of the isotope.

A preliminary isolation yielding about one microgram of $Pu^{239}$ was carried out in August, 1942, in order to prove a satisfactory separation and isolation procedure. At the time the isolation was performed it had not yet been shown that a self-sustaining nuclear reaction leading to the production of substantial amounts of $Pu^{239}$ could be carried out, and therefore the plutonium used in the preliminary isolation was produced by the irradiation of natural uranium with neutrons produced by a $d,n$ reaction on beryllium. Five kilograms of uranyl nitrate hexahydrate were irradiated using 12-Mev deuterons from the 60-inch cyclotron at the University of California Radiation Laboratory at Berkeley. The plutonium produced, approximately one microgram, was separated by a series of "fluoride cycles" from uranium and fission products and concentrated with 5 mg of cerium and 5 mg of lanthanum in 15 ml of 0.5 $M$ $H_2SO_4$. These, and later, bulk separations of the large mass of uranium were carried out at Berkeley by A. C. Wahl and J. W. Gofman and at Chicago by A. H. Jaffey, T. P. Kohman, D. E. Koshland, Jr., and E. H. Turk. The solution of cerium, lanthanum, and plutonium was concentrated by evaporation and the fluorides precipitated by the addition of HF and KF solutions. The fluoride precipitate was then converted to a soluble sulfate by fuming with sulfuric acid and the plutonium oxidized to the "fluoride-soluble" oxidation state by addition of solid argentic oxide. Upon addition of hydrofluoric acid the rare earths were precipitated and the plutonium remained in solution. It was separated and recovered by centrifuging the solution, removing the supernatant, and fuming the supernatant with sulfuric acid to convert the plutonium to a soluble sulfate. Repeated cycles identical to this were carried out with ever smaller quantities of rare earth carrier until finally, on August 18, 1942, a pure sample of plutonium fluoride was precipitated—the first isolation of a synthetic element. This material was not satisfactory for gravimetric work but it did indicate that the fluoride-cycle method was satisfactory for concentrating and purifying plutonium at all concentrations of

Presented as part of the Symposium on Inorganic Chemists in the Nuclear Age before the Division of History of Chemistry and the Division of Inorganic Chemistry at the 134th Meeting of the American Chemical Society, Chicago, September, 1958.

plutonium and rare earth carrier. Accordingly, another isolation was performed on about 30 micrograms of plutonium which had been produced by irradiating 90 kilograms of uranyl nitrate hexahydrate with neutrons produced by the reaction of beryllium and deuterons from the cyclotron at Washington University, St. Louis. In this experiment the bulk of the uranium was removed by ether extraction and the plutonium concentrated by means of successive fluoride cycles with decreasing amounts of lanthanum carrier. Finally the lanthanum was removed by a fluoride precipitation carried out with the plutonium oxidized to the fluoride-soluble state. The plutonium in the supernatant solution was fumed with sulfuric acid to yield soluble plutonium sulfate, the hydroxide was precipitated with ammonium hydroxide and washed and then dissolved with dilute nitric acid. From this solution plutonium iodate was precipitated, metathesized to the hydroxide, dissolved in dilute nitric acid, and reprecipitated. Metathesis of this plutonium iodate to the hydroxide yielded a pure material which was dissolved in dilute nitric acid to give a stock solution of about 20 micrograms of plutonium nitrate with the solution concentration approximately 0.01 $M$ in plutonium.

Several small portions of this solution were used for direct-weighing determinations of the specific activity of $Pu^{239}$. The mass determination was done on a Salvioni type microbalance which had been constructed and calibrated by two independent methods. The first method consisted of constructing two additional Salvioni balances of lesser sensitivity and calibrating the less sensitive of the pair with a standard 1-milligram analytical weight. This calibration was used to determine the mass of a platinum wire, which was then used to calibrate the more sensitive second balance; similarly, a knowledge of the relation between load and displacement for the second balance allowed a calibration to be obtained for the third balance, the most sensitive one and the one on which the plutonium was to be weighed. A check on this calibration was made by an independent method. A 1-liter solution of thorium nitrate was prepared and the concentration of the solution was determined by ordinary analytical techniques. Then a known volume, about 1 microliter, of the solution was delivered onto the previously weighed platinum weighing pan of the Salvioni balance. The pan was then ignited until a constant weight was attained. The two calibrations agreed within 0.3% and indicated a sensitivity of ±0.00126 microgram. On September 10, 1942, the first weighing of a pure compound of a synthetic element was made when an aliquot of the plutonium solution was delivered onto the previously weighed platinum weighing pan, dried, and ignited. The deflection of the balance indicated a weight of $PuO_2$ of 2.77 micrograms. This material was not used for further experimentation but was preserved intact. Two more weighings were made of $PuO_2$, sample weights 4.55 and 2.20 micrograms, and these were used for specific-activity determinations which we now know indicated a purity of the plutonium stock solution of >95%. Additional experiments were carried out, using the same plutonium stock solution, to determine the oxidation number of plutonium in plutonium iodate and to determine the approximate solubilities of various plutonium compounds. This information was of importance in connection with the problems involved in designing chemical methods for the large-scale extraction, decontamination, and purification of plutonium. The chemical separations process at Hanford was successful from the beginning of operation and represented a scale-up factor of $10^9$ over the ultramicrochemical experiments.

The isolation of plutonium required microchemical techniques of great ingenuity. Both new techniques and the modification of previously developed techniques were used. In the latter the work of P. L. Kirk and associates and M. Cefola and A. A. Benedetti-Pichler should be mentioned.

## Neptunium

Neptunium was the first of the transuranium elements discovered, but it was not isolated until about two years after Cunningham and Werner had isolated pure plutonium. The neptunium isolation was carried out at the Metallurgical Laboratory of the University of Chicago by L. B. Magnusson, now of the Argonne National Laboratory Chemistry Division, and T. J. LaChapelle, currently employed in industry in California. Neptunium-237 with an alpha-decay half life of more than one million years was the isotope available. Two objectives stimulated the isolation of neptunium. First, an accurate value for the half life, determined by means of a direct-weighing specific-activity measurement, was desired because of the fundamental importance of this constant and for accurate standardization of the radiometric method of mass determination. In addition, a more accurate and detailed knowledge of the chemistry of neptunium was needed than could be obtained from tracer experiments. It was especially desired to establish one or more of the oxidation states of neptunium along with the formula of a dry compound.

Two sources of $Np^{237}$ yielded approximately equal amounts of neptunium. One source was 64 pounds of uranium metal which had been bombarded by fast neutrons produced by the reaction of beryllium with deuterons from the cyclotron at the University of California Radiation Laboratory, Berkeley. The other source was uranium from a chain-reacting pile. Both sources produced neptunium-237 as a result of the $n$, $2n$ reaction on uranium-238, which yields the beta-decaying $U^{237}$ of about 7 days half life. A total of 45 micrograms of neptunium was isolated by utilizing the fact that neptunium is precipitated by fluoride ion under certain conditions and yet can be rapidly oxidized to a fluoride-soluble state by bromate ion. The neptunium was separated from uranium by precipitating it, along with lanthanum carrier and plutonium, by adding HF to the solution previously treated with reducing agent. Separation of the neptunium and plutonium was achieved by dissolving the fluoride precipitate and adding potassium bromate. Under the conditions used plutonium was oxidized very slowly, and precipitation of lanthanum and plutonium fluorides left the oxidized fluoride-soluble neptunium in the supernatant. The supernatant solution was then treated with excess sulfur dioxide and the neptunium recovered as a fluoride which could be dissolved by any one of several means. Repeated bromate cycles separated the neptunium from contaminants until finally a pure neptunium fluoride was obtained. This was dissolved and a hydroxide precipitated. After being washed, the precipitate was fired and ignited and about 10 micrograms of the resulting oxide was scraped into an X-ray capillary. The remaining oxide was recovered and used for further preparation of neptunium compounds and measurement of their solubilities and crystal structure.

An X-ray-diffraction analysis of the ignited neptunium hydroxide was made by W. H. Zachariasen. He obtained a diffraction pattern which showed the oxide to be isomorphous with $ThO_2$, $UO_2$, and $PuO_2$, thus establishing a +4 oxidation state for neptunium. With this information about the preparation of a compound of definite composition, a specific-activity determination was undertaken. Two weighings of 3.82 and 3.75 micrograms of $NpO_2$ were made on a Kirk, Craig, Gullberg, Boyer quartz-fiber torsion microbalance, with a precision of about 0.02 microgram, and the balance pans then were counted directly in an alpha counter of ~50% geometry. The half life calculated from this specific-activity measurement, $2.20 \times 10^6$ years, is within 1% of the value obtained in recent years by using large quantities of $Np^{237}$, and demonstrates clearly the purity of the neptunium isolated so neatly by Magnusson and LaChapelle.

## Americium

Element 95, americium, is the third element following uranium in the periodic table, but it was the fourth transuranium element discovered—following curium, element 96, by a few months—and unlike all the other transuranics it was isolated in the form of pure compounds less than one year after it was discovered. The isolation was carried out at the Metallurgical Laboratory of the University of Chicago by B. B. Cunningham, who three years previously had achieved, in association with L. B. Werner, the isolation of the first synthetic element ever isolated, plutonium.

After the discovery of and prior to the isolation of americium, rather extensive tracer experiments on the chemistry had been carried on by the discoverers, Seaborg, James, and Morgan, and also by Thompson, Morgan, James, and Perlman. These investigations demonstrated the pronounced stability of the tripositive oxidation state of americium and the great similarity between the aqueous tripositive ions of the rare earth elements and americium. In three respects the problem of isolating americium differed from those encountered in the isolations of neptunium and plutonium. First, on the basis of the tracer experiments it appeared that it was difficult, if not impossible, to obtain any oxidation state other than +3 for americium. Also, the only methods of separating americium from the naturally occurring rare earths on a microgram scale involved prohibitive losses. Thirdly, the half life of $Am^{241}$, the principal isotope, was uncertain by at least an order of magnitude, which meant that the amount of americium expected in the isolation was uncertain, and from an amount obtained there was no way of judging its probable purity. The americium-241 was produced by pile irradiation of plutonium, which by multiple neutron capture produced $Pu^{241}$, which yielded $Am^{241}$ by beta decay. Necessity for separation of the americium from rare earths was avoided by subjecting the plutonium to extensive purification before irradiation and carefully avoiding any rare earth contamination from reagents or apparatus during the isolation. The americium produced in the irradiated plutonium was concentrated by hydroxide precipitation following precipitation of the bulk of the plutonium as peroxide. This cycle was repeated several times and a final americium-plutonium separation performed by oxidizing the plutonium to the fluoride-soluble +6 state and precipitating the americium fluoride with HF. The americium fluoride was dissolved, and after some further purification a very small portion of the americium solution was subjected to spectrographic analysis carried out by M. Fred and F. Tomkins. Lead and iron were the detected impurities, and these were removed by a lead sulfide precipitation and precipitation of the americium as fluoride to separate it from iron. On the basis of the chemistry which had been carried out on the sample, and from observation of its color, this was believed to be a pure americium compound. This fluoride was therefore used for a direct-weighing specific-activity measurement to determine the half life of $Am^{241}$. The ignited fluoride yielded a black oxide which was weighed on a quartz-fiber torsion microbalance and then counted in a low-geometry alpha counter. On the assumption that the several micrograms of oxide was $AmO_2$—an assumption later verified by X-ray-diffraction analysis—a half life of 498 years was calculated. The americium oxide was dissolved off the platinum boat and 20% of it used for spectrographic analysis which indicated 2% La, 0.1% Mg, and 6% Pt, the latter presumably dissolved from the weighing boat when the oxide was dissolved.

The remaining americium was purified and precipitated as hydroxide. The hydroxide was dissolved in dilute nitric acid and used for further studies of the oxidation states of americium in aqueous solution: oxidation states both higher and lower than +3 were looked for without definite success. In addition, the aqueous-solution absorption spectrum of Am(III) was determined. The absorption spectrum tended to verify the validity of Seaborg's actinide hypothesis: the difference between the spectra of americium and plutonium was similar to the difference between the spectra of europium and samarium. This lent weight to the argument of Seaborg that the new elements were part of an actinide series analogous to the rare earth or lanthanide elements.

## Curium

The actinide hypothesis also predicted that element 96, curium, would be the seventh member of a series in which the $f$ orbitals lay at progressively lower levels. Curium was postulated to be an analogue of gadolinium and a special stability was expected for Cm(III), presumed to have a configuration of seven $5f$ electrons. This had been borne out by tracer studies which indicated that only +3 curium was stable in aqueous solution. The problem of isolating curium from irradiated americium thus resolved itself into one of separating two tripositive ions similar to two adjacent rare earths. This separation and the isolation of curium were successfully accomplished by L. B. Werner, associated earlier with the plutonium isolation, and I. Perlman at the University of California Radiation Laboratory, Berkeley.

A quantity of 4.48 milligrams of $Am^{241}$ was irradiated for one year with a high flux of slow neutrons to produce about 150 micrograms of curium-242. The separation of the curium from americium was effected by means of a cation-exchange column using citric acid eluant. Additional ion-exchange separations were made on americium-contaminated fractions until 115 micrograms of $Cm^{242}$ was obtained free of americium in 50 milliliters of solution. This material was concentrated by readsorption on several small portions of ion-exchange resin and then batchwise elution from the resin with citrate solution. After decomposition of the citrate with nitric and sulfuric acids, curium hydroxide was precipitated. Handling $Cm^{242}$, which decays by alpha-particle emission with a half life of only 162 days, leads to problems other than just those of manipulating small quantities of radioactive material. Decomposition of the aqueous solution occurs as a consequence of the high alpha-decay rate, and both buildup of peroxide and evolution of gas are observed. This gas formation in the solution causes a precipitate to be stirred up within a few seconds after it has been compacted by centrifugation. Another concomitant of the short half life of curium-242 is the growth in the curium at the rate of 0.5% per day of daughter $Pu^{238}$. Except immediately after a separation plutonium is always present as an impurity.

The curium hydroxide was dissolved and the absorption spectrum of the solution examined. After purification of the curium from plutonium two 1-microgram samples were used for spectrographic analysis, which indicated that only lead was a major impurity. After precipitation of lead sulfide a 5-microgram sample was sparked to obtain a more complete measure of the spectral lines attributable to curium and to check for impurities. A further check on impurities was made by performing a direct-weighing specific-activity determination. Unlike the transuranium elements isolated earlier, the curium-242 had a half life so short that it was known from direct decay observations. A specific-activity determination on curium would thus check the purity of the compound weighed. On the assumption that the composition of the oxide was $Cm_2O_3$, about 40 micrograms of curium was weighed on a quartz fiber torsion microbalance and then dissolved and counted. A purity of 85 to 93% was found for the oxide preparation.

## Berkelium and Californium

In September, 1958, at the 2nd Geneva Conference on the Peaceful Uses of Atomic Energy, a paper was presented entitled "First Macroscopic Observations of the Chemical Properties of Berkelium and Californium." Thus the fifth and sixth transuranium elements have now been isolated. This work was done during the spring and summer of 1958 by B. B. Cunningham and S. G. Thompson at the University of California Radiation Laboratory, Berkeley.

Prolonged neutron irradiation of $Pu^{239}$ produced about a microgram each of berkelium, element 97, and californium, element 98. A mixture of isotopes was produced in each case, but those present in greatest abundance were $Bk^{249}$, a 300-day $\beta^-$ emitter, and $Cf^{252}$, a 2-year $\alpha$-emitting isotope. Prior to this work by Cunningham and Thompson the only knowledge of the chemical properties of these elements had been obtained by tracer experiments. This knowledge was actually extensive enough to allow the transplutonium elements to be concentrated by means of ion-exchange techniques which had been tested repeatedly. The final purifications of both berkelium and californium also consisted of elution from a very small ion-exchange column. The solution coming off the column passed directly into a capillary cell with optically flat windows, where the absorption spectrum of the elements could be studied. Approximately $1/2$ microgram of berkelium and double that amount of californium in dilute HCl were studied in the cell, and revealed no absorption lines in the visible region of the spectrum. The absence of detectable absorption lines of Bk(III) in the visible region of the spectrum was expected, but the absence of lines for Cf(III) suggested that in the heavier (as contrasted with the lighter) actinides the transition probabilities were decreasing for transitions from the $^6H_{15/2}$ ground state to the various $^6F$ levels. Additional studies of the absorption spectrum of Cf(III) by photographic methods revealed the presence of two broad weak absorptions which may correspond to transitions in analogous states of Dy(III).

Magnetic-susceptibility measurements on tripositive berkelium and californium were also made. The separate ions were sorbed on single beads of Dowex-50 resin and the beads suspended in a magnetic field by means of a plastic basket sealed to a fine quartz fiber. Gd(III) was used as the reference standard. The experimental results agreed best with moments derived on the assumption that the electrons occupy $f$ orbitals and interact by unperturbed pure L-S coupling.

Ten transuranium elements are now known, and of these ten, six have been isolated in amounts such that macroscopic properties could be observed or pure compounds weighed. Element 99, einsteinium, will perhaps be isolated in the near future, but it may well be the last element available in macro quantities. Thereafter the half lives are so short that even if sufficient quantities of the transeinsteinium elements could be produced the isolation would be difficult.

## References

*Np:* MAGNUSSON, L. B., AND LaCHAPELLE, T. J., *J. Am. Chem. Soc.*, **70**, 3534 (1948).

*Pu:* CUNNINGHAM, B. B., AND WERNER, L. B., *J. Am. Chem. Soc.*, **71**, 1521 (1949).

*Am:* CUNNINGHAM, B. B., paper 19.2, The Transuranium Elements, National Nuclear Energy Series Div. IV, **14B**, (1949).

*Cm:* WERNER, L. B., AND PERLMAN, I., *J. Am. Chem. Soc.*, **73**, 5215 (1951).

*Bk and Cf:* THOMPSON, S. G., AND CUNNINGHAM, B. B., "First Macroscopic Observation of the Chemical Properties of Berkelium and Californium," published in the Proceedings of the Geneva Conference on the Peaceful Uses of Atomic Energy (1958).

*General:* "The Chemistry of the Actinide Elements," KATZ, J. J., AND SEABORG, G. T., Wiley, New York, **1957**.

"The Transuranium Elements," SEABORG, G. T., Yale University Press, New Haven, **1958**.

"The New Elements," A Chem Ed Symposium, SEABORG, G. T., ET AL., *J. CHEM. EDUC*, **36**, 2-44 (1959).

**Martin D. Kamen**
University of California
San Diego

# The Early History of Carbon-14

**W**hen, how, and why was carbon-14 discovered?

As T. S. Kuhn has remarked (1), discovery is seldom a single event that can be attributed wholly to a particular individual, time, or place. He notes that some discoveries, such as those of the neutrino, radio waves and missing isotopes or elements, are predictable and present few problems, as far as establishment of priority is concerned. Others, such as the discoveries of oxygen, X-rays, and the electron, are unpredictable. These put the historian in a "bind" when he tries to decide when, how, who, and where of the discovery. Much more rarely does he have a basis for an answer to the question "why?"

I propose in this narrative of the "prenatal" history of $^{14}C$, to provide the answers to my leading questions. These will make a story which is a fragment of the whole record that must be constructed by future historians who seek to probe the events of a period in which there has been an unparalleled impact of intellectual curiosity and scientific creativity on the structure of society.

The tremendous outburst of technology in the past half-century, consequent to the rise of nuclear science, has crowned man's quest for the philosopher's stone so successfully as to be hardly credible even to the most optimistic alchemist. Tracer methodology, an offspring of nuclear science, has provided essential support for the ever-widening and deepening knowledge of structure and function in biological systems, expressed as the dynamic science of molecular biology.

These developments have profound, but unknown, implications for the future of our social structures. They obviously bring with them an unexampled load of grist for the mills of cultural historians, social scientists, and philosophers. Perhaps the novelists will dig into the record of these exciting times for fresh insights into the age-old drives of mankind.

Carbon-14, the long-lived carbon isotope, is the most important single tool made available by tracer methodology, because carbon occupies the central position in the chemistry of biological systems. Thus, it plays, and will continue to play, an essential role in the elucidation of biochemical mechanisms—knowledge of which is essential in the further development of molecular biology. Obviously, the circumstances surrounding its discovery are valid objects of interest for the historian.

I am happy that this opportunity has arisen to record a deeply felt personal tribute to two former associates, Dr. Franz N. D. Kurie and Dr. Samuel Ruben. The interruption of Dr. Kurie's career by a debilitating illness a few years ago deprived nuclear physics of a foremost investigator. The untimely death of Dr. Ruben, at the age of 29 while engaged in research in chemical warfare in 1943, was an unmitigated catastrophe for modern biochemistry.

## The Initial Phases, 1934–6

In the early 1930's, nuclear physicists, well-immersed in the great traditions of the Cambridge school led by Ernest Rutherford, were concerned primarily with observations of processes associated with the scattering of elementary nuclear particles by various atomic nuclei. Reports in those times show painstaking determinations of range-energy relations for the fundamental projectiles (protons, deuterons, alpha particles). The energies used did not exceed ~10 Mev, because of the limitations set by the relatively primitive accelerators and by the radiation characteristics of available naturally radioactive materials. The rationale for such work, which often involved much labor and tedious attention to detail, was that if enough precise facts were put together, accurate binding energies for nuclei could be deduced. From these, it was reasoned, could be derived a solid basis for further attack on the problem of the nature of nuclear forces.

By 1933, such data—as binding energies, angular distributions in scattering experiments, etc.—had demonstrated that nuclear forces could be described as analogous to saturation exchange forces, like those

### The Cover

The photograph shows the author installing a $B_2O_3$ target for cyclotron bombardment. This and the other photographs accompanying the text were taken by *Life* photographer Peter Stackpole in 1938 and are used here by special permission of *Life Magazine*. The editor also acknowledges with thanks the gracious cooperation of Dr. Philip Abelson, Editor of *Science*, and one-time associate of Dr. Kamen. The text of this paper will also appear in the May 10 issue of *Science*.

This paper is an abridged version of a lecture presented at the meeting of the American Chemical Society in Los Angeles, California, April, 1963, on the occasion of the 1963 Award for Nuclear Applications in Chemistry.

[1] A brief account, concerned mainly with technical aspects, has appeared previously, see KAMEN, M.D., "Isotopic Tracers in Biology," 3rd ed., Academic Press, New York, **1957**, p. 300 *et seq.*

postulated previously for chemical bonding. The so-called "alpha-particle" model of the nucleus already contained the seeds of what was to be the full-fledged modern "shell" theory of nuclei, to be developed later by Maria Mayer, Eugene Feenberg, and others.

As to my part in this, I was a young eager student and had just begun doctoral research, using the Wilson cloud chamber to study the angular distribution of neutrons scattered in collisions with protons and other nuclei. These researches were part of a general program initiated in the laboratory of Professor W. D. Harkins in the Chemistry Department at the University of Chicago (2). My decision to work in this field was largely owing to the influence of Dr. D. M. Gans, Professor Harkins' associate and also an assistant professor in the department. I am happy to record here my great debt to Dr. Gans and also to Dr. Henry W. Newson, my immediate predecessor in the research. Both of these scientists were most patient and helpful in my successful induction into a research career.

Most significantly for this history, similar work was also underway at Yale, where Dr. F. N. D. Kurie was investigating neutron-induced disintegration of light elements, and had obtained certain anomalous results for the angular distributions of protons in collisions with neutrons. In 1934 he proposed a radical interpretation (3) of certain events he noted in the cloud chamber. When nitrogen was exposed to fast neutrons, for instance, he found that in some cases the ejected nucleus exhibited a very long, thin track. This he ascribed to a proton, rather than an alpha particle. Thus, he supposed that the usual reaction, $^{14}N (n, ^{4}He)^{11}B$, was accompanied by a less frequent but readily observable reaction, $^{14}N(n, ^{1}H)^{14}C$. (As far as I am aware, this is the first suggestion in the literature that $^{14}C$ might exist.) Kurie also suggested, however, that the tracks he was observing might be those arising from $^{2}H$, or even $^{3}H$, so that the reactions, $^{14}N(n, ^{2}H)^{13}C$ and $^{14}N(n, ^{3}H)^{12}C$, were also possible. In fact, he felt the reactions with emission of $^{2}H$ and $^{3}H$ were more likely because they resulted in nuclei of known stability.

What was radical about Kurie's suggestion was the idea that something other than an alpha particle could emerge in a disintegration of a nucleus like $^{14}N$. Thus the physicists at the time assumed from their everyday experience that the alpha particle was much the most likely nucleon to be formed in such a nuclear reaction. This belief found a ready basis in the relatively great stability of the alpha-particle which was considered to exist as an entity in all nuclei because of its relatively enormous binding energy per nucleon, and because invariably in natural radioactivity it was the only heavy nucleon ejected.

In the meantime, T. W. Bonner and W. M. Brubaker (4) published observations on the energies of recoils induced by neutrons in inelastic collisions with nitrogen nuclei. Assuming the usual reaction, $^{14}N$-$(n, ^{4}He)^{11}B$, they calculated from the mass values given by Hans Bethe (5) that Q, the heat of reaction, was ~1.5 Mev. Most significantly, however, Bonner and Brubaker (3, 4) and W. Chadwick and M. Goldhaber (6, 7), independently, reported that the disintegration of $^{14}N$ occurred also with *slow* neutrons.

This, it turned out, was the crucial observation in the "prenatal" history of $^{14}C$, because it prompted a re-evaluation of the assumptions on which analyses of the nitrogen disintegration tracks were based.

Chadwick and Goldhaber had detected disintegrations in an ionization chamber connected to a linear amplifier and oscillograph. From the size of the oscillograph deflections they had deduced that Q was ~0.5 Mev. Bonner and Brubaker had used a cloud chamber and observed a group of tracks with a sharply defined range of 1.06 cm air (STP) which they thought to be alpha particles. On this basis, they had calculated a Q value of 2.33 Mev. The discrepancy in the two Q values was far beyond any experimental error. W. E. Burcham and Goldhaber (8) then were inspired to suggest that both sets of data were referred to the wrong reaction, and that if the disintegration were assumed to take place with proton emission, i.e., $^{14}N(n, ^{1}H)^{14}C$, then the value of Q taken from the range observed by Bonner and Brubaker, became 0.58 Mev, in good agreement with the value of Q deduced from the ionization measurements. Bonner and Brubaker not only concurred, but advanced further evidence in support of this suggestion by noting that when they measured Q for a related reaction, $^{11}B(^{2}H,n)^{12}C$ they found a value of 13.5 Mev, which, together with Q values known for some other reactions, enabled them to construct a reaction cycle in which the $^{14}N(n, ^{4}He)^{11}B$ reaction turned out to be endergonic, Q = −0.28 Mev, rather than exergonic, Q = 2.33 Mev. Thus, the alpha particle emission could not have taken place with slow neutrons, at least if one believed the rather marginal negative value for Q.

Burcham and Goldhaber proceeded to use the visualization technique of nuclear emulsions, in which they could distinguish more certainly between protons and alpha particles. They showed conclusively (8) that alpha particles were not emitted in the slow neutron disintegration of $^{14}N$, and proposed that the recoil particles be assigned definitely to the reaction with $^{14}C$ as a product. They could not exclude experimentally the possibility that $^{2}H$ or $^{3}H$ particles, rather than protons, might account for the recoil tracks observed. On the other hand, they remarked that reactions that could produce such particles were unlikely on energetic grounds. Thus, Kurie's original intuitive suggestion based on the appearance of certain unusually thin, long tracks in his cloud chamber experiments of 1933–4, were raised to the status of a practical certainty by 1936.

I think it is safe to say that in the *physical* sense the discovery of $^{14}C$ had been established by the observations of Burcham and Goldhaber. But as to the discovery of $^{14}C$ in the *chemical* sense—which I must say has turned out to be the more important—many obstacles lay in the way. Referring again to the remarks of Kuhn (1), the discovery of $^{14}C$ in a physical sense belongs in the "expected" category but its discovery in the chemical sense does not.

### The Intermediate Phases, 1936–8

Meanwhile, back at the ranch—so to say—I was plugging away collecting proton recoils produced by collisions with neutrons from a pathetically weak MsTh-Be source of a few millicuries equivalent. By the end of 1936, I received a PhD on the basis of results obtained from an analysis of 730 tracks which showed a marked asymmetry in the angular distribution of protons in the energy range from $\sim$0.1 to 3 Mev (9). This result confirmed those obtained by Kurie a few years previously (10). But, at the time, these results were in contradiction to theoretical expectations. Before this anomaly could be taken seriously, it was required that greater numbers of events be analyzed—an objective quite unrealizable with the feeble neutron sources available. It had taken three years of constant labor to produce and analyze a few hundred proton recoils—in fact, 10 man-hours per track had been required! This statistic shows how slender were the means available for researches in nuclear physics in 1936, which after all is not so long ago.

It was natural in the mid-1930's to look toward Berkeley where Ernest O. Lawrence was assembling the nucleus of a group of young physicists drawn by the prospect of a greatly enhanced particle source—the cyclotron.

Thus, in January of 1937, I found myself at the Berkeley Radiation Laboratory, along with Kurie who had arrived there a short time before. Because of our mutual interest in neutron scattering, we quickly began a collaboration in which we proposed to investigate not only the various apparent anomalies in the neutron-proton interactions, but neutron-nuclear interactions in general. The neutron fluxes available with the cyclotron, even in its primitive form as the 27-in. machine in 1937, were already four or five orders of magnitude greater than any with which we had been familiar.

Unfortunately, this neutron flux was not a well-collimated beam with minimal energy spread. The cyclotron contained innumerable scattering sites from which great numbers of neutrons emerged in a welter of undefined directions and energies. To achieve some measure of order in the neutron beam, a major effort was begun by Lawrence and his group, with responsibility vested largely in Dr. Arthur Snell. The procedure was to lead the deuterium beam away from the main vacuum accelerating chamber so that it would hit a beryllium target at some distance from the scattering bulk of the cyclotron. The emergent neutrons from the $^9Be(^2H,n)^{10}B$ reaction were to be piped through a hole in the water shield around the cyclotron. It was hoped that, with judicious use of auxiliary absorbers, the whole effect of this effort, called "snouting," would produce a relatively well-collimated intense beam of neutrons with a small energy spread downward from the maximum available in the reaction.

Kurie and I found that a cloud chamber filled with hydrogen as target, placed at either side of the hole, showed relatively few recoil pictures compared to an enormous yield when the chamber was directly in front of the hole. A typical single expansion, in front of the snout hole with an exciting deuteron beam of a few microamperes incident on the beryllium target, exhibited more recoil tracks than either Kurie or I had seen in all our previous experience with naturally radioactive sources of magnitude then available, e.g., hundreds of millicurie equivalents of Po or Ra, mixed with Be.

Mindful of the previous results on $^{14}C$ production, we decided to exploit them in our researches on neutron disintegration of $^{14}N$. The slow neutron reaction on $^{14}N$ with its characteristic recoil product—protons of a homogeneous range of 1.06 cm in air as dictated by the $Q$ value of 0.58 Mev—manifested itself almost every other expansion in the cloud chamber as a short, stubby track with a knob on the starting end. This track arose from the proton which, because of its relatively low mass, took up practically all the energy of the reaction as kinetic energy, while the knobby stub was the $^{14}C$ recoil, which because of its relatively high mass, possessed very little of the kinetic energy released in the reaction. These characteristic short, stubby tracks provided a convenient and accurate internal monitor for calibration of the stopping power of the nitrogen gas–water vapor mixture in the cloud chamber. In this way, we solved a very bothersome technical problem—the precise value of stopping power to use in calculations of ranges for determinations of recoil energies. Thus, $^{14}C$ was sufficiently well established as an entity by early 1937 so that it could be used in the calibrations of cloud chamber experiments!

However, nothing was known about its physical characteristics. One could attempt some predictions. First, it seemed certain that $^{14}C$ was radioactive and that it must emit negative $\beta$-rays in transformation to $^{14}N$. This followed from the observation that in all known cases among the elements of low atomic number, there were no examples of neighboring isobaric pairs in which more than one of the pair was stable, e.g., as in the pairs, $^6He$–$^6Li$, $^7Be$–$^7Li$, $^{10}Be$–$^{10}B$, $^{11}C$–$^{11}B$, etc. So, one might expect that for the isobaric pair $^{14}C$–$^{14}N$, the stability of $^{14}N$ required that $^{14}C$ be unstable and decay to $^{14}N$ by transformation of a neutron into a proton, with emission of a negative beta particle and a neutrino. Secondly—and here a great uncertainty arose—the rate of decay could be expected to be fairly rapid, because in two known analogous cases in which a nucleus with two excess neutrons decayed to a nucleus with equal numbers of neutrons and protons, i.e., $^6He$–$^6Li$ and $^{10}Be$–$^{10}B$, the expected decay rate was in quite good agreement with those actually observed. Thus, $^6He$, with an upper energy limit for $\beta$-rays of 3.5 Mev and a spin difference no more than 1 unit possible, could be expected to decay with a period of the magnitude $10^{-1}$ to $10^1$ sec. Its half life was, in fact, 0.8 sec. $^{10}Be$ with its enormously long half life—of the order of $10^6$–$10^7$ years (11)—corresponded to a highly forbidden transition despite a fairly high beta ray energy maximum of $\sim$0.5 Mev. In this case, a high degree of forbiddenness could be rationalized on the basis of the shell model available, i.e., a large spin difference was possible. The case of $^{14}C$ was quite analogous to that of $^6He$–$^6Li$, with a maximum spin difference of 1. The lower energy limit to be expected depended on the mass difference between $^{14}C$ and $^{14}N$. Thus, for the production reaction with slow neutrons,

$$(n-{}^1H) = ({}^{14}C - {}^{14}N) + Q$$

For the masses as then known and for $Q = +0.58$, the maximum energy expected for the emergent beta particles was $\sim$0.3 Mev. On this basis, a tentative maximal estimate for the $^{14}C$ half life of a few hours or days was made by P. Morrison and J. R. Oppenheimer. Thus, it appeared that $^{14}C$ was probably quite short-lived. If attempts to make it proved negative, it could be assumed that the half life was too short for the isotope to be isolated, rather than that it was too long, i.e., $t^{1}/_{2}$ was expected to be in the order of seconds, rather than centuries.

None of these arguments were wholly convincing for it was recognized that the state of beta decay theory was quite unsatisfactory; nevertheless they were sufficiently impressive to discourage determined efforts to isolate $^{14}C$ at that time. E. M. McMillan had noted that some very long-lived activities were present in old cyclotron targets and bits of metal scraped from various parts of the acceleration chamber. With what now is seen to be extraordinary intuition, he surmised that these activities could represent radioactive species of Be and C. In an abstract (11) submitted to a meeting of the Physical Society in 1936, he described two activities residual in an old Be target. The major activity was a very soft component, with a decay rate consistent with a half life of 10 years or longer. This component, he thought, might be assigned tentatively to $^{10}Be$. The other activity which was weaker, but harder, and decayed with a half life of a few months, was suggested as owing to a radioactive isotope of carbon, in particular $^{14}C$. In later years (12) he published a final summary of work done with S. Ruben in the years 1938–40, in which the activity assigned to $^{10}Be$ was reassigned with some certainty to $^{3}H$. The other activity obviously could not have been $^{14}C$, because, as we know now, the half life of $^{14}C$ is $\sim$5700 years. In an effort to produce $^{14}C$ by the $^{14}N(n,^{1}H)^{14}C$ reaction, McMillan exposed solid ammonium nitrate to the intense neutron flux of the 37-in. cyclotron for several months in 1938–1939, but this experiment ended when the bottle containing the salt was inadvertently knocked off the magnet coil tank and smashed.

However, a new—and what was to prove decisive—factor entered late in 1937. As we all know, the ancient alchemists' ascribed to the "philosopher's stone" two magical powers—the first was the ability to transmute elements, the second was the ability to banish disease. The old alchemical treatises bear constant witness to the state of mind which supported through centuries what were tedious, disappointing, and often fatally hazardous searches. Even after chemistry was well established and alchemy in some disrepute, Robert Boyle could still make his well-known statement (13).

There may be some agent found out so subtle and powerful, at least in respect of those particular compounded corpuscles, as to be able to resolve them into those more simple ones, whereof they consist.

With the discoveries of radioactivity by Becquerel and X-rays by Roentgen at the end of the nineteenth century and the experiments of Rutherford early in this century, the prophecy of Boyle and the hopes of the alchemists had been realized. Lawrence saw even greater potentialities in the exploitation of the immensely more powerful agents available from artificial radioactivity and man-made accelerators and was eager to see them applied. For this purpose, he had

interested his brother, Dr. John Lawrence in the possibilities of the neutron as a therapeutic agent and had assigned P. C. Aebersold, then a graduate student, to help him to establish the physical and radiological procedures involved. A small beginning had already been made in the use of the radioactive isotopes of phosphorus, sodium, and iodine as tracers in biological research. To facilitate a rapid development of such researches both at Berkeley and elsewhere, I was asked to assume responsibility as staff chemist to develop procedures whereby target materials could be bombarded, processed, and delivered in forms suitable for direct applications in biological systems. The problems involved were sufficiently challenging and urgent so that from the early months of 1937 until well into 1940, most of my energies were channeled into this activity.

Almost immediately, I found it necessary to devise a procedure for rapid and reproducible preparation of the 21 min $^{11}C$, for use by S. Ruben, W. Z. Hassid, and I. L. Chaikoff in some researches in which they proposed to investigate carbohydrate metabolism by means of $^{11}C$-labeled sugars prepared photosynthetically from $^{11}CO_2$. (See Figures 1–3.) In a short time, it became apparent (14) that $B_2O_3$ powder, bombarded by deuterons in a special external target chamber designed by Kurie, evolved much of the $^{11}C$ produced in the $^{10}B(^{2}H,n)^{11}C$ reaction as $^{11}CO_2$. The success of this procedure which eliminated hazardous radiation exposure incidental to manipulation of target material, expedited the researches sufficiently so that Ruben was encouraged to initiate researches on photosynthesis itself—an undertaking into which I was soon drawn full time outside of my duties as radiochemist.

In the meantime, Ruben observed in May, 1938, that a number of graphite targets, which I had been using to make $^{13}N$ by the $^{12}C(^{2}H,n)$ reaction for some researches on nitrogen fixation (15), contained no residual long-lived activity isotopic with carbon. He concluded that any $^{14}C$ formed by the $^{13}C(^{2}H,^{1}H)$ reaction with a half life of up to 200 years could have been detected. This finding underscored the probability that $^{14}C$, if it existed, was a short-lived isotope.

External target for C$^{11}$ production. Assembly on the right contains window and main chamber. Middle section shows $B_2O_3$ target material. This section was clamped into the main section so that the whole constituted a closed system cooled by the water pipes shown. The $B_2O_3$ powder was held to the target plate by a frame and window assembly (parts shown on left). The target, as shown, had just survived bombardment with 30–50 $\mu$amps of 7–8 Mev deuterons for 20 minutes.

My constant exposure to cyclotron targets kept me in a steady state of radioactive contamination which rendered me *persona non grata* around radioactivity assay equipment. I recall, as an example, an experience during a collaboration with Philip Abelson sometime in late 1937 when we were attempting to use an apparatus consisting of an ionization chamber connected to an FP-54 Pliotron tube amplifier. We were harassed by occurrence of an eccentric and irregular background drift of variable magnitude. Finally, Abelson noted that the effect was correlated with my movements toward and away from the apparatus. While I stood in a corner, he systematically stripped me and established that the disturbance originated from the front of my pants. Likewise, in my collaboration with Ruben, it was necessary to keep me away from the counting equipment. In our researches, we came to a logical arrangement whereby Ruben assumed sole responsibility for assay and I concentrated on tracer isotope production.

I cannot leave this section of my presentation without mentioning that Ruben was responsible, almost single-handedly, for the growth of interest in tracer methodology which occurred at Berkeley in the years 1937–8. His unique combination of experimental skills, energy, wide-ranging interests, and quick grasp of essentials when confronted with new and unfamiliar areas of science, provided a focus for the efforts of an ever-increasing number of able investigators.

By the middle of 1938, the demands for cyclotron time made by biologists and clinicians was so great that it was mandatory to initiate round the clock operation of the cyclotron—by now a 37-in. machine. In addition the pressure to build bigger machines had impelled Lawrence to seek additional subsidies from biologically oriented foundations as sources likely to support such projects. As an argument, Lawrence cited preliminary results obtained with neutron therapy and by applications of radioactive isotopes, such as $^{24}Na$, $^{32}P$, and $^{59}Fe$, in medical diagnosis. A 60-in. machine was almost ready for operational

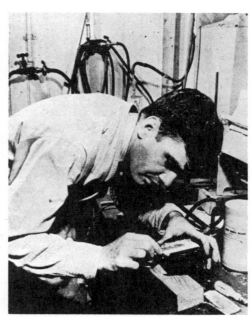

The author preparing a $B_2O_3$ target.

tests and further development depended critically on favorable responses from medically and biologically oriented sources of funds which had been solicited. Added urgency was generated by the demonstration that ultimate energies and ion currents were likely to be far in excess of the limits earlier thought to be reasonable.

The researches of R. R. Wilson in this period were of considerable importance in pointing the direction for further developments of cyclotron design. Wilson showed that very large beam currents at energies somewhat lower than those emergent in the external target area circulated inside the accelerating electrodes (*16*). He realized that if a means could be devised to use these internal beams, bombardments of much greater magnitude than those possible with external targets could be effected. Moreover, he was able to show that a large fraction of the internal circulating ion current could be intercepted by appropriately designed "probes" without appreciable diminution of external beams. However, the problems which arose in the achievement of acceptable internal targets were formidable and sufficiently difficult to discourage immediate efforts to exploit the internal ion currents. As an example, the external beams of 7–8 Mev and 50–100 $\mu$amp required dissipation of 300 to 800 watts—a power input which, even with well cooled targets of good heat conductance, required sequestration of target material from the cyclotron vacuum by the use of aluminum or other metal foil windows. Internal beams with ion currents as much as several milliamperes and energies only slightly less than 6–7 Mev, generated power inputs of an order of magnitude greater than those associated with the external beams.

However, the cyclotron was increasingly unable to keep up with the demands for radio-isotopes, as well as for bombardment time for clinical trials; even the enforcedly modest needs for essential nuclear physical research could not be satisfied. This led Wilson and me to try to devise acceptable internal targets for radio-isotope production—an enterprise in which we succeeded late in 1938. This research was to prove the turning point in the sequence of events comprising the prenatal history of $^{14}C$. In fact, as we remarked at that time (*17*),

Obviously, the method of internal targets should find its most important application in the preparation of radio-isotopes which are long-lived and difficult of activation, as well as in the demonstration of the existence of many radio-isotopes as yet undiscovered.

### The Final Phase, 1938–40

The search for funds proceeded with some success through 1938 and into 1939, so that both cyclotrons were in operation on a full schedule when the discovery of nuclear fission burst on the world in January, 1939. In the meantime, the ambitions of Lawrence to produce an even greater machine had been spurred by the successful operation of the 60-in. cyclotron. He pressed for more support from the same biologically-oriented sources he had tapped previously, on the basis of the considerably expanded collection of clinical data as well as the enormously developing tracer program at Berkeley and elsewhere which was made possible by the Berkeley cyclotrons.

In our own researches on photosynthesis, [11]C had by this time been exploited to its ultimate limits (18).

As an example of our difficulties, we had found it essential to try an ultracentrifugal determination of the molecular weight of the labeled intermediates produced during photosynthesis in the presence of $^{11}CO_2$. The necessary apparatus was at Stanford University, 50 miles away from the Berkeley cyclotrons through heavy traffic. We calculated that it would be possible to make the $^{11}CO_2$, incubate algae with it, extract the resultant intermediates and drive to Stanford. There would be insufficient time, however, to do a proper centrifuge run. We considered a number of possible courses of action, such as arranging a police escort for the motor trip to Stanford, posting one of us at Stanford to have the counting apparatus ready, etc., but one night a brilliant solution occurred to Sam Ruben. He woke me at 2 A.M. to suggest carrier pigeons!

Fortunately, this problem was finally resolved by the discovery that an apparatus identical with that at Stanford was available at the Shell Oil Company research laboratories only 10 min drive from the cyclotron. Even with this dispensation, we found it impossible to obtain the precision needed to establish with certainty the average size of the early intermediates in photosynthesis.

In a gloomy conference late in September, 1939, Ruben and I reached the conclusion that without a long-lived isotope of carbon our researches were at an end. I suggested one last desperate try to make [14]C by means of the internal target technique. The difficulty was that, in view of the pessimism about the probability of a long-lived isotope, it was not possible to liberate any of the internal targets from their constant use for production of $^{32}P$ and $^{59}Fe$.

S. Ruben (left) and W. Z. Hassid (right) examine reaction vessel containing C*O$_2$ and photosynthesis leaf system.

It was with some amazement therefore, that I found myself shortly after this conference being told by Lawrence that both cyclotrons must be diverted forthwith to a full time effort to make sure that long-lived isotopes of hydrogen, carbon, nitrogen, and oxygen did, or did not, exist. The reason emerged soon. During Lawrence's most recent efforts to ensure increased and continued subsidies for further cyclotron development, he had found that some doubts had been raised as to the real value of radioactive isotopes in biological research, relative to the rare stable isotopes, such as $^2H$, $^{13}C$, $^{15}N$, and $^{18}O$. Thus, while these very useful stable isotopes existed as tracers for the elements of primary importance in biology, there were no comparable radioactive isotopes with reasonably long life-times available; i.e., no radioactive hydrogen isotope existed (it was thought that tritium was stable relative to $^3He$). the carbon isotopes[10]C and [11]C were limited by their half lives of 8 sec and 21 min, respectively, and only very short-lived [13]N and [15]O were known for nitrogen and oxygen.

Lawrence asked me to organize a complete and systematic campaign to probe every possibility for the existence of long-lived isotopes anywhere in the first row of the periodic table—but especially for H, C, N, and O. From the experience gained in previous years, it was a simple matter to draw up a comprehensive plan which included a detailed set of protocols for every nuclear reaction possible with the projectiles available, including the choice of target materials and target chemistry. It was natural to concentrate first on carbon. An abridged plan taken from my notebook, as drawn up in September, 1939, is shown in Table 1. Similar plans were devised for nitrogen and oxygen activities based on bombardments of $B_2O_3$, graphite, BN and $(NH_4)_2F_2$ targets. Every possibility was assumed— even that there might be long-lived isomers of stable nuclei (e.g., [12]C, [13]C) or of short-lived nuclei (e.g., [13]N, [15]O).

The first trials involved bombardment of $B_2O_3$ with 16 Mev alpha particles in the 37-in. machine (Sept. 27–29). A 5 μamp hr exposure yielded no long-lived activity in the gas space, assayed by direct introduction of the target gases into an ionization chamber-pliotron apparatus. The residual powder was burned with a small bit of filter paper as a carbon carrier, but the resultant gases were also inactive. It could be concluded that the 16 Mev alpha particles were inadequate to produce significant quantities of [13]N, [14]N, [13]C, or the isotope [14]C by means of the ($^4$He,n) or ($^4$He,$^1$H) reactions. Next, $B_2O_3$ was bombarded for 34 μamp hr with 16 Mev deuterons in the 60-in. machine. In this experiment, E. Segré collaborated and examined the

Table I.   Plan—Production Reactions for Possible Long-Lived Carbon Isotope, September, 1939

| Reaction[a] | Target material | | | | | Target chemistry | |
|---|---|---|---|---|---|---|---|
| $^9$Be($^4$He,n)C$^{12}$* | BeO | (atmosphere 3% CH$_4$ in O$_2$) | | | | Collect C*O in gas, burn residue to CO$_2$, | |
| $^{10,11}$B($^4$He, $^1$H)$^{13}$*,$^{14}$C | B$_2$O$_3$ | ( " | " | " | " ) | with carrier C | |
| $^{11}$B($^1$H, $\gamma$)C$^{12}$* | " | ( " | " | " | " ) | " | " |
| $^{11}$B($^2$H,n)C$^{12}$* | " | ( " | " | " | " ) | " | " |
| $^{12,13}$C($^2$H, $^1$H)$^{13}$*,$^{14}$C | Graphite ( " | " | " | " ) | | " | " |
| $^{14,15}$N(n, $^1$H)$^{14,15}$C | Ammonium nitrate (nitrate) | | | | | " | " |
| | | | | | | Aspirate CO$_2$-free air through solution, burn emergent gases and trap C$^a$O$_2$ | |

[a] Energies available:  protons (4-8 Mev), deuterons (8-10 Mev), alphas (16-32 Mev).

activities produced in the gas phase which were introduced again directly into an ionization chamber detector. He found the expected $^{11}C$ in enormous quantities and also an activity with a half life of 112 min. Unfortunately, we traced this to $^{18}F$ produced by the $(^{2}H,2n)$ reaction on $^{18}O$. By October 16, 1939, I had reached the conclusion that none of the alpha particle induced reactions were feasible—it appeared that at least $5 \times 10^{5}$ $\mu$amp hr of 32 Mev alpha particles would be needed to produce one $\mu$curie of radioactivity with $t^{1}/_{2} \sim 1$–3 hr.

On October 17, I tried exposure of methane to 20 $\mu$amp hr of 16 Mev deuterons in the 60-in. machine and obtained only the expected $^{13}N$ (several hundreds of millicuries), $\sim$0.01 $\mu$curie of $^{18}F$ from a small amount of contaminant oxygen, and again no long-lived activity.

In the meantime, I had begun continuous exposure of a graphite probe target introduced through the north port of the 37-in. machine. This probe was allowed to collect stray deuterons in the internal cyclotron beam for nearly a month throughout January, 1940. The probe was inserted so as to intercept practically all deuterons during night operation and retracted to allow normal operation in the day. I undertook the night bombardments, aided occasionally by others who needed the copious supply of neutrons produced for further studies on the uranium fission reactions. The probe target was not designed properly to withstand intense bombardment. I had merely smeared colloidal graphite on the water-cooled copper surface and counted on replacement during frequent inspections of whatever graphite was found to be blasted off. The weather was unusually violent, even for January, and most nights witnessed heavy drenching rains and wind storms. The noise of the rain on the laboratory tin roof, interspersed with cannonades from cyclotron high-voltage discharges created an appropriate fanfare for the birth of $^{14}C$ which was fated to come during this bombardment.

This experiment had been regarded as the most likely to make $^{14}C$. It was performed with mixed desperation and resignation, and involved considerable hazard from radiation exposure as it was necessary to examine the intensely radioactive probe nightly to insure that some graphite still clung to the target surface. Occasionally, I found the irradiated graphite almost on the verge of flaking off and so had to cement it back on with more graphite.

On February 15, during a particularly violent storm, I terminated this bombardment which had involved exposure of the graphite to 5700 $\mu$amp hr of 7–8 Mev deuterons. Shortly before dawn, I left the graphite, which looked like bits of gravel, in a weighing bottle on Ruben's desk. On the way home to get some sleep for the first time in several days, I must have presented a sorry spectacle—unshaven, red-eyed and dazed—for I was intercepted and questioned by police looking for an escaped convict who had committed several revolting murders earlier in the evening. Fortunately, I failed to pass muster and was released to continue stumbling onwards to sleep.

On awakening some hours later, I phoned Ruben who had found the sample, burned it to $CO_2$, precipitated it as $CaCO_3$, and noted some activity when he examined the precipitate inside a screen-wall counter of a type designed by W. F. Libby (19) to permit assay inside the sensitive volume of a Geiger-Müller tube. No activity could be detected with the usual thin-walled tubes. The effect was very small—about four times the counting background—but reproducible. In some excitement, I hurried back to the laboratory, prepared a new probe target made up of graphite solidly bonded to copper and then joined Ruben to press on further with the identification of the activity. By Tuesday afternoon, February 27, we had disposed of the last uncertainty—that the activity might have arisen from $^{35}S$ produced by the $(^{2}H,^{1}H)$ reaction on the sulfur as a possible contaminant of the graphite used—but had left only about $\sim^{1}/_{8}$ of the original activity. We wrote a preliminary account for publication as a letter and later as an abstract in the Physical Review (18), and on Wednesday evening motored to Lawrence's home to acquaint him with the result. Lawrence was resting in an attempt to banish a cold before his appearance the next night, Thursday, February 29, to receive the Nobel Award in Physics. His pleasure was unbounded and shook our own certainty as we revived nagging doubts about the reality of the activity we were ascribing to $^{14}C$. After all, it was only an activity half of the counting background when counted as solid $CaCO_3$ even though it had persisted through repeated cycles of precipitations with $CaCO_3$ and acidification to $CO_2$. It was a comfort to realize that, of all the elements in the periodic system, only carbon possessed an oxide which could be liberated repeatedly from acid solutions under oxidizing conditions—a fact which ensured that the activity observed was in fact isotopic with carbon.

The new probe target, with its improved mode of bonding, withstood much more intense probe beams, so that in a week it had accumulated 13,500 $\mu$amp hr of exposure to 3–4 Mev deuterons on a probe inserted in the south port of the 37-in. machine. The activity obtained was 10–20 times counting background and sufficient to establish the isotopic assignment as $^{14}C$, to show that the beta-energy maximum lay in the neighborhood of $\sim$120 kv, and that the half life was certainly greater than 20 years. I was able to make an estimate for $t^{1}/_{2}$ based on the following considerations. The first probe sample, after 5700 $\mu$amp hr, had shown a total activity of $\sim$100 disintegrations sec$^{-1}$. From a knowledge of the cross section at 3–4 Mev for the reaction $^{12}C(^{2}H,^{1}H)^{13}C$ and the assumption that the cross section for $^{13}C(^{2}H,^{1}H)^{14}C$ was similar, it could be calculated that the ratio of $^{14}C$ nuclei made to deuterons stopped in the graphite would have been $\sim$1/60,000 assuming 100% $^{13}C$ or $[1/(6 \times 10^{6})]$ for the graphite which had the normal isotope content of 1% $^{13}C$. The total number of deuterons was $\sim$1.2 $\times$ 10$^{20}$ (5700 $\mu$amp hr), hence the number of $^{14}C$ nuclei produced ($N_{^{14}C}$) was (1.2 $\times$ 10$^{20}$/6 $\times$ 10$^{6}$), or 2 $\times$ 10$^{13}$. Knowing $N_{^{14}C}$ and $dN_{^{14}C}/dt$ (100 dis/sec), it was simple to deduce the $t^{1}/_{2}$ as $\sim$4 $\times$ 10$^{3}$ years! This value was remarkably close to the true disintegration half life of $\sim$5700 years determined many years later, but the agreement was quite accidental, as this 1940 estimate was uncertain by as much as an order of magnitude in either direction. However, it did shed light on the reason for the negative results of previous years—the half life of $^{14}C$ was too great to permit production in significant quantities until the internal target technique had been developed so that bombardments of 5000 $\mu$amp hr and upward were possible. Moreover, it was clear that $^{14}C$ had an enormously long half life—a result most surprising on theoretical grounds, as remarked previously.

In all of these exercises, the basic assumption was that the ($^2H$,$^1H$) reaction on $^{13}C$ would be much the most likely to succeed. This type of reaction exhibited the largest cross sections among those excited by charged particles, and had the advantage that target chemistry was simple and dilution of isotopic material minimal. The reaction of slow neutrons with $^{14}N$, which had led to the initial postulation of $^{14}C$, was regarded as a possible, but not promising, process as a basis for $^{14}C$ production. It may come as a surprise to many of you that this impression prevailed in 1940 in view of the fact that the $^{14}N(n,{}^1H)^{14}C$ reaction is the method of choice now.

There were many cogent reasons for neglecting the slow neutron reaction. First, the neutrons produced in the cyclotron were not primaries, but secondary particles with ranges up to many meters in dense media so that only a fraction could be captured by $^{14}N$ nuclei, even with the best possible geometry. On the other hand, all deuterons produced as primaries with very small ranges could be absorbed in a minimal amount of target. Second, cross sections for slow neutron capture were high only for the $(n,\gamma)$ process with which the $(n,{}^1H)$ process was expected to compete poorly. Thirdly, the recoil $^{14}C$ nuclei produced would not be expected to reach equilibrium in chemical species sufficiently uniform to permit simple, efficient extraction. Nevertheless, two carboys, each containing 5 gal. of saturated ammonium nitrate solution were placed near a good source of neutrons—the deflector region of the 60-in. cyclotron—in January. Prior to exposure, the solutions were acidified with dilute nitric acid, aspirated with $CO_2$-free air to remove contaminant carbonate, which would dilute excessively any radioactive carbonate formed (not that we expected to see any!), and sealed tightly. The success with the graphite probes had quite completely distracted my attention from these carboys, and I was busily engaged in an attempt to improve the ($^2H$,$^1H$) yields by fabrication of $^{13}C$ enriched graphite probes when an angry deputation from the 60-in. cyclotron paid me a visit and issued an ultimatum to remove the carboys, which had sprung leaks and were proving an intolerable nuisance. The deflector region was in constant need of attention for deflector adjustments; and the cyclotron crew was weary of the constant pushing and pulling to move the box, especially a box wet with acid, to get at the deflector controls.

So, with no great enthusiasm, I went over to the 60-in. cyclotron with a cart and moved the box to Ruben's laboratory in a ramshackle hut, affectionately labeled the "Rat House." Ruben and I decided to make a gesture and aspirate some air, freed of $CO_2$ by passage through soda lime, through the carboys in the hopes some $^{14}C$ might be entrained and removed as ${}^{\cdot 14}CO_2$. A copious precipitate of $CaCO_3$ which formed in the $Ca(OH)_2$ trap after passage of the effluent gases

through a combustion train lent no encouragement, as it indicated large quantities of $CO_2$ had diffused into the ammonium nitrate solutions and that any activity formed was likely to have been lost because of excessive dilution. To our astonishment, we found that a small fraction of this precipitate was so active it completely paralyzed the screen wall counter! In a short time, we ascertained that we had several microcuries of $^{14}C$— a quantity two or three orders of magnitude greater than any we had seen from the probe bombardments. Needless to say, our interest in the $^{13}C(^2H,{}^1H)^{14}C$ reaction vanished, never to return.

Where had I gone astray in denigration of the slow neutron process? All the assumptions about poor cross-sections and complex target chemistry were eminently sound and eminently wrong! As it developed later, the $(n,{}^1H)$ process for $^{14}N$ was favored heavily over the $(n,\gamma)$ process—possibly the only exception to the general rule. It is remarkable that the only other instance of appreciable yield from $(n,{}^1H)$ process with slow neutrons also involves production of an important radioactive tracer (20)—$^{35}S$ from the $(n,{}^1H)$ reaction on $^{35}Cl$. Moreover, as we found in further experimentation (21) and as was later confirmed by P. E. Yankwich, T. H. Norris and G. K. Rollefson (22), well over 80% of the recoil $^{14}C$ found its way into the volatile oxides of carbon (CO and $CO_2$) and so made possible a simple, practically quantitative recovery of the $^{14}C$ from any amount of bulk solution. The realization of all these facts caused some talk shortly thereafter of a syndicate to build a battery of cyclotrons designed solely for $^{14}C$ production.

In the meantime, Lawrence authorized construction of a special set of stainless steel cans with aspirator inlets and outlets to be mounted as a permanent shield around the 60-in. cyclotron. This set-up was expected to produce hundreds of microcuries of $^{14}C$ monthly. After these cans had been in place a month, however, worries about ammonium nitrate solutions as a possible explosion hazard, however remote, induced Lawrence to order them removed. A few years later, in 1944, these cans were to serve as a source of $^{14}C$ in the first published tracer researches with $^{14}C$, carried out in collaboration with Dr. H. A. Barker (23).

The story of the birth of $^{14}C$ ends here. But, of course, there were many other chapters to come, e.g., the expansion of $^{14}C$ production from the microcurie to the curie level which followed the development of nuclear reactors, and the resultant proliferation of $^{14}C$ as a tracer isotope in every area of biological research. Another chapter—which ties into a last thread from the early history up to 1940—concerns what may prove of great significance in the future of nuclear theory, namely, the anomalously low rate of $^{14}C$ decay. All through the period from 1938–40 the search for $^{14}C$ was conducted under a cloud of certainty that the half life of $^{14}C$ was probably in the order of seconds, or less. When it was seen by July of 1940 that the half life of the material we had produced was certainly of the order of years, in fact millenia, active doubts were expressed that the activity observed was isotopic with carbon. Even the testimony of algae, which absorbed the activity photosynthetically, and the chemical behavior of the activity failed to still these doubts at the time! The question raised—why is $^{14}C$ so long-lived?—remains with us today.

Explanations have been offered *seriatim:* first, that there is a change in parity, secondly, that $^{14}C$ is wholly $'S_0$ and $^{14}N$ purely $^3D$, so that a transition between them is $\Delta L$ forbidden: thirdly, there is a fortuitous cancellation in the matrix element for decay (24). The last suggestion is favored at present (25) but is not wholly acceptable. The first two are definitely excluded on experimental as well as theoretical grounds (24, 25). It is apparent that the riddle of $^{14}C$ decay implies an answer which should be an important part of the future history of nuclear theory. In conclusion, I quote as a moral for our story, the words of the late psychiatrist, E. Winzholz—"We never let our theories interfere with our practice."

## Literature Cited

(1) KUHN, T. S., *Science,* **136,** 760 (1962).
(2) HARKINS, W. D., GANS, D. M., and NEWSON, H. W., *Phys. Rev.,* **44,** 529 (1933).
(3) KURIE, F. N. D., *Phys. Rev.,* **45,** 904 (1934); *ibid.,* **46,** 330 (1934).
(4) BONNER, T. W., AND BRUBAKER, W. M., *Phys. Rev.,* **48,** 469 (1935).
(5) BETHE, H., *Phys. Rev.,* **47,** 633 (1935).
(6) CHADWICK, W., AND GOLDHABER, M., *Nature,* **135,** 65 (1935).
(7) CHADWICK, W., AND GOLDHABER, M., *Proc. Camb. Phil. Soc.,* **31,** 612 (1935).
(8) BURCHAM, W. E., AND GOLDHABER, M., *Proc. Camb. Phil. Soc.,* **32,** 632 (1936).
(9) HARKINS, W. D., KAMEN, M. D., GANS, D. M., AND NEWSON, H. W., *Phys. Rev.,* **50,** 980 (1936).
(10) KURIE, F. N. D., *Phys. Rev.,* **49,** 461 (1933).
(11) McMILLAN, E. M., *Phys. Rev.,* **49,** 875 (1936).
(12) McMILLAN, E. M., AND RUBEN, S., *Phys. Rev.,* **70,** 123 (1946).
(13) *See* PANETH, F., in the Introductory Lecture of his "Radio-elements as Indicators," The Baker Lectures, **1928,** McGraw-Hill Book Co., New York.
(14) RUBEN, S., HASSID, W. Z., AND KAMEN, M. D., *J. Amer. Chem. Soc.,* **61,** 661 (1939).
(15) RUBEN, S., HASSID, W. Z., AND KAMEN, M. D., *Science,* **91,** 578 (1940).
(16) WILSON, R. R., *Phys. Rev.,* **54,** 240 (1938).
(17) WILSON, R. R., AND KAMEN, M. D., *Phys. Rev.,* **54,** 1031 (1938).
(18) RUBEN, S., AND KAMEN, M. D., *Phys. Rev.,* **57,** 549 (1940), see also KAMEN, M. D., AND RUBEN, S., *Phys. Rev.,* **58,** 194 (1940).
(19) LIBBY, W. F., *Phys. Rev.,* **46,** 196 (1934).
(20) KAMEN, M. D., *Phys. Rev.,* **60,** 537 (1941); *ibid.,* **62,** 303 (1942).
(21) RUBEN, S., AND KAMEN, M. D., *Phys. Rev.,* **59,** 349 (1941).
(22) YANKWICH, P. E., ROLLEFSON, G. K., AND NORRIS, T. H., *J. Chem. Phys.,* **14,** 131 (1946).
(23) BARKER, H. A., AND KAMEN, M. D., *Proc. Nat. Acad. Sci. U. S.,* **31,** 219 (1945).
(24) INGLIS, D. R., *Revs. Mod. Phys.,* **25,** 390 (1953).
(25) SHERR, R., GERHART, J. B., HORIE, H., AND HORNYAK, W. F., *Phys. Rev.,* **100,** 945 (1955).

---

## Friedrich Rochleder (1819–74)

*Continued from page 151*

acid. Schunck had already in 1848 obtained this substance, which he called rubian, in impure form. In 1854 Rochleder and Schwarz prepared pure saponine from Levantine soap root.

Rochleder also published two theoretical communications (1853 and 1854). In these he expressed the view that methyl is the fundamental radical. Other radicals can be considered to arise by stepwise substitution of methyl or phenyl for the hydrogen atoms of methyl. Unsaturated radicals, that is, those which can add hydrogen or halogens, were thought to be radicals which contained empty spaces (free valence units).

When Rochleder died (1874), his assistant was Zdenko Hans Skraup[3] (1850–1910). In 1874 appeared a preliminary communication by Rochleder and Skraup on cinchonine. Skraup continued this study after the death of his teacher. In 1879 he published his work on the composition of cinchonine. Thus, shortly before his death, Rochleder led Skraup into the field of the quinine alkaloids, in which Skraup later became one of the chief investigators.

If Rochleder had had a longer life, science could have expected much more from him. Destiny willed otherwise. Yet his pupils, H. Hlasiwetz and Zd. H. Skraup, were able to increase richly the values which they obtained from him.

### ACKNOWLEDGMENT

I obtained the picture of Friedrich Rochleder through the courtesy of the National Library in Vienna by the efforts of Mrs. Mathilde Raschka, who kindly acted as intermediary between the library and myself.

[3] KOHN, M., *ibid.,* **20,** 471 (1943).

---

## The Search for Tritium—The Hydrogen Isotope of Mass Three

*Continued from page 208*

(14) OLIPHANT, M., P. HARTECK, AND E. RUTHERFORD, *Nature,* **133,** 413 (1934).
(15) SELWOOD, P. W., H. S. TAYLOR, W. W. LOZIER, AND W. BLEAKNEY, *J. Am. Chem. Soc.,* **57,** 780 (1935).
(16) RUTHERFORD, E., *Nature,* **140,** 304 (1937).
(17) SHERR, R., L. G. SMITH, AND W. BLEAKNEY, *Phys. Rev.,* **54,** 388 (1938).
(18) ALVAREZ, L. W., AND R. CORNOG, *ibid.,* **56,** 613 (1939).
(19) O'NEAL, R. D., AND M. GOLDHABER, *ibid.,* **57,** 1086 (1940)
(20) O'NEAL, R. D., AND M. GOLDHABER, *ibid.,* **58,** 574 (1940).
(21) BROWN, S. C., *ibid.,* **59,** 687, 954 (1941).
(22) O'NEAL, R. D., *ibid.,* **60,** 359 (1941).
(23) EIDINOFF, M. L., *J. Am. Chem. Soc.,* **69,** 977 (1947).
(24) LIBBY, W. F., *Phys. Rev.,* **69,** 671 (1946).

# AUGUSTE LAURENT—GUIDE AND INSPIRATION OF GERHARDT[1]

## CLARA deMILT
Newcomb College, Tulane University, New Orleans, Louisiana

AUGUSTE LAURENT was one of the founders, probably the most important, of modern organic chemistry. Few chemists, however, even in his native France, have recognized his contributions to the development of chemistry. Whenever his name is mentioned in accounts of the history of organic chemistry it is usually associated with that of Charles Gerhardt, his collaborator, as if Laurent had not won a distinctive place among the chemists of his time, that included such leaders as Berzelius, Liebig, Wohler, Graham, and Dumas, several years before Laurent began to correspond with Gerhardt and ten years before Gerhardt moved to Paris in 1848 to collaborate with him.

The writings of Adolphe Wurtz are partly responsible for this misconception of the importance of Laurent. Wurtz was a great admirer of both Laurent and Gerhardt, and it was the enthusiasm of Wurtz for the new chemistry, called at that time the unitary system, that finally led to its official adoption in France after 1890. In 1862 Wurtz published an *éloge* of Laurent and Gerhardt in which he says: "The great figure of Gerhardt will not be separated from Laurent: their work was collective, their talent complementary, their influence reciprocal.[2] In 1868 he expressed the same idea.[3] Since that time most of the writers dealing with this period have accepted this opinion of Wurtz, and as a result have credited to the collaboration of Laurent and Gerhardt what was in truth the work of one of them, Laurent.

There have been published only two accounts of the life of Laurent based on original sources. Both of these are short. The earliest is the obituary published in the *Journal of the Chemical Society* of London.[4] It is not signed but was probably written by Alexander Williamson. The other is by Édouard Grimaux.[5] The account of Laurent's life which follows is a composite of these two, corrected, and amplified to a small extent, by reference to publications in the journals of the period, and to the letters of Laurent and Gerhardt in Grimaux's comprehensive work on Gerhardt.

Auguste Laurent was born November 14, 1807, at La Folie, a small village near Langres in the province of Haute Marne in northeastern France. His father, a wine merchant, intended him to succeed to the business and insisted that he learn bookkeeping. Laurent had no interest in business; he preferred to investigate the plants, rocks, and marshes in the countryside. He constructed a small mill which became an object of admiration by all who knew anything of the difficulties of such work. Laurent's teachers recognized his talent in science and obtained his father's consent to direct his courses toward preparation for college. In his memoirs on chemistry his predilection for names and terms founded on Greek roots is the result of his training in the classics at this period. One of the reasons that has been offered for the failure of the French chemists of his day to recognize the value of his ideas was the elaborate, though logical, system of nomenclature, originated by Dumas but developed by Laurent, that he used in his papers. Among Laurent's own inventions that have survived are phenyl and anhydride.

With his brother Charles he was sent to the small college at Gray near his home, and in 1826, with the help of a maternal uncle, he entered the School of Mines in Paris as a day student. In 1828 he was sent on a mission to Germany where he visited mines and factories, on which he made careful observations and took notes that he later used in his work on inorganic chemistry. His first laboratory research in chemistry was on the ores of cobalt and arsenic. In his last year at the School of Mines he began the study of theoretical organic chemistry.

Laurent received his diploma as an engineer of mines December 30, 1830, and shortly afterward became Dumas' assistant at the Central School of Arts and Manufactures, a technical college founded in 1828 by Dumas and three others, all of whom were engineers. Working with Dumas, a great master of analysis and laboratory technique, Laurent learned organic analysis and began research. Dumas suggested the topic: a better method for the isolation of naphthalene from coal tar, its purification and analysis (then in doubt), and its reactions with the halogens and nitric acid. His first memoir on naphthalene appeared in 1832.[6] He described the purified naphthalene crystals, confirmed the formula of Faraday, $C_5H_2$ (C = 6, the atomic weight of carbon advocated by Gay-Lussac), and reported the vigorous reactions of chlorine, bromine, and

[1] Presented before the Division of the History of Chemistry at the 117th Meeting of the American Chemical Society at Philadelphia, Pennsylvania, April 12, 1950.

[2] WURTZ, ADOLPHE, *Le Moniteur Scientifique*, **4**, 482 (August 1, 1862).

[3] WURTZ, A., "Dictionnaire de Chimie," **1868**, xxxvii. WURTZ, A., "A History of Chemical Theory," Translated and edited by Henry Watts, 1869, p. 83.

[4] *J. Chem. Soc.*, **7**, 149 (1855).

[5] GRIMAUX, É., "Auguste Laurent," *Rev. Sci.*, [4] **6**, 161–163 (1896).

[6] *Ann. Chim. et Phys.*, [2] **49**, 214 (1832).

nitric acid with the hydrocarbon. The following year the first of his many papers on the chlorination of naphthalene appeared. In this paper are his first speculations on the chlorine substitution and addition products of naphthalene.[7] He had prepared two chlorides: a solid and a liquid. He suggested that the oily chloride is probably analogous to "Dutch liquid" (ethylene chloride) on which he had already begun to work.[8] In the second volume of *Annales de Chimie et de Physique* for 1835 Laurent described and outlined his theory of fundamental and derived radicals.[9]

At the beginning of 1833 he had been appointed by Alexandre Brongniart to direct the testing laboratory at Sèvres. At this time he discovered and published the process for the analysis of silicates by the action of hydrofluoric acid.[10] Analytical work in this porcelain factory was not congenial to him so he resigned, and in 1835 he moved to a garret in Rue ᵻSt. André des Arts where he fitted up a laboratory and opened a school. His pupils became deeply attached to him and many of them remained his friends as long as he lived. To his dismay he discovered that teaching students laboratory technique took up so much of his time that he had less for research in organic chemistry than he had had at Sèvres. He dismissed the students and spent all his time on research. When his money was gone he re-opened the school and the students returned in a body, paying him regularly eighty francs a month. Again he dismissed the students. Once more he found himself without the funds to purchase the materials he needed, so he accepted the offer of a perfumer to work in his shop, where Laurent distilled essences and tested their purity. According to the account in the *Journal of the Chemical Society* he was so absorbed in his own researches carried out in this shop in Rue Bourg-l'Abbé, that he never demanded a regular salary and only occasionally asked for a five franc piece. When Laurent left the shop his employer settled his account and presented him with 10,000 francs! Soon afterward he lost this money in an industrial venture and this sobering experience convinced him that it would be wise for him to devote his life to pure science.

In this shop Laurent worked happily and effectively for almost two years; here he carried out the first of his famous experimental researches in organic chemistry. During this period he developed his ideas on substitution reactions and worked out a classification of organic compounds based on the fundamental hydrocarbon radical of which they were derivatives, a radical composed always of the same number of carbon atoms. His published memoirs brought him into conflict, first with Dumas over the theory of substitution, later with Liebig and Berzelius. Thus, before he ᵻwas thirty he began the struggle for the recognition of his ideas, a

Courtesy of the Edgar F. Smith Collection, University of Pennsylvania, Philadelphia, Pa.

**Auguste Laurent**

struggle that would continue without interruption until his death in 1853 at the age of forty-six. This struggle would end in the overthrow of the dualistic theory of the composition of organic compounds, which had been set up by Berzelius, based on Berzelius' electrochemical theory of the constitution of inorganic oxides, salts, acids, and bases.

Laurent presented and defended his theory of fundamental and derived radicals (later called by Laurent the nucleus theory) as a thesis for the degree of Doctor of Science, December 20, 1837, before a committee of the Academy of Sciences composed of Dumas, Dulong, Beudant, and Despretz. One can be sure that of those who heard him only his former teacher, Dumas, understood the import of his assumptions. His thesis presented a theory of the constitution of organic compounds supported by experimental evidence based on his own work on the reactions of chlorine, bromine, and nitric acid on organic compounds, mostly hydrocarbons.[11] Laurent's thesis was the first organized attack on the dualistic theory of Berzelius.

[7] *ibid.*, [2], **52**, 275 (1833).

[8] LAURENT, A., "Méthode de Chimie," **1854**, 227; W. ODLING, "Chemical Method," Trans. of "Méthode de Chimie," **1855**, 187.

[9] *Ann. Chim. Phys.*, [2], **59**, 376 (1835); É. GRIMAUX, *loc. cit.*, 164.

[10] LAURENT, A., "Nouveau procédé pour analyses les silicates alcalines," *Ann. Chim. Phys.*, [2] **58**, 428 (1835).

[11] His thesis was a summary of papers already published. He illustrated his theory by likening the fundamental radical to a geometrical figure. A fundamental radical, as $C^8H^{12}$, might be thought of as a 4-faced prism with eight carbon atoms occupying the eight corners and with twelve hydrogen atoms attached to the middle points of the twelve edges. A. LAURENT, *loc. cit.*, p. 237; A. LADENBURG, "A History of Chemistry," 2nd ed., trans. by Leonard Dobbin, **1900**, p. 144; E. GRIMAUX, *loc. cit.*, p. 164.

**Charles Gerhardt**

Early in 1838 Laurent accepted a position in a porcelain factory in Luxembourg. His stay there was short. Not long after his return to Paris he was named professor of chemistry in the Faculty of the University of Bordeaux. In May, 1839, he married the daughter of a judge of the Superior Court in Luxembourg. Grimaux in his biography says that the widow of Laurent told him (in 1896) that Laurent's vacations from the university were always spent at the home of his wife's parents despite the long journey from Bordeaux.

At Bordeaux he found no laboratory, so that during the first year there, while he was fitting up a laboratory from his own small income, he spent much of his time with his associates on the faculty, especially with Lebesgue, a distinguished mathematician, and with the dean, Count de Collegno, professor of geology. The amount of his experimental work in this poorly equipped laboratory is truly amazing, especially when it is remembered that he worked alone. His investigations center around three projects: (1) the study of the components of coal tar, which led in 1841 to the isolation of phenol and the preparation of its derivatives one of which, called by him nitrophénisique acid, was proved to be identical with picric acid, already known; (2) the study of indigo, from which he prepared isatin and its derivatives; (3) the completion of the work on the derivatives of naphthalene, which included the correction of some of the formulas and relationships he had proposed in earlier papers, for example that of phthalic acid.

Besides these beautiful researches he found time for an investigation of pine tar, from which he isolated pimaric acid, to say nothing of his occasional papers on some of the fatty acids, on complex salts of the metals, and on silicates.

In all this work Laurent was collecting facts to support the great idea conceived sometime in 1834: the organization of organic compounds and their reactions on a logical and understandable foundation. On February 15, 1845, he wrote to Gerhardt: "Your classification is poor; (Laurent is criticizing volume one of Gerhardt's "Précis," his first textbook on organic chemistry published in July, 1844).... Do you ever develop anything from your classification? No, nothing, absolutely nothing because there is no idea in it. A classification should offer a series of relationships. It is my opinion that without a dominating idea it is impossible to do anything."[12]

In 1838 the attacks on Laurent's so-called theory of substitution (opposition to the electrochemical theory) began in earnest. To Laurent this was not primarily a theory of substitution and therefore was not in any sense at variance with Dumas' law of substitution. It was a theory of the constitution of organic compounds (what Dumas in 1840 called the type theory) the validity of which was demonstrated by substitution and oxidation reactions. Liebig in the first number of the *Annalen* for 1838 devoted thirty-one pages to an attack on Laurent and his speculations.[13] Compared with many of Liebig's polemics against those who did not agree with him, his remarks on Laurent are mild. Liebig most certainly does not refute Laurent's suppositions; most of the paper is taken up with a criticism of his analyses made in 1835, when Laurent's laboratory facilities were inadequate. By the time this paper was written he had reported the correction of most of these analyses. In 1835 Laurent had published a paper on the benzoyl radical[14] in which he describes benzil prepared by passing a current of chlorine into fused benzoin. He treated benzil with strong potash and obtained an acid, which he did not analyze but which according to this theory he assumed to be benzoic acid (the acid was benzilic acid; this is the benzilic acid rearrangement). Liebig repeated the work and three years later reminded Laurent that because of his speculations he failed to discover a new acid. This paper of Liebig's, which begins with his classic definition of a radical, is often quoted to the detriment of Laurent.[15] Liebig's attack was followed by a more serious one by

[12] GRIMAUX, É., "Charles Gerhardt, sa vie, son oeuvre, sa correspondance," 1900, p. 344.

[13] "Ueber Laurent's Theorie der Organischen Verbindungen," *Ann.*, 25, 1 (1838).

[14] *Ann. Chim. Phys.*, [2] 59, 397 (1835).

[15] LADENBURG, A., *loc. cit.*, pp. 149, 163; E. VON MEYER, "History of Chemistry," 3rd ed., trans. by George McGowan, 1906, p. 290.

Berzelius,[16] who remarks on Laurent's rare talent for research, "the value of which is considerably diminished by his bizarre theories." Berzelius, however, had mistakenly assumed that the idea that electronegative chlorine could replace electropositive hydrogen without essentially altering the nature of the substance was that of the French school, and he therefore directed the attack against Dumas. Dumas answered Berzelius.[17] He reminded Berzelius that his contribution was the law of substitutions, not a theory. He implied also that the work of Laurent was not to be relied upon. Laurent defended his position. He would assume all responsibility for the ideas opposed to the electrochemical theory as it applies to the constitution of organic compounds.[18]

Late in the summer of 1838 Dumas prepared trichloracetic acid. In April, 1839, the detailed paper on its reactions, its salts, and esters appeared. At the end of this paper Dumas announced a theory of types.[19] In February, 1840, Dumas presented to the Academy his now famous paper on the type theory.[20] Laurent's claim to the priority of the theory of substitution (opposition to the electrochemical theory) and of types or derived radicals appeared in the March 9 issue of the *Comptes rendus*. This is the beginning of the contest between Dumas and Laurent that continued several years.[21]

Berzelius, whose dualistic theory had been given its death blow by the theory of types, was the first to recognize the priority of Laurent. Liebig's recognition followed. In the summer of 1844 Laurent visited Giessen, where he gave "by request of the students in the laboratory an extempore discourse on his theories. . . . . Liebig offered him at that time an entire number of his *Annalen* for the publication of a review of his labors and of the ideas which had guided him in his researches; and three of the students offered to translate the work into English, German, and Italian."[22] In 1845 Liebig's student, A. W. Hofmann, in his paper on the chloroanilines discussed at some length Laurent's ideas, pointing out that his own work offered additional proof of their validity.[23]

It was during this period that the correspondence

between Laurent and Gerhardt began, probably in the winter of 1843–44, as the first letter that has been preserved, one from Laurent to Gerhardt, dated July 4, 1844, begins, "Mon cher collègue." Gerhardt in 1842 had written an article published in Dr. Quesneville's *Revue Scientifique et Industrielle* claiming the priority of the discovery of Laurent's "draconic" acid for his friend Cahours. Gerhardt pointed out that draconic acid was identical with Cahour's anisic acid reported earlier. In November, 1842, Laurent, convinced of the identity of the two acids and also of the younger chemist's priority in the matter of publication, graciously conceded Cahour's priority. Dr. Quesneville, who realized that Laurent and Gerhardt would have many interests in common, since both were opposed to the dualistic theory of Berzelius, arranged for a meeting of these two chemists at his home in Paris in the summer of 1843.

Laurent's letters to Gerhardt written during the winter of 1844–45 show signs of his growing discontent with his life at Bordeaux. Gerhardt, also dissatisfied with his isolation at Montpellier,[24] said nothing in his replies to calm Laurent's now rebellious spirit. His intellectual activity at Bordeaux had been intense and by 1845 he must have been exhausted. At long last his brilliant experimental work had been recognized in Paris. April 29, 1844, he was named *chevalier de la Legion d'honneur;* on August 11, 1845, he was elected a corresponding member of the Academy, replacing Faraday who was promoted to an associate. For some time he had entertained a hope of obtaining a position at the Mint. In the fall of 1845 he asked for a leave of absence, and with his wife and son left Bordeaux. He arrived in Paris with little money, as he had received only one-half of his salary, and with no immediate prospect of a position. For the next two and a half years he divided his time between the instruction of students and researches of little consequence, mainly inorganic, carried out in the laboratories of his friends. His spirits were low, as is shown by his letters to Gerhardt. His friends were urging him to break off relations with Gerhardt, whose dictatorial manner and harsh denunciations of the work of other chemists had made him both feared and disliked. Liebig wrote to Laurent on January 30, 1846: ". . . If you associate yourself with him [Gerhardt], it is you who will lose because he has nothing to lose. Read with attention my article ("Herr Gerhardt und die organische Chemie," *Ann.*, **57**, 93, 1846) and tell me whether this man has the truth in his soul? . . . . I believe you to be a man of perfect loyalty and honesty who . . . has linked his destiny with that of a man without character and without morality."[25]

On March 13, 1848, Laurent wrote to Gerhardt that he had been nominated assayer at the Mint to succeed Péligot. This position gave him no laboratory for his own work but the income enabled him to equip one. Thus, in "a corner of the Hôtel de la Monnaie, in a kind

[16] *Compt. rend.*, **6**, 633 (1838); *Ann. Chim. Phys.*, [2], **67**, 312 (1838); E. Hjelt, "Geschichte der organischen Chemie," 1916, p. 103.

[17] *Compt. rend.*, **6**, 647, 699 (1838); C. Schorlemmer, "The Rise and Development of Organic Chemistry," 1894, p. 35.

[18] *Ann. Chim. Phys.*, [2], **72**, 403 (1839).

[19] *Compt. rend.*, **8**, 609 (1839); "Premier mémoire sur les types Chimiques," *Ann. Chim. Phys.*, [2], **73**, 73 (1840); *Ann.*, **35**, 129 (1840).

[20] "Memoire sur la loi des substitutions et la theorie des types," *Compt. rend.*, **10**, 149 (1840). Dumas went too far in his enthusiasm over this idea and Wöhler's letter in the *Annalen* [**33**, 308 (1840)], signed S. C. H. Windler, pointed this out. For the English translation of this letter see H. B. Friedman, "The theory of types—A satirical sketch," J. Chem. Educ., **7**, 635 (1930).

[21] Grimaux, É., *Rev. Sci.*, [4] **6**, 168 (1896).

[22] Nicklès, J., "Auguste Laurent," *Am. J. Sci.*, [2], **16**, 103 (1853).

[23] *Ann.*, **53**, 3 (1845).

[24] Ostwald, W., "Grosse Männer," 1909, 229, 250.

[25] Grimaux, É., "Charles Gerhardt," 1900, p. 125.

of cellar, dark, damp, and unhealthy''[26] Laurent carried out his last researches in organic chemistry[27] and here he contracted tuberculosis. Now that Laurent had a laboratory where the two friends could work together, Gerhardt decided to join him; so, also without the prospect of a position, Gerhardt left Montpellier on March 17, 1848. For two and a half years these two dissenters collaborated in most of their papers relating to the theory of organic chemistry. There is not the slightest doubt in the mind of this author that without this daily association with Laurent, Gerhardt could not have written his great treatise on organic chemistry.[28] His book would have been just another in the field, and Gerhardt's name would be as little known as that of a host of able men working in Paris at this same time.

[26] *J. Chem. Soc.*, **7**, 154 (1855).
[27] In 1850 he prepared the acid which bears his name. *Compt. rend.*, **31**, 537 (1850).
[28] GERHARDT, C., "Traité de Chimie Organique," Vol. 1, **1853**; Vols. 2 and 3, **1854**; Vol. 4, **1856**.

Courtesy of Professor Colin M. Mackall, The George Washington University, Washington, D. C.

### Statue of Auguste Laurent

This bronze monument, designed by Péchiné, was erected in 1903 in the Place de l'Hôtel de Ville in Langres. The author has received word from l'Abbé F. Rabin, adjointau Maire de Langres, that it was removed by the Germans in World War II.

The influence of Laurent's laboratory in the rapid development of the new organic chemistry has never been appreciated. The author (Williamson?) of the obituary in the *Journal of the Chemical Society* has given an excellent account of the activity there and also of the manner of work of Laurent: "His laboratory was the rendezvous of a great number of scientific men; there was no lack of news there; and Laurent had every day some new result to announce, or some new idea to develop. Raw materials were also sent to him from all sides for examination.... Laurent possessed a degree of analytical tact never before known; his researches on naphthaline, indigo, bitter-almond oil, etc., remain as monuments to a genius for investigation which, unfortunately, will not soon be equalled.... [He] used a small number of reagents...: chlorine, nitric acid, ammonia, sulfuric acid, potash.... Water, alcohol, ether, and the goniometer served him for the recognition of his products. He was the first to employ the goniometer as a reagent, and no one knew better how to manage it."

In November, 1846, Laurent published his last important paper on theoretical chemistry.[29] In this paper he develops at length the difference between an atom and a molecule and explains the basis for the new notation used in the formulas of the organic compounds of nitrogen given in tables. A molecule is defined; the hypothesis of Avogadro (always referred to by Laurent as Ampère's hypothesis) is discussed; the atom is distinguished from the molecule and from the equivalent.[30] In the last part of the paper (pages 293–298) Laurent outlines the water-type theory that was to be used in 1850 by Williamson, and by Chancel in the synthesis of the ethers, and by Gerhardt in 1852 in the synthesis of the acid anhydrides. The great importance of this idea, however, was pointed out first by T. Sterry Hunt.[31] In later papers Hunt extended Laurent's idea and on the basis of these papers claimed priority to the water-type theory in 1861.[32] There is much justice in Hunt's claim, but that is another story.

Among those who had followed the work of Laurent none was more conscious of its value than Leopold Gmelin. In 1847 word reached Paris that Gmelin in the first volume on organic chemistry (published in 1848) of the 4th edition of the "Handbook" had adopted Laurent's classification of organic compounds. At the anniversary meeting of the London Chemical Society of March 30, 1850, Laurent was elected a foreign member, along with Brongniart, Chevreul, Gay-Lussac, Gmelin, Kopp, Mitscherlich, Pelouze, Regnault, Rose, Thénard, and Wöhler.[33] Laurent's work had been

[29] "Recherches sur les combinaisons azotées," *Ann. Chim. Phys.*, [3], **18**, 266 (1846).
[30] Laurent's adoption of Gerhardt's so-called equivalents, and certain other aspects of his work, will be discussed in an article in *Chymia*, **4** (1951).
[31] *Am. J. Sci.*, [2] **6**, 173 (1848).
[32] HUNT, T. S., "On the Theory of Types," *Am. J. Sci.*, [2] **31**, 256 (1861).
[33] *J. Chem. Soc.*, **3**, 97 (1850).

recognized in foreign countries but his native France had yet to offer him a laboratory.

Late in 1850 Pelouze resigned the chair of chemistry in the Collège de France. Gerhardt applied but was told that he had no chance for the place. This left as candidates Balard and Laurent. Jean Baptiste Biot, who for many years had been professor of physics in this school, appeared in person before the faculty to support Laurent. The vote in the faculty was thirteen to nine in favor of Laurent. The final decision, however, rested with the Academy. Biot wrote a letter to the committee of the Academy pointing out that Laurent with no laboratory was doing important research, whereas Balard with two fine laboratories was doing little in either of them. Biot's efforts were in vain. The final vote in the Academy of twenty-five to eleven gave the chair to Balard.[34]

Laurent's last hope of a well-equipped laboratory was gone. Shortly after he received the news he collapsed. His physicians ordered him to give up all laboratory work. His laboratory was closed. His part—the major part—of the reform[35] movement was over. After Laurent's laboratory was closed, Gerhardt organized his School of Practical Chemistry. Kekulé attended Gerhardt's conferences from May, 1851, until April, 1852, but Kekulé never saw Laurent.[36] The friends of Laurent, especially Biot, Nicklès, and Balard urged him to organize his ideas and theories in the form of a systematic work. At this, his last contribution to the advancement of the science to which he had devoted his life, he worked as long as he could hold a pen. The manuscript of "Méthode de Chimie,"[37] published in 1854, after his death, was recently presented to the French Academy for its Archives.[38]

In January, 1852, Laurent was granted a three-months' leave; he spent part of the summer of 1852 in the country, and on his return in the fall he was sufficiently improved to present three papers to the Academy, on September 20, November 2, and November 22. These are his last published memoirs. He died April 15, 1853. Gerhardt on May 16, 1853, wrote to Chancel, then at Montpellier, that even though he had been prepared for this sad event for a long while, it had affected him deeply. Then he says: "I know nothing about it. I learned of it only ten hours before the burial, as you did, through a simple announcement.... The burial was very sad, twenty or thirty persons at the most. Not a word at the grave!" Ostwald writing of

this in his life of Gerhardt says: "Thus ends one of the blackest pages in the history of French science."[39]

The personality of Laurent was described in the first two obituaries published after his death; in the one by Nicklès in the American Journal of Science and in the obituary in the Journal of the Chemical Society. The remarks in the French journals are copied from the latter. The following is quoted from this source also. "Laurent was of a very kind and obliging disposition, extremely indulgent to others, and his friendship was capable of standing the severest tests. To a just sentiment of his own dignity, he united great firmness of his convictions; his mind revolted from injustice, and he was always ready to acknowledge his errors and even go to the side of his adversary, as shown especially in his discussions with Gerhardt in 1844 [1843] on the constitution of draconic acid, etc. [This is the only mention of Gerhardt in the obituary.] He was one of those persons of whom it may be said that they improve upon acquaintance. Cold and reserved at first, he soon became confiding and expansive, and removed any unfavourable opinion of him formed from hearsay. He may have been envied, but he had no enemies; he sometimes met with ingratitude, even from those on whom he had conferred the greatest benefits:—such ingratitude, in fact, embittered his last moments."

What is the implication in this last sentence? To whose ingratitude is the author referring? He is undoubtedly referring to that of Gerhardt. It seems to the author of this paper that this conclusion is inescapable. Here is some of the evidence: (1) Gerhardt's letter to Chancel; (2) the omission of Gerhardt's name as his friend in the obituary in the Journal of the Chemical Society; (3) the letter of Williamson to Gerhardt written April 28, 1853, asking for details of Laurent's life and Gerhardt's reply of May 7, 1853[40]; (4) the omission of Gerhardt's name as his friend in the account by Nicklès and the remarks about Laurent's character; (5) the obituary of Gerhardt by Nicklès[41] in which Laurent's name is mentioned several times but not as Gerhardt's friend; (6) the silence of the English chemists for the next twenty-five years about what the German chemists called "Gerhardt's system and his type theory."

What caused the parting of the ways of Laurent and Gerhardt the last few months of Laurent's life and turned Laurent's friends and admirers against Gerhardt

[34] GRIMAUX, É., Rev. Sci. [4] 6, 162 (1896).

[35] For another and different view of this reform movement see the article by Maurice Daumas in Chymia, 1, 155 (1948).

[36] ANSCHÜTZ, R., "August Kekulé," 1929, p. 28.

[37] Translated by William Odling as "Chemical Method" and published in 1855 by the Cavendish Society.

[38] The presentation was made by Marc Tiffeneau in the name of Madame Hermann Laurent, widow of the only son of Auguste Laurent. Tiffeneau's remarks are worth quoting. He said: "This work, which marks an epoch in the history of chemistry, contains all the principles of the work of reformation accomplished by Laurent and Gerhardt." Compt. rend., 209, 585 (1939).

[39] OSTWALD, W., loc. cit., p. 247.

[40] GRIMAUX, É., "Charles Gerhardt," 1900, p. 242. Williamson writes, "You, certainly, more than any other person know the details of his life" (trans. from the French of Grimaux). Gerhardt in his reply speaks of Laurent's manuscript of "Méthode de Chimie," and adds: "I know only about its content, Laurent having told me some time ago (dans le temps) of certain parts ... it is full of new and arresting views. I await its publication with impatience." This letter was written after April 27, the date of Nicklès' communication on Laurent to the editor of the American Journal of Science, in which Nicklès says that he has the manuscript in his hands and that the printing of it will shortly follow.

[41] Am. J. Sci., 23, 102 (1856).

after Laurent's death? No definite answer can now be given to this question. One can only make a guess: the appropriation of the water-type theory by Gerhardt in 1852 after his discovery of the acid anhydrides.[42]

What were these "greatest benefits" that Laurent had conferred upon Gerhardt? Before Gerhardt moved to Paris in March, 1848, to work in Laurent's laboratory, Laurent in long letters criticized Gerhardt's classification of organic compounds in the "Précis" and also in his papers; he pointed out to Gerhardt his mistake in disregarding entirely the theory of radicals so that Gerhardt developed his theory of residues; he explained to him in great detail that the terms, "atoms, equivalents, and volumes" are not synonymous![43] (So stated in the "Précis.") Gerhardt in February, 1848, published a small but important book: "Introduction to the Study of Chemistry by the Unitary System." It is dedicated to Laurent. It could not have been written by Gerhardt unless he had had Laurent's instruction, for the ideas are primarily those of Laurent. Gerhardt had an excellent memory, and great talent for the organization and generalization of facts; his chief interest was in writing. His great treatise is written in the clear, easily followed, expositional style so characteristic of all his work and this accounts in large measure for its popularity. But he possessed little or no originality; he had almost no talent for and no real interest in experimental research, and he did not grasp new ideas readily. His confusion about principles stimulated Laurent's thinking, and there is no question that Laurent's association with Gerhardt helped Laurent to clarify and express his own ideas. Laurent could never have written a treatise that would have won over the German chemists of the time to the new organic chemistry. He was much too philosophic, too interested in speculation, and too devoted to experimentation for this kind of work and he knew it. Gerhardt with his aggressive, dictatorial manner promoted Laurent's ideas, and tried in so doing to promote his own interests, but because of his manner and his positive assertions he built up resistance, at least in Paris, to both of them. After Laurent's death Gerhardt did no experimental work of any importance. The master who had guided him and inspired him to interpret the facts of chemistry was no longer there to direct the channels of his thinking. But he finished his treatise.

Had Gerhardt in the preface to the first volume of this great work acknowledged his debt to Laurent; had he written an introduction to "Generalities," the last and by far the most important section of volume four of the "Traité," an introduction in which credit was given where credit was due, to Hofmann, Frankland, Williamson, Hunt, and, above all, to Laurent for their contributions to the theory of types; had he pointed out that Laurent was the first to clarify the terms equivalent, atom, molecule, the first to apply Ampère's hypothesis to the determination of the molecular weights of volatile organic compounds—the history of organic chemistry as it has been written would be different.

In the preface to volume one Gerhardt attributed the first type theory (1840) to Dumas. This from a man who had earned part of his income by writing for Dr. Quesneville's *Revue Scientifique et Industrielle*, in which Laurent's papers claiming his priority to this theory had appeared! The preface is dated June, 1853. Was it written before this and did Laurent learn of his so-called friend's perfidy before the book went to press? Perhaps. Kekulé is said to have read volume one in manuscript in 1852. Laurent's friends, and most certainly Dumas himself, recognized Gerhardt's gesture to Dumas for what it was—a deliberate misstatement to further the interests of a man whose over-powering ambition had motivated his entire life. What Gerhardt desired most was a position in Paris. What Dumas offered him, and what he accepted, were two professorships at Strassburg, where once again he found himself isolated from the center of activity in chemistry—Paris. Here he died August 19, 1856.

When Gerhardt wrote the "Generalities" he had Laurent's "Méthode de Chimie" in front of him, for he refers to it on page 599; but except for this reference to "Laurent et moi," Laurent's name is mentioned only in the discussion of certain experimental work. Gerhardt writes of "my classification," "my distinction between equivalents, atoms, and molecules," "my idea of types." He assumes the credit for all of them—hydrogen, hydrochloric acid, ammonia, water—not one of which originated with him.

His four-volume treatise was translated into German immediately following the appearance of the volumes in France. Cannizzaro and the German chemists at the Congress at Karlsruhe spoke only of Gerhardt's system. After 1862, due to the efforts of Wurtz, some of them added the name of Laurent.

## ACKNOWLEDGMENT

The author wishes to thank the staff of the Stanford University Libraries and the staff of the Chemists Club Library in New York for their courtesies to her. Especially does the author thank Robert F. Sutton, Curator of the Edgar F. Smith Collection at the University of Pennsylvania, for locating information about Laurent and his publications. Part of the expenses of gathering the material for this paper was met by a Carnegie grant-in-aid given the author by the University Council on Research of Tulane University.

---

[42] For a discussion of this the reader is referred to the account given by Grimaux in the life of Gerhardt, and to Ostwald's comments on Grimaux's excuses for Gerhardt's behavior. The papers of Williamson, Chancel, and Gerhardt are enlightening, especially those in the *Annalen*.

[43] GRIMAUX, É., *loc. cit.*, p. 531.

Herbert C. Brown
Purdue University
Lafayette, Indiana

# Foundations of the Structural Theory

One hundred years ago the simple concepts of the structural theory were published by two young chemists, August Kekulé (1) and Archibald Scott Couper (2). Working entirely independently, each had arrived at an understanding of the tetravalence of carbon and the self-linking of carbon atoms. With these simple concepts they brought an end to the "Age of Confusion" of organic chemistry.

For several decades chemists had been seeking some principle to provide a basis for understanding organic substances and their reactions. Polemics raged as opposing schools advanced conflicting proposals. Once presented, the structural theory provided so simple, and, yet, so useful an interpretation of organic substances and their reactions that it quickly converted most of the disputants (3–5).

At once the chains restraining the progress of the science were ruptured. In contrast to the slow empirical progress of previous years, organic chemical research bounded ahead.

From the structures of the simple saturated derivatives, chemists progressed to an understanding of unsaturated compounds with multiple carbon-to-carbon bonds. Next the structures of benzene and related organic molecules were worked out. In 1874 van't Hoff accounted for the existence of optical isomers in terms of a tetrahedral configuration of the carbon atom. Thus, within sixteen years of the original proposal of the structural theory, all of the basic concepts had been advanced.

Today we discuss the chemistry of hundreds of thousands of organic molecules in terms of their structures. We interpret the behavior of high polymers in terms of their molecular constitution and configuration. We interpret the behavior of drugs in terms of their molecular dimensions and shapes and their ability to occupy molecular sites of related shape requirements in biological systems. Finally, we are making active progress in unraveling the structures of those amazing, versatile polymers of life—the proteins.

One hundred years of structure—one hundred years of amazing progress! We owe a real debt of gratitude to the two young chemists who first pointed the way to this magnificent highway of chemical investigation. It is fitting that we commemorate their contribution and honor their memory.

When I was invited to join with the various Divisions in this honor to Kekulé and Couper, I accepted with pleasure. All of us, active in research today, owe a deep debt of gratitude to these two pioneers. However, when I considered the precise form that my tribute should take, I found my decision less easy.

One possibility was to discuss recent triumphs and present problems. It is always pleasant to review an area of research in which one has direct, active interests.

The Kekulé-Couper Centennial Celebration commemorating the pioneering papers by F. A. Kekulé and A. S. Couper on the tetravalence and self-linking of carbon atoms was held on September 10, 1958, at the Chicago Meeting of the American Chemical Society. In the morning a symposium on the Development of Theoretical Organic Chemistry was held under the auspices of the History of Chemistry Division. Papers presented at the symposium will appear in forthcoming issues of THIS JOURNAL.

In the afternoon, Herbert C. Brown, Professor of Chemistry at Purdue University, delivered the Kekulé-Couper Centennial Lecture before the Divisions of Chemical Education, History of Chemistry, and Organic Chemistry. For many years the lecturer has had an active interest in the history of chemistry. He has, in addition, made major contributions to the theory of organic chemistry, contributions that are in direct line of descent from the papers this lecture commemorates.

In fact there exists a close parallelism between the period in which Professor Brown initiated his researches into steric effects and the period preceding the enunciation of the structural theory. Both periods were characterized by the dominance of an electrochemical theory. In the 1830's Berzelius' dualistic theory of chemical combination was decisively challenged by the demonstrations of Dumas and Laurent that replacement of hydrogen by chlorine did not greatly alter the chemical characteristics of many compounds. In the 1930's a highly successful electronic theory seemed likely to explain by electrical concepts almost all chemical effects of atoms or groups.

The development by Professor Brown of a quantitative method for estimating the magnitude of steric strains made possible a new understanding of the importance of the steric factor in chemical behavior. Herbert Brown was, of course, not alone in reemphasizing nonelectrical factors. Bartlett, Ingold, Newman, Westheimer, and many others have contributed to our present understanding of steric effects. Undoubtedly, however, Herbert Brown deserves major credit for rescuing steric concepts from the disrepute into which they had generally fallen, and for re-establishing them as factors of great significance in the total understanding of organic chemistry. Therefore, it is particularly appropriate to have Professor Brown participate in this tribute to the founders of the structural theory.

O. T. BENFEY
*Earlham College*
*Richmond, Indiana*

A second possibility was to trace the course of development of the structural theory from its original proposal to its highly developed stage today. One hundred years of structural chemistry—a truly stirring story of success in chemistry and a most inspiring topic for a lecture! Finally, there was the possibility of reviewing the confusing background against which the structural theory made its appearance. This period has been reviewed in various histories of chemistry (3–5) and was thoroughly treated in Japp's magnificant Memorial Lecture to Kekulé (6). Such a review offered little possibility for a truly original contribution.

However, after careful deliberation, I turned away from the temptations of the first two possibilities and adopted the last. I was influenced in this decision by the following considerations.

## The Lessons of History

Little attention is paid to the history of chemistry in our graduate schools today. In part, this is the result of an ever growing, ever more crowded curriculum; in part, it arises from the great youth and vigor of chemical research in America. Let us go back a mere 25 years. The state of organic chemistry in this country may be indicated by pointing out that not a single advanced organic chemistry textbook, originating in the United States, was then available. Not until 1937 did the first such book, by Frank C. Whitmore, appear (7).

These 25 years have witnessed a remarkable upsurge of organic chemistry in this country. Chemical research is being pursued with vigor and intensity. It is a recognized characteristic of youth to ignore the past. And the history of chemistry has been ignored. Little attention is paid to the lessons that history can teach.

An incident at the last Organic Symposium illustrates the point. At that time I made the statement that a sound principle to adopt in chemical research is that chemistry is *simple*, and *appears* complicated only when the experimental data are poor or when the currently accepted theory used to account for the data is unsatisfactory. This position appeared to amuse the audience. Yet it can be supported by numerous examples from the chemical history.

There appears to be at the present time a tendency to glorify the importance of empirical observations and to expect that any new theory should account immediately for all experimental observations on record. This ignores the lesson that a considerable fraction of experimental observations made without the benefit of the careful scrutiny provided by a sound theory has invariably turned out to be erroneous in the past. Consequently, the worker who proposes a new theory or interpretation must attempt to separate the apparently sound and consistent data from other results which fail to fit the proposed theory. These results must then be re-examined experimentally in order to test the new theory.

This has been the course of theoretical developments in the past. There is no reason to anticipate that it will not be the course in the future.

Unfortunately, our present graduates in chemistry have had so little contact with the lessons of chemical history that this view is foreign to them. We have

numerous textbooks available today which give the present position of chemical hypotheses and theories. Such textbooks point out the various facts that these theories satisfactorily interpret. They fail to review the difficult and tortuous paths which led to the present positions. Not a single advanced textbook which I examined even mentioned the background against which the structural theory was proposed. Consequently, I decided that I should be rendering a service to the younger chemists of today, as well as giving a proper tribute to Kekulé and Couper, by emphasizing once again these important lessons of history, illustrated by the origins of the structural theory.

## The Age of Confusion: Background for Structural Theory

Let us then briefly review the background against which the contribution made by Kekulé and by Couper in 1858 appeared. In 1808 Dalton proposed his atomic theory (8), and a rapid development of chemical theory based on this important contribution might have been anticipated. Unfortunately, this was not realized. Chemical theory rapidly degenerated into a morass of confusion, so that some eminent chemists such as Liebig expressed disgust at the state of theory and retired to the simpler problems of practical and applied chemistry.

The half century preceding the foundation of the structural theory in 1858 is the "Dark Age of Organic Chemistry," an "Age of Confusion," with numerous currents and counter-currents, violent polemics, and relatively little progress (3–5).

On the practical side, a number of important advances were made. Organic analysis became precise. Methods of separation became refined. Numerous organic substances were isolated, analyzed, and characterized. Acids, such as acetic, butyric, stearic, tartaric, and succinic were recognized materials. Fats were shown to be composed of fatty acids and glycerol. Alkaloids such as morphine, strychnine, brucine, and quinine were isolated and characterized.

The difficulty arose in attempting to proceed from the analytical results to a molecular formula. Considerable confusion existed as to the correct atomic weights. At various times carbon was assigned a weight of 6 and oxygen 8 (on the basis of hydrogen equal to 1). At other times, the accepted values were carbon 12 and oxygen 8, or carbon 6 and oxygen 16. Still others championed the present values, but with most of the metals having half the present atomic weights.

It is highly unfortunate that this confusion existed, since all of the tools were at hand to construct a con-

─ *The Cover* ────────────────

The Kekulé-Couper Centennial commemorates the papers on the tetravalence and chain-forming capacity of carbon atoms. The titles of the two papers (KEKULÉ, *Ann.*, **106**, 129 (1858); Couper, *Compt. rend.*, **46**, 1157 (1858)) are reproduced together with photographs of the same period. Source of Kekulé photo: Fig. 56, p. 233, in RICHARD ANSCHÜTZ, "August Kekulé," Vol. I, Verlag Chemie, Berlin, **1929**.

ANNALEN

DER

# CHEMIE UND PHARMACIE.

CVI. Bandes zweites Heft.

Ueber die Constitution und die Metamorphosen der chemischen Verbindungen und über die chemische Natur des Kohlenstoffs;

von *August Kekulé.*

Vor einiger Zeit\*) habe ich Betrachtungen „über die s. g. gepaarten Verbindungen und über die Theorie der mehratomigen Radicale" mitgetheilt, deren weitere Ausführung und Vervollständigung jetzt, um Mifsverständnissen vorzubeugen, zweckmäfsig erscheint.

Meine damalige Mittheilung hat von Seiten Limpricht's Bemerkungen\*\*) veranlafst, auf deren gröfseren Theil näher einzugehen ich mich nicht veranlafst finde\*\*\*). Eine der-

\*) Diese Annalen CIV, 129.

\*\*) Daselbst CV, 177.

\*\*\*) In Betreff der Berechtigung meiner damaligen Aussprüche vergleiche man : Diese Annalen CII, 249 : «neue Ansicht»; »ist die *neue* Ansicht" u. s. w. Diese Annalen CII, 259 : „Es hiefse den Thatsachen geradezu widersprechen, wenn man die Sulfobenzoësäure noch fernerhin als *gepaarte Schwefelsäure* u. s. w. auffführen wollte". Diese Annalen CIII, 71 : „Als gepaarte Säuren bleiben dieser Begriffsbestimmung nach noch übrig : 3) diejenigen, welche aus einer organischen und einer zweibasischen unorganischen sich bilden, von denen *nur* die mit *Schwefelsäure gepaarten* bekannt sind".

Annal. d. Chem. u. Pharm. CVI. Bd. 2. Heft.        9

follows that each compound substance, regardless of the number of its constituent principles, may be divided into two parts, of which one is electrically positive and the other negative. Thus, for example, sulfate of soda is not composed of sulfur, oxygen and sodium, but of sulfuric acid [$SO_3$] and soda [$NaO$] which both may again be divided into two elements, one positive and the other negative.

The confusion introduced by this combination of erroneous (and variable) atomic weights, indefinite molecular weights, and the interpretation of composition in terms of the dualistic system may be understood by examining the representation of calcium acetate, acetic acid, ethyl alcohol, and ethyl ether (5).

Since a salt is a combination of the metal oxide and the acid, calcium acetate, $C_4H_6O_4Ca$ (C = 6, O = 8), must be represented as $C_4H_6O_3$ + CaO. Therefore acetic acid must be $C_4H_6O_3$. (The fact that glacial acetic acid contains one more molecule of water than required by this formula was ignored.) Since acetic acid can be obtained by oxidation of ethyl alcohol, the latter was written $C_4H_{12}O_2$. Ethyl ether arises from the dehydration of ethyl alcohol. Its composition was represented as $C_4H_{10}O$.

The study of ammonium salts had earlier led to the idea of a radical, ammonium, which could perform the functions of a metal. Consequently, it was a natural step to seek to analyze the composition of these oxygen compounds further into a combination of a hydrocarbon radical and oxygen. At different times the derivatives of ethanol discussed previously were postulated to be composed of the etherin radical, $C_4H_8$, the ethyl radical, $C_4H_{10}$, or the acetyl radical, $C_4H_6$. Originally, it was assumed that these radicals, like the metals they were supposed to resemble, could exist in the free state.

Apparently, we owe to a development in industrial chemistry the immediate experimental developments which resulted in the overthrow of this approach to organic chemistry. It is reported that at an important social function in Paris at the Tuileries, the guests were annoyed by irritating fumes, presumably hydrogen chloride, emitted by the burning candles. Dumas investigated the phenomenon. He discovered that the wax used in the manufacture of the candles had been bleached with chlorine. Thereupon, he proceeded to study the action of chlorine and bromine on various organic compounds.

He soon recognized that it was possible to replace one or more hydrogen atoms in various compounds by an equivalent number of halogen atoms without a marked change in chemical behavior. In 1839 he transformed acetic acid into trichloroacetic acid and noted that the chemical behavior of the two acids was very similar. It was obviously counter to the tenets of the dualistic system that electronegative chlorine should be capable of displacing electropositive hydrogen without significant change in the chemical nature of the product.

Berzelius and his followers attacked vigorously. I feel confident that many have enjoyed reading the satire published by S. C. H. Windler (i.e., "schwindler") in 1840 in which he reports his remarkable results on chlorinating manganous acetate. First he replaces the hydrogens of the acetate groups and observes that the product is similar to the original reactant. Further chlorination replaces the oxygen atoms, then

sistent scale of atomic weights. In 1808 Dalton had proposed that the chemical elements were composed of small, ultimate particles which retained their identity in chemical reactions. All of the ultimate particles of a given element were identical. He stressed the importance of proceeding from analytical data to a determination of the relative weights of these particles and to their numbers in the molecules of various substances. In 1811 Avogadro clearly distinguished between the atom and the molecule of an element and pointed the way to the determination of atomic and molecular weights by comparing the densities of gases (9). Unfortunately some cases of dissociation led to apparent anomalies and to the consequent abandonment of his proposal, so that only after 1858 was it finally adopted as a result of Cannizzaro's clear exposition of its merits (10).

A second major difficulty was the general acceptance of the "dualistic system" of Berzelius. Impressed by the electrochemical results of Davy, he carried out simple experiments in which he observed the simultaneous formation of an acid and a base in the electrolysis of various salts. Consequently, he concluded that chemical combination must be an electrical phenomenon. His view is expressed in the following quotation (11).

If these electrochemical views are correct, it follows that all chemical combination depends solely on two opposing forces, positive and negative, and that each combination should be composed of two parts united by the effect of their electrochemical reaction, provided that there exists no third force. Whence it

the carbon, and finally the manganese. He achieves a substance which contains only chlorine but which possesses all the properties of the original manganous acetate (12).

In spite of such attacks and ridicule, the fact of substitution could not be dismissed. It required a major change in the formulation of organic compounds and led to the "unitary theory." The molecule was regarded as a unit, parts of it being capable of substitution without alteration of its chemical type. Although organic radicals were soon incorporated into the formulation of compounds, it was generally assumed that these radicals were incapable of independent existence, but were merely assemblages of atoms which were transferred without change from one structure to another in the course of reaction. No attempt was made to inquire into the structure of the radical or into the nature of the forces holding together the assemblage of atoms.

Once the molecule was treated as a unit, certain similarities as to type were recognized. In 1850 Hofmann investigated the amines and showed that they could be formulated as $NH_3$ in which one, two, or three hydrogen atoms were replaced by a corresponding number of organic radicals. Similarly, Williamson clarified the relationship between water, alcohol, and ether. Finally, in 1857 Kekulé proposed the methane type and pointed out that many simple carbon compounds, such as methyl chloride, chloroform, and chloropicrin, could be simply related to the parent molecule.

One further development must be mentioned at this time. Frankland, an adherent of the old radical theory, undertook to prepare free radicals. He treated ethyl iodide with zinc and obtained a substance which he considered to be free ethyl, apparently providing a powerful support for the radical theory. In the course of this investigation, he isolated the zinc alkyls for the first time, investigated their chemical behavior, and demonstrated their utility in organic synthesis.

During his investigation of organometallics, Frankland became impressed by the observation that the presence of alkyl groups reduced the number of other atoms which combined with the metal atom. In other words, oxygen derivatives of the metal alkyls were not the simple oxides associated with organic radicals; they were the oxides with one or more oxygen atoms replaced by organic radicals. Consideration of this phenomenon led him to the concept of valence. To quote (13):

When the formulae of inorganic chemical compounds are considered, even a superficial observer is impressed with the general symmetry of their construction. The compounds of nitrogen, phosphorus, antimony, and arsenic, especially, exhibit the tendency of these elements to form compounds containing 3 or 5 atoms of other elements; and it is in these proportions that their affinities are best satisfied: thus in the ternal groups we have $NO_3$, $NH_3$, $NI_3$, $NS_3$, $PO_3$, $PH_3$, $PCl_3$, $SbH_3$, $SbCl_3$, $AsO_3$, $AsH_3$, $AsCl_3$, etc.; and in the five-atom groups, $NO_5$, $NH_4O$, $NH_4I$, $PO_5$, $PH_4I$, etc. Without offering any hypothesis regarding the cause of this symmetrical grouping of atoms, it is sufficiently evident, from the examples just given, that such a tendency or law prevails, and that, no matter what the character of the uniting atoms may be, the combining-power of the attracting element, if I may be allowed the term, is always satisfied by the same number of these atoms.

A half century of confusion—opening on the promising note of the atomic theory of Dalton but closing on a most pessimistic phase. Organic chemists were no longer hopeful of describing the composition of molecules or of ascertaining the forces operating to hold the molecular assemblages together. Their main hope was to recognize simple types which would permit them to predict the results of simple chemical reactions.

Even in this dark age of organic chemistry, all was not black. In A. W. Hofmann's laboratory in London, a young student, W. H. Perkin, undertook to synthesize quinine by the oxidation of an aniline derivative. In terms of the empirical formulas in use at the time, the chemical transformation appeared to be a simple one. In terms of our knowledge of chemical structure, the change is highly improbable, to say the least. Perkin failed to obtain quinine, but he did obtain the color, mauve, and thereby initiated the coal tar dye industry (14).

It is certainly a gratifying experince to be able to close one's eyes in an unmarked, unknown wilderness, set out for a specific objective, and stumble across another highly desirable goal. However, such a fortunate occurrence is rare. We are far happier to find ourselves in the midst of a carefully charted area, able to proceed with open eyes to our objective in new uncharted areas with the aid of well-tried theories and methods.

That this is the situation at the present time we owe to the pioneering efforts of Kekulé and Couper.

( 1157 )

CHIMIE GÉNÉRALE. — *Sur une nouvelle théorie chimique; par* M. A. COUPER. (Note présentée par M. Dumas.)

« J'ai l'honneur d'exposer à l'Académie les traits principaux d'une nouvelle théorie chimique que je propose pour les combinaisons organiques.

« Je remonte aux éléments eux-mêmes dont j'étudie les affinités réciproques. Cette étude suffit, selon moi, à l'explication de toutes les combinaisons chimiques, sans qu'on ait besoin de recourir à des principes inconnus et à des généralisations arbitraires.

« Je distingue deux espèces d'affinité, savoir :

« 1°. L'affinité de degré ; 2° l'affinité élective.

« J'entends par affinité de degré, l'affinité qu'un élément exerce sur un autre avec lequel il se combine en plusieurs proportions définies. Je nomme affinité élective, celle que différents éléments exercent les uns sur les autres, avec des intensités différentes. Prenant pour exemple le carbone, je trouve qu'il exerce son pouvoir de combinaison en deux degrés. Ces degrés sont représentés par $CO^2$ et $CO^4$, c'est-à-dire par l'oxyde de carbone et l'acide carbonique, en adoptant pour les équivalents du carbone et de l'oxygène les nombres 12 et 8.

« En ce qui concerne ses affinités électives, le carbone s'éloigne des autre éléments et montre, pour ainsi dire, une physionomie particulière. Les traits qui caractérisent cette affinité élective du carbone sont les suivants :

« 1°. Il se combine avec des nombres d'équivalents égaux d'hydrogène, de chlore, d'oxygène, de soufre, etc., qui peuvent se remplacer mutuellement pour satisfaire son pouvoir de combinaison.

« 2°. Il entre en combinaison avec lui-même.

« Ces deux propriétés suffisent à mon avis pour expliquer tout ce que la chimie organique offre de caractéristique. Je crois que la seconde est signalée ici pour la première fois. A mon avis, elle rend compte de ce fait important et encore inexpliqué de l'accumulation des molécules de carbone dans les combinaisons organiques. Dans les composés où 2, 3, 4, 5, 6, etc., molécules de carbone sont liées ensemble, c'est le carbone qui sert de lien au carbone.

« Ce n'est pas l'hydrogène qui peut lier ensemble les éléments des corps organiques. Si, comme le carbone, il avait le pouvoir de se combiner à lui-même, on devrait pouvoir former les composés $H^2 Cl^2$, $H^3 Cl^3$, $H^4 Cl^4$.

150..

## Kekulé's Contribution

Kekulé was born in 1829 in Darmstadt, Germany, Originally designed for a career in architecture, he was converted to chemistry by Liebig. But let us hear about his training from Kekulé himself (15).

In high school I showed particular aptitude in mathematics and drawing. My father, who was a close friend of a number of famous architects, decided that I should study architecture. It seemed to be the fact that parents normally decide the vocations of their sons. Accordingly, I entered the university (as *studiosus architecturae*) and followed with commendable diligence under Ritgen's guidance descriptive geometry, perspective, shadow-theory, stonecutting, and other interesting subjects. But Liebig's lectures tempted me to change subjects and this I decided to do....

My years of apprenticeship took me to Paris, where I was able to listen to what I believe were the last lectures of the famous Dumas. I spent much time with Wurtz with whom a close friendship later developed. By accident I met and became friends with Gerhardt, who at that time was discovering the acid anhydrides and was preparing the completed manuscript of his famous textbook for the printer. A stay of a year and a half at a lonely Swiss Castle [chemical assistant to Baron von Planta] gave me ample leisure to assimilate independently the insights I had gained from the still unpublished manuscript. My travel years took me farther to London. While Paris gave me the opportunity to become acquainted with the unpublished views of Gerhardt, so now I had the good fortune to become good friends with Williamson and to familiarize myself with the mode of thought of this philosophical intellect. Originally a student of Liebig, I had become a student of Dumas, Gerhardt, and Williamson. No longer did I belong to any one school.

This circumstance and the direction which my earlier architectural studies gave my intellect—an irresistible urge to visualize everything—these seem to be the reasons why the chemical ideas which were in the air twenty-five years ago found suitable soil inside my head. The human being, it seems clear, is the product of the conditions in which he grew up; no merit accrues to him for what he becomes.

Kekulé's account of how he arrived at the conception of the structural theory is famous.

During my stay in London I resided for a considerable time in Clapham Road in the neighborhood of Clapham Common. I frequently, however, spent my evenings with my friend Hugo Müller at Islington at the opposite end of the metropolis. We talked of many things, but most often of our beloved chemistry. One fine summer evening I was returning by the last bus, "outside," as usual, through the deserted streets of the city, which are at other times so full of life. I fell into a reverie (Traümerei), and lo, the atoms were gamboling before my eyes. Whenever, hitherto, these diminutive beings had appeared to me, they had always been in motion; but up to that time I had never been able to discern the nature of their motion. Now, however, I saw how, frequently, two smaller atoms united to form a pair; how a larger one embraced the two smaller ones; how still larger ones kept hold of three or even four of the smaller; whilst the whole kept whirling in a giddy dance. I saw how the larger ones formed a chain, dragging the smaller ones after them but only at the ends of the chain. I saw what our past master, Kipp, my highly honored teacher and friend, has depicted with such charm in his "Molekularwelt;" but I saw it long before him. The cry of the conductor, "Clapham Road," awakened me from my dreaming; but I spent a part of the night in putting on paper at least sketches of these dream forms. This was the origin of the "Structure Theory."

Kekulé's important paper, "On the Constitution and Metamorphoses of Chemical Compounds and on the Chemical Nature of Carbon" appeared in May, 1858, when he was but 29 years old. In this paper Kekulé clearly presents the proposal that carbon is tetravalent and is capable of uniting with itself to form chains. In his own words (1, 16):

If only the simplest compounds of carbon are considered (marsh gas, methyl chloride, carbon tetrachloride, chloroform, carbonic acid, phosgene gas, carbon disulfide, prussic acid, etc.), it is striking that the amount of carbon which the chemist has known as the least possible, as the *atom*, always combines with four atoms of a monatomic or two atoms of a diatomic, element, that generally, the sum of the chemical unities of these elements which are bound to one atom of carbon is equal to 4. This leads to the view that carbon is *tetratomic* (or tetrabasic)....

For substances which contain more atoms of carbon, it must be assumed that at least part of the atoms are held just by the affinity of carbon and that the carbon atoms themselves are joined together, so that naturally a part of the affinity of one for the other will bind an equally great part of the affinity of the other.

The simplest, and therefore the most obvious, case of such linking together of two carbon atoms is this, that one affinity unit of each atom is bound to one of the other....In other words, one group of two atoms of carbon = $C_2$ will be hexatomic, it will form compounds with six atoms of a monatomic element....

When comparisons are made between compounds which have an equal number of carbon atoms in the molecule and which can be changed into each other by simple transformations (e.g., alcohol, ethyl chloride, aldehyde, acetic acid, glycolic acid, oxalic acid, etc.) the view is reached that the carbon atoms are arranged in the same way and only the atoms held to the carbon skeleton are changed.

It is appropriate to close this review of Kekulé's contribution with a further quotation from his 1890 address:

One cannot explore new countries in express trains, nor will the study of even the best textbook qualify a man to become a discoverer. Whoever is content to follow well-laid promenades until he reaches some pleasant eminence frequented by tourists, may, by striking into thickets, gather some forgotten flower; or if cryptograms, mosses and lichens satisfy him he may even bring home a well-filled vasculum; but anything essentially new he will not find. Whoever wishes to train himself as an investigator must study the traveler's original works; and that, too, so thoroughly that he is able to read between the lines—to divine the author's unexpressed thought. He must follow the paths of the Pathfinders; he must note every footprint, every bent twig, every fallen leaf. Then, standing at the extreme point reached by his predecessors, it will be easy for him to perceive where the foot of a further pioneer may find solid ground.

## Couper's Contribution

Archibald Scott Couper (17, 18) was born in 1831 at Kirkintilloch, in Scotland. As a child his health was poor and he received most of his education at home. His university studies began in Glasgow and emphasized the humanities and languages. In 1852, at the age of 21, he attended the University of Edinburgh, where he studied logic, metaphysics, and moral philosophy. Certainly an unusual background for a future chemist!

Some time between the years 1854 to 1856 Couper decided to study chemistry. After relatively brief preparative work at Edinburgh, he went to Wurtz's laboratory in Paris and almost immediately began independent work. His first paper, "Recherches sur la benzine" was published in 1857 and reported the preparation of two new compounds, bromobenzene and *p*-dibromobenzene. A second paper, on salicylic acid, was presented to the French Academy of Sciences in 1858.

A few months earlier Couper had arrived at the concept of the tetravalence of carbon and the self-linking of carbon atoms. He described his ideas in a paper entitled "On a New Chemical Theory" and requested Wurtz to present it to the French Academy. Unfortunately, Wurtz failed to act, and Kekulé's paper appeared on May 19, 1858. Couper's contribution was then presented to the academy by Dumas, on June 14, 1858.

Couper was deeply affected by Wurtz's unfortunate delay which had resulted in his views being anticipated by Kekulé, albeit by less than a month. He returned to Scotland in the role of second assistant to Lyon Playfair, Professor of Chemistry. Unfortunately, he soon suffered a nervous breakdown, from which he never fully recovered. It is not possible to say whether his severe disappointment was a factor. His life for the next thirty-four years was spent at his home in Kirkintilloch, away from any significant intellectual activity.

Couper's approach is illustrated by these quotations from his paper (2).

> The end of chemistry *is its theory*. The guide in chemical research *is a theory*.
>
> \*     \*     \*
>
> There are two conditions which every sound theory must fulfil:
> 1. It must be proved to be empirically true.
> 2. It must no less be philosophically true.

After discussing the Theory of Types, he concludes that the empirical truth of the theory must be admitted. He then points out, "The philosophical test demands that a theory be competent to explain the greatest number of facts in the simplest possible manner." He then proceeds to point out that the Theory of Types makes no attempt to explain the facts.

Just as Kekulé used his earlier architectural training in his approach, Couper utilized his earlier linguistic training in criticizing the Theory of Types.

> Should the principle which is therein adopted be applied to the common events of life, it will be found that it is simply absurd. Suppose that some one were to systematize the formation of letters into words that formed the contents of a book. Were he to begin by saying that he had discovered a certain word which would serve as a type, and from which by substitution and double decomposition all others are to be derived,—that he by this means not only could form new words, but new books, and books almost ad infinitum,—that this word also formed an admirable point of comparison with all others,—that in this there were only a few difficulties, but that these might be ingeniously overcome,—he would certainly state an empirical truth. At the same time, however, his method would, judged by the light of common sense, be an absurdity. . . .
>
> The sure and invincible method of arriving at every truth which the mind is capable of discovering is always the one and the same. It is that, namely, of throwing away all generalization, of going back to first principles, and of letting the mind be guided by these alone. It is the same in common matters. It is the same in science. To reach the structure of words we must go back, seek out the undecomposable elements, viz. the letters, and carefully study their powers and bearing. Having ascertained these, the composition and structure of every possible word is revealed.

Applying his method to the analysis of carbon compounds, he arrived at the conclusion that carbon exhibits a combining power of 4 and it is capable of uniting with itself utilizing units of the combining power of the atoms involved.

In several respects his publication goes beyond that of Kekulé. The latter considered that carbon must have an invariant valence of 4; Couper is willing to assign carbon valences of both 2 (in carbon monoxide) and 4 (in carbon dioxide and methane). In his paper Kekulé nowhere attempted to write structural formulas for the compounds discussed. Couper clearly represents such molecules as methyl and ethyl alcohol, ethyl ether, propionic acid, and ethylene glycol by means of structural formulas, showing bonds between atoms linked to each other. Finally, he attempts a structural formula for salicylic acid. Although the molecule is shown as an open-chain derivative, he does show the phenolic hydroxyl and the carboxyl groups on neighboring carbon atoms, and the reaction product with phosphorus pentachloride as a ring compound in which the phosphorus atom has displaced the two acidic hydrogen atoms. Carbon atoms are linked by both single and double bonds—only a shift of a hydrogen atom and formation of a ring is required to transform it into a structure which would be acceptable today.

All in all, this is a remarkable contribution from a young man, 27 years of age, whose studies in chemistry had begun but 2 to 3 years previously.

Kekulé died in 1896. He had a long and fruitful research career. His important contributions were widely recognized and he was repeatedly honored in the course of his life.

On the other hand, Couper's chemical life was exceedingly brief. His contribution, important as it was, was soon forgotten. We are indebted to Kekulé's successor at Bonn, R. Anschütz for uncovering and pointing out to the chemical world Couper's major contribution (19).

We may also contrast the different approaches of the two workers. Kekulé was very well versed in the chemical theory of the day. He had studied chemistry intensively for a number of years. He was so accustomed to the Theory of Types that he found it difficult to avoid presentation of his researches in terms and symbols customary to that theory even after the publication of his revolutionary paper.

On the other hand, Couper was a relative novice in chemistry. He had little prejudice to overcome in developing his theory. Which is to be more admired—the man who proved capable of surmounting previous training and prejudice, or the novice who attained such a remarkable insight into chemical structure with so little prior training?

## One Hundred Years of Structural Theory

The publications of Kekulé and Couper merely provided the first opening for modern theory, a mere crack in the dike confining organic theory for half a century. However, that crack was all that was needed. Organic research could now be directed in effort, rather than blinded. The crack was made into a fault, the rivulet into a stream, and then into a mighty river, the full flood of organic accomplishments providing a relatively smooth, rapid transit toward his objectives for the organic investigator of today.

In 1865 Kekulé proposed his structure for benzene and related aromatic compounds (20), and by 1874 his student Körner had demonstrated the power of isomer number in fixing the structures of benzene isomers (21). In 1874 van't Hoff (22) and Le Bel (23) extended the two dimensional representations of Kekulé into three dimensions, providing a simple explanation of optical isomerism. At the same time van't Hoff also used the tetrahedral carbon atom to account for *cis-trans* geometric isomers.

It was a basic tenet of the structural theory that there existed at most but one structure for each and every substance. However, cases soon were recognized where a given substance apparently required two structural formulas to describe its behavior. However the phenomenon of tautomerism was soon understood and brought within the structural theory.

Molecular rearrangements sometimes provided major difficulties in the determination of structures. Indeed more than 30 structures were proposed for camphor and its degradation product, camphoric acid, before their constitutions were satisfactorily interpreted.

The study of small ring compounds led to recognition of the strains resulting from the presence of distorted angles (24). In 1889 Kehrmann noted that certain substituted quinones exhibited markedly decreased reactivity and led him to postulate a steric effect resulting from the steric requirements of the substituents (25). The concept was developed further by Victor Meyer in his studies of the rates of esterification of ortho substituted benzoic acids (26). The idea revealed its importance to the structural theory in accounting for the isomerism observed in ortho substituted biphenyls (27).

## In Conclusion

The path of the organic theorist is not an easy one. The man who synthesizes a new class of compounds receives ready recognition and acclaim. One who discovers a new reaction is applauded and will doubtless soon have his contribution recognized by having his name attached to the reaction in question, to the confusion of future generations of students.

However, consider the lot of the theorist. Should he propose a new interpretation or a new theory, his proposed interpretation or theory is immediately attacked. The referees of his paper are almost certain to point out that alternative interpretations are possible, so that the paper should not be published. Or they may state that the germ of the idea has already been suggested by someone in an obscure reference. Or they may fall back on the position that the proposed interpretation fails to account for all the published data and the author should do additional experimental work (preferably forever) before he publishes his proposal.

Should he be successful in overcoming these objectives, he faces new difficulties. Immediately upon publication other workers point out that the ideas are obvious, that these ideas had occurred to them long ago but had not been considered worthy of publication. Various workers carry out inaccurate experiments and immediately rush into print with their data to refute the new theory.

We teach our students that theories come, and theories go, but practical results stand forever.

Yes, theoretical developments are treated quite differently than are practical developments. It is not surprising that many chemists begin their work with a theoretical inclination but end their days primarily interested in the practical aspects of chemical research.

To all discouraged theoretical chemists, the achievement of Kekulé and Couper provides a beacon of encouragement. One hundred years have passed—yet their contribution shines even brighter. Both the practical worker and the organic theorist are deeply indebted to them for their magnificent contribution 100 years ago.

### Literature Cited

(1) KEKULÉ, A., *Ann.*, **106**, 129–59 (1858).
(2) COUPER, A. S., *Compt. rend.*, **46**, 1157–60 (1858); *Phil. Mag.* [4] **16**, 104–16 (1858). Alembic Club Reprints No. 21, "On a New Chemical Theory and Researches on Salicylic Acid," Edinburgh, 1933.
(3) VON MEYER, E., "History of Chemistry," Macmillan and Co., Ltd., London, 3rd ed., 1906, pp. 196–355.
(4) PARTINGTON, J. R., "A Short History of Chemistry," The Macmillan Co., New York, 1937, pp. 216–98.
(5) MOORE, F. J., "A History of Chemistry," McGraw-Hill Book Co., New York, 1939, pp. 175–246.
(6) JAPP, F. R., *J. Chem. Soc.*, **73**, 97 (1898).
(7) WHITMORE, F. C., "Organic Chemistry," D. Van Nostrand Co., Inc., New York, 1937.
(8) DALTON, J., "A New System of Chemical Philosophy," Part I, Manchester, R. Bicherstaff, London, 1808.
(9) AVOGADRO, L.R.A.C., *J. de physique*, **73**, 58–76 (1811). Alembic Club Reprints, No. 4, "Foundations of the Molecular Theory," Edinburgh, 1899.
(10) CANNIZZARO, S., *Il Nuovo Cimento*, **7**, 321–66 (1858). Alembic Club Reprints, No. 18, "Sketch of a Course of Chemical Philosophy by Stanislao Cannizzaro," Edinburgh, 1910.
(11) BERZELIUS, J. J., "Essai sur la Théorie des Proportions chimiques et sur l'influence chimique de l'électricité," Paris, 1819. LEICESTER, H. M., AND KLICKSTEIN, H. S., "A Source Book in Chemistry," McGraw-Hill Book Co., New York, 1952, p. 261.
(12) WINDLER, S. C. H., *Ann.*, **34**, 308 (1840).
(13) FRANKLAND, E., *Phil. Trans.*, **142**, 417 (1852).
(14) ROBINSON, R., *J Chem. Educ.*, **34**, 54 (1957).
(15) KEKULÉ, A., *Ber.*, **23**, 1302 (1890). BENFEY, O. T., *J. Chem. Educ.*, **35**, 21 (1958).
(16) LEICESTER, H. M., AND KLICKSTEIN, H. S., *op. cit.*, pp. 419–20.
(17) BENFEY, O. T., "Archibald Scott Couper," contribution to "Lives of Great Chemists," Eduard Farber, Editor, Interscience Publishers, in press.
(18) IRVINE, J. C., *J. CHEM. EDUC.*, **7**, 2808 (1930).
(19) DOBBIN, L., *J. CHEM. EDUC.*, **11**, 331 (1934).
(20) KEKULÉ, A., *Ann.*, **137**, 129 (1865).
(21) KORNER, W., *Gazz. chim. ital.*, **4**, 305 (1874).
(22) VAN'T HOFF, J. H., *Archives Néerlandaises*, **9**, 445 (1874).
(23) LE BEL, J. A., *Bull. Soc. Chim.* [2] **22**, 337 (1874).
(24) BAEYER. A., **18**, 2269, 2277 (1885).
(25) KEHRMANN, F., *J. prakt. Chem.*, **40**, 257 (1889).
(26) MEYER, V., *Ber.*, **27**, 510 (1894).
(27) TURNER, E. E., AND LEFÉVRE, R. J. W., *Chem. & Ind.*, **45**, 831 (1926).

+ + +

# Kekulé-Couper Centennial

## Introduction[1]

**W**ithin one month in 1858 two papers appeared that were to have decisive influence on the development of theoretical organic chemistry. August Kekulé's article was entitled "On the Constitution and Metamorphoses of Chemical Compounds and on the Chemical Nature of Carbon" and contained the passage:

I regard it as necessary and in the present state of chemical knowledge, as in many cases possible, to explain the properties of chemical compounds by going back to the elements themselves.[2]

Couper's "On a New Chemical Theory" began:

I go back to the elements themselves of which I study the mutual affinities.[3]

Each then repeated the axiom of the tetravalence of carbon already in the literature and propounded for the first time the concept of chain formation of carbon atoms. These two principles represent the cornerstone of the structural theory.

### Hundredth Anniversary Commemorated

The hundredth anniversary of the structural theory was commemorated in Chicago, London, Ghent, and Heidelberg.

*Chicago.* A Centennial Symposium on the Development of Theoretical Organic Chemistry was held as part of the fall meeting of the American Chemical Society. Further, Herbert C. Brown delivered the Kekulé-Couper Centennial Lecture.[4] The symposium papers published in this issue of the JOURNAL deal first with Kekulé's experimental work prior to 1858 and its bearing on Kekulé's theoretical views (by E. Hiebert). This is followed by a careful analysis by H. Leicester of the contrasting claims made in recent years as to the relative significance of Kekulé and Butlerov. The final three papers deal with developments in theoretical organic chemistry necessitated by the discovery of phenomena not explained by the original structural theory. On the one hand there were discovered certain instances where several compounds corresponded to the same structural formula. The philosophical problems underlying the present conception of "optical isomerism" are developed by J. Senior, while the field of geometrical isomerism is dealt with in the first half of the Ihde paper. On the other hand are instances where a substance seemed to correspond more or less exactly to several structural formulas. Tautomeric phenomena are discussed in the latter part of Ihde's paper, while the early history of the resonance concept is developed by E. Campaigne.[5]

*London.* Under the auspices of the Organic Chemistry Section of the International Union of Pure and Applied Chemistry, the Chemical Society (London) organized "The Kekulé Symposium on Theoretical Organic Chemistry." It was held September 15–17, 1958, and consisted of 18 papers on current theoretical problems by some of the leading chemists of Western Europe and America. The symposium was preceded by a booklet of abstracts published by the Chemical Society which also included an excellent biographical article "August Kekulé" by P. E. Verkade of Delft, President of the Organic Section of the IUPAC.[6] It contains a few passing references to Couper, who was otherwise completely ignored by the planners of the symposium.[7]

*Ghent.* Kekulé was called to the professorship of the University of Ghent in the fall of 1858. That university opened on November 12 an exhibition of Kekulé materials from the period of his stay in Ghent (1858–67). J. Gillis, Professor of Chemistry and Pro-Rector of the university, organized the exhibition and wrote a brief study of Kekulé's Ghent period.[8]

*Heidelberg.* Kekulé was *Privat-Dozent* in Heidelberg from 1856–58. There he worked in a privately furnished laboratory because Bunsen who held the chair of chemistry at the university refused to let men of Kekulé's rank use the Chemical Institute for research! On November 30, 1957, Heinz A. Staab delivered an inaugural address entitled "A Hundred Years of Organic Structural Chemistry."[9] He reviewed the development of the structural theory since 1857, discussed the achievements and limits of classical structural chemistry, and ended with an analysis of the potentialities of modern structural studies. He emphasized the distinction between the statics and dynamics of moleculed and the still very enigmatic position of the concept of a "transition state."

### The Continued Neglect of Couper

Reviewing these celebrations and their origin, the relative neglect of Archibald Scott Couper is remarkable. At least the Chemical Society, one would have imagined, would have insisted on Couper's equal claim with Kekulé as an originator of the Structural Theory. Richard Anschütz's monumental efforts to restore Couper to his deserved eminence seem once more to have been ignored.[10]

Undoubtedly Couper originated with Kekulé the basic tenets of the structural theory. Couper's paper was commented on by Butlerov and Kekulé, while Wurtz, his teacher, was also influenced by him. But his claim to fame is further strengthened by other contributions made in 1857–58. He was the pioneer in the use graphical formulas for organic compounds, using lines to join the atoms.[11] He wrote a ring formula for cyanuric

[1] Supported by National Science Foundation Grant G-4207.

[2] KEKULÉ, A., *Ann.*, **106**, 129 (1858).

[3] *Compt. rend.*, **46**, 1157 (1858). The title pages of these two articles are reproduced in THIS JOURNAL, **36**, 106, 107 (1959).

[4] BROWN, H. C., J. CHEM. EDUC., **36**, 104 (1959).

[5] For an analysis of the failures of the structural theory *cf.* O. T. BENFEY, J. CHEM. EDUC., **34**, 286 (1957).

[6] Also in *Proc. Chem. Soc.*, **1958**, 205.

[7] A summary of the symposium was published in the *Proc. Chem. Soc.*, **1958**, 298. The full text of lectures and papers will be published for the International Union by Butterworths, London, in 1959.

[8] *De Brug*, II, No. 2, 65–75, (April-June 1958); available as a separate issue from the University of Ghent, Belgium.

[9] The complete text appeared in *Angew. Chem.*, **70**, 37–41 (1958).

[10] *Cf.* L. DOBBIN, "The Couper Quest," J. CHEM. EDUC., **11**, 331 (1934).

[11] It is of interest that Wm. Higgins much earlier used lines for a similar purpose, but his approach was never followed up in organic chemistry; *cf.* E. R. ATKINSON, J. CHEM. EDUC., **17**, 3 (1940).

acid $(O=8)$[12] seven years before Kekulé conceived of a cyclic arrangement of atoms (for benzene), and he advo-

HO—O—Az—C—AzO—OH
| C
| Az { C
|   O—OH

cated the necessity of variable valences against Kekulé's determined opposition.   Experimentally he was one of

the early workers to become aware of the lack of reactivity of benzene and was the first to synthesize bromo- and p-dibromobenzene.   Following on Wurtz's successful conversion of ethylene dibromide via the diacetate to ethylene glycol, Couper had thought to convert the seemingly highly unsaturated benzene to the corresponding glycol.   He discovered that bromine vapor attacked by substitution rather than addition, that it attacked very slowly, producing the mono- and dibromo derivatives, and that the products were remarkably inert to silver acetate.[13]   Finally he used the term "structure" by analogy with its use in linguistics, to signify order and arrangement of atoms rather than spatial distribution, thus accurately recognizing the topological as contrasted with a geometrical character of the original structural theory.[14,15]

O. T. Benfey, *chairman of symposium*
Earlham College, Richmond, Indiana

[12] *Ann. chim. phys.* (3), **53,** 489 (1858); reprinted by R. Anschütz in *Proc. Roy. Soc. Edinb.,* **29,** 265 (1909). English Version in Alembic Club Reprint No. 21, Edinburgh, **1953,** p. 33.
[13] *Compt. rend.,* **45,** 230 (1857).
[14] *Cf.* SENIOR, J., J. CHEM. EDUC., **15,** 464 (1938).
[15] BENFEY, O. T., "Archibald Scott Couper" in "Lives of Great Chemists," Eduard Farber, Editor; Interscience, in press.

Erwin N. Hiebert
University of Wisconsin
Madison

# The Experimental Basis of Kekulé's Valence Theory

**B**etween 1850 and 1892 August Kekulé (1829–96) published over a hundred papers.   The majority of these were experimental communications in organic chemistry and related topics.[1]   Even a superficial examination of the papers shows that Kekulé's knowledge of the chemistry of his day was extraordinarily comprehensive.   We can readily accept his claim that he had studied the historical development of chemistry from the time of his first acquaintance with chemistry, and that he had spent a good deal of time mastering its classics before he accomplished anything on his own.   Indeed, he maintained that prior to the

Presented as part of the Kekulé-Couper Centennial Symposium on the Development of Theoretical Organic Chemistry before the Division of History of Chemistry at the 134th Meeting of the American Chemical Society, Chicago, September, 1958.

[1] ANSCHÜTZ, RICHARD, "August Kekulé," 2 vols., Verlag Chemie, Berlin, **1929:** Vol. I, Leben und Wirken; Vol. II, Abhandlungen, Berichte, Kritiken, Artikel, Reden.   The second volume contains 75 papers authored by Kekulé, 28 papers coauthored by Kekulé and 28 other items including book reports, technical comments and speeches, in German, French, and English.   Anschütz was a student and colleague of Kekulé's for 21 years and his successor in Bonn in 1898.   At the *Versammlung Deutscher Naturforscher und Aerzte* in 1896, the year of Kekulé's death, Emil Fischer urged Anschütz to write a detailed obituary notice for the *Berichte.*   The eventual outcome of this request was a two volume biography and collection of papers published 33 years later on the 100th anniversary of Kekulé's birth.   Since 1929 these volumes have been the most indispensable and reliable single guide for all Kekulé studies.   Passages quoted from the works of Kekulé have been translated by the author of this paper.

time of any of his theoretical papers his friends had considered his fund of chemical knowledge more reliable then Berzelius' *Jahresberichte.*[2]   Thus we learn, from an analysis of his papers, that he attacked his own specific research problems only after having virtually mastered all the related chemical literature on the subject. In addition, in many instances, his papers reveal rather precisely how the work of previous investigators provided him with a point of departure for his own experiments, or how another author's work was corrected, challenged, expanded, or reinterpreted to explain a new situation.   Characteristically, the complete and considerate recognition of the labors of his predecessors formed an integral part of all his published works. The list of chemical investigators who benefited directly from Kekulé's various activities on some point of technical detail, over a period of some forty fruitful years, is impressive indeed.   That subject would merit a full study by itself.

Hardly less important for the evaluation of Kekulé's over-all contribution is the observation that his most significant discoveries taken together exhibit great overall unity.   This was the result of his remarkable command over a great and complex mass of factual experi-

[2] Vital information on the earliest period of Kekulé's chemical career is available in two speeches which he delivered toward the end of his life:   the first in 1890 at a *Kekuléfeir* sponsored by the Deutsche Chemische Gesellschaft in Berlin (*Ber.,* **23,** 1265–1312 (1890) and Anschütz II, 937–47);   the second in 1892 at the Chemical Institute in Bonn on the occasion of the 25th year of his professorship there (Anschütz, II, 947–52).

mental information concerning the properties and reactions of individual organic compounds, coupled with a passionate search for some organizational principle which would shed new light upon the question of the molecular consitution of organic compounds in terms of certain well-known and characteristic reaction types. Even Kekulé's earliest works contained refreshingly straightforward attempts to give an answer to that question, and eventually he provided one of the most explicit nineteenth century formulations of a chemical philosophy on the whole broad subject of molecular constitution.

Kekulé was twenty-nine years of age when he formulated the valence theory which provided a great new stimulus to theoretical organic chemistry. We may well emphasize at the outset that he was not led to the theory because of any specific experimental discoveries. It was an organizational achievement accomplished in its concise final form by a few deft strokes of the pen—a mere sentence or two. The theory was simple, and its value was almost immediately obvious to most chemists. All of the specific experimental information which Kekulé marshalled together in support of his valence theory in the famous statement of 1858 must have been available to a great number of eminently competent contemporary chemists, but the fact remains that only he and Couper were able to suggest the crucial theoretical concepts which laid the foundation for modern structural organic chemistry.

It is the object of this paper to discuss the experimental basis of Kekulé's valence theory of 1858 as seen in the progressive stages of his own experimental career prior to that time. An adequate exposition of Kekulé's theoretical papers of 1857/8[3] would require a great deal more time than is available here, and we shall do no more than to indicate where his experimental work bears directly on the theory of the quadrivalency and self-linking characteristics of carbon.

### Darmstadt and Giessen (1848–51)

Kekulé remarked late in life that it had been Liebig's chemistry lectures which had enticed him to abandon a planned career of *studiosus architecturae*. Between 1848 and 1851 he studied analytical chemistry in the Darmstadt Technical School with Friedrich Moldenhauer, and in Giessen with Heinrich Will and Theodor Fleitmann (discoverer of sulfur matches). In addition he attended Liebig's lectures in experimental, theoretical, and agricultural chemistry, Kopp's lectures on crystallography, stoichiometry, and mineralogy, Knapp's lectures on chemical technology, and Strecker's lectures on organic chemistry. His first experimental communication was a carefully performed but routine analytical investigation on amyl sulfuric acid, its salts and their distillation products; it was sponsored by Heinrich Will in Giessen in 1850 and became his doctoral dissertation.[4]

The only Kekulé work on record from Liebig's private laboratory was an analysis of gluten and wheat bran.[5] Liebig's continued influence upon Kekulé's chemical views was probably not very great. The two men were never on very congenial terms with one another. Kekulé in the 1850's praised Liebig highly, but presumably because he needed his recommendation in order to obtain a professorial chair in chemistry in a German university. That was something Kekulé wanted above all else. By 1850 Liebig had more or less abandoned his active interest in organic chemistry for agricultural and physiological chemistry, and thereafter no longer kept up in his lectures with the newer theoretical developments. While Liebig was dogmatic in his pronouncements, Heinrich Will in his lectures on organic chemistry radiated a noncommittal attitude on the question of the consitution of organic compounds. Reinhold Hoffmann, one of Kekulé's most intimate student associates at Giessen, wrote later: "At that time already in our circles the sentiment was aroused, partly unconsciously, that the rigorous radical theory was not the all-redeeming dogma of chemistry."[6]

### Paris (1851–52)

In 1851 Kekulé left Giessen to undertake further studies in Paris. Liebig had told him that in Paris he would extend his horizons, learn a new language, and experience the great city, but learn no chemistry. Concerning the latter, Liebig could not have been more in error. While en route to Paris, Kekulé was absorbing Charles Gerhardt's *Introduction à l'étude de chimie par le système unitaire* (Paris, 1848).

In Paris Kekulé attended lectures at the Sorbonne, the Ecole de Médicine, the Conservatoire des Arts et Métiers and the Collège de France. He listened to the lectures of Dumas, Cahours, Wurtz, Payen, Magendie, Regnault, and Pouillet. It was by chance that he met Charles Gerhardt in Paris. Their first conversation lasted twelve hours and thereafter they met at least twice every week for over a year. Much of that time was spent in weighing Gerhardt's various proposals for schemes of classification of organic compounds, the overall object being to try and account for a number of series of compounds on the basis of a single type theory. The close association with Gerhardt in Paris was later to have the profoundest effect upon the direction of Kekulé's theoretical ideas.[7]

### Switzerland (1852–53)

In 1852 Kekulé became for one and a half years the private assistant to the chemist Alfred von Planta in Reichenau/Chur, Switzerland. In this beautiful, secluded and idyllic mountain spot Kekulé expected to rework and rethink his newly acquired scientific information; and especially, as he later remarked, that portion of it which he had learned from studying the manuscript of Gerhardt's as yet unpublished famous

[3] The two crucial theoretical papers were: "Ueber die s. g. gepaarten Verbindungen und die Theorie der mehratomigen Radicale," *Ann.*, **104**, 129–50 (1857); "Ueber die Constitution und die Metamorphosen der chemischen Verbindungen und über die chemische Natur des Kohlenstoffs," *Ann.*, **106**, 129–59 (1858).

[4] KEKULÉ, "Ueber die Amyloxydschwefelsäure und einige ihrer Salze," *Annalen*, **75**, 275–93 (1850).

[5] LIEBIG, *Chemische Briefe*, 3rd ed., Heidelberg, **1851**, Letter No. 28, pp. 592, 595.

[6] ANSCHÜTZ, I, 16–17.

[7] GRIMAUX, ED., AND GERHARDT, CH., *Charles Gerhardt, sa vie son oeuvre, sa correspondence, 1816–1856*. Document d'histoire de la chimie. Paris, 1900. This volume gives a very full account of Gerhardt's theory of types and of its connection with the chemical activities of Williamson, Chancel, Wurtz, Odling, Dumas, Frankland, Hofmann, Kopp, and Kekulé. For the years of friendship between Gerhardt and Kekulé (1851–56) see esp. Pt. I, Chaps. VII and VIII and Pt. II, Chaps. VI and VII.

four volume *Traité de chimie organique* (Paris, 1853–56). Concerning this time of his life Kekulé adopted for himself the sentence from Heine: "Mein Kopf war damals ein zwitscherndes Vogelnest von confiscierlichen Büchern."

Four joint publications with Planta appeared between 1853 and 1854. Two of these dealt with the quantitative analysis of gallstones and a number of minerals. More important were the two papers on the volatile alkaloids, nicotine and coniine, whose study was then of obvious interest in light of A. W. Hofmann's discovery in 1851 of the mode of formation of primary, secondary, and tertiary amines, and the quaternary ammonium bases. Kekulé in later life never again returned to the investigations of the alkaloids, but it is worth noting, first, that this work put him in contact with Gerhardt once more,[8] and second, that all of these papers indicate that Kekulé had mastered the earlier literature on the subject—a characteristic exhibited by every paper that he ever published.

## London (1853–55)

In 1853, upon the recommendation of Liebig, Kekulé reluctantly accepted a private assistantship at St. Bartholomew's hospital in London in the laboratory of Liebig's former student, Professor John Stenhouse.[9] Bunsen had advised him to go to London to learn a new language, even, if no chemistry. Bunsen turned out to be just as mistaken about Kekulé's sojourn in London as Liebig had been about his stay in Paris two years earlier. For, in London, Kekulé almost immediately joined a friendly circle of former Giessen students who spent a good part of their time in vigorous discussions on the new theoretical chemistry of Gerhardt, Laurent, and Kolbe. Before long Kekulé's acquaintances in London included Hugo Müller who had been a student of Wöhler's in Göttingen, A. W. Hoffmann, Thomas Graham, Edward Frankland, William Odling, and in particular Alexander Williamson who was Professor of Practical Chemistry in University College, London. Kekulé's roommate in London, Reinhold Hoffman, who was then employed as an assistant in Williamson's laboratory, wrote to Anschütz that many of the ideas which Kekulé acquired at that time in London only became prominent in his later work; such for example were his persistent attempts to reduce the properties of organic compounds and radicals to the elements themselves. By refusing to accept the radicals or the various types as something absolute, Kekulé was not far removed, thought Hoffman, from the idea that "in the organic compounds, only the valences of carbon are decisive for the combining ability with other elements and groups of atoms and for the transformability of the compounds."[10]

Kekulé's work under Stenhouse was routine and unchallenging, but fortunately interrupted by frequent visits to University College. There he felt himself drawn into the excitement of the chemical disputes which were being conducted by Williamson and his colleagues against Hermann Kolbe on the question of the theory of formation of water, ethers, and acids. Wil-

liamson's mixed ether experiments of 1850/52[11] had already indirectly provided a demonstration of the views of Laurent and Gerhardt regarding the equivalents to be used in writing the formulas for alcohol and ether. The production of mixed ethers being derived from two alcohols, Williamson represented ether as the oxide of the two ethyl groups, and alcohol as the oxide of ethyl and hydrogen.

Williamson's notion of chemical formulas, written so as to exhibit their chemical constitution through the arrangement of interdependent atoms, was first developed in his paper of 1852: "On the Constitution of Salts."[12] His use of bivalent oxygen for linking together hydrogen and hydrocarbon radicals was limited essentially to compounds of the water type. Odling and Frankland extended the idea to elements other than oxygen as the linking agent, and Gerhardt added other types to Williamson's water type but the latter were mere "types of double decomposition" without the structural significance of Williamson's conception.[13]

Kekulé, who was in close contact with Williamson and in the midst of discussions related to all of these matters, soon arrived at the idea of using phosphorus sulfide to replace the oxygen in organic acids and esters with sulfur. This was after Cahours had already succeeded in replacing the oxygen of monocarboxylic acids with chlorine by means of phosphorus pentachloride. When Kekulé communicated his ideas to Williamson the latter suggested that if he did not undertake the experiments immediately he would attempt them in his own laboratory. Kekulé's position under Stenhouse did not easily lend itself to private investigations. Nevertheless he began the experiments at St. Bartholomew's in the early morning hours, much to the consternation of Stenhouse who had no difficulty in discovering from the sulfurous odors that something foreign to his specific research concerns was going on in his own private laboratory. Kekulé's paper "On a new Series of Sulphuretted Acids" was handed in to the Royal Society of London by Williamson and delivered there in April of 1854 by Kekulé under the presidency of Graham.[14]

Kekulé introduced his paper as follows:

Adopting the idea that the series of organic compounds, of which sulphuretted hydrogen is the type, corresponds in every respect with the series of which water is the type, I concluded that not only mercaptans and neutral sulphides, which correspond to the alcohols and ethers, but also compounds corresponding to the acids, anhydrous acids, and ethers of acids might be produced; I therefore endeavoured to obtain reactions which would enable me to replace oxygen in the compounds of the latter series by sulphur.

By fusing amorphous phosphorus and sulfur in an atmosphere of carbonic acid Kekulé produced the tersulfide ($P_2S_3$) and the pentasulfide ($P_2S_5$), and demonstrated that they acted on the members of the water series in a manner analogous to the action of the corresponding compounds of phosphorus and chlorine ($PCl_3$

[8] Anschütz, I, 33–35.

[9] Kekulé said later, "Aber ich hatte wenig Lust anzunehmen, weil ich ihn, [Stenhouse] wenn ich mir den Ausdruck gestatten darf, für einen Schmierchemiker hielt." Anschütz, II, 950.

[10] Anschütz, I, 41.

[11] WILLIAMSON, A. W., "Theory of Etherification," *Phil. Mag* [3], **37**, 350–56 (1850); "On Etherification," *J. Chem. Soc.*, **4**, 229–39 (1852); See also Alembic Club Reprints, No. 16 for papers by Williamson, and cf. Chancel, G., "Sur l'éthérifaction et sur une nouvelle classe d'éthers," *Compt. rend.*, **31**, 521–23 (1850).

[12] WILLIAMSON, A. W., *J. Chem. Soc.*, **4**, 350–55 (1852).

[13] DIVERS, EDWARD, Obituary Notice for Williamson, *Roy. Soc. Proc.*, London, [A], **78**, xxiv–xliv (1907).

[14] KEKULÉ, *Proc. Roy. Soc.*, London, **7**, 37–40 (1854); more detailed German version in *Ann.*, **90**, 309–16 (1854); abridged French version in *Annales de chimie*, [3], **42**, 240–42 (1854).

and $PCl_5$), although less violently. But there was this difference,

> . . . that by using the chlorine compounds the product is resolved into *two* groups of atoms, while by using the sulphur compounds there is obtained only *one* group; a peculiarity, which, according to the dibasic nature of sulphur, must have been expected. . . . By acting on these compounds of sulphur and phosphorus with water, one atom of sulphuretted hydrogen is obtained, while the chlorides give two atoms of hydrochloric acid.

Kekulé then listed the series of sulfuretted organic compounds obtainable from hydrogen sulfide, indicating that they were precisely analogous to the compounds corresponding to the water type, viz.: "mercaptan,"

$$\left. \begin{array}{c} C_2H_5 \\ H \end{array} \right\} S$$

and "sulfide of ethyl,"

$$\left. \begin{array}{c} C_2H_5 \\ C_2H_5 \end{array} \right\} S$$

which could be obtained by reacting alcohol or ether with pentasulfide of phosphorus; or as had been demonstrated previously in the literature, by replacing one or two atoms of hydrogen or of metal with organic radicals in sulfuretted hydrogen, sulfide of potassium, or sulfide of hydrogen and potassium. He furthermore prepared "othyl hydrosulfuric acid" (also called "thiacetic acid"),[15]

$$\left. \begin{array}{c} C_2H_3O \\ H \end{array} \right\} S$$

by the action of tersulfide of phosphorus on monohydrated acetic acid or of pentasulfide of phosphorus on fused acetate of soda. Similarly, "othyl-sulfide of othyl" (also called "thiacetic acid anhydride" or "anhydrous sulfuretted acetic acid"),

$$\left. \begin{array}{c} C_2H_3O \\ C_2H_3O \end{array} \right\} S$$

was prepared by heating pentasulfide of phosphorus with anhydrous acetic acid. He also reported "othyl-sulfide of ethyl" ("thiacetic acid ether"),

$$\left. \begin{array}{c} C_2H_3O \\ C_2H_5 \end{array} \right\} S$$

in which he was later shown to have been mistaken.

The more detailed German version of this paper of 1854 was more decidedly on the side of Gerhardt and Williamson against Kolbe in the manner of writing formulas. While Kekulé remarked that he had not intended his formulas to be an exact representation of the facts, since he was uncertain about the intermediate products, he nevertheless had no reservations about adopting the Gerhardt formulas based on an "equivalent" of carbon equal to 12, i.e., consistent with the formula $H_2O$ for water in place of HO or $\left\{ \begin{array}{c} HO \\ HO \end{array} \right\}$ which latter would follow from the use of an "equivalent" of 6

for carbon.[16] Kekulé argued that according to the HO view, alcohol and ether ought to be written

$$\left\{ \begin{array}{c} C_4H_5O \\ HO \end{array} \right\} \quad \text{and} \quad \left\{ \begin{array}{c} C_4H_5O \\ C_4H_5O \end{array} \right\}$$

respectively. But how would one then account for the observation that the sulfide of phosphorus produced alcohol mercaptan,

$$\left\{ \begin{array}{c} C_4H_5S \\ HS \end{array} \right\}$$

while the chloride of phosphorus gave ethyl chloride, $C_4H_5Cl$, + HCl in place of

$$\left\{ \begin{array}{c} C_4H_5Cl \\ HCl \end{array} \right\}$$

All of these matters were explained perfectly, thought Kekulé by assuming "that the amount of chlorine equivalent to a single indivisible atom of oxygen is divisible by 2, while the sulfur, like oxygen itself, is *dibasic*, so that 1 atom is equivalent to 2 atoms of chlorine."

Gerhardt, Williamson, Hofmann, and Stenhouse all recognized the importance of Kekulé's experimental investigation in the preparation of the sulfuretted organic acids, and they praised the work highly.[17] In effect, Kekulé's paper helped to confirm Williamson's formula for acetic acid, according to which the oxygen was shared between hydrogen and "othyl," ($C_2H_3O$); for he had shown that the phosphorus sulfides when allowed to act upon acetic acid or its anhydride or ester, produced substances in which only half of the oxygen was replaced by sulfur.

Now if we accept at face value the statements in 1890 of the 61-year-old Kekulé reminiscing about his days in London[2] then we are led to believe that in the year of this paper on sulfuretted acids he was already preoccupied with the fundamentals of his valence theory, i.e., four years before he put any such ideas into any of his papers. According to his own account, which he said contained the "most indiscrete disclosures from my inner life," the first visions of the structural theory came to him while dozing on the outside deck of an om-

---

[15] "Othyle" for "oxygen-ethyle" had been introduced by Williamson for the acid radical $C_2H_3O$. (*J. Chem. Soc.*, 4, 238 (1852)). Gerhardt called the same radical "acétyle" (*Annales de chimie*, [3], 37, 339 (1853)). Kekulé preferred to reserve the name "acetyl" for $C_2H_3$ and so he accepted Williamson's "othyl."

[16] Gerhardt, Laurent, Chancel, and Williamson had by this time all supported the $H_2O$ view, (H = 1, O = 16, C = 12, S = 32) against the HO view (H = 1, O = 8, C = 6, S = 16), which latter was so long defended by Kolbe and others.

[17] Gerhardt wrote that Kekulé's paper had produced a great sensation in the chemical world by opening up a novel way of scientific investigation. The facts and new substances discovered by Kekulé, he wrote, were of such a nature as to contribute considerably to the discussions of certain fundamental questions with which contemporary chemists were occupied. Williamson wrote: "Dr. Kekulé unites great intellectual acuteness and power of generalization with a singularly profound and complete acquaintance with chemical science. . . . The last research of Dr. Kekulé on a new series of organic acids has opened up to science an entirely new field for investigation. . . . These brilliant researches have gained Dr. Kekulé an European reputation among scientific chemists. . . ." Hofmann wrote, "Seine Untersuchung, welche aus einer consequenten Durchführung der Gerhardt'schen Anschauungsweise geflossen, hat die Chemiker mit einer Reihe höchst merkwürdiger Verbindungen bekannt gemacht, deren Existenz in dem System klar gegründet ist, deren Darstellung aber bis jetzt nicht gelungen war." Even Stenhouse attributed to Kekulé an excellent familiarity with theoretical and practical chemistry, but especially "with the views of the more modern French school." See letters in behalf of Kekulé's intended candidature at Zürich, Anschütz, I, 55–58.

nibus after a strenuous evening of chemical discussions with his friend Hugo Müller in London. Diminutive atoms gamboled before his eyes, the smaller ones uniting to form pairs, the larger ones embracing the smaller ones and dragging them behind in a whirling giddy dance. "Thus, the structural theory came into being." But two of Kekulé's friends at Heidelberg "shook their heads in doubt" when he developed his ideas on paper for them. So he quietly put his manuscript in the drawer: "Nonumque prematur in annum." He needed more time to test those dreams "by the awakened understanding."

Kekulé was obviously in no hurry to publish his ideas, but he was constantly preoccupied with them. Von Baeyer remarked in Munich in 1905,[18] on the occasion of his 70th birthday, that while his own motivation for chemical research had been "whatever was fun," his teacher Kekulé was a "born chemical general" who wanted to "command nature." Baeyer said concerning himself: "I did not carry out my experiments to see whether I was right, but to see how substances are related to one another." In contrast, he characterized Kekulé's attitude as one which was basically critical, and directed mainly toward the reorganization of a "mighty amount of material." "Kekulé," said Baeyer, "had no interest in substances themselves, but was only concerned whether they conformed to his ideas. When that was the case, it was fine; if not, they were rejected."

Two years after his famous 1890 speech in Berlin Kekulé was speaking to another audience in Bonn on "selected chapters (aphorisms) from the history of chemistry."[2] He remarked that "age makes one gossipy, and the old are inclined to speak much about themselves." On that occasion he mentioned again that his theory of valency and the structural chemistry had originated in his thinking during his stay in London. He said, "Such ideas were then in the air, [and] sooner or later they would have been expressed; perhaps a year or two later, perhaps in another way than I did." Kekulé went on to attribute his success, both to a preoccupation with architecture, which had led him to think about the spatial representation of atom groups, and to his manifold travels from which he had learned how to separate the good from the bad. He remarked, "I had become an eclectic. I was not captured by the spirit of a narrow school." From Liebig's pupil, to an adherent of the chemical philosophy of Dumas, Gerhardt, and Williamson, Kekulé had become, so he said, a proponent of no school at all. He had become a critic of the theory of types and of compound radicals.

Kekulé made these statements some 32 to 34 years after he had enunciated his valence theory. He was then world famous for it. We might suggest that his views in the 1854 paper were noticeably oriented in the direction of valency considerations, but they certainly were not explicit. Let us then examine some of the experimental investigations which he completed prior to 1858 but in the period after he left London.

## Heidelberg (1856–58)

In 1855, after Kekulé had failed to obtain the candidature for the professorial chair of pure chemistry at the Polytechnic School of Zürich, mostly because Liebig would not recommend him for it, he sought formal admission to an academic lectureship in the faculty of a German university. He eventually chose Heidelberg believing that he would be able to draw large classes in organic chemistry there. Bunsen, who was in charge of the largest laboratory in all of Germany, had by 1855 turned all of his attention to analytical, inorganic, and physical chemistry at Heidelberg and so organic chemistry more or less fell into Kekulé's lap. It did not take long for the unaffected and congenial Kekulé, who was an irresistible academic lecturer, to capture an enterprising group of young men who later distinguished themselves in some branch of chemistry. Among those who were in Heidelberg at the time were Emil Erlenmeyer, Adolf von Baeyer, Hans Landolt, Freidrich Beilstein, Lothar Meyer, Alexander M. Butlerow, and Henry E. Roscoe. Kekulé could speak to the English, French, and Italians in their native tongues, and he knew quite well what was going on in their own countries, chemically speaking.

Lothar Meyer relates[19] what an exciting place Heidelberg was at that time for chemists. Gerhardt's *Traité* was in the process of being published, but the fourth volume containing the key to Gerhardt's whole chemical system had not yet appeared when Kekulé arrived in Heidelberg early in 1856. Kekulé, the young *Dozent*, was an eager apostle of Gerhardt's type theory, and initiated debates against the authority of the traditional dualistic theory which lasted for hours and days, and in which he won his ground point for point. His great dismay was that the inorganic chemists had not yet freed themselves from "the swindle of electro-chemical-dualistic addition."[20] The names of Gerhardt and Williamson were constantly referred to during the organic chemistry lectures, which he delivered with "wahrer Liebhaberei"—so he wrote Williamson in 1856.

Adolf von Baeyer, who left Bunsen's laboratory to join Kekulé in his small one-window laboratory, spoke of the latter as the "Reformator der Chemie," who with his French and English ideas opened up a new world in theoretical chemistry. In his *Erinnerungen aus meinem Leben*[21] Baeyer wrote:

Charmed by the logical consistency of the new theory, which later was baptized as the structural theory, he [Kekulé] constructed, before his enthusiastic listeners, the structure of theoretical chemistry in which we still live today. And even if the fundamental idea of interpreting the types by the valence of the atoms was started by Williamson, and if Couper simultaneously pronounced the tetravalency of carbon, he still has the glory of having founded a unitary system of organic chemistry and having proclaimed it to the world with the enthusiasm of a prophet.

Anschütz has examined a 400-page notebook of a student who attended Kekulés lectures on organic chemistry in the winter semester of 1857/58.[22] It contains a 39-page section entitled "Konstitution und Systematik der organischen Verbindungen," and an appendix with an historical treatment of Gerhardt's type theory. Noteworthy is the fact that Kekulé was then already using the graphic formulas which he introduced into the

[18] Vorfeier des 70. Geburtstages von Adolf von Baeyer, *Z. für ang. Chemie*, **18**, 1617–22 (1905).

[19] MEYER, LOTHAR, Obituary notice for Leopold von Pebal, *Ber.*, **20**, 1000 (1887).

[20] Letter to Williamson, November 1856, Anschütz, I, 70/1.

[21] BAEYER, A. VON, *Gesammelte Werke*, 2 Vols., Braunschweig, 1905, I, xv.

[22] Anschütz, I, 71–72.

first issue of his *Lehrbuch der organischen Chemie* (Erlangen, 1859), in which the mode of union of the atoms in the molecules are made clear.

Kekulé's first experimental communication from his private laboratory in Heidelberg, a paper on the constitution of the fulminate of mercury, was delivered in January of 1857 to the newly-founded *Naturhistorisch-medizinischer Verein* of Heidelberg.[23] By 1857 fulminic acid and the fulminates had been the subject of numerous investigations for over half a century. Howard, Berthollet, Gay-Lussac, Liebig, Berzelius, and Gerhardt had initiated important work on the subject. Gerhardt in his *Précis* in 1844/5 had suggested that fulminic acid was $C^2H^2N^2O^2$ and that the fulminates belonged to a nitrogenous species having the formula $C^2 (H^2X) N$ where X is equivalent to $NO^2$. Accordingly the fulminates, thought Gerhardt, should belong to the genus of the cyanides homologous with the normal species designated by $C^2H^3N$.[24] In his *Traité* of 1854 Gerhardt did not suggest any structure and merely mentioned that while the constitution of fulminic acid was difficult to account for, it seemed reasonable to suppose that it contained $NO_2$ or $NO_4$ groups because of its explosive nature.[25] We should note that the Gerhardt formulas given above are based on an equivalent of 12 for carbon, unlike Kekulé's formulas in the discussion which follows.

In Kekulé's investigations the fulminates were subjected to a number of reactions with chlorine and bromine. The experimental details are unimportant here. He concluded that half of the nitrogen contained in fulminate of mercury was present as $NO_4$, and the other half was combined with carbon as $C_2N$, giving the formula $C_2(NO_4)Hg \ Hg(C_2N)$. "This formula," said Kekulé, "indicates at first glance, that the composition of fulminate of mercury shows the greatest analogy with a large number of known substances, to which, e.g., chloroform belongs: $C_2 \ H \ Cl \ Cl \ Cl$." Kekulé then listed ten substances with their formulas so arranged as to exhibit a marsh gas-like structure, conforming to the type: $C_2 \ H \ H \ H$. He remarked that fulminate of mercury could be looked upon either as nitrated chloroform, i.e., chloropicrin, $C_2(NO_4)Cl \ Cl \ Cl$, in which the chlorine had been replaced in part by cyanogen $(C_2N)$ and in part by mercury; or as acetonitrile, i.e., $C_2 \ H \ H \ H(C_2N)$, which had been nitrated and in which both hydrogens had been replaced by mercury. This would make fulminic acid: nitro methyl cyanide, i.e., nitroacetonitril, or $C_2(NO_4) \ H \ H \ (C_2N)$.

In this paper Kekulé introduced a new type—the marsh gas type—which had not been suggested prior to this time except in a paper delivered to the Royal Institution by William Odling[26] in March of 1855, 22 months prior to Kekulé's report to the *Verein* in Heidelberg. Kekulé may not have known about this work although he expressly mentioned another work of Odling's in his theoretical paper of 1857 which we have already mentioned previously.[3]

[23] KEKULÉ, "Ueber die Constitution des Knallquecksilbers," *Ann.*, **101**, 200–13 (1857); **105**, 279–86 (1858).
[24] GERHARDT, C., *Précis de chimie organique*, 2 vols., Paris, 1844/45. I, 382–84; II, 445.
[25] GERHARDT, C., *Traité de chimie organique*, Vol. 2, 384, Paris, 1854.
[26] ODLING, W., "On the Constitution of the Hydro-carbons," *Roy. Inst. of G. Brit.*, *Proceedings*, **2**, 63–66 (1854–58).

In that theoretical paper Kekulé stated:

In order to avoid detailed historical considerations, I mention at the outset, that most of what follows at least does not lay claim to originality; but [it] rather shall be nothing more than a further explanation of the leading ideas, which Williamson has communicated on occasion and which one might call "the theory of polyatomic radicals": ideas, which Odling first extended in his work on the constitution of acids and salts [*J. Chem. Soc.*, **7**, 1–22 (1855)]; which also have been often repeated in German works since Gerhardt adopted these in part in his IVth volume of his *Traité* (without however conceiving them strictly in the sense of Williamson), and whose suitability now most likely can no longer be questioned, since they have led to the discovery of a great number of exceptionally interesting compounds.

We recall that Odling was Williamson's pupil, and that Kekulé's associations with Williamson in London had been very congenial. There seems to be little doubt that Williamson himself was close to similar ideas. He actually deserves considerable credit for the notion of valency, at least in so far as the combining power of radicals is concerned. For as we have shown, he maintained that oxygen held the hydrogen and ethyl radicals together. Still the notion of valency had to be generalized. In particular it needed to be extended to include the element carbon. In this regard Gerhardt was of no help to Kekulé, and it is unlikely that Kekulé arrived at his marsh-gas-like fulminate formulas through any of Gerhardt's views on the subject. Gerhardt had not used marsh gas as a type, but had accepted the formula $C^4H^2H^6$ for marsh gas as Regnault and Dumas had formulated it. In the last analysis even Kekulé was not quite convinced about his proposed structures when he said, "I am far removed from believing that the suggested reasonable formula is proved from the facts which I have communicated for the fulminate of mercury, and will try next, whether new grounds can be produced for my opinion through a synthesis."

In his second paper on the fulminate of mercury,[22] which was delivered eleven months later, (December 1857), Kekulé attempted, on the one hand, to strengthen his previous argument through additional experiments, and on the other, to criticize the recently suggested structure for fulminate of mercury which had been published by the Russian chemist, Schischkoff, who was then working on this same subject in a laboratory in Heidelberg.[27] Kekulé decided in this second paper that by combining some new reactions of his own on fulminate of mercury with information taken from Schischkoff's paper (which we might suggest was superior experimentally but not theoretically to Kekulé's work) that he could add three new items to the list of substances written to conform with his newly designated marsh gas structure. "All these bodies of one series," said Kekulé, "can be included in one mechanical type; all contain the same number of atoms if one considers the nitro-group $[NO_4]$ and the cyanogen $[C_2N]$ as radicals analogous to the elements; at the same time they

[27] SCHISCHKOFF, L., *Ann.*, **101**, 213–17 (1857). We notice that Kekulé's first paper on fulminate of mercury and Schischkoff's paper were both submitted to Liebig on December 26, 1856; they were published consecutively in the *Annalen*. But this was not done until after Liebig, as editor of the *Annalen* had recommended in a letter to Kekulé (Anschütz, I, 74) that the two men publish their investigations jointly as he and Wöhler had done—which suggestion Kekulé did not follow. See also CHICHKOFF, "Sur la constitution de l'acide fulminique et une nouvelle série de corps dérivés de l'acide acétique." *Ann. chim., Paris*, [3], **49**, 310–38 (1857).

exhibit great differences in their individual properties, being occasioned by the differences in dynamic nature of the elements which have entered into them.''

There is one thing about these two Kekulé papers on the fulminates which is peculiarly puzzling. It is that Kekulé made use of the Kopp-Gmelin-Dumas-Liebig equivalents instead of the Gerhardt-Williamson equivalents. Thus he wrote $C_2H_4$ for marsh gas, instead of $CH_4$; and $C_4H_2N_2O_4$ for fulminic acid instead of $C_2H_2N_2O_2$, etc. Let us recall that in his experimental paper on thiacetic acid, written two years earlier and discussed above,[14] and in the theoretical paper of 1857[3] which falls between the two papers on fulminate of mercury, Kekulé adopted the Gerhardt-Williamson view.

The question which automatically presents itself is whether Kekulé was converted during this time to the older view. It is more plausible to suppose, as Anschütz suggests,[28] that Kekulé was making a concession in conforming to familiar German usage, so that the chemists who would be reading his papers in Liebig's *Annalen* would find the formulas to be in agreement with the editor's own usage and would thus be in a position to judge more readily the value of his work when placed alongside that of Schischkoff's paper on the same subject in the same issue of the *Annalen*. In an unpublished manuscript Kekulé says as much.

The situation with respect to equivalents is also clarified considerably on examining Gerhardt's views. In the *Précis* of 1844/45 Gerhardt used only the newer system of atomic weights (O = 16, C = 12), yet a decade later he used the older system (O = 8, C = 6) in the first three volumes of his *Traité* (1853–56). Then in the fourth volume of that work, published posthumously in 1856, Gerhardt reintroduced his original system in order to spell out the theoretical foundations of the preceding three volumes. Gerhardt, in that volume, clearly stated that his own private position had been consistent all along.[29] He too had apparently conformed to familiar usage. Kekulé could very well have been the only adherent of the Gerhardt-Williamson views in Germany in 1857/58.

One final observation in the light of the above remarks. It may not be unreasonable to suppose that the formulas according to which Kekulé arranged the fulminates by mechanical type analogous to the structure of methane, represent a first theoretical attempt on his part to test the notion of the quadrivalence of carbon. This is accomplished by replacing each $C_2$ by a C in his formulas. I am suggesting that Kekulé may well have conformed to familiar formula usage by writing $C_2$'s (where C = 6) while holding on to his own mental picture of C's (where C = 12). At least so it

seems in retrospect. And even beyond that one might note that in those cases where there are more than two $C_2$'s per formula,[30] that Kekulé was on the threshold of the idea of the self-linking of carbon. This would require that each $C_2$ be replaced by a C and that one designate, in addition, a feasible graphical scheme to show the linkage.

It goes without saying, that the theoretical importance of these two fulminate papers for the growth of Kekulé's valence theory stands, even if we now know that the fulminates have no such structure as he imagined. The final clarification on the question of the structure of the fulminates began in the 1880's and was only completed by John Ulric Nef of the University of Chicago, who proved the carbyloxime structure in 1894.

We must still provide brief comments to the other experimental papers which Kekulé completed in Heidelberg by 1858 before he left for Ghent. A paper on the formation of glycolic acid from acetic acid was delivered to the Heidelberg *Verein* on March 1858.[31] The theoretical importance of this work was that the product obtained from boiling the barium and calcium salts of monochloroacetic acid was identical with glycolic acid which had been obtained by other means. There were not two different modifications as Wurtz had contended. In this paper we also find the beginning of Kekulé's classification of the alcohols and the carboxylic acids as given in the *Lehrbuch* of 1859. Remember, however, that in his paper on glycolic acid, as well as in his papers on fulminate of mercury, Kekulé used the old style formulas written to correspond to the "equivalents" of common usage.

More important, Kekulé recognized this as "the first example of the formation of a *diatomic* (zweiatomig) acid from a *monatomic* (einatomig) acid, of the acetic acid group; in the series of these acids, being precisely what the formation of glycol from alcohol is to the series of the corresponding alcohol." In other words, Kekulé drew attention to the analogy which exists between alcohol and acetic acid when compared respectively with glycol and glycolic acid, in so far as alcohol and acetic acid are both transformed in the process from "monatomic" to "diatomic" substances by the substitution of a diatomic oxygen atom for a monatomic hydrogen atom. In two later theoretical papers of 1857/8 Kekulé demonstrated how to construct a whole structural system of organic chemistry on the basis of experimentally determined substitutions of monatomic atoms by diatomic, triatomic, and tetratomic atoms or groupings.

Three other experimental papers originated in Kekulé's laboratory in Heidelberg. One of these was on "chloralid," which was first identified by Wallach in 1875 as trichlorolactic acid ethylidene chloride ether. The other two papers were on chemical physiology. The first of these, on saccharification in the liver, was an investigation in which Claude Bernard's *matière glycogène* was prepared in pure form and analyzed. The

[28] ANSCHÜTZ, I., 85–86; GRAEBE, C., *Geschichte der organischen Chemie*, Berlin, **1920**, p. 180.

[29] GERHARDT, C., *Traité de chimie organique*, Vol. 4, Paris, **1856**, p. 586, "Quelques chimistes cependant, saisissant mal ma pensée, supposent à mes types la même signification qu'aux types moléculaires sur lesquels M. Dumas a développé, il y a longtemps déjà ["Mémoire sur la loi des substitutions et la théorie des types," *Comptes Rendus*, **10**, 149 (1840)] des spéculations fort ingenieuses; mais je dois réclamer contre cette assimilation, quelque précieux qu'un si haut patronage puisse être pour le succès de mes vues; car à la vérité, il n'y a de semblable que le nom, emprunté à la langue vulgaire, et mes types signifient tout autre chose que les types de M. Dumas, ceux-ci se rapportant à l'arrangement supposé des atomes dans les corps, arrangement qui, dans mon opinion, est inaccesible à l'experience. Mes types sont des *types de double décomposition*."

[30] As in Kekulé's fulminic acid, $C_2(NO_4)H\ H(C_2N)$; fulminate of mercury, $C_2(NO_4)Hg\ Hg(C_2N)$; acetonitrile, $C_2\ H\ H\ H(C_2N)$; and trichloroacetonitrile, $C_2\ Cl\ Cl\ Cl(C_2N)$.

[31] KEKULÉ "Bildung von Glycolsäure aus Essigsäure," *Verhandlungen des naturhistorischmedizinischen Vereins zu Heidelberg*, **1**, 105–107 (1857–59); *Ann.*, **105**, 286–92 (1858).

other paper, by Friedrich and Kekulé, was on the degeneration of the so-called amyloids (starches) of the spleen. None of these papers need concern us further here, but they do indicate the breadth of Kekulé's experimental undertakings.

The most important experimental work to come from a student in Kekulé's private laboratory at Heidelberg was Baeyer's paper on the constitution of cacodyl compounds.[32] In this communication Baeyer demonstrated that the addition of chlorine to cacodyl chloride (dimethyl arsenic chloride) was analogous to the addition of chlorine to ammonia. The resulting addition product was easily decomposed with mild heat yielding methyl chloride and monomethyl arsenic dichloride. In Baeyer's paper, as in Kekulé's on the fulminate of mercury, the formulas for the cacodyls were written in a schematic way designed to indicate the type.

A rather revealing aspect of Baeyer's paper was his observation that, whereas Dumas' plan to designate organic compounds according to mechanical type, based on similar genetic series, had not been widely accepted, the constitution of certain organic substances had in fact, he believed, already been elucidated by the drawing of mechanical analogies in reactions where the disruption of the substance was accomplished by a replacement of one element with an element of another kind. The example which Baeyer cited was Frankland's work on zinc ethyl where he compared the binding of metal and oxygen to that of ethyl and oxygen, specifically calling attention to the fact that the ethyl was analogous to hydrogen and not to oxygen. The difficulties vanish, Baeyer contended, "if the right atomic weight of oxygen is taken, and if the formulas, which contain an odd number of atoms of the same, are doubled." We know that one of the most pressing chemical problems in the 1850's was connected with the search for unambiguous values of the saturation capacity, atomicity, or valency of the elements. Frank-

land's experiments (1850–54)[33] with the metal alkyls provided a basic solution to that problem, at least for a limited group of organometallic compounds. The reference to the zinc alkyls in Baeyer's paper indicates that precisely those Frankland papers were well known in Kekulé's laboratory which Frankland later mentioned in connection with his own claims as discoverer of the valence theory.

This completes our discussion of Kekulé's experimental activities relative to the question of his valence theory up until and including the year of his fundamental theoretical paper on the quadrivalency and self-linking characteristics of carbon in 1858. We have seen that he had carried out publishable experimental investigations in Will's laboratory in Giessen on amylsulfuric acid (1850), in Von Planta's private laboratory in Switzerland on volatile alkaloids and mineral analyses (1853/54), in Stenhouse's laboratory at St. Bartholomew's Hospital in London on thiacetic acid (1854), and finally as a *Dozent* in his own privately arranged and financed laboratory at Heidelberg on fulminate of mercury, glycolic acid from acetic acid, saccharification of the liver and the so-called amyloids of the spleen (1857/58). This is not an unimpressive record for a young man of age 29.

It remains to be shown how Kekulé manipulated his own experimental results and those of others to formulate an explicit and general valence theory for organic compounds based upon the assumption of a quadrivalent and self-linking carbon atom. It is beyond the scope of this paper to present that aspect of Kekulé's contribution, since it would entail a careful analysis of his two theoretical papers of 1857 and 1858. Much of what Kekulé had to say in those papers had already been implied in the early experimental papers which we have discussed above. To spell out the detailed implications of Kekulé's more mature treatment of the theory would constitute a further investigation into the developmental history of the modern valence theory.

[32] BAEYER, A. VON, "Ueber die organischen Arsenverbindungen," *Ann.*, **105**, 265–76 (1858).

[33] FRANKLAND, E., *J. Chem. Soc.*, **2**, 263–96 and 297–99 (1850); **3**, 30–52 and 322–47 (1851); **6**, 57–71 (1854).

---

# ● ADOLF VON BAEYER

**RALPH E. OESPER**
**University of Cincinnati, Cincinnati, Ohio**

ADOLF BAEYER (born at Berlin, October 31, 1835) succeeded Liebig at the University of Munich in 1875. Here he built up not only the physical facilities but developed the most outstanding chemical school in Germany—perhaps in the world. He trained many leaders of the growing German chemical industry and an astounding number of the most distinguished university teachers and investigators came from his circle of students. He had an uncanny ability to pick out men of promise and to keep the inept at a distance. He was the leader of the movement to insure a high quality of chemical instruction throughout all of Germany.

His work on phthaleins, acetylene, indigo, the constitution of benzene, oxonium compounds, etc., testifies to his caliber as an organic chemist. His strain theory rendered yeoman service for many years. He followed the advice he gave his young associates: "Whatever you choose, do not seek to carry out easy tasks; devote

yourselves especially to difficult problems." He was a master in limiting himself to the essential things; he had no love for the complicated. Test-tube experimentation was his specialty. He once wrote: "What makes the great scientist? He should not dominate but listen, and adapt himself to what he has heard and change himself accordingly. The old empiricists did this, they laid their ears to nature. The modern scientist does the same, and I have tried to follow this method. Men are affected in a peculiar manner when they get close to nature. They then develop in a manner quite different from one who approaches nature with a preconceived idea."

His health was excellent throughout his entire life. Not until he reached 80 did the infirmities of old age become insistent enough to lead to his retirement. He died on August 20, 1917, and is buried in the Waldfriedhof in Munich.

Henry M. Leicester
College of Physicians & Surgeons
San Francisco, California

# Contributions of Butlerov to the Development of Structural Theory

The basic theory enunciated by Kekulé and Couper in 1858 made possible all the modern developments of structural organic chemistry, but neither Kekulé nor Couper at first went beyond a bare theortical statement or attempted to make any practical applications. Nevertheless, almost as soon as the theory was announced, one investigator realized its full significance and began to think in essentially modern terms. Alexander Mikhailovich Butlerov (1), on the basis of the doctrine of the tetravalence of carbon, was able to establish the principles upon which organic chemistry made its greatest advances. He coined the term "chemical structure," recognized the existence of structural isomers and the number of theoretically possible isomers for a given empirical formula, explained tautomerism, and used the theory as a guide in the synthesis of new and important classes of compounds. All of this was accomplished in the early years of the 1860's, while most other chemists were still trying to free themselves from the confusion of the various type theories.

However, the implications of the structural theory soon began to impress many younger organic chemists, and they too began to use structural ideas, often without realizing that such ideas had already been expressed. Butlerov was keenly aware of his priority in this field, and when he was directly challenged, he did not hesitate to state his claims. Toward the end of the decade, a rather bitter controversy over the question of priority took place between Butlerov and Lothar Meyer. The bitterness was perhaps intensified by a certain spirit of nationalism which is apparent behind the immediate statements of the participants. The Russian school of chemists tended to feel that western scientists neglected their work, while the Germans were not inclined to undervalue the work of their compatriots. It is worth noting, however, that Kekulé himself took no part in the controversy, and Butlerov only entered it when he felt directly attacked, and then his statements were calm and well reasoned. A survey of this controversy casts much light on the early development of the structural theory.

Butlerov had been appointed professor of chemistry at the University of Kazan in 1854, but he had not carried out any important original work during his first years in the chair. In 1857 he was sent abroad for a year of study in Germany and France. During this critical period, in which Kekulé and Couper were developing their theories and preparing them for publication, Butlerov made the personal acquaintance of both men. He made a lengthy visit to Heidelberg during which he developed a lasting friendship for Kekulé, and he studied for five months in the laboratory of Wurtz in Paris, where Couper was also working. There is no doubt that during this year he became well acquainted with the theory of "the chemical nature of carbon."

When he returned to Kazan in August, 1858, he had already begun to develop his ideas on structure. The basic starting point of his thought was that for any given structural formula there existed only one compound, and for any individual compound only one formula could be written. He discarded the idea of Gerhardt who had said that the formula for a compound should vary according to its different methods of synthesis or reaction. Thus Butlerov discarded the type theory altogether. Kekulé continued to use type formulas in his textbook for several years.

By 1861, Butlerov's formulation was so clear to himself that he felt able to present it to western chemists. He read a paper to a meeting of German naturalists at Speyer on September 19, 1861 (2) in which he first used the term "chemical structure."[1] His definition was as follows:

Starting from the assumption that each chemical atom possesses only a definite and limited amount of chemical force (affinity) with which it takes part in forming a compound, I might call this chemical arrangement, or the type and manner of the mutual binding of the atoms in a compound substance by the name of "chemical structure" (4).

When Butlerov returned to Kazan, he made a report to the University Senate in which he summed up his impressions of chemical theory in western Europe.

None of the ideas which I found in western Europe seemed especially new to me. Laying aside here misplaced false modesty, I can say that these ideas and conclusions have been quite familiar in recent years in the Kazan laboratory and they have not been considered especially original; they were part of the general chemical inheritance and some were introduced into the lectures (5).

Butlerov now began to contribute a number of papers on aliphatic hydrocarbons and alcohols to western chemical journals. In these he showed that on the basis of structural theory it was possible to predict the number of isomers of various homologous hydrocarbons. His exposition was essentially that used at present in introducing the concept of isomerism in elementary organic chemistry courses.

Other chemists, with increasing frequency, gradually began to use similar structural formulas without realizing that Butlerov had preceded them. At length, in

Presented as part of the Kekulé-Couper Centennial Symposium on the Development of Theoretical Organic Chemistry before the Division of History of Chemistry at the 134th Meeting of the American Chemical Society, Chicago, September, 1958.

[1] Menshutkin (3) has pointed out that this term was actually first applied by Lomonosov in 1760, but this usage did not become generally known.

1867, he felt that he must assert his claims to priority. He appended a footnote to his discussion of the number of isomers of $C_4H_{10}$ theoretically possible (6), in which he said:

. . .I have given the theoretically possible structures of the hydrocarbons $C_5H_{12}$. One of these, $C(CH_3)_4$, is completely analogous to the case of $C(CH_3)_2(C_2H_5)_2$; a hydrocarbon which has this latter structure was recently discovered by Friedel and Ladenburg. It is clear that if once the formula $C(CH_3)_4$ is given, so must also the structural case $C(CH_3)_2(C_2H_5)_2$ be foreseen. It appears, however, that Friedel and Ladenburg have neglected the fact that the view which they have newly expressed is entirely analogous to that already given by me much earlier. I must expressly mention that in the chemical literature of recent years such ideas as those I have already published are presented as new and original (without citation).

He then indicated that many chemists, including Lothar Meyer, had made unjustified claims, and concluded,

The estimation of the mutual chemical method of binding elementary atoms in molecules (the principle of chemical structure) will more and more be the chief basis of most chemical speculations in the newer chemistry; of the need for this estimation I have already spoken, and I am now obliged to assert that to me belongs an important part of the priority for complete and consequential development of this principle. This assertion of mine, as I hope, will be found to be solidly based, if one will make a closer acquaintance with my publications which have appeared since 1861.

The mention of Lothar Meyer resulted from a paper which the latter chemist had published in 1866 (7) in which he discussed the presence of "unsaturated affinities" (double bonds) in ethylene chloride as follows:

Without the assumption of unsaturated affinities, the constitution of both compounds would be identical, namely: HHCCHCl; with the other assumption there are three possible cases:

.HHCCHCl.        ..HCCHHCl        ..ClCCHHH

where the monovalent atom next to the C atom is held by this atom and the unsaturated affinity is expressed by a dot.

It can be seen that Meyer was actually using a structural formula in these cases, and he apparently felt that Butlerov was aiming a personal attack at him. He therefore published a bitter counterattack at his assumed foe, which he entitled "To the Defense" (8).

In setting up this formula I have neither intended nor believed that I was establishing a claim to priority. Nor does such a right in the least belong to Prof. Butlerov. This and a thousand other formulas are the obvious consequence of the two propositions that carbon is a tetravalent element and that its atoms and all other elements in its compounds are arranged in chains. Both propositions are a part of the rich heritage developed through the tireless work of numerous investigators of organic chemistry. But the first of these propositions was clearly recognized and expressed first and only by A. Kekulé in 1857. The discovery of the second proposition Kekulé divided with A. S. Couper. Kekulé, however, combined these propositions long before Prof. Butlerov, who learned of the chain formation from Kekulé and suggested calling it structure. The establishment of these formulas, carried out through a long series of combinations, permutations, and calculus of variables, required in concrete cases neither unusual genius nor great gifts of discovery. Whether one chemist should express schematically the series of signs which expressed the order of atoms from left to right, as is usual in Europe, or like the Hebrew, from right to left, or like the Chinese, from above down, is merely a matter of taste. Whoever by writing down formulas of this type intends to establish a property right deceives himself. . .he claims things as his newly discovered property which are the common goods of science through the services of others years before.

It can here be seen that Meyer completely misinterpreted the real significance of Butlerov's contributions, reading them as a mere manipulation of symbols and that he committed the very common error of claiming that because a given point of view was becoming obvious to everyone, the man who first realized the meaning of this point of view deserved no credit.

Butlerov was not slow to accept this new challenge. At the time he was making a third trip to western Europe, largely for the purpose of defending his claims, and he was at this time in Nice. From there he sent his reply, which he entitled simply "An Answer" (9).

I always was and still am far from misunderstanding the brilliant services of Kekulé in the theoretical and practical branches of our science. I hold, like Herr Meyer, that the idea of chemical structure is a consequence of the recognition of the valence of elements and especially the proposition first recognized and expressed by Kekulé that carbon is tetravalent. I also believe that the idea of chain formation by atoms cannot be neglected. Also I believe that the views expressed by Couper (unfortunately only briefly) are almost identical with those generally accepted and that the formulas given by Couper are actually rational formulas in the present sense of the word, that is, constitutional formulas or formulas of chemical structure.

But what Herr Meyer says about the development and expanded use of these new propositions will, as I believe not be accepted completely by an impartial man.

Aside from the recognition of the new propositions, we still find for several years longer much which had either become superfluous or did not agree with these propositions. This includes the use of types, both compound and mixed, the old way of determining formulas by reaction only, so that for one and the same substance several rational formulas could be given, etc. Similarly, assumptions which did not entirely agree with the new principles were not entirely absent from the writings of Kekulé even *after* I expressed my views on chemical structure and made them the basis for the chief principles of my theoretical speculations. . . . I place no value on the outward appearance of formulas.

After a challenge to Meyer to reread his various papers, Butlerov concluded that he would not "shrink my contribution to developing the new principles to the mere name 'chemical structure' and the use of a certain way of writing formulas."

This reply seems to have ended the polemical part of the battle. It is probable that Butlerov's acknowledgment of the importance of Kekulé's work silenced the German critics. At the same time he stated his own contribution so clearly that it could scarcely be denied. Instead, another fate overtook it. It became so much a part of the basic framework of organic chemistry that it was taken for granted, and the work of the originator was forgotten. This is usually the fate of those who make the initial steps in what later becomes a whole new science in itself.

## Literature Cited

(1) LEICESTER, H. M., J. CHEM. EDUC., 17, 203 (1940).
(2) GUMILEVSKIĬ, L., "Alexander Mikhailovich Butlerov, 1828–1886," Moscow, 1952, p. 152.
(3) MENSHUTKIN, B. N., "Chemistry and the Way of Its Development," Moscow and Leningrad, 1937, p. 204.
(4) KAZANSKIĬ, B. A., PETROV, A. D., AND BYKOV, G. V., "Selected Works of A. M. Butlerov in Organic Chemistry," Moscow, 1951, p. 557.
(5) MENSHUTKIN, N. A., J. Russ. Phys. Chem. Soc., 19, Butlerov Memorial No., 2–12 (1887).
(6) BUTLEROV, A. M., Ann., 144, 9 (1867).
(7) MEYER, L., Ann., 139, 286 (1866).
(8) MEYER, L., Ann., 145, 124 (1868).
(9) BUTLEROV, A. M., Ann., 146, 260 (1868).

**Aaron Ihde**

University of Wisconsin,
Madison

# The Unraveling of Geometric Isomerism and Tautomerism

## Geometric Isomerism

After he had introduced the concept of the tetrahedral carbon atom and used it to explain the optical isomerism of the tartaric acids, malic acid, sugars, camphor, and other compounds, Van't Hoff turned to another type of isomerism which appeared to be a consequence of the tetrahedral atom, namely, *"The influence of the new hypothesis upon compounds containing doubly linked carbon atoms.* Double linking is represented by two tetrahedrons with one edge in common. . ." *(1)*.[1]

Van't Hoff pointed out that when two tetrahedrons are joined on an edge (Fig. 1) and the four points carry

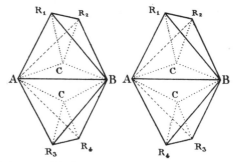

Fig. 1. Isomers possible by joining the edges of tetrahedra (after Van't Hoff).

univalent groups, $R_1$, $R_2$, $R_3$, and $R_4$, possibilities for isomerism occur when $R_1$ differs from $R_2$ and $R_3$ differs from $R_4$. This does not preclude an identity of, for example, $R_1$ and $R_3$ and $R_2$ and $R_4$.

Van't Hoff then called attention to several instances of isomerism where the structures had not been properly resolved, but which were amenable to his interpretation. Let us look at the case of fumaric and maleic acids, his first example.

Malic acid was isolated from apple juice by Scheele in 1785. Dry distillation of this acid led to the discovery, in 1817, of fumaric and maleic acids by Braconnot and independently by Vauquelin. Studies by Pelouze in 1836 pointed toward the isomerism of the two acids although the state of organic formulation at this date was too chaotic for certainty on this matter. Liebig in 1838

Presented as part of the Kekulé-Couper Centennial Symposium on the Development of Theoretical Organic Chemistry before the Division of History of Chemistry at the 134th Meeting of the American Chemical Society, Chicago, September, 1958.

[1] This Dutch publication *(1)*, carrying Van't Hoff's paper in French, appeared in September, two months before Le Bel's paper on the same subject in *Bull. soc. chim.*, **22**, 337–47 (1874). Van't Hoff's paper was published in enlarged French translation in 1875 under the title, "La chimie dans l'espace." Both papers are found in English translation in Richardson *(2)*. Quotation from the latter, p. 42.

also obtained the same composition for the two acids but considered the higher melting fumaric acid to be a polymer of maleic acid. Erlenmeyer put forth this explanation in 1870 and again in 1886. Kekulé *(3)* succeeded in reducing both acids to succinic acid in 1861. Later, when attempting to write structures for such isomers, some chemists were inclined to assume the presence of a bivalent carbon atom, as in the case of carbon monoxide. Kekulé, however, was firmly committed to the quadrivalency of the carbon atom and considered the only really appropriate structures to be,

$$
\begin{array}{ll}
-\mathrm{CH \cdot COOH} & \mathrm{CH_2 \cdot COOH} \\
\ \ \ | & \ \ \ | \\
-\mathrm{CH \cdot COOH} \ \text{and} & =\mathrm{C-COOH} \\
\text{"Fumaric acid"} & \text{"Maleic acid"}
\end{array}
$$

The problem of the structure of maleic and fumaric acids was closely associated with the three isomeric acids, $C_3H_4(COOH)_2$, produced from citric acid by pyrolysis. These acids, named itaconic, citraconic, and mesaconic, were first encountered by Lassaigne *(4)* in 1822 and were extensively studied in Kekulé's laboratory by Swarts *(5)*. These investigators postulated four possible structures, each with the carboxyl groups at the ends of straight carbon chains and with two unattached valence bonds on one or two of the central carbon atoms. Kekulé and Swarts believed that such structures were consistent with the properties, but in the second paper they arrived at a genuine double bond in an alternative structure for mesaconic acid when explaining the conversion of itaconic and citraconic acids to mesaconic acid by hydrobromic acid. An analogy to fumaric acid led to the formulas,

$$
\begin{array}{ll}
\mathrm{CH \cdot COOH} & \mathrm{CH \cdot COOH} \\
\ \ \| & \ \ | \\
\mathrm{CH \cdot COOH} & =\mathrm{C \cdot COOH} \\
\text{"Fumaric acid"} & \text{"Maleic acid"}
\end{array}
$$

which were popular for several years.

Still another formula for maleic acid was introduced by Richter *(6)*.

$$
\begin{array}{l}
\mathrm{CH_2} \\
\ \| \\
\mathrm{C(COOH)_2}
\end{array}
$$

Kekulé rejected this since it was inconsistent in properties with other compounds where two carboxyl groups were present on the same carbon atom. Maleic acid lost water on heating, being converted into an anhydride, whereas such dicarboxylic compounds as isosuccinic acid lost carbon dioxide on heating,

$$
\underset{\substack{\text{Isosuccinic acid} \\ \text{(Methyl malonic acid)}}}{\mathrm{CH_3 \cdot CH \cdot (COOH)_2}} \xrightarrow{\Delta} \underset{\text{Propionic acid}}{\mathrm{CH_3 \cdot CH_2 \cdot COOH} + CO_2}
$$

Maleic acid with the Richter formula should therefore decompose to acrylic acid.

$$CH_2\!\!=\!\!C(COOH)_2 \xrightarrow{\Delta} CH_2\!\!=\!\!CH\cdot COOH + CO_2$$

Furthermore, on hydrogenation it should yield isosuccinic acid rather than succinic acid.

$$CH_2\!\!=\!\!C(COOH)_2 \xrightarrow{H_2}$$
$$CH_3\cdot CH\cdot(COOH)_2 \quad [HOOC\cdot CH_2\cdot CH_2\cdot COOH]$$
Presumed \qquad\qquad Observed

Van't Hoff recognized that the dilemma might be easily resolved by the application of his principle involving the joining of two tetrahedral carbon atoms on an edge. This gave the structures,

H—C·COOH \qquad\qquad H—C—COOH
H·C—COOH \qquad\qquad HOOC—C—H
Maleic Acid \qquad\qquad Fumaric Acid

He saw signs of similar isomerism in such pairs as brommaleic acid and iso-brommaleic acid, citraconic and mesaconic (methylmaleic and methylfumaric) acids, and liquid and solid crotonic acids.

Solid crotonic acid was discovered in the seeds of *Croton tiglum* by Pelletier and Caventou (7), and isolated from croton oil by Schlippe (8). Will and Körner (9) prepared the acid synthetically from allyl cyanide. As a result of this synthesis the formula was considered to be

$$\dot{C}H_2\!\!=\!\!CH\cdot CH_2\cdot COOH \qquad\qquad (1)$$

A decade later Kekulé (10) found that crotonaldehyde was formed during the condensation of acetaldehyde. He went on to show that the formula of the solid crotonic acid formed therefrom by air oxidation had the formula,

$$CH_3\!\!-\!\!CH\!\!=\!\!CH\cdot COOH \qquad\qquad (2)$$

and showed that crotonic acid formed from allyl cyanide also had formula (2), as the result of the migration of the double bond during synthesis. However, a liquid crotonic acid was known and the assumption was made that this had formula (1) (11).

Van't Hoff argued that it was more logical to assume that the liquid and solid crotonic acids both had formula (2) since they both gave almost quantitative yields of acetic acid upon fusion with KOH, both gave acetic and oxalic acid on oxidation, and the liquid acid isomerized to the solid acid on heating at 170–180°C. He felt that the isomerism that existed was similar to that found in maleic and fumaric acids. The correctness of his reasoning was shown later when vinylacetic acid was synthesized and found to have structure (1) (12). Van't Hoff included in this same class the chlorocrotonic and chloroisocrotonic acids prepared by Geuther (13).

The papers of Van't Hoff and Le Bel were received with a good deal of skepticism and since Van't Hoff's was more imaginative and broader in its scope he naturally came in for the bulk of the criticism. Le Bel had introduced the concept of the asymmetric carbon atom but had not gone on to suggest a geometry of the atom. Van't Hoff had, on the other hand, directed the four valences of the carbon atom toward the corners of a tetrahedron and used the tetrahedron freely in his explanations. He had also dealt with the nature of double and triple bonding which Le Bel had overlooked in his original treatment of the subject.

Kolbe, in typically cantankerous fashion, castigated Van't Hoff as an example of the backward trend in German chemical research, the regeneration of the discredited *Naturphilosophie* which had stood discredited for fifty years as the result of investigations in exact science. He dismissed the work with (14):

A Dr. J. H. van't Hoff, of the veterinary school at Utrecht, finds as it seems, no taste for exact chemical investigation. He has thought it more convenient to mount Pegasus (obviously loaned by the veterinary school) and to proclaim in his "La chimie dans l'espace" how during his bold flight to the top of the chemical Parnassus, the atoms appeared to him to have grouped themselves throughout universal space.

Fittig opposed the Van't Hoff proposals for fumaric and maleic acids, preferring to use the Kekulé formulas. Fittig and his students (15) studied the removal of hydrogen bromide from the two isomeric dibromsuccinic acids and postulated the following changes:

CHBr·COOH \qquad\qquad CHBr·COOH
CHBr·COOH \quad—HBr→ \quad =C·COOH
Dibromsuccinic acid \qquad "Brommaleic acid"

CH₂·COOH \qquad\qquad CH·COOH
CBr₂·COOH \quad—HBr→ \quad CBr·COOH
"Isodibromsuccinic acid" \qquad "Bromfumaric acid"

Claus (16), Lossen (17), and Hinricksen (18) were among those who criticized the theory on the basis of incompatibility with physical laws (19). The physical science of the time was not prepared for a concept in which the forces of the atom were oriented in several different directions.

There were, however, certain organic chemists who overlooked the alleged taint with *Naturphilosophie* and the incompatibility with physical theory to apply the concepts to the practical problems of structural organic chemistry facing them at the time. There were numerous cases of structurally unexplained isomerism to which the new concepts were applicable. Johannes Wislicenus was clearly the leader in recognizing the value of the new theory. Soon after seeing the French version of Van't Hoff's book he wrote enthusiastically to the author urging translation of the work into German. Felix Hermann, one of Wislicenus' students, undertook the translation which was published in 1877 as "Die Lagerung der Atome im Raume," with a preface by Wislicenus.

Wislicenus was active, during the next two decades, in the pursuit of structural problems. It was partly his early work with lactic acid which had led Van't Hoff to recognize the nature of the asymmetry of optically active carbon compounds. Now Wislicenus proceeded, through the application of Van't Hoff's theoretical constructs, to work out the structure of a variety of compounds. A large part of his work dealt with optical isomerism but his work with the isomers of monochloropropylene, bromobutylene, dibromobutylene, chlorocrotonic acid, and the maleic-fumaric acid pair represented significant pioneering with the new concept of geometric isomerism (20). At the same time a number of other workers, notably Fittig, Erlenmeyer, Michael, Beilstein, and Anschütz, were attempting to solve structural problems without use of the new concepts. After a succession of failures some of these workers slowly came to accept the new viewpoint (21).

The correct selection of *cis* or *trans* configuration for individual isomers was seldom an easy matter and in certain cases could not be made for many years. In the case of maleic and fumaric acids the *cis* form was assigned to maleic acid by Van't Hoff because of the ease with which the anhydride was formed upon warming the acid.

HC—COOH        HC—C     O
                              \
   ‖              →     ‖       O
                −H₂O          /
HC—COOH        HC—C     O

Of course this was not clear proof since it was known that isomerization took place under a variety of conditions, particularly in the presence of halogens and halogen acids. Fumaric acid gave the same anhydride but much more slowly and at higher temperatures. Studies on the cold water hydrolysis of maleic anhydride formed from either maleic or fumaric acids always resulted in the formation of maleic acid.

The research which had been done on the two acids was subjected to a lengthy and critical analysis by Wislicenus (*22*) who concluded that the *cis* form for maleic and the *trans* form for fumaric acid were most consistent with the facts. This was based very largely on the addition reactions of the two unsaturated acids and on the rearrangements brought about by the halogens and hydrohalogen acids. Ossipoff (*23*), Anschütz (*24*), Petri (*25*), and Kekulé had made such studies with the finding that maleic esters were readily converted into the more stable fumarate form.

Kekulé (*26*) and Anschütz (*27*) showed that the oxidation of maleic with alkaline permanganate resulted in the formation of *meso* tartaric acid whereas the oxidation of fumaric acid gave the racemic mixture of *dl*-tartaric acids. Wislicenus (*28a*), assuming that no rearrangement took place during the permanganate oxidation, argued that the opening of the double bond of maleic acid would result in formation of the internally compensating form of tartaric acid regardless of which bond was opened (see Fig. 2).[2] With fumaric acid, however, the opening of one bond (2,2′) would give *d*-tartaric acid, the other (1,1′) would give *l*-tartaric acid (see Fig. 3). Wis-

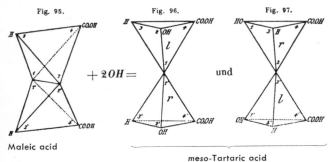

Figure 2.

Maleic acid

meso-Tartaric acid

² Figures 2–5 are from Wislicenus' paper (*20*).

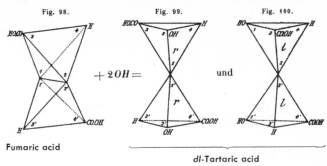

Fumaric acid

dl-Tartaric acid

Figure 3.

oratory their optical behavior was not clearly established. In 1925 Terry and Eichelberger (*29*) showed that *cis* addition is not characteristic of bromination, maleic acid yielding *dl*-dibromosuccinic acid, fumaric acid the *meso* form.

Wislicenus was aware of the influence of halogens and hydrohalogen acids in the conversion of maleic into fumaric acid. There were also cases where one acid was converted into a derivative of the other. In extensive researches Wislicenus (*28b*) showed that, following halogenation, quantities of hydrohalogen acids became detectable in the reaction mixture. This led him to suggest a mechanism in which halogenation was followed by rotation to a "most favored position" and splitting out of a hydrohalogen molecule (*28c*). Thus, for maleic acid ("Fig. 78") bromination produced dibromosuccinic acid ("Fig. 79") which then rotated to the "most favored position" ("Fig. 80"), after which hydrogen bromide split out to give bromofumaric acid ("Fig. 81").

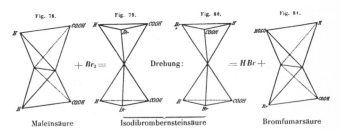

Maleïnsäure        Isodibrombernsteinsäure        Bromfumarsäure

Figure 4.

In a similar manner he explained the formation of bromomaleic acid from fumaric acid in the presence of bromine ("Figs. 74–77"). By analogous reasoning he showed that in the presence of hydrobromic acid, maleic acid would be converted into fumaric acid, whereas fumaric acid would remain unconverted. This was in accord with experimental observations.

Wislicenus went on to apply his reasoning to other cases of geometric isomerism. For the three pyrolysis products of citric acid he showed that itaconic acid could

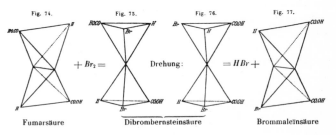

Fumarsäure        Dibrombernsteinsäure        Brommaleïnsäure

Figure 5.

licenus went on to suggest that the characteristics of the dibromosuccinic acids formed on bromination of maleic and fumaric acids must be entirely analogous. While these acids had been prepared in Kekulé's lab-

show no geometric isomerism and was assigned the formula below. Citraconic acid, because of its easy convertibility into mesaconic acid by hydrobromic acid was assigned the *cis* form.

$$CH_2$$
$$|$$
$$C—COOH \qquad\qquad CH_3—C—COOH \qquad\qquad CH_3—C—COOH$$
$$| \qquad\qquad\qquad\quad ‖ \qquad\qquad\qquad\qquad ‖$$
$$CH_2·COOH \qquad\quad H·C—COOH \qquad\qquad HOOC—C—H$$

Itaconic acid $\qquad$ Citraconic acid $\qquad$ Mesaconic acid

Although Wislicenus attempted to deal with the isomerism of solid crotonic and liquid crotonic acids he was unable to relate them to an unambiguous reference compound, and his analysis of their reactions led him to assign the *cis* form to solid crotonic acid.

The correct orientation of the crotonic acids was not finally established until 1923 when Von Auwers (*30*) was able to relate the solid acid to fumaric acid by preparation of each acid from a common substance under conditions where rearrangement around the double bond was unlikely.

$$CCl_3—C—H \qquad\quad Zn, HAc \qquad\quad CHCl_2—C—H \qquad\quad Na(Hg) \qquad\quad CH_3—C—H$$
$$‖ \qquad\qquad\quad\longrightarrow \qquad\qquad ‖ \qquad\qquad\quad\longrightarrow \qquad\qquad ‖$$
$$H—C—COOH \qquad\qquad\qquad\quad H—C—COOH \qquad\qquad\qquad H—C—COOH$$
$$\qquad\qquad\qquad\qquad\qquad\qquad\qquad\qquad\qquad\qquad\qquad\qquad\qquad\qquad Crotonic\ acid$$
$$\qquad\qquad\qquad\qquad\qquad\qquad\qquad\qquad\qquad\qquad\qquad\qquad\qquad\qquad (solid)$$

Conc. $H_2SO_4$ at 30° $\qquad\qquad\longrightarrow \qquad\qquad HOOC—C—H$
$$‖$$
$$H—C—COOH$$
Fumaric acid

Cinnamic acid shows the same relationship, the higher-melting natural form having the *trans* configuration. Here again Wislicenus attempted to deal with the orientation but confessed inability to make a decision with certainty. He tentatively but erroneously decided in favor of the *cis* form for the natural acid.

Following the pioneering work of Wislicenus there has been continued progress in establishing the geometric structure of unsaturated compounds although the problem is frequently fraught with danger when superficial studies are made. Greatest confidence can be had in those cases where the *cis* isomer can be related to a compound of unquestionable structure through ring closure or ring opening. After the structure of a number of isomers was clearly established, physical properties were found to vary in a definite manner between isomers and this has become a useful tool, at least for indicative value. Melting points were found to be lower for *cis* isomers, while solubility in inert solvents, dissociation constants (of acids), and heats of combustion were found lowest for *trans* isomers (*31*). Debye (*32*) established the configuration of the two dichloroethylenes by measuring the distance between chlorine atoms from X-ray diffraction patterns. In the lower melting isomer, which had been termed *cis*, the distance was 3.6 Å whereas in the other isomer the distance was 4.1 Å. Other physical properties have been utilized with some success.

The geometric isomerism of nitrogen compounds was recognized about 1890. Goldschmidt (*33*) observed two isomeric benzildioximes ($C_6H_5C:NOH)_2$, as early as 1883. Victor Meyer and Von Auwers (*34*) verified the isomerism of these two compounds and discovered a third isomer. They sought to explain the isomerism by postulating restricted rotation between two of the car-

bon atoms. About this time Beckmann (*35*) prepared an isomer of benzaldoxime, $C_6H_5CH:NOH$, which he considered to be a structural isomer. Goldschmidt (*36*), however, established the general structural identity of the two isomers as oximes.

In 1890, Hantzsch and Werner (*37*) pointed out that if the three valences of nitrogen did not lie in the same plane, the oximes might be expected to show a *cis-trans* type of isomerism. Thus, the two benzaldoximes were formulated as

$$C_6H_5—C—H \qquad\qquad\qquad C_6H_5—C—H$$
$$‖ \qquad\qquad\qquad\qquad\qquad\qquad ‖$$
$$N—OH \qquad\qquad\qquad\qquad HO—N$$

*syn*-Benzaldoxime $\qquad\qquad$ *anti*-Benzaldoxime

and the three benzildioximes as

$$C_6H_5—C—C—C_6H_5 \qquad C_6H_5—C————C—C_6H_5$$
$$‖ \quad ‖ \qquad\qquad\qquad ‖ \qquad\qquad ‖$$
$$HO—N \quad N—OH \qquad\qquad NOH \quad HON$$

$$\qquad\qquad\qquad\qquad\qquad\qquad C_6H_5—C————C—C_6H_5$$
$$\qquad\qquad\qquad\qquad\qquad\qquad ‖ \qquad\qquad ‖$$
$$\qquad\qquad\qquad\qquad\qquad\qquad N—OH \quad N—OH$$

*anti* $\qquad\qquad$ *syn* $\qquad\qquad$ *amphi*

This type of reasoning was found consistent with the experimental knowledge of the known aldoximes, ketoximes, dioximes, oximido acids, hydrazones, and related compounds, although some problems were encountered with such oximes as were involved in tautomeric phenomena.

Once the tetrahedral character of the nitrogen valences was established it was apparent that geometric isomerism should be observed not only in those compounds with a carbon to nitrogen double bond but also in those with a nitrogen to nitrogen double bond. Isomeric diazo compounds, which began to be reported during the nineties, were at first interpreted by their discoverers as structural isomers. It was largely through the work of Arthur Hantzsch at Leipzig that the matter was clarified as another instance of geometric isomerism (*38*).

**Tautomerism**

During the 1860's and 1870's various pieces of evidence were accumulating which suggested that certain compounds had properties which were consistent with more than one formula. This was the case with Kekulé's explanation of the failure to observe two *ortho*-disubstituted benzenes, but it was even more striking in the case of certain other compounds. The compound of greatest interest was acetoacetic ester but there were enough other examples to show that the phenomenon was not unique to this compound.

Acetoacetic ester was first prepared in 1863 by Geuther (*39*) who believed that acetic acid contained replaceable hydrogen atoms and attempted to prepare a sodium salt of ethyl acetate by reaction with metallic sodium. The evolution of hydrogen was observed along with the formation of a crystalline compound having the formula, $C_6H_9O_3Na$. It was learned that ethyl alcohol needed to be present in the reaction mixture so that sodium ethoxide, which served as a catalyst, would be formed. Acidification of the crystalline compound gave a liquid which was neutral to litmus but reacted with bases to form salts. The sodium salt with ethyl iodide gave an ethyl derivative. The compound was named ethyl diacetic ester and was formulated as,

$$CH_3 \cdot \overset{OH}{\underset{}{C}} = CH \cdot \overset{O}{\underset{}{C}} - OC_2H_5$$

The nature of the reactions involved was not clearly understood until the work of Wislicenus (40) more than a decade later.

Shortly following Geuther's original work the same compound was prepared by Frankland and Duppa (41). In contrast to Geuther, they observed the ketonic character of the compound and named it acetone carboxylic ester which came to be formulated as

$$CH_3 \cdot \overset{O}{\underset{}{C}} \cdot CH_2 \cdot \overset{O}{\underset{}{C}} \cdot OC_2H_5$$

Various investigators who studied the compound reported variant properties. The structural formulas proposed for the ester emphasized the presence of unsaturation and an active hydroxyl group on the one hand, ketonic character on the other. Through the work of Claisen, this and similar compounds came to have great usefulness in organic syntheses.

Butlerov (42) prepared two isomeric di-isobutylenes in 1877 by the action of sulfuric acid on trimethyl carbinol. He assumed the formation of these isomers on the assumption of an equilibrium between the two hydrocarbons, water, and the corresponding alcohols. Butlerov suggested the existence of such isomerism even in the absence of a reagent. "In these cases in every investigation concerning the chemical structure of the substance, the molecule will always behave in two or more isomeric forms. It is clear that the chemical reactions of such a substance must occur in accordance sometimes with one and sometimes with the other chemical structure, depending on the reagent and on the experimental conditions." He used as examples the cases of cyanic and prussic acids, the former suggesting an equilibrium mixture of carbimide and cyanogen hydroxide, the latter a mixture of the nitrile and isonitrile. These speculations were to ultimately receive experimental support (42a).

When Erlenmeyer (43) in 1878 attempted to isolate alcohols with the hydroxyl group directly attached to double-bonded carbon by treatment of appropriate halogen derivatives with metal hydroxides he obtained in every case the isomeric carbonyl compound, and concluded that alcohols of this type undergo conversion into carbonyl compounds at the moment of formation. Baeyer (44) encountered similar difficulties when he isolated two isomeric methylisatins with the formulas,

(I)                    and                    (II)

These supposedly came from the same parent compound (IV) since he was unable to isolate the equivalent of formula (III) which would be expected to be

(III)                    (IV)

the precursor of (I).

The name *tautomerism* (Gr., *tauto*, the same) was introduced for such cases by Conrad Laar (45) when he discussed the phenomenon in 1885. He pointed out that one substance could combine the properties of two isomers, giving as examples, isatin, ethyl acetoacetate, and the identity of *para*-nitrosophenol and quinone monoxime, and of benzeneazo-alpha-naphthol and alpha-naphthaquinonephenylhydrazone. He postulated a change in the position of a hydrogen atom, resulting in the existence of two structures in equilibrium with one another. As Schorlemmer remarked a few years later (46),

The atoms within the molecule are in continual motion, and thus one form of a compound changes into another; the light atoms of hydrogen, the comet of the elements, moving the quickest, gets outside the sphere of attraction of a heavier atom, and comes within the sphere of attraction of another one. But if we replace hydrogen by an element or radical, moving more slowly, the latter does not get beyond the sphere of attraction, and the unstable form becomes a stable one.

Thus, the formula for acetoacetic ester came to be written in two forms, for which Brühl (47) proposed the names *enol* and *keto*.

*Enol* form                    *Keto* form

P. Jacobson (48) objected to the term, *tautomerism*, since he felt that it implied a continuously changing constitution. He preferred to believe that both forms of the compound were present in a stable state with change from one into the other occurring only under the influence of certain reagents. He proposed the term *desmotropy* (Gr., *desmos*, ligament; *tripein*, to change) which suggested a change in atomic linkage. Hantzsch and Hermann (49) proposed that both terms be used, *desmotropes* for such compounds as could be isolated in one form or both, *tautomers* for such cases where isolation of a pure structural form was not possible. *Desmotropy* has gradually fallen into disuse with *tautomerism* referring to the dynamic equilibrium of two readily interconvertible isomers.

Butlerov (42) was the first to recognize a case of such equilibrium through his preparation and study of the di-isobutylenes in 1877. The acid-catalyzed equilibrium was postulated to be

$$(CH_3)_3C \cdot CH = \overset{CH_3}{\underset{}{C}} \cdot CH_3 \rightleftharpoons (CH_3)_3C \cdot CH_2 \cdot \overset{CH_3}{\underset{}{C}} = CH_2$$

Twenty years later Wilhelm Wislicenus (50) isolated two ethyl formlyphenylacetates, a solid unreactive toward ferric chloride and a liquid which gave a color with the iron salt. On standing the solid slowly isomerized to the liquid form

$$\underset{\underset{\text{Solid}}{\overset{|}{\text{HC}}=\text{O}}}{\text{C}_6\text{H}_5\cdot\text{CH}\cdot\text{COOC}_2\text{H}_5} \qquad \underset{\underset{\text{Liquid}}{\overset{|}{\text{HC}}-\text{OH}}}{\text{C}_6\text{H}_5\cdot\text{C}\cdot\text{COOC}_2\text{H}_5}$$

About this same time Claisen (51) reported results of studies which led to the isolation of dibenzoyl acetone in two solid modifications. While the molecular weights were identical they showed marked differences in their chemical properties, especially toward metallic salts and alkalies. One form exhibited acid properties and with ferric chloride gave an intensely colored salt. The other form exhibited no acidic properties and was indifferent toward ferric chloride. This indifferent form, however, passed into solution upon standing but the salt formed was that of the other modification. Claisen diagnosed the two forms to be the *enol* and *keto* forms in 1896 and suggested the structures,

$$\underset{\underset{\text{\textit{Enol} form (reactive)}}{\overset{|}{\text{OH}}}}{\text{CH}_3\cdot\text{C}=\text{C}(\text{COC}_6\text{H}_5)_2} \qquad \underset{\underset{\text{\textit{Keto} form (inert)}}{\overset{||}{\text{O}}}}{\text{CH}_3\cdot\text{C}\cdot\text{CH}(\text{COC}_6\text{H}_5)_2}$$

Hantzsch (52) isolated two isomers of phenylnitromethane, a solid form with acidic character and a neutral liquid. Claisen and others obtained similar results with other compounds. In some cases at least two pure solid substances in *keto* and *enol* form were shown to be capable of passing into each other without a reagent being present. An equilibrium mixture was formed. If a reagent capable of reacting with one form was added the reactive form was constantly regenerated from the non-reactive form until the reaction is complete. The cases studied by Claisen were all slow-reacting which made it possible to observe what was happening. Claisen never recognized the reversibility of the change because he never obtained his *keto* form in pure state. W. Dieckmann (52a) later demonstrated this fact and proved the interconvertibility.

At an earlier point W. Wislicenus and L. Knorr recognized the reversibility of the change. Wislicenus obtained a liquid *enol* and a crystalline *keto* form of a certain compound and showed that the equilibrium mixture could be obtained from either direction.

In 1911 Knorr (53), and independently, K. H. Meyer (54), succeeded in obtaining ethyl acetoacetate in two modifications. The crystalline *keto* form was obtained by cooling a concentrated solution of the ester in petroleum ether, hexane, or methyl ether at $-78°C$. The *enol* form was obtained by decomposing a suspension of the sodium compound in petroleum ether with a limited amount of hydrogen chloride at the same low temperature. The *keto* crystals melted at $-39°C$. They gave no coloration with ferric chloride and remained stable at ordinary temperatures for several days if catalysts were rigidly excluded. Hydrochloric acid, ferric chloride, or even a trace of tobacco smoke caused them to revert to the equilibrium mixture in a few seconds. The *enol* ester gave an immediate intense coloration with ferric chloride but on holding it passed into the same equilibrium mixture as was obtained from the *keto* form.

With the growth of use of electronic structures in explaining organic combination it was natural that electronic mechanisms would be introduced into the explanation of tautomerism. From an analysis of electron affinity J. F. Thorpe, Robert Robinson, and particularly C. K. Ingold deduced the effects of neighboring groups on nearby electrons (55). Of course, there have been numerous cases where the existence of separate forms in equilibrium has not been demonstrable, yet a single formula is inadequate to explain the properties of the compound. Here the resonance concept of Pauling (56) has been of great value in the interpretation of structure.

## Literature Cited

(1) *Archives néerlandaises des sciences exactes et naturelles*, 9, 445–54 (1874).
(2) "Foundations of Stereochemistry. Memoirs by Pasteur, Van't Hoff, Le Bel, and Wislicenus," transl. and ed. by G. M. Richardson, New York, 1901.
(3) Kekulé, A., *Ann.*, Suppl. 1, 129 (1861); Suppl. 2, 85 (1862).
(4) Lassaigne, J. L., *Ann. chim. phys.*, [2], 21, 100 (1822).
(5) Swarts, Th., *Z. für Chem.*, n.s., 2, 721 (1866); 3, 646 (1867).
(6) Richter, V. von, *Z. für Chem.*, n.s., 4, 453 (1868).
(7) Pelletier, P. J., and Caventou, J., *J. Pharm.*, 4, 289 (1818).
(8) Schlippe, T., *Ann.*, 105, 21 (1858).
(9) Will, H., and Körner, W., *Ann.*, 125, 273 (1863).
(10) Kekulé, A., *Ann.*, 162, 77, 309 (1872); *Ber.*, 6, 386 (1873).
(11) Geuther, A., *Z. für Chem.*, n.s., 6, 27 (1870).
(12) Fittig, R., and Roeder, F., *Ber.*, 16, 2592 (1883).
(13) Geuther, A., *Jena. Z. Med. Naturw.*, 1, 265 (1864).
(14) Kolbe, H., *J. prakt. chem.*, n.s., 15, 473 (1877).
(15) Fittig, R., and Dorn, L., *Ann.*, 188, 87 (1877); Fittig, R., *Ann.*, 95; Fittig, R., and Petri, C., *Ann.*, 195, 56 (1879).
(16) Claus, A., *Ber.*, 14, 432 (1881).
(17) Lossen, W., *Ann.*, 204, 336 (1880); *Ber.*, 20, 3306 (1887).
(18) Hinricksen, F. W., *Ahren's Samml. Chem. u. Chem-Techn. Vorträge*, 7, 189 (1902).
(19) Sementsov, A., *Am. Scientist*, 43, 97 (1955).
(20) Wislicenus, J., *Ber.*, 20, 1008 (1887); *Abhandl. königl. sachs. Gesell. Wissensch. Leipzig.*, *Math-Phys. Classe*, 14, 1 (1887). Cited hereafter as *Abhandl.*
(21) Friedrich, R., *Ann.*, 219, 362 (1883); Beilstein, F., *Ber.*, 17, 2262 (1884); Michael, A., *Ann.*, 215, 249 (1882); *Ber.*, 15, 16 (1882); 19, 1378, 1381 (1886); 20, 550 (1887).
(22) Wislicenus, J., *Abhandl.*, p. 27.
(23) Ossipoff, J., *Ber.*, 12, 2095 (1879).
(24) Anschütz, R., *Ber.*, 12, 2282 (1879); *Ann.*, 226, 191 (1884).
(25) Petri, C., *Ann.*, 195, 62 (1879).
(26) Kekulé, A., *Ann. Suppl.*, 2, 91 (1863); *Ann.*, 130, 1 (1864).
(27) Kekulé, A., and Anschütz, R., *Ber.*, 13, 2150 (1880); 14, 713 (1881).
(28) (a) Wislicenus, J., *Abhandl.*, pp. 35–36; (b) *Ann.*, 246, 61 (1888); (c) *Abhandl.*, p. 32.
(29) Terry, E. M., and Eichelberger, L., *J. Am. Chem. Soc.*, 47, 1067 (1925).
(30) von Auwers, K., and Wissenbach, H., *Ber.*, 56, 715 (1923).
(31) Ostwald, W., *Z. physik. Chem.*, 3, 242, 278, 380 (1889); *Ber.*, 24, 1106 (1891); Bader, R., *Z. physik. Chem.*, 6, 315 (1890); Walden, P., *Z. physik. Chem.*, 8, 495 (1891); Kortright, F. L., *Am. Chem. J.*, 18, 370 (1896); Stohmann, F., *Z. physik. Chem.*, 10, 416 (1892); Louguinine, W., *Ann. chim.*, [6], 23, 189 (1891); Roth, W. A., and Stoermer, R., *Ber.*, 46, 260 (1913); Roth, W. A., and Ostling, G. J., *Ber.*, 46, p. 317.
(32) Debye, P., *Physik. Z.*, 31, 142 (1930).
(33) Goldschmidt, H., *Ber.*, 16, 2176 (1883).
(34) Meyer, V., and von Auwers, K. F., *Ber.*, 21, 784, 3510 (1888); von Auwers, "Die Entwicklung der Stereochemie," Heidelberg, 1890, pp. 54–133.
(35) Beckmann, E. O., *Ber.*, 20, 2766 (1887); 22, 429 (1889).
(36) Goldschmidt, H., *Ber.*, 22, 3113 (1889).
(37) Hantzsch, A., and Werner, A., *Ber.*, 23, 11 (1890).
(38) Hantzsch, A., *Ber.*, 27, 701 (1894) *et seq.*; "The Elements of Stereochemistry," transl. by C. G. L. Wolf, Easton, Pa., 1901, p. 172, *et seq.*

(39) GEUTHER, A., *Jahresbericht*, 1863, 323; *Nachrichten Königl Gesellschaft Wissensch., Göttingen*, 1863, 281.

(40) WISLICENUS, J., *Ann.*, 186, 161 (1877); 190, 257 (1878); 192, 159 (1878); 206, 308 (1881); *Ber.*, 7, 683 (1874); 10, 2226 (1877); 11, 251 (1878); 14, 843 (1881).

(41) FRANKLAND, E., AND DUPPA, B. F., *J. Chem. Soc.*, 19, 395 (1866); 20, 102 (1867).

(42) BUTLEROV, A., *Ann.*, 189, 76 (1877).

(42a) WERNER, E. A., *J. Chem. Soc.*, 103, 1010 (1913); USHERWOOD, E. H. (Ingold), *J. Chem. Soc.*, 121, 1604 (1922).

(43) ERLENMEYER, E., *Ann.*, 192, 119 (1878); *Ber.*, 13, 309 (1880).

(44) BAEYER, A., *Ber.*, 15, 2093 (1882); 16, 2193 (1883).

(45) LAAR, C., *Ber.*, 18, 648 (1885); 19, 730 (1886).

(46) SCHORLEMMER, C., "The Rise and Development of Organic Chemistry," Rev. Edn., London, 1894, p. 183.

(47) BRÜHL, J. W., *J. prakt. Chem.*, 50, 123 (1894).

(48) JACOBSON, P., *Ber.*, 20, 1732 (1887); 21, 2628 (1888).

(49) HANTZSCH, A., AND HERMANN, F., *Ber.*, 20, 2801 (1887).

(50) WISLICENUS, W., *Ann.*, 291, 147, 160, 176 (1896); *Ber.*, 32, 2839 (1899).

(51) CLAISEN, L., ET AL., *Ann.*, 277, 162, 184 (1893); 291, 25, 93 (1896).

(52) HANTZSCH, A., *Ber.*, 29, 2256 (1896); 32, 622 (1899); 39, 1084 (1906).

(52a) DIECKMANN, W. *Ber.*, 49, 2203 (1916).

(53) KNORR, L., *Ber.*, 44, 1138 (1911).

(54) MEYER, K. H., *Ann.*, 380, 220 (1911).

(55) BAKER, JOHN W., "Tautomerism," New York, 1934, pp. 1–11, *et passim*.

(56) PAULING, L., "The Nature of the Chemical Bond," 2nd ed., Ithaca, N. Y., 1948, pp. 424–29, *et passim*. Also see SIDGWICK, N. V., TAYLOR, T. W. J., AND BAKER, W., "The Organic Chemistry of Nitrogen," Oxford, 1937, *passim*.

---

# The Contributions of Fritz Arndt to Resonance Theory

E. Campaigne
Indiana University
Bloomington

**K**ekulé's ideas on tetravalence and self-linking of carbon atoms, which were so important in the development of structural theory, were described in 1858, just one hundred years ago. Only seven years later, in 1865, Kekulé (*1*) showed how these ideas could explain the composition and anomalous behavior of the "aromatic" substances, by assuming the structure of benzene as a nucleus of six carbon atoms in a ring, with alternating single and double bonds. Kekulé believed, but was unable to prove, that the six combining positions of benzene were identical. The Kekulé structure has been called "the most fruitful single suggestion in the history of organic chemistry"(*2*).

During the next decade, Kekulé's first postulate that the six combining valences of benzene were equivalent was quickly demonstrated by Ladenburg and Wroblewsky and then by Körner, with the first applications of what was later to be called the "absolute" method. Thus within ten years the structure of benzene as a symmetrical hexagon with six equivalent hydrogen atoms was pretty well established. At the same time, a much more difficult problem was presented, that of the actual location and function of the six carbon valences of benzene which are not needed to hold the atoms in place. Kekulé himself soon suggested (*3*) that oscillation occurring between the two possible arrangements of the double bonds (I) would account for the non-existence of certain isomers of disubstituted benzenes, and be more consistent with the apparent lack of

unsaturation in aromatic compounds.

(I)

However, the concept of moving bonds in molecules was never quite satisfactory, and several other suggestions to account for the unused carbon valences in a manner consistent with the "aromatic" chemical properties of benzene were put forward. Among these were the Claus *para*-bond formula, II, and the Armstrong-

(II)      (III)

Baeyer centric formula III. Perhaps the best of these suggestions was advanced by Thiele (*4*), and was based on his ideas of partial valence used to explain the α-, γ-reactions observed in olefins containing alternating single and double bonds. This he called "conjugation," and he pointed out that in benzene the conjugation was cyclic and endless, and therefore unreactive. This suggestion was valuable in that it related "aromatic" character to the behavior of certain aliphatic compounds, but, like previous suggestions, it depended on unorthodox valence concepts.

Regarding these suggestions, F. G. Arndt states (*5*):

Kekulé's idea of the oscillating double bonds in benzene was the closest approximation to the resonance interpretation of benzene and similar molecules achieved during all the time from Kekulé up to 1924. I think this is so because Kekulé's idea represented the state of benzene as one in which both Kekulé formulas have equal shares, without altering the valencies as such; whereas all the later theories of Thiele, Kauffmann, Werner, Weitz, and others, introduced "partial valencies," "secondary valencies," "free

Presented as part of the Kekulé-Couper Centennial Symposium on the Development of Theoretical Organic Chemistry before the Division of History of Chemistry at the 134th Meeting of the American Chemical Society, Chicago, September, 1958. Contribution No. 877 from the Chemistry Laboratories of Indiana University.

valencies," etc., which turned up and disappeared again arbitrarily. All these attempts within the framework of unitarian theory, though useful in detail, were contradictory to the fundamentals of stoichiometry which are based on the *indivisible* units of valence. So Kekulé's idea, and the theories of Thiele, Weitz, and others cannot be regarded as anticipations of the theory of resonance because they missed the main point, namely, the interrelation between valencies and *ionic changes*. In all resonating systems zwitterionic structures are involved, even in the case of benzene where the reaction formulas for aromatic substitution are zwitterionic.

With the development of the electronic theory of valence about 1916, ideas based on the work of Langmuir, Lewis, and others on electrical charges began to be applied to organic molecules. An important idea presented at this time was the suggestion (6) regarding the amino-acids as molecules containing separated charges (Zwitterions). However, the problem of the non-bonding valences of benzene was still being considered in terms of unusual partial valence or oscillating valence concepts in the early 1920's (7).

In 1924, Fritz Arndt published the first paper containing the "resonance hybrid" idea (8), which within the next ten years was firmly established as the proper explanation of aromatic behavior by the molecular orbital calculations of Hückel (1932) and the valence-bond treatment of Pauling and Wheland (1933). In 1934, Ingold (9) used the term "mesomerism" meaning "between the parts" for this concept, and this term has been widely adopted to describe modern views of resonance.

Arndt (8) dealt with the nature of bonds in pyrone ring systems. It was well known the $\gamma$-pyrones (V) did not exhibit the characteristic reactions of olefins or ketones, such as addition of halogens or reaction with phenylhydrazine, etc. Nor does $\gamma$-pyrone give the

(IV)   (V)   (VI)   (VII)   (VIII)

characteristic halochromic reaction of the doubly unsaturated ketones in strong acid. To explain this peculiar "aromatic" character of $\gamma$-pyrone, Collie (10) had suggested the oxonium oxide formula, VI, containing a tetracovalent ring oxygen atom. In 1924 (8) Arndt wrote formulas IV and VII, showing $\gamma$-pyrone and $\gamma$-thiopyrone as zwitterion dipolar molecules. More important, he clearly recognized that the two formulas, betainic dipoles, IV and VII, on the one hand and unsaturated ketones, V and VIII, on the other, were limiting structures only. He wrote (11):

It is to be emphasized that both formulas, and especially formula VII, represent formulations of extremes; dimethylthiopyrone, as shown by its solubilities, etc., is certainly not such a clear-cut betainic dipole as formula VII would indicate. But with the new views (Zwitterions) according to which no new bond across the ring is involved but all boils down to a shift of electronic orbitals, any intermediate states (Zwischenstufen) can be conceived.

Regarding this publication, Arndt later wrote (5):

You see that in this paper I have, to save space, not inserted the Collie formula, but at once translated it into the zwitterionic

formulas IV and VII. Later on I had reason to regret this: some authors got it into their heads that my zwitterionic formula was Collie's. Confronting the Collie formula and formula IV would have better shown the decisive transition from classical unitarian theory to electronic theory. What I had in mind in 1923–24 was this: The objections of earlier authors (WILLSTÄTTER AND PUMMERER, *Ber.*, **38**, 1463 (1905)) to the Collie inner salt idea of the pyrones were due to Collie's misleading formula based on classical onium theory. But a few years before 1924 Pfeiffer had shown that inner salts have to be regarded as zwitterions (see footnote 7 on page 1905).[1] So the Collie formula has to be replaced by formula IV. But this formula, in contrast to the Collie one, shows no bond between the two oxygen atoms, so the objections are no longer valid; and it shows the same order of sequence of all the linked atoms as does the ketonic formula V (or VIII). And in such cases the real state of the system can be regarded as being in between the two formulas; the real intermediate state depends on constitutional factors as shown all over paper 1 (Ref. 8). It should be noted that Sir Robert Robinson, one of the first pioneers of electronic theory, formulated in 1925, i.e., only one year after my first paper, the potential electronic shifts in pyrones and similar systems which would lead from distribution V to distribution IV. In doing so he made a more detailed use of electronic theory than I had at first done; but he did not speak of a definite "intermediate state" of the molecule in between V and IV.

Although the 1924 paper referred experimentally only to pyrones and thiopyrones, the Zwischenstufe theory was quite a general one; but to revert to it in other papers I had to wait for experimental material. During 1924–29 my co-workers, e.g., Eistert and the students who attended my Breslau lectures, heard much more about it. During the 1920's every author of organic papers in Germany had to contend with severe rules of utmost brevity; it happened very often that papers were returned for abbreviation, and any organic theory was frowned upon. So I could express theoretical views only in connection with experimental work, and even then only very shortly. In 1927 I tried to publish a general theoretical paper on the idea of "Zwischenstufe" and "Zwischenzustand" (resonance), but I was told to insert such views in experimental papers.

In 1925, it was shown (12) that when the extra electron pairs of the sulfur atom in 1-thio-$\gamma$-pyrone (IX)

(IX)   (X)

are tied up by oxidation to the sulfone (X), the resonance is no longer possible and the 1-thio-$\gamma$-pyrone dioxide shows, in fact, the typical functional group reactions of a diolefinic ketone, in contrast to the behavior of IX. These ideas were applied to nitrogen heterocycles in 1929 (13) when in discussing the chemistry of carbostyril (XI) the betaine-bond system XII was

(XI)   (XII)

proposed to account for the inactivation of the ring double bond. In 1930, a paper on $\gamma$-pyridones appeared (14) in which the difference between tautomeric equilibrium and Zwischenstufe was discussed in modern terms of electron resonance. "Formulas VIII and IX" (Keto and Zwitterion formulas of $\gamma$-pyridones) "show the

---

[1] This footnote reads, "Formula IV stands in the same relationship to the Collie formula as the Pfeiffer betaine formula does to the old ring formula of Betaine." Ref. 8, p. 1905, footnote 7.

Figure 1. The Breslau Laboratories, 1928. Seated, front, left to right: Amende, Arndt, unidentified. Standing, rear, left to right: Martius, unidentified, Eistert, unidentified, Bakir, Partale.

same position of all atomic nuclei and differ only in the electron orbitals, whose shifts proceed so fast that every pair of formulas represents one single molecule..." (15). Arndt writes (5):

As this paper was partly misunderstood by Von Auwers, I at long last succeeded in getting the general paper (16) (on Equilibrium and Intermediate stages) accepted. This paper sums up, I think, the whole theory as far as it could be developed at that time, with no quantum mechanics. To get it published I had to do some bickering with the Editors; the physical chemists among them made me insert the lines on page 2964 about "Verweilzeit" (duration) and "Ubergangzeit" (transition time) and on p. 2965 about "Quantenstufe"; but as I did not want to commit myself so much to the oscillation model of Zwischenstufe I then inserted the lines on page 2965 which I translate: "Whether the limiting states symbolized by the formulas are reached at all (and, therefore, the Zwischenzustand has to be expressed by a time integral of electronic motion) or whether the electronic system remains, even in the strictest sense, always suspended in balance between the limiting states, that is a question which can perhaps be raised and answered from the point of view of quantum and wave mechanics; from the chemical point of view it is irrelevant." As you know, the answer was given three or four years later by the quantum mechanical work of Pauling and Hückel, and rather in favor of the second alternative.

In 1932, similar ideas regarding Zwischenstufe in amide linkages, particularly in the case of cyclic amides, appeared in a paper with Martius (17). The subject of mesomerism of the amide group and the aromaticity of cyclic amides appeared in many later papers with Eistert and others.

Regarding the development of the Zwischenzustand theory, Arndt wrote (5):

During the years 1924–32 my publications referring to the general chemical theory of Zwischenstufe (resonance hybrid) and Zwischenzustand (resonance) were too scattered and the whole idea too unconventional, to be generally accepted or even universally noticed. It only gained momentum when, in 1933–35 the quantum mechanical work of Pauling, Hückel, and Ingold confirmed it independently and put it on a much sounder physical basis. At that time I was already at Istanbul as a refugee from the Nazi regime. In 1935 Eistert wrote me: "Look here, Meister, your views which I have known for 10 years are now emerging in the theory of resonance; you simply must publish something to connect the two." But as a black sheep in Nazi Germany I could not hope to publish such a paper alone, so Eistert did it together with me. (This paper, entitled "About Resonance and Zwischenstufen Ideas in Organic Substances with Multiple Bonds and Their Electronic Formulas" (18) relates the chemical ideas of previous papers to current ideas on resonance, and provides an excellent bibliography of the early work leading to resonance concepts.) A year later the concept of Zwischenzustand or resonance was spoken of and used for a rational mecha-

nism of the Claisen condensation: (in a paper with Eistert (19)) on page 2382 both of these terms were replaced by Ingold's term mesomerism, and since then the term Mesomerie has been the current one in German and French literature.

In 1938 the need was felt in Germany for a book elucidating the importance of electronic theory in general and its application to tautomerism and mesomerism. Under normal circumstances, Arndt probably would have been invited to write such a book, but at that time his book publications were forbidden by the Nazis An excellent review by his former colleague, Eistert (20) was published.

Arndt's appreciation of the implications of the Zwischenstufe theory are indicated by the work done while visiting the laboratories of Robinson, after leaving Germany in 1933. In a paper entitled, "Studies on Dielectric Polarisation, XII. Dipole Moments and Structures of Thiopyrones and Related Compounds" (21), it was pointed out that 2,6-diphenylthiopyrone cannot exist exclusively either as the ketone (XIII) nor as the betainic dipole (XIV) since the calculated mo-

ment for XIII was 1.5 and that of XIV nearly 20, whereas the observed value was 4.4. Moreover, using data of Lorentz obtained at Breslau (22) on heats of combustion of XIII, the related saturated compound XV, and their respective sulfones XVI and XVII, it was shown that compound XIII possessed $80 - 47 = 33$ kcal of "resonance" stabilization.

Heats of combustion

| XIII | = 2165 kcal | XV | = 2268 kcal |
|------|-------------|-----|-------------|
| XVI | = 2118 kcal | XVII | = 2188 kcal |
| $\Delta_1$ | $= -47$ kcal | $\Delta_2$ | $= -80$ kcal |

### Fritz Arndt

Fritz Georg Arndt was born in 1885. After receiving the doctorate from Freiburg in 1908, he worked as research assistant to Von Auwers and Gatterman at Freiburg. He was appointed University Assistant at Kiel in 1910, and Lecturer in Chemistry there in 1912. In 1915 Arndt became Professor of Chemistry at the Imperial Ottoman University of Constantinople. Following the Armistice, he returned to Germany in 1918 and was appointed extraordinary Professor of Chemistry at Breslau, being promoted to Professor in 1927 (see Fig. 1). Dismissed by the Nazis in 1933, he was invited to join the Department of Organic Chemistry at Oxford as researcher and guest lecturer. In 1934 he left Oxford to accept the chair of General Chemistry at the University of Istanbul. He was a guest lecturer at a Conference on Organic Sulfur Compounds, held at Indiana University in the summer of 1951, and he was

Figure 2. Fritz Arndt (Visiting Professor, Indiana University, 1954).

visiting Professor of Chemistry at Indiana University in the spring of 1954 (see Fig. 2). During this visit to the United States he delivered the Reilly lectures at Notre Dame and the Priestley Lecture at Pennsylvania State University. He retired from the University of Istanbul in 1955, and is now lecturing at Hamburg University as an honorary professor. In the spring of 1957 he circled the globe, giving lectures in Egypt, Australia, and various universities in the United States, on new problems regarding resonance in unusual heterocycles.

His continued interest in problems of resonance and mesomerism is illustrated by the great number of his later papers in which research was undertaken to provide evidence for the correctness of the theory, including its more modern refinements, one of the most recent appearing in 1956. Concerning these, Arndt wrote (5):

The most important "refinement" which I used later on is the influence which coplanarity has on mesomerism and resonance energy. This very important knowledge is due exclusively to the quantum mechanical theory of resonance. I had not anticipated it and I do not think it could have been arrived at from chemical evidence alone.

The attached bibliography will serve as a guide to these later papers on mesomerism. It is not intended to be exhaustive, but rather as a guide to the general trend of Arndt's later work on resonance.

It is apparent from the preceding that Fritz Arndt was one of the very first to clearly appreciate the difference between tautomerism and resonance, and to conceive of a stable resonance hybrid structure for aromatic compounds. His contributions to this area of chemical thought have been many and continuous from 1924 until the present.

## Acknowledgment

I am indebted to Professor Arndt for many enlightening letters and conversations, and for a large collection of reprints. In particular I wish to acknowledge his several long letters during the summer of 1957, when I requested his assistance in preparing this paper, and the photograph of the early days at Breslau.

## Bibliography

ARNDT, F., AND SCHOLZ, H., "Carbonyl and Sulfonyl Chlorides and Diazomethane," Ber., 66, 1912–14 (1933).

ARNDT, F., "Action of the Sulfonyl Group," J. Am. Chem. Soc., 59, 759–60 (1937).

ARNDT, F., AND EISTERT, B., "Tautomerism and Mesomerism of the Carbonamide Group, and Their Relation to Light Absorption," Ber., 71, 2040–49 (1938).

ARNDT, F., AND LOEWE, L., "Stereoisomeric Enolethers, Acetals and the Claisen Condensation," Ber., 71, 1631–40 (1938).

ARNDT, F., EISTERT, B., AND JENSEN K. A., "Stereoisomerism and Mesomerism. Structural Requirements for Mesomerism," Ber., 72, 202–212 (1939).

ARNDT, F., LOEWE, L., AND CAPUANO, L., "The Production, Tautomerism, and Reactions of γ-Chloroacetoacetic ester," Rev. Fac. Sci., Istanbul, 8, 122–52 (1943).

ARNDT, F., "Tautomerism and Aromatic Resonance in Cyclic Carbonamides," Rev. Fac. Sci., Istanbul, 9, 19–29 (1944).

ARNDT, F., LOEWE, L., AND GINKOK, R., "Enolization, Solvation and Chelation," Rev. Fac. Sci., Istanbul, 11, 147–67 (1946).

ARNDT, F., LOEWE, L., AND ERGENER, L., "The Problem of the Fine Structure of Carbon-Containing Ring Systems," Rev. Fac. Sci., Istanbul, 13, 103–26 (1948).

ARNDT, F., LOEWE, L., AND TARLAN, A., "Tautomerism and Methyl Derivatives of Urazoles," Rev. Fac. Sci., Istanbul, 13, 127–46 (1948).

ARNDT, F., "Problem of the Fine Structure of Heterocyclic Oxygen Compounds," Angew. Chem., 61, 397–400 (1949).

ARNDT, F., LOEWE, L., UN, R., AND AYEA, E., "Cumarindiols and Cumarin-Chromone Tautomerism," Chem. Ber., 84, 319–29 (1951).

ARNDT, F., ERGENER, L., AND KUTLU, O., "Structure of 4-Oxycarbostyrils and Their Methyl-Derivatives," Chem. Ber., 86, 951–57 (1953).

ARNDT, F., ERGENER, L., AND KUTLU, O., "Py-Dioxy-derivatives of Carbostyrils and the So-called Homoanthroxan Acids," Chem. Ber., 86, 957–64 (1953).

ARNDT, F., "Note on the Theory of the Aromatic State," Chem. Ber., 89, 730–31 (1956).

## Literature Cited

(1) KEKULÉ, A., Bull. soc. chim., 3, 98 (1865).
(2) BAKER, WILSON, in "Perspectives in Organic Chemistry," Sir A. Todd, ed., Interscience, N. Y., 1956, p. 30.
(3) KEKULÉ, A., Ann., 162, 77–124 (1872).
(4) THIELE, J., Ann., 306, 125–42 (1898).
(5) ARNDT, F. G., private communication, 1957.
(6) (a) ADAMS, E. C., J. Am. Chem. Soc., 38, 1503–10 (1916); (b) PFEIFFER, P., Ber., 55B, 1762–69 (1922).
(7) cf. INGOLD, C. K., J. Chem. Soc., 121, 1133–43 (1922).
(8) ARNDT, F., SCHOLZ, E., AND NACHTWEY, P., Ber., 57, 1903–11 (1924).
(9) INGOLD, C. K., Nature, 133, 946 (1934).
(10) COLLIE, J. N., J. Chem. Soc., 85, 971–80 (1904).
(11) Ref. (8), p. 1906.
(12) ARNDT, F., NACHTWEY, P., AND PUSCH, J., Ber., 58, 1633–44 (1925). See also ARNDT, F., AND BEKIR, N., Ber., 63, 2393–97 (1930).
(13) ARNDT, F., EISTERT, B., AND ENDER, W., Ber., 62, 44–56 (1929).
(14) ARNDT, F., AND KALISCHEK, A. Ber., 63, 587–96 (1930).
(15) Ibid., p. 587, footnote 2.
(16) ARNDT, F., Ber., 63, 2963–66 (1930).
(17) ARNDT, F., AND MARTIUS, C., Ann., 499, 228–87 (1932).
(18) ARNDT, F., AND EISTERT, B., Zeit. fur phys. Chem., 31, 125–31 (1935).
(19) ARNDT, F., AND EISTERT, B., Ber., 69, 2381–93 (1936).
(20) EISTERT, B., "Tautomerie and Mesomerie," Enke, Stuttgart, 1938.
(21) ARNDT, F., MARTIN, G. T. O., AND PARTINGTON, J. R., J. Chem. Soc., 1935, 602–4.
(22) LORENZ, L., AND STERNITZKE, H., Z. Elektrochemie, 49, 501 (1934).

**G. V. Bykov**
The Institute of the History of
Natural Science and Technology
USSR Academy of Sciences
Moscow

# The Origin of the Theory of Chemical Structure

**S**everal articles appeared in 1958 and 1959 devoted to the centenary of the theory of chemical structure (1), linking its appearance with works by Kekulé (2) and Couper (3). However, in works published in recent years in the Soviet Union, the theory is regarded to have originated in 1861, when Butlerov read a report on "The Chemical Structure of Substances" (4) at the Congress of German Natural Scientists in Speyer.

We have recently explained the basic reason for the divergence in views on the question (5). It is that there are two conceptions of the substance of the classical theory of chemical structure. According to one of them, the theory boils down to the theses of the tetravalency of carbon and the capacity of its atoms to link in chains, and of the use of these theoretical propositions for drawing up formulas for chemical compounds (6). According to the other point of view, both the theses are only premises for the creation of a theory of chemical structure, which combines closely bound propositions, the chief of them being the dependence of the chemical properties of molecules (i.e., their behavior in chemical reactions) on chemical structure. It is thus, beginning with Butlerov's "Introduction to a Complete Study of Organic Chemistry" (Kazan, 1864–66; Leipzig, 1867–68), that the theory of chemical structure has been presented in textbooks. Since the system of propositions mentioned above was first advanced in Butlerov's report in 1861, there is some ground to maintain that 1961 makes the centennial of the founding of structural theory.

We shall review the history of the theory of structure from this point of view, which may be somewhat new to the reader if he is not acquainted with works in Russian on the history of chemistry. We shall also draw attention to several facts in support of this idea of the origin and development of the theory.

## The Basic Premises for Developing a Theory of Chemical Structure

The very conception of chemical structure could be formulated only at a definite stage in the development of theoretical chemistry. Butlerov formulated it (4) as follows:

Proceeding from the fact that each *chemical* atom[1] bears a definite, limited amount of chemical force (affinity) with which it participates in forming a body, I would call that chemical binding, or manner of the mutual uniting of atoms in a complex body, the *chemical structure*.

From this definition, we see that the concept of chemical structure could only have been advanced after the concepts of the atom (and consequently of the molecule), of valency (or atomicity as it was then called), and of interatomic binding were crystallized and accepted.

The establishment of a correct conception of chemical atoms and the discarding of the equivalent signs of the elements from formulas was promoted in particular by the International Chemists Congress in Karlsruhe, in 1860.

The rejection of the equivalents cleared the way for developing a conception of valency, and consequently, for a theory of structure. We point out that Couper used the symbol for oxygen as if it had an atomic weight of eight. The artificiality of his arguments was apparent to many and to a certain extent justified the sceptical attitude his contemporaries had toward his work.

Just as important was the establishment of the concept of the molecule and of ways to determine the molecular weight of organic compounds. In his "Historical Essay of the Development of Chemistry for the Past Forty Years," in 1879–80, Butlerov wrote (7) that the elaboration of this conception was the most essential achievement in chemistry during the middle of the 19th century:

After that, when the conception was established, and due to an aspiration for a more exact determination of the chemical nature of substances, a conception . . . of chemical structure developed.

The idea of valency was originated primarily by Kekulé. Though Frankland advanced the idea before Kekulé that "no matter what the character of the uniting atoms may be, the combining power of the attracting element . . . is always satisfied by the same number of these atoms" (8), his views seem not to have attracted due attention because of his use of equivalent symbols for oxygen, carbon, and certain other elements. Kolbe is an exception; on the basis of similar considerations, he reached the conclusion in 1857 about the

---

[1] By chemical atoms he meant the smallest amounts of the element in the molecule, i.e., chemically indivisible, without predetermining the possibility of further division into still smaller particles, physical atoms, which cannot be further divided.

tetraatomicity of "carbonyl," the "double" atom of carbon, $C_2$, in which the "C" equals the equivalent, or semi-atom, of carbon (9). At any rate, the theory of valency accepted by chemists since the close of the 1850's first appeared in the works of Kekulé in 1858 (2), though it entailed rejection of the thesis of constant atomicity, or valency, of elements, which he continued stubbornly to support even during the second half of the 1860's.

The concept of union between atoms was noted quite clearly by Kekulé and especially by Couper, who originated the line connecting the symbols of the elements.[2] We will not dwell in detail on Kekulé's and Couper's views in this matter; it has been done repeatedly. But we shall attempt to discover whether the theses they examined are sufficient to establish the chemical structure of organic compounds.

Couper used both correct and incorrect formulas. His formula for ethylene glycol is correct, for example, while his formula for glycerine is wrong. His only attempt to connect the chemical properties of molecules (in particular the acidic properties) with their structure, by the supplementary hypothesis that molecules have electric poles, led to his formula for oxalic acid:

$$C \begin{cases} O_2 \\ O_2 \end{cases}$$
$$\Big| $$
$$C \begin{cases} O—OH \\ O—OH \end{cases}$$

which is also incorrect. It is not surprising that Wurtz (10) found Couper's formulas "too arbitrary and too far removed from experiment," while Butlerov (11) wrote:

Of course, they express certain relations for the affinity of the elements when forming bodies resulting from their union, but the question nevertheless arises why the symbols for oxygen and hydrogen . . . are placed as they are, and not otherwise, among the carbon atoms.

Nevertheless, in his "Historical Essay," Butlerov subsequently expressed a very high opinion of Couper's work for his

definite conception of chemical structure . . . . Together with correct views, Couper presented views not quite correct, and even quite incorrect ones, . . . but at any rate, his article is a remarkable advance in chemical theory.

It can be demonstrated that Kekulé also did not hold his formulas expressing "the relations between mutually linked atoms (*Beziehungen der sich gegenseitig bindenden Atome*)" (12) superior to typical or even empirical formulas.

Kekulé also used graphic formulas, mainly to illustrate the factors complicating the composition of organic compounds. Of course, for his time, this was of enormous value. But according to Kekulé, these formulas of his had the shortcoming of not giving any idea of the *relative position of the atoms in space;* it was that, he believed, which primarily determined the chemical properties of the molecule. Thus, Kekulé

explained the diverse behavior of chlorine in organic compounds by the fact that in some cases (13)

the chlorine is located in a place inaccessible to the active substance, and to a certain extent within the substance, while in most of the bodies (chlorides), it is easily accessible, can easily be attacked, and thus is subjected to the action of the reagent.

Later, in the third part of the same volume, released in 1861, we also find a correct surmise about the reasons for the definite reaction faculty of acetic acid (14):

Out of four hydrogen atoms, primarily one moves off in certain reactions, perhaps because it alone is directly joined to the carbon group; moreover, it is especially easily substituted by metals and metal-like radicals, perhaps owing to its position near two oxygen atoms. The other three hydrogen atoms are capable of substitution by chlorine . . . perhaps because they are directly bound with carbon . . . .

Nevertheless, Kekulé did not prefer the formula for acetic acid showing the bonds between the atoms, but the conventional, typical

$$\begin{matrix} C_2H_3O \\ H \end{matrix} \Big\} O$$

For more complex substances, he considered "fully expanded" formulas altogether impossible (15);

. . . atoms spaced side by side in a molecule cannot be grouped on the surface of paper in such a way as to show atoms joined in various transformations side by side in a single formula.

Kekulé continued to use type formulas in the first part of the second volume of his textbook, released in 1863, though he stopped using them in his original works back in 1861, considering them inadequate and declaring that he would change over to empirical formulas. He made this declaration at the Congress in Speyer (16), two days after the report on chemical structure by Butlerov.

## Butlerov's Report "On the Chemical Structure of Substances" (1861)

Butlerov criticized the whole idea of typical formulas, both the mineral types of Gerhardt and the carbon types of Kolbe. He rejected the typical theory just as categorically as Couper did three years before him. Among the arguments against it, Butlerov referred in particular (as did Couper) to the impossibility of expressing addition reactions by typical formulas.

Having rejected typical conceptions, Butlerov pointed to the atomicity of elements as a conception that "could serve as a foundation for a general theory and to allow us to advance rather far in our scientific thinking."

Butlerov formulated the concept of chemical structure which we have given above. Of course, the "relations between mutually linked atoms" of Kekulé and the "constitution" of Couper's formulas coincide in their contents with the "chemical structure" of Butlerov. However, his merit consists in the fact that he defined "chemical structure" as a scientific concept, clearly separating it from the concept of "constitution" as used by Gerhardt and his followers in the sense of "mechanical structure of molecules," or the arrangement of atoms in space (17).

The error in the view that Butlerov used the term "chemical structure" here *for the first time* should be noted. Actually, it has been found in Russian works on chemistry as far back as 1845, but either in the sense of

---

[2] In all fairness it must be said that in 1789 W. Higgins applied in his formulas the lines joining "particles" of oxygen, sulfur, and "dephlogisticated air." See ATKINSON, E. R., J. CHEM. EDUC., **17**, 3 (1940).

the mechanical structure of molecules or for describing the composition of molecules by typical formulas (18). Butlerov adopted the term from them, together with certain others. He put new meaning into them and, making them express new ideas, introduced them into the theory of chemical structure.

Butlerov formulated *the basic thesis of the theory of chemical structure:*

I would believe it possible meanwhile to change the accepted rule that the nature of a complex molecule is determined by the *nature, quantity, and position* of its elementary component parts, to the following statement: *the chemical nature of a complex molecule is determined by the nature of its elementary component parts, their quantity, and chemical structure.*

We call this the basic thesis of the theory for two reasons. First, because most other concepts are a more or less direct outcome of it, and second, because it is a substantially new idea, counterposed to the old accepted point of view. In confirmation of the fact that this was the Rubicon chemists had to cross when accepting the theory of chemical structure, we refer to the following opinion voiced by Kekulé in 1872 (19):

The main trend of contemporary chemistry doubtlessly consists in studying the constitution of compounds, but this latter does not refer, as previously, to the position of atoms in space, but rather to their mutual binding in the molecule.''

Of course, Butlerov did not attach absolute infallibility to this thesis, noting that chemical properties depend on chemical structure (and composition) in the first place only. But while posing the question thus, he continued in his report:

... we will deal with problems that can be solved through chemical experiment. . . . further development of the view expressed here will show how much the chemical properties of substances depend on chemical structure, and how inadequate the rule is.''

Butlerov showed ways to determine chemical structure and offered a few rules. He believed that all reactions known to chemists could be applied for this purpose, but he prefered synthetical reactions to decomposition or double exchange reactions. He said that it was desirable to select conditions so that the residues of the molecules, or radicals formed during the reaction, would preserve their chemical structure. At the same time, Butlerov provided for the possibility of rearrangements during the reaction, and consequently, of extra difficulties in determining chemical structure. He noted, however, "we may hope that after a detailed study of substances from the point of view of their chemical structure, general laws will be developed for such cases too.''

He added a few rules to these general theses, "developed from facts, and in part already accepted by most chemists.'' More than half of them presented the basic theses and conclusions of the current theory of valency, including the possibility of atoms of one and the same element uniting. Among the rules, some gave an elementary explanation of the addition reaction mechanism.

It follows from the basic thesis of the theory of chemical structure that the structural formulas must give an idea of chemical properties of molecules. Butlerov wrote in his report that "when the general laws of the dependence of chemical properties of substances on their chemical structure become known,

such formulas will express all the properties.'' However, he did not offer any method for writing them. "Time and experience,'' he said, "will show just what the formulas for chemical structure should be like.'' Time and experience have shown that the most suitable formulas are Couper's, with their lines describing bonds; Butlerov in the 1860's preferred formulas using braces, though they might be confused with typical formulas.

At the end of his report, Butlerov wrote, "I am far from intending to offer a new theory here.'' But this must not be regarded as an underestimation of the value for chemistry of his system of views, because he concluded his report with a suggestion to substitute them for the prevalent theory of types in all its forms. Probably Butlerov's words reflect his habitual modesty and also, perhaps, covert contrast to Couper, who had promptly announced a "New Chemical Theory'' he had created.

After Butlerov's death, Markovnikov, his closest pupil and the first to deal with the history of the theory of chemical structure, said that this report (20)

is of especially great importance in the history of modern theory. It is a document showing that A. M. (Butlerov) was not only the first to outline the chief essentials of present doctrine quite clearly and definitely; he also developed them in as much detail as possible in a magazine article. In fact, when we now reread this symbol of faith in the theory of structure, we find no difference in it from the principles guiding contemporary (1887) chemists.

## Elaboration and Development of the Theory of Chemical Structure

We will outline only the principal stages in the further development of the theory of chemical structure.

*Isomeric* phenomena were among the big problems of theoretical chemistry for decades. True, some were explained by the typical theory, like the isomerism of methyl acetate with ethyl formate. But there was another group of isomers, differing only in the position of their substitutes for the carbon skeleton, and still another, with isomer skeletons. The second group was first explained by Butlerov in 1863, in a big article, "On Different Ways of Explaining Various Cases of Isomerism'' (21).

The general explanation of isomerism follows from the basic thesis of the theory of chemical structure; since isomers are substances which (having a similar composition) differ in their chemical properties, they differ also in their chemical structure. In the same article, Butlerov examined the views of Kekulé and Kolbe on isomerism critically and in detail. He discovered trimethylcarbinol the next year and pointed for the first time to the possibility of skeletal isomerism in the alcohol series and then of saturated hydrocarbons (22). He himself confirmed his forecasts of new alcohols and hydrocarbons in experiments during the next three years.

The dependence of chemical properties on chemical structure are especially manifested in isomeric molecules. Butlerov explained in his article on isomerism that this is so because though the atoms in isomeric molecules are the same, they are influenced by other atoms, depending on the chemical structure, to acquire differing *"chemical significance,"* i.e., differing behavior in chemical reactions. Of course, before the idea of electrons appeared in chemistry, there could be no correct view of the mechanism of the *mutual influence of atoms.*

Butlerov devoted much attention to this question in his textbook, concluding it with the chapter, "An Essay on the Chemical Significance of Elementary Atoms in the Molecules of Carbon Compounds." His pupil, Popov, made an extensive study of the laws of the oxidation of ketones and other organic compounds (*23*). Markovnikov studied substitution reactions from the same point of view and revised written works, formulating several rules concerning substitution, addition, decomposition, and isomerization reactions, though only one of these rules of his is usually attributed to him. Markovnikov wrote a special monograph, "Materials on the Question of the Mutual Influence of Atoms in Chemical Compounds" (Kazan, 1869). Part of it was incorporated in his articles in German (*24*). Subsequently, van't Hoff made a systematic study of this entire field from the theoretical point of view (*25*).

Though other chemists also discovered particular cases of the interdependence between the chemical structure and chemical properties of the molecule in their experiments, the first *systematic* research was done by Butlerov's school.

Butlerov and his pupils studied saturated organic compounds and suggested the formulas for their chemical structure. But in the mid 1860's, the theory also expanded to include unsaturated open chain compounds and aromatic ones.

Before this, many chemists, including Kekulé and Butlerov, had approached the idea of *multiple bonds,* but it was first voiced definitely following experimental tests (though not very convincing ones) by Erlenmeyer, who gave the familiar formula of ethylene, $H_2C = CH_2$, and acetylene, $HC \equiv CH$ (*26*), while Kekulé suggested his famous formula for benzene in 1865.

## Questions of Priority

Most divergencies in the written history of the theory of structure occur in questions of priority, falling into three basic trends. Some authors (*1*) ascribe the origin of theory of chemical structure to Kekulé or to Kekulé and Couper together.[3] Others, chiefly authors writing in Russian, regard Butlerov as the founder of the theory. The third group regards the theory of chemical structure as a simple development of the theory of valency, and therefore do not draw a line between the two. For example, this view was advanced by Pauling in his Nobel Prize speech (*27*).

However, the very fact that the terms "structure theory" and "structure chemistry" are used extensively in the literature compels us in the historical aspect, too, to regard the structure theory as something independent of the theory of valency. Actually, as noted above, the thesis that the chemical properties of molecules depend on chemical structure is in no degree a logical conclusion from the theory of valency.

The theory of chemical structure has just as much right to independence as the typical theory of Gerhardt, because the very idea of types, and even types of water and ammonia, had been suggested prior to Gerhardt; and just as much as the stereochemical conceptions of van't Hoff and Le Bel, because the idea of the carbon tetrahedron is found prior to them in Butlerov (1862), Kekulé (1867), and Paternò (1869). The idea of molecular dissymmetry as a cause of optical activity is met in Herschel's work back in 1833, and in Pasteur's in 1860. Finally, the idea that certain isomers ought to be explained by various arrangements of atoms in space given a similar chemical structure was clearly expressed by Wislicenus in 1869 and 1873, and served as the point of departure for the reasoning of van't Hoff.

For the same reasons, it is a questionable procedure to identify the theory of chemical structure with the views of Kekulé and Couper. It can only be done when there is a formal approach to the theory as a simple manipulation with symbols, restricted merely by the rules of element valency. Such an attitude is characteristic, for example, for L. Meyer, who entered into polemics with Butlerov about it in 1868.[4]

The question remains to be answered: How and why did the tradition arise in the history of chemistry to deny Butlerov's role in originating the theory of chemical structure and to attribute it to Kekulé or to Kekulé and Couper together? Only Giua noted in his "History of Chemistry" (*28*) that the theory of chemical structure appeared in 1861, and attributed the chief role in originating it to Butlerov.[5] Delacre (*29*) sees the beginnings of the structure theory in works by Kolbe, though he highly praises Butlerov's role.

Kekulé's famous story that the "structure theory" came into his head on the upper deck of a London omnibus in 1856 was taken on good faith. In 1864 he deemed it necessary to note in an article (*30*) that his views on the way atoms unite in the molecule would not change in essence ("wesentlich") if "chemical structure" were to be used to express them. In that same year, 1864, he even maintained at the beginning of the second part of the second volume of his textbook that he had presented these ideas in an earlier textbook also. This was not a true statement; Markovnikov spoke out energetically against it (*31*).

Historians of chemistry also apparently have been insufficiently acquainted with utterances by Butlerov himself and by Markovnikov about priority.

When he returned from the Congress of German natural scientists in Speyer, Butlerov wrote about a feature of German conventions that had impressed him at that time. He mentioned the "hypertrophied national feeling" of the Germans which "makes them insufficiently appreciate every other nationality" (*32*). And then, he more than once complained in his published writings that his views were often cited without

---

[3] The historians of chemistry undervalued a long time the profundity and insight of Couper's conception. It looks as if his name faded away in the blaze of Kekulé's fame. But, as it was recently pointed out by O. T. Benfey [in THIS JOURNAL, **36**, 319 (1959)], neglect of Couper continues.

[4] The episode has been described by H. M. Leicester in the pages of THIS JOURNAL, **36**, 328 (1959).

[5] Butlerov's role in the history of classical structural theory also is very well outlined in Leicester's above-mentioned article. Complying most willingly with what the author said there, I should like to note that his paper and mine complement one another in this respect.

260

any mention of his name, and in a reply to L. Meyer, he wrote plainly that he found his opinions *constantly* smothered.

Butlerov went abroad in 1867–68 to stand up for his priority. The trip was arranged by the University of Kazan in particular in order to "provide Mr. Butlerov himself the opportunity to make clear to foreign chemists his right to the leading role in developing the trend of contemporary chemistry" (*33*).

In reply to a letter from Butlerov (from Kazan) which has not been preserved, Markovnikov wrote from Leipzig in October, 1866 (*34*):

"From what you write, I see that the main purpose (of the trip abroad, G. V. B.) is to compel recognition of your priority, historically, in the current views of chemistry. It is not only a delicate business, but difficult too. From Buff's book (*35*), you see that anyone who has written anything about it imagines that he has created the theory. Some people describe it without mentioning names, while still others, less conceited and less selfish, refer it all to such authorities as Kekulé."

Further, Markovnikov advised Butlerov to come to Germany after the first part of the German translation of his textbook was issued. "Then," he wrote, "when they read it here, at least the first part, you can point out that you developed the principle of chemical structure before any Kekulés or Buffs did." Later, Markovnikov named Butlerov on various occasions as the founder of the theory of chemical structure.[6] True, he did not develop and did not always support these assertions of his. It has been done by Soviet historians of chemistry, who began a systematic elaboration of the history of the classical theory of chemical structure in the late 1940's. In this article we have attempted to describe the basic conclusions reached.

## Acknowledgment

The author is deeply grateful to the editor and reviewers of this paper for valuable comments.

## Literature Cited

(1) Staab, H. A., *Angew. Chem.*, **70**, 37 (1958); Grohn, H., *Chem. Techn. (Berlin)*, **10**, 501 (1958); Verkade, P. E., *Proc. Chem. Soc.*, 205 (1958); Farrer, W. V., and Farrer, K. R., *Proc. Chem. Soc.*, 285 (1959); Brown, H. C., J. Chem. Educ., **36**, 104 (1959); and "Kekulé–Couper Centennial Symposium," J. Chem. Educ., **36**, 319–39 (1959).

(2) Kekulé, A., *Ann. Chem. Pharm.*, **106**, 129 (1858).

(3) Couper, A. S., *Phil. Mag.*, [4], **16**, 104 (1858); *Ann. chim. phys.*, [3], **53**, 467 (1858).

(4) Butlerov, A., *Z. Chem. Pharm.*, **4**, 541 (1861).

(5) Bykov, G. V., *Proc. Chem. Soc.*, 210 (1960); see also Bykov, G. V., "History of the Classical Theory of Chemical Structure," USSR Acad. of Sci. Publication, Moscow, 1960.

(6) Meyer, L., *Ann. Chem. Pharm.*, **145**, 124 (1868).

(7) Butlerov, A. M., "Collected Works," Moscow, 1958, Vol. 3, p. 169.

(8) Frankland, E., and Brodie, B. C., *Phil. Trans.*, 417 (1852).

(9) Kolbe, H., *Ann. Chem. Pharm.*, **101**, 257 (1857).

(10) Wurtz, A., *Rép. chim. pure*, **1**, 49 (1858).

(11) Butlerov, A., *Ann. Chem. Pharm.*, **110**, 51 (1859).

(12) Kekulé, A., "Lehrbuch der organischen Chemie oder der Chemie der Kohlenstoffverbindungen, Bd. 1, Erlangen, 1859–61, p. 174.

(13) *Ibid.*, p. 173.

(14) *Ibid.*, p. 523.

(15) *Ibid.*, p. 522.

(16) Kekulé, A., *Z. Chem. Pharm.*, **4**, 613 (1861).

(17) Hjelt, E., "Geschichte der organischen Chemie von ältester Zeit bis zur Gegenwart," Braunschweig, 1916, p. 249–50.

(18) Bykov, G. V., "Problems of the History of Natural Science and Technics," Moscow, 1957, Vol. 4, p. 179.

(19) Kekulé, A., *Verh. d. naturhistor. Vereines d. preussischen Rheinlande u. Westphalens (Bonn)*, Sitzungsberichte **29**, 15 (1872).

(20) Markovnikov, V. V., "Selected Works," Moscow, 1955, p. 827.

(21) Butlerov, A. M., *Z. Chem. Pharm.*, **6**, 500 (1863).

(22) Butlerov, A. M., *Z. Chem. Pharm.*, **7**, 385, 513 (1864).

(23) Popov, A., *Z. Chem.*, [2], **4**, 619 (1868); *Z. Chem.*, **7**, 4 (1871); *Ber. deut. chem. Ges.*, **4**, 720 (1871); *Ann. Chem. Pharm.*, **161**, 285 (1872); *Ann. Chem. Pharm.*, **162**, 151 (1872); Popov, A., and Zincke, T., *Ber. deut. chem. Ges.*, **5**, 384 (1872).

(24) Markovnikov, V. V. *Ann. Chem. Pharm.*, **146**, 339 (1868); **153**, 228 (1870).

(25) van't Hoff, H. J., "Ansichten uber die organische Chemie," Braunschweig, Th. 1, 1878; Th. 2, 1881.

(26) Erlenmeyer, E., *Verh. d. naturhist.-med. Vereins zu Heidelberg*, **4**, 31 (1865); *Ann. Chem. Pharm.*, **137**, 327 (1866).

(27) Pauling, L., *Science*, **123**, 255 (1956).

(28) Giua, M., "Storia della chimica dall'alchimica alle dottrine moderne," Torino, 1946, pp. 181, 204.

(29) Delacre, M., "Histoire de chimie," Paris, 1920.

(30) Kekulé, A., *Ann. Chem. Pharm.*, **130**, 1 (1864).

(31) Markovnikov, V. V., *Z. Chem.*, [2], **1**, 280 (1865).

(32) Butlerov, A. M., "Collected Works," USSR Acad. of Sci. Pub., Moscow, 1958, Vol. 3, p. 78.

(33) Butlerov, A. M., "Scientific and Pedagogical Activity. A Collection of Documents," USSR Acad. of Sci. Pub., Moscow, 1961, p. 84.

(34) Letters from Russian Chemists to A. M. Butlerov, Nauchnoye nasledstvo, USSR Acad. of Sci. Pub., Moscow, 1961, Vol. 4, p. 235.

(35) Buff, H. L., "Grundlehren der theoretischen Chemie und Beziehungen zwischen den chemischen und physikalischen Eigenschaften der Körper," Erlangen, 1866.

[6] See Ref. *20*, pp. 280, 648, and 684.

---

## CHEMIKER-ANEKDOTEN[1]

R. B. Woodward. "Woodward, auf der Münchener Hauptversammlung der GDCh (1955), läuft mit einem blauseidenen Binder herum, auf dem die Konstitutionsformel des Strychnins aufgestickt ist. Am anderen Tag neutraler Binder. Frage: Warum heute keine Strukturformel? Antwort: Bin heute inkognito."

(*See page 266*)

[1] "Chemiker-Anekdoten," Verlag Chemie, Weinheim/Bergstr., Germany, 1957, p. 63.

# Emil Fischer's Discovery
# of the Configuration of Glucose[1]

## A Semicentennial Retrospect

### C. S. HUDSON

*National Institute of Health, U. S. Public Health Service, Washington, D. C.*

EMIL FISCHER'S first publication on sugars was in the year 1884, when he described their phenylosazones and recognized that he had thereby in hand for the first time crystalline derivatives which are of general applicability for the identification of sugars (*1*). He soon found that glucose and fructose yield the same osazone, that galactose yields another one and that sorbose gives a third. The analyses of the three osazones proved conclusively that the four sugars are hexoses (*1, 2*). The steps of the osazone reaction were not clear at first but in 1887 he discovered the phenylhydrazones (*2*) and was able thereby to supply the needed information and write the stoichiometric equations that are in the textbooks of today. At this early stage he discovered a new hexose, our mannose, through its phenylhydrazine derivative; the gentle oxidation of mannitol with nitric acid and the testing of the resulting products with phenylhydrazine led to the isolation of the rather insoluble mannose phenylhydrazone (*2*), from which he prepared the new hexose and named it mannose (*3*). The discovery of mannose proved of vital importance for the development of Fischer's further sugar researches: it led him to the synthesis of the substances of the mannitol group (*4*) which brought him world-wide fame; he himself has said that mannose was the key that opened the gate to this field of synthesis ["Untersuchungen," p. 11]. Mannose also led him in a direct path to his establishment of the configurations of the sugars. His study of mannose soon led to a remarkable result; glucose, fructose, and mannose yield the same phenylosazone (*5*). From this fact he drew the conclusion, now so familiar to all, that glucose and mannose are epimeric aldoses, fructose being the configurationally related 2-ketose. It is at this stage that Fischer uses for the first time the Le Bel-van't Hoff theory of the asymmetric carbon atom; he concludes that mannose is an aldehyde of mannitol, that glucose is epimeric in configuration with mannose and that consequently glucose must be the aldehyde of some alcohol other than mannitol. This last conclusion must have aroused general interest at the time because only mannitol had ever been found by the reduction of glucose with sodium amalgam.

Experiment quickly supplied the decision; Meunier (*6*) and also Vincent and Delachanal (*7*) found that the true reduction product of glucose is sorbitol, mannitol being the result of a secondary reaction in the alkaline solution. Fischer verified these results and further showed that the reduction of fructose yields a mixture of mannitol and sorbitol (*8*), as would be expected from the Le Bel-van't Hoff theory.

Kiliani's discovery in 1885 of the addition of hydrocyanic acid to reducing sugars, which led him to the synthesis of acids (and their lactones) possessing one more carbon atom, was of fundamental importance in the development of Fischer's sugar researches because four years later Fischer discovered that the lactones of the sugar group can be reduced to corresponding aldoses (*10*); the synthesis of higher carbon sugars and also the reduction of the lactones of the dibasic acids of the sugar group to uronic and even to aldonic acids became possible. By this reduction he changed saccharic acid to the naturally occurring glucuronic acid (*11*). Thierfelder (*12*) had recently reduced glucuronic acid to a new and beautifully crystalline hexonic acid lactone, which he had described with precision; it is our L-gulonic lactone. Fischer showed that this lactone may be obtained in one operation by the reduction of lactonized saccharic acid, through the intermediate glucuronic acid. He and Thierfelder named the new acid gulonic acid and Fischer reduced its lactone to our L-gulose; as would be expected, the oxidation of gulonic acid yielded saccharic acid and Fischer emphasized that here for the first time had been found an example where two different hexoses (glucose and gulose) give on oxidation one and the same dibasic acid (saccharic acid), a fact which was readily interpretable (*13*) through the Le Bel-van't Hoff theory.

The story of arabinose is an interesting one. The sugar was first prepared by Scheibler (*14*) in 1868 by the acid hydrolysis of beet pulp. It was regarded as another hexose but in 1887 Kiliani (*15*) proved that it is a pentose; by hydrocyanic acid addition he converted it to a new hexonic acid and the oxidation of this yielded in turn a new six-carbon dibasic acid. It was in this same year of 1887 that Fischer discovered mannose (our D-mannose). In 1889 he prepared D-mannonic acid from mannose (*16*) by Kiliani's method of oxidation with bromine water, and in 1890 he showed (*17*) that its lactone is the optical antipode of the lactone from the hexonic acid that Kiliani had made from natural arabinose by the cyanide synthesis. Here were the D- and L-forms of mannonic lactone, and

[1] Publication authorized by the Surgeon General, U. S. Public Health Service. An address delivered before the Division of Sugar Chemistry and Technology at the 101st meeting of the American Chemical Society, St. Louis, Missouri, April 10, 1941, on the occasion of the commemoration of the semicentennial anniversary of this discovery, under the honorary chairmanship of Dr. H. O. L. Fischer.

Fischer emphasized that they represent the first known pair of enantiomorphs in the sugar group. He oxidized D-mannonic acid to D-mannosaccharic acid (18) which proved to be the enantiomorph of the dibasic acid that Kiliani had discovered; the latter was accordingly recognized as L-mannosaccharic acid. Both acids, of course, are optically active. In 1889 Fischer and Passmore discovered the phenylhydrazides of the aldonic acids, crystalline substances which proved most useful in the separation and identification of such acids (19). Applying the new tool quickly, Fischer found (20) that natural (our L-) arabinose yields by the cyanide synthesis L-gluconic acid in addition to L-mannonic acid and that the two acids are interconvertible through heating with quinoline. These important discoveries confirmed his view that glucose and mannose are epimers. The reduction product of arabinose, crystalline arabitol, had been discovered in 1887 by Kiliani (15) who had reported that it showed no rotatory power; Fischer (21) now tested it in 1891 in a solution containing borax, following an old observation of Vignon (22) that borax augments the rotation of mannitol. The result was decisive in showing that arabitol is an optically active alcohol (our L-arabitol).

The sugar xylose next comes into consideration. It had been discovered by Friedrich Koch (23) through the acid hydrolysis of wood gum in 1886, just one year before Fischer discovered mannose. In 1889 Wheeler and Tollens (24) prepared its osazone for the first time and the analysis indicated that xylose was probably a pentose. Fischer (25) undertook then a study of xylose, after making the proper arrangement with Wheeler and Tollens. In 1891 he reported (21) that xylose yields by the cyanhydrin synthesis a hexonic acid which we now designate D-gulonic acid, and that this acid passes on oxidation to L-saccharic acid. He also found that the alcohol which results from the reduction of xylose, namely xylitol, shows no rotation even in the presence of borax. Arabitol was undoubtedly active, xylitol appeared to be inactive. But xylitol was a sirup; he had indeed purified it through its crystalline benzylidene derivative but the matter was of such importance that he desired further evidence. He therefore prepared the crystalline trihydroxy-glutaric acids from arabinose and xylose, respectively; the one from arabinose was active, the one from xylose was inactive. He then published his proof (26) of the configurations of these various sugars and derivatives, the proof that we commemorate today. The following is the introductory sentence of his proof. "*All previous observations in the sugar group are in such complete agreement with the theory of the asymmetric carbon atom that the use of this theory as a basis for the classification of these substances seems justifiable.*" To me, this sentence announces the formal advent of a theoretical chemistry of the carbohydrates.

I shall now present this proof, but not quite in its original form. Conventions of expression in this field have changed during the past fifty years and I think that the use of modified symbols and a different order

for presenting the steps of the proof are in the interest of clearness. In introduction to the proof, it should be stated that it was well known at the time that the carbon chain of mannitol is a normal one because the substance yields normal hexyl iodide by reduction with hydriodic acid. It was also known that D-glucoheptonic acid yields normal heptylic acid by hydriodic reduction. The chains of glucose and mannose were thus known to be normal.

Write the formulas for a pentose and the two hexoses which it yields by the Fischer-Kiliani cyanhydrin synthesis as shown in the accompanying diagram, using Fischer's convention that the asymmetric carbon atoms (tetrahedra) have the lower edge in the plane of the paper and the corners which carry the H and OH groups lie above this plane. The arrangement of the H and OH groups is then decided through the following steps, in which the pentose is selected to be D-arabinose and in consequence the hexoses become D-glucose and D-mannose.

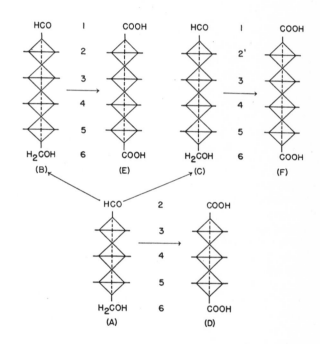

Step 1—By convention for the D-configurational series OH is on the right of C-5.

Step 2—(D) is optically active hence OH is on the left of C-3.

Step 3—D-Glucose and D-mannose are epimeric, hence the OH's on C-2 and C-2' are opposed. Either (B) or (C) may be selected as having OH on the right, without changing the final result; here the OH is placed to the right of C-2 and consequently to the left of C-2'.

Step 4—Since both saccharic and manno-saccharic acids are optically active the configuration of neither of them can possess end-to-end symmetry; hence the OH on C-4 must be on the right. (If it were on the left, (E) would have end-to-end symmetry.)

At this stage the configuration of D-arabinose and its dibasic acid (D) have become established. D-Glucose and D-mannose have been limited to the configurations (B) and (C), but the correlation within this limit remains to be established. This is done by:

Step 5—Saccharic acid is obtainable from the oxidation of each of two hexoses, namely, glucose and gulose. (E) must therefore refer to D-saccharic acid because (F) cannot result from the oxidation of two hexoses. Hence (B) refers to D-glucose, (C) to D-mannose, and (F) to D-manno-saccharic acid.

The proof is now complete and the formulas become:

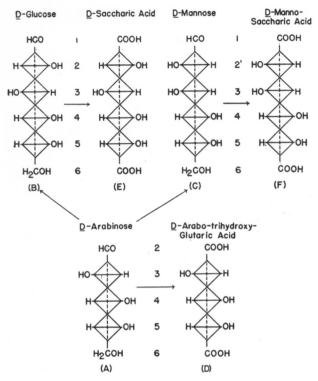

various modifications of Fischer's proof. It is rare that one finds a textbook of today which follows the steps of the original proof. Possibly the preceding statement of his proof in the conventional terms of today may serve to popularize among teachers and students this classic example of exact mathematical reasoning in an experimental science.

One of the many corroborations of Fischer's proof is of some interest because of its simplicity. Referring to the third diagram, which will be understood from the preceding ones, it is noted that the inactivity of this glucoheptitol was shown by Fischer (27). This manno-octitol was first prepared by Fischer and Passmore (28); its optical inactivity was shown later (29).

Step 1—By convention for the D-configurational series OH is on the right of each C-7.

Step 2—By end-to-end symmetry C-2' has OH on the right and C-3 has OH on the right.

Step 3—Since D-arabitol is optically active, C-5 must have OH on the left.

Step 4—By end-to-end symmetry C-4' must have OH on the left.

Step 5—Since glucose and mannose are epimeric, C-4 must have OH on the right.

Step 6—By end-to-end symmetry C-6 has OH on the right.

Step 7—By end-to-end symmetry C-3' has OH on the right.

Corollary: Since carbon atoms 3', 2', and 1 of (F) have been added by cyanhydrin syntheses beginning from the carbonyl carbon 4 of (A), the carbons 4', 3', 2', and 1 of (F) must represent a normal chain; hence by end-to-end symmetry the whole chain of (F) must be normal and therefore the chains of all the structures are normal.

When these steps have been completed the formulas become:

Discoveries which have been made subsequent to 1891, several of them by Fischer himself, are the basis of

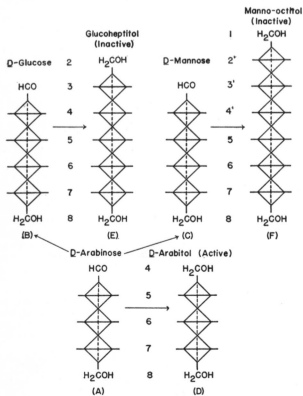

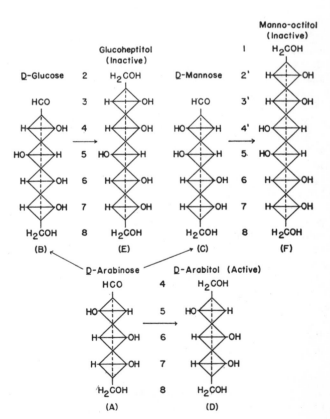

Have there arisen during these fifty years any new findings which have thrown doubt on the validity of Fischer's proof? At the end of Fischer's article of 1891 we find the statement that his arguments assume, first, that the theory of the asymmetric carbon atom is valid, and, second, that stereochemical rearrangements do not occur in the cyanhydrin synthesis of hexoses from pentoses. Five years later Paul Walden (30) discovered what have come to be known as the "Walden inversions." In 1908 Fischer (31) stated that he had been surprised that no corrections for his configurations had arisen, and attributed this to what he termed the "lucky" circumstance that his arguments had been based upon reactions which do not involve substitution on an asymmetric carbon atom. However, there arose again this question of Walden inversion through the remarkable discovery by Richard Kuhn and F. Ebel (32) in 1925 that the *cis* form of ethylene oxide dicarboxylic acid passes to racemic rather than to meso tartaric acid. This reaction is:

$$2 \begin{array}{c} COOH \\ | \\ HC \\ \\ HC \\ | \\ COOH \end{array} \!\!\!\! \bigg\rangle O + 2H_2O = \begin{array}{c} COOH \\ | \\ HCOH \\ | \\ HOCH \\ | \\ COOH \end{array} + \begin{array}{c} COOH \\ | \\ HOCH \\ | \\ HCOH \\ | \\ COOH \end{array}$$

Ethylene oxide Dicarboxylic acid (*cis*)     D-Tartaric     L-Tartaric

Racemic acid

We know now that the sugars are mostly cyclic structures, and Kuhn and Ebel raised the question whether the opening of the rings at the oxygen atom may not be accompanied by a stereo change, such as they had found. On such a view the aldehydo form of D-glucose would indeed possess the accepted configuration (I) but the α-D-glucopyranose would not be (II), as generally believed, but rather (III), the formula that we commonly assign to β-L-idopyranose. W. Hückel

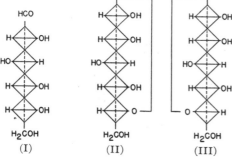

(I)      (II)      (III)

(33) published a critique of this view in which he called attention to the fact that the cyclic sugar structure is that of a cyclic hemi-acetal rather than an oxide and that Walden inversions have never been known to occur in the formation or breaking of acetal unions; he concluded therefore that the present cyclic sugar configurations are probably correct as commonly written. It seems to me that we have today additional experimental evidence that the old configurations are correct. The ring of cyclic forms of the sugars and

their glycosides can be opened in two ways. The first way is by action on the oxygen atom of the ring; it is the way that Kuhn, Ebel, and Hückel discuss. The second way is by the breaking of the carbon chain of the ring with per-iodic acid; it is the reaction which E. L. Jackson and I (34) have carried out in the case of the methyl-D-glucopyranosides, for example, and by which we have shown that the carbon 5 of the pyranoside has the accepted configuration of the D-glyceric acid of the Fischer system. The matter is illustrated by the accompanying formulas.[2]

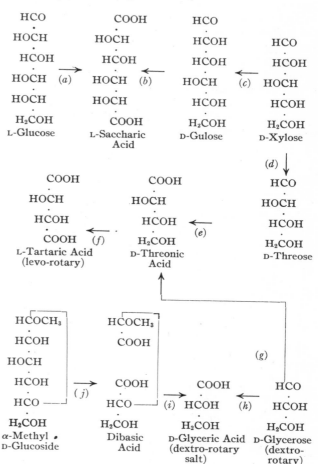

If Kuhn and Ebel's view were correct we should have obtained L-glyceric acid. The addition which we have made to Hückel's argument is that in our reactions the acetal which is hydrolyzed is not a cyclic acetal and therefore there can be no question of the opening of an

[2] The following references describe these reactions: (a) FISCHER, *Ber.*, **23**, 2611 (1890), ["Untersuchungen," (see ref. *1* for complete title) p. 372]; (b) FISCHER AND STAHEL, *Ber.*, **24**, 528 (1891), ["Untersuchungen," p. 394]; (c) FISCHER AND STAHEL, *ibid.*; (d), (e), (f) HOCKETT, *J. Am. Chem. Soc.*, **57**, 2260, 2265 (1935), which gives the earlier literature references; (g) WOHL AND MOMBER, *Ber.*, **50**, 455 (1917); (h) WOHL AND SCHELLENBERG, *Ber.*, **55**, 1404 (1922); (i) (j) JACKSON AND HUDSON, ref. *34*. The configuration of L-tartaric acid was established by FISCHER [*Ber.*, **29**, 1377 (1896)], ["Untersuchungen," p. 519] through the oxidation of the methyltetrose from natural rhamnose to yield D-tartaric acid (dextro-rotary).

oxygen ring in a *cis* or *trans* direction. There is thus today no valid criticism of the Fischer configurations as applied to the cyclic forms of the sugars.

The stereochemistry of the sugars that arose with Fischer's proof has developed amazingly during the subsequent half century; today we classify by his configurational formulas nearly all the simple and compound sugars and some of the polysaccharides, and his system has been extended to the amino acids and polypeptides, various types of the hydroxy acids, the inositol cyclic group of alcohols, most of the natural and synthetic glycosides, and at least one of the vitamins (ascorbic acid). In all this broad field there appears to be no established fact which disagrees with the Le Bel–van't Hoff theory of the asymmetric carbon atom; its use by Fischer to classify the sugars has proved so successful that it is today the guiding principle of the theoretical chemistry of the carbohydrates.

Throughout Emil Fischer's publications and addresses on carbohydrates one finds the most generous acknowledgment of assistance from the concurrent discoveries of others in the sugar field. He was especially appreciative of Kiliani's (*35*) work. Maquenne's (*36*) careful analyses of perseitol, which proved the substance to be a hepta-atomic alcohol rather than an isomer of mannitol as long believed, aroused his admiration (*37*). Tollens' (*38*) discovery that mannose occurs in nature (a polysaccharide in salep mucilage), followed shortly by Reiss's (*39*) preparation of it from the readily available vegetable ivory, was of the greatest practical value to Fischer, which he took occasion to emphasize (*40*). Thierfelder's (*41*) reduction of glucuronic lactone to gulonic lactone was very helpful to Fischer and the two joined in selecting the gulose name. Meunier's (*42*) discovery of the crystalline benzylidene derivative of sorbitol, through which the relationship of fructose to sorbitol was so rapidly established by Fischer, came at an opportune time in the development of Fischer's proof, as he has stated (*43*). With these delightful examples of friendly coöperation and courteous appreciation among the members of this noble group of sugar chemists of fifty years ago I shall close my story of one of the classic dramas of chemical science.

LITERATURE CITED

(1) FISCHER, *Ber.*, **17**, 579 (1884). ["Untersuchungen über Kohlenhydrate und Fermente," Verlag Julius Springer, Berlin, **1909**, Vol. I, p. 138.]

(2) FISCHER, *Ber.*, **20**, 821 (1887). ["Untersuchungen," *op. cit.*, p. 144.] Fischer did not include arabinose in his early osazone studies, presumably (C. S. H.) because Kiliani was investigating this sugar. It had always been believed to be a hexose but in 1887 Kiliani (ref. *15*) published the first analysis of arabinose osazone, which showed the sugar to be a pentose.

(3) FISCHER AND HIRSCHBERGER, *Ber.*, **21**, 1805 (1888). ["Untersuchungen," p. 289.]

(4) FISCHER, *Ber.*, **23**, 2114 (1890). ["Untersuchungen," p. 1.]

(5) FISCHER AND HIRSCHBERGER, *Ber.*, **22**, 265 (1889). ["Untersuchungen," p. 294.]

(6) MEUNIER, *Compt. rend.*, **111**, 49 (1890).

(7) VINCENT AND DELACHANAL, *ibid.*, **111**, 51 (1890).

(8) FISCHER, *Ber.*, **23**, 3684 (1890). ["Untersuchungen," p. 377.]

(9) KILIANI, *Ber.*, **18**, 3066 (1885); **19**, 767 (1886).

(10) FISCHER, *ibid.*, **22**, 2204 (1889). ["Untersuchungen," p. 315.]

(11) FISCHER AND PILOTY, *Ber.*, **24**, 521 (1891). ["Untersuchungen," p. 381.]

(12) THIERFELDER, *Z. physiol. Chem.*, **15**, 71 (1891).

(13) FISCHER AND STAHEL, *Ber.*, **24**, 528 (1891). ["Untersuchungen," p. 397.]

(14) SCHEIBLER, *Ber.*, **1**, 58, 108 (1868).

(15) KILIANI, *ibid.*, **20**, 341, 1233 (1887).

(16) FISCHER AND HIRSCHBERGER, *ibid.*, **22**, 3218 (1889). ["Untersuchungen," p. 311.]

(17) FISCHER, *Ber.*, **23**, 370 (1890). ["Untersuchungen," p. 330.]

(18) FISCHER, *Ber.*, **24**, 539 (1891). ["Untersuchungen," p. 401.]

(19) FISCHER AND PASSMORE, *Ber.*, **22**, 2728 (1889). "Untersuchungen," p. 222.]

(20) FISCHER, *Ber.*, **23**, 2611 (1890). ["Untersuchungen," p. 362.]

(21) FISCHER AND STAHEL, *Ber.*, **24**, 528 (1891). ["Untersuchungen," p. 389.]

(22) VIGNON, *Ann. chim. phys.*, [5], **2**, 440 (1874).

(23) KOCH, *Pharm. Ztg. für Russland*, **25**, 619 (1886). This journal is in the Library of the Surgeon General of the Army, Washington, D. C.

(24) WHEELER AND TOLLENS, *Ann.*, **254**, 304 (1889).

(25) FISCHER, *Ber.*, **23**, 2625 (1890). ["Untersuchungen," p. 329.]

(26) FISCHER, *Ber.*, **24**, 1836, 2683 (1891). ["Untersuchungen," pp. 417, 427.]

(27) FISCHER, *Ann.*, **270**, 64 (1892). ["Untersuchungen," p. 605.]

(28) FISCHER AND PASSMORE, *Ber.*, **23**, 2226 (1890). ["Untersuchungen," p. 579.]

(29) HANN, MACLAY, KNAUF, AND HUDSON, *J. Am. Chem. Soc.*, **61**, 1268 (1939). Compare PEIRCE, *J. Biol. Chem.*, **23**, 327 (1915).

(30) WALDEN, *Ber.*, **29**, 133 (1896).

(31) FISCHER, "Untersuchungen," p. 81.

(32) KUHN AND EBEL, *Ber.*, **58**, 919 (1925).

(33) HÜCKEL, *Z. angew. Chem.*, **39**, 849 (1926).

(34) JACKSON AND HUDSON, *J. Am. Chem. Soc.*, **59**, 994 (1937).

(35) FISCHER, ref. *4*. ["Untersuchungen," p. 3.]

(36) MAQUENNE, *Ann. chim. phys.*, [6], **19**, 1 (1890).

(37) FISCHER AND PASSMORE, *Ber.*, 2226 (1890). ["Untersuchungen," p. 574.]

(38) TOLLENS AND GANS, *Ber.*, **21**, 2150 (1888); *Ann.*, **249**, 256 (1888).

(39) REISS, *Ber.*, **22**, 609 (1889).

(40) FISCHER AND HIRSCHBERGER, *ibid.*, **22**, 3218 (1889). ["Untersuchungen," p. 308.]

(41) THIERFELDER, ref. *12*. ["Untersuchungen," p. 381.]

(42) MEUNIER, *Compt. rend.*, **110**, 579 (1890); **111**, 52 (1890).

(43) FISCHER, *Ber.*, **27**, 3189 (1894). ["Untersuchungen," p. 38.]

——————————◆——————————

## CHEMIKER-ANEKDOTEN—R. B. WOODWARD

AT THE Munich (1955) meeting of the Gesellschaft deutscher Chemiker, Woodward roamed the halls carrying a big notebook in a blue silk cover on which was embroidered the structural formula of strychnine. The next day he appeared bearing a cover innocent of any embroidery. Asked a friend, "Why no structural formula?" Quipped Woodward, "Oh, I'm traveling incognito today."

(*See page 261*)

**Rolf Huisgen**
Institute of Organic Chemistry
University of Munich
Germany

# Richard Willstätter

From the large number of enthusiasts striving for new knowledge, a few titans arise to guide us to new horizons and uncover new territories of science. These pioneers—with their gift of creative imagination, clarity of thinking, and extraordinary will power—command the attention of the historians of chemistry. "All his ascents are first ascents" was said epigrammatically of Richard Willstätter (Fig. 1) when he was awarded an honorary degree.

Willstätter was born in 1872 in Karlsruhe, which at that time was the residence of the grand duke of Baden. He decided at the age of 12 to become a scientist and at 18, after hearing Adolf v. Baeyer's impressive lectures at the University of Munich, he knew that chemistry would be his future field. Baeyer, who as Liebig's successor contributed so much to the reputation of the Munich laboratory, had begun to grow old at that time and accepted only a limited number of co-workers. It was only after Willstätter had asked the alkaloid chemist Professor Einhorn for a subject for his thesis that Baeyer became aware of the highly gifted young man; Baeyer then looked after him so intensively that Willstätter later considered himself mainly a disciple of Baeyer.

Figure 1. Richard Willstätter (Engraving by P. Halm).

## Early Research: Alkaloids

When Willstätter graduated summa cum laude at 22, some results of his thesis struck him as being in-

compatible with the cocaine structure as proposed by Einhorn in analogy to the formulation of tropine by Ladenburg and Merling. Einhorn was engaged in the synthesis of model compounds showing the anesthetic activity of cocaine. Assuming a wrong structure for cocaine, he discovered the famous local anesthetic novocaine. Einhorn insisted that Willstätter promise not to continue work on cocaine. What was young Willstätter's reaction? He switched to the kindred atropine.

Willstätter, possessed by a "furor experimentalis," within two years carried out the now classical degradations which proved conclusively the structure of tropine. Some transformations which characterize tropine as a derivative of a cyclic unbranched chain of seven carbon atoms are formulated below.

**Evolution of tropine formula**

$$
\begin{array}{ll}
HC{\overset{CH_2}{\diagup}}{\underset{}{\diagdown}}CH_2 & CH \\
\end{array}
$$

A. Ladenburg (1887)          G. Merling (1891)

R. Willstätter (1897)

**Proof of the unbranched carbon skeleton**

$$H_2C-CH-CH_2-COOR \quad \xrightarrow[60°]{K_2CO_3} \quad H_2C-CH=CH-COOR \quad \xrightarrow[OH^\ominus]{CH_3J}$$

$$H_2C-CH=CH-COOR \quad \xrightarrow[amalgam]{Na-} \quad HOOC-(CH_2)_5-COOH$$
pimelic acid

(R. Willstätter, 1898)

Baeyer requisitioned this brilliant opus immediately for the *habilitation*,[1] the ceremony and process which in Germany mark the beginning of the academic career. Willstätter's determination to dedicate his life to scientific research originated from an incidental observation. The methiodide of tropinic ester, on gentle warming with potash, underwent degradation to the tertiary amine; this anomalously easy Hofmann degradation is a special property of $\beta$-aminocarbonyl derivatives.

In his biography, written in exile in 1940, Willstätter disclosed that this observation, though relatively minor, gave him an overpowering feeling of the dis-

Presented as the Carl Schurz Lecture on April 27, 1959, at the University of Wisconsin, Madison, Wisconsin. The author gratefully acknowledges the help of Dr. B. Witkop, Washington, in preparing the English text. The Verlag Chemie kindly gave permission to reproduce pictures from R. Willstätter's biography.

[1] When a green Ph.D. wants to enter an academic career in Germany, he must spend five years in independent research work to demonstrate his capability. Then, after being examined by the faculty, he is "habilitated" and is permitted to lecture.

covery of something unprecedented. He regrets that the element of adventure at the outset of scientific investigation cannot carry through to the reader of the eventual complete publication.[2]

The hydrocarbon tropilidene, obtained from tropine by Merling in 1881, was recognized as *cycloheptatriene*. Willstätter not only succeeded in the transformation of cycloheptanone to cycloheptatriene by a clear-cut route, he was able to reintroduce the nitrogen bridge into the molecule and to synthesize tropine by a multi-step procedure. The proper conclusions with regard to the structure of cocaine were quickly drawn. The elegant synthesis of ecgonine was carried out two decades later, at which time Willstätter's interest had turned to other subjects. Dioxosuberic ester, prepared by the Kolbe electrolysis procedure, with methylamine yielded pyrrolidine diacetic ester; intramolecular condensation then resulted in the desired ring system.

---

[2] In this connection I may mention some of Willstätter's philosophical remarks from his autobiography. A purposeful overestimation of the importance of the special problem under investigation helps to supply the needed vigor for the attack. Sometimes, the person too well-read and too critical is unable to adopt this attitude of overestimation. Then the enthusiasm and the driving force for the experimental activity is gone. Willstätter felt that this overestimation of a minor research goal is no longer possible after a great and fundamental discovery has been made. He pointed out that Röntgen, after his discovery of X-rays, was unable to work or publish on minor problems.

[3] The *extraordinarius* in Germany corresponds roughly to an associate professor, while the German *ordinarius* is the counterpart of the full professor.

---

**Structure of cocaine**

A. Einhorn (1893)

R. Willstätter (1898)

**Synthesis of e gonine**

Kolbe Electrolysis

Tropinone

Ecgonine and ψ-ecgonine

(R. Willstätter, A. Pfannenstiel and M. Bommer, 1918)

## Research on Quinones

When Willstätter became professor extraordinarius[3] in 1902, he was faced with the conflict familiar to every chemistry professor: the problem of how to divide his time between teaching and research. He paid due tribute to teaching in lectures and laboratory courses. Willstätter never regarded teaching as secondary; he knew that ingenious *but untrained* students were incapable of great achievements.

Willstätter's researches on quinones give eloquent testimony of the high educational standard of his co-workers. The red *o*-benzoquinone and its colorless

light red
o-Benzoquinone

colorless
p-Benzoquinonimines

(R. Willstätter and A. Pfannenstiel, 1904)

4.4'-Diphenoquinone
(R. Willstätter and L. Kalb, 1905)
golden yellow

amphi-Naphthoquinone
(R. Willstätter and J. Parnas, 1907)
brick red

modification, still unexplained today, as well as the mono- and diimines of *p*-benzoquinones, were all prepared for the first time. The isolation of *amphi*-naphthoquinone was the fruit of three semesters' work. The directions for the preparation of all of these quinones are so short and devoid of any reference to the extraordinary experimental difficulties that unjustified doubts as to their reproducibility were expressed during the first years after publication.

The important elucidation of the character of the Wurster dyes adds to the rich harvest in the quinone field. These red and blue dyes, formed on oxidation of *p*-phenylenediamines, are not quinone-imonium salts,

---

**R. Willstätter's Synthesis of Tropine**

Suberone

$HN(CH_3)_2$

$CH_3J$ / $Ag_2O$

quinoline 150°

Tropilidene

+HBr

$HN(CH_3)_2$

Na in Alcohol

+Br$_2$

-HBr

-CH$_3$Br

Tropidine

+HBr / HOAc

dil. H$_2$SO$_4$ 200°

ψ-Tropine

CrO$_3$ / Zn/HJ

Tropinone

Zn/HJ

Tropine

for Willstätter found these to be only yellow in color. Wurster's Red results from the combination of one equivalent each of the benzenoid and quinonoid species. Willstätter's term for this phenomenon was *meriquinonoid principle*. The present interpretation of Wurster's dyes as semi-quinones came much later.

**Preparation of cyclooctatetraene from psuedopelletierine**

(R.Willstätter, E.Waser and M.Heidelberger, 1912/13)

**Wurster's Red as meriquinonoid salt**

colorless    light yellow                    dark red

(R.Willstätter and J. Piccard, 1908)

**Modern formulation as semiquinonone**

Willstätter regarded the clarification of the mechanism of oxidation of aniline to the well-known black dye as his most eminent contribution to aromatic chemistry. "Aniline black" is quantitatively hydrolyzed by acids to *p*-benzoquinone. Today, we should immediately ask the further question whether cations or radicals act as precursors of the dye. Yet, even today, we cannot help admiring the craftsmanship of the master in the separation and structural determination of the 2-, 4- and 8-nuclear anilino-quinones.

**Oxidation of aniline to aniline black**

light yellow

Blue imine

Red imine

Emeraldine (dark blue)

Fourfold quinonoid aniline black

(R.Willstätter, C.W.Moore and S.Dorogi, 1907/1909)

Richard Willstätter never bothered about "small potatoes." With forethought and deliberation he came to grips with the most difficult problems of his time. Johannes Thiele explained the stability of benzene by the compensation of the so-called partial valencies. Willstätter saw in cyclooctatetraene, the higher vinylog of benzene, a suitable model for checking Thiele's hypothesis. In a backbreaking piece of work extending over eight years, the alkaloid pseudopelletierine was transformed to a few grams of the yellow tetraene which, in contrast to benzene, displayed the character of a reactive olefin. The molecular-orbital theory accommodates the observed high reactivity; 8 $\pi$-electrons in cyclic conjugation is a violation of the Hückel rule. The valence bond method rationalizes the *non*-aromatic character by the lack of coplanarity.

In his 1942 biography Willstätter complained that the preparation of the remarkable yellow hydrocarbon had not been repeated for more than a generation, though important physical constants were still lacking. But it so happened that at that very time cyclooctatetraene was being obtained by the tetramerization of acetylene in the Badische Anilin- und Sodafabrik. I suppose that Walter Reppe in 1941 had the first pounds of that yellow hydrocarbon in hand.

Willstätter's endeavors to prepare *cyclobutadiene* as a lower vinylog of benzene failed. This problem remained unsolved for many decades. Finally, in 1959, R. Criegee succeeded in isolating tetramethyl-cyclobutadiene as its crystalline, deeply colored complex with nickel chloride. C. Nenitzescu isolated in the same year a silver nitrate complex of cyclobutadiene itself.

The birthplace of cyclooctatetraene was Zürich. In 1905 Willstätter accepted a call as full professor of chemistry to the Swiss Polytechnic Institute (Eidgenössische Technische Hochschule) in Zürich. The teaching obligations at this institute at that time were known to be terrifying. Of the predecessors in that chair, Victor Meyer had lost his nerve and Eugen Bamberger his mind. Despite this heavy teaching burden, the six years at Zürich were the height of Willstätter's scientific productivity. Preparing the numerous demonstrations for the introductory lectures was troublesome, but apparently his successors in Zürich lightened this load considerably. Leopold Ruzicka, Willstätter's grandson as it were in the professorship, in his first lecture addressed the audience: "Gentlemen, can you imagine that on mixing two colorless solutions a red color develops?" After the affirmative answer of the students, Ruzicka continued: "Then we need not carry out that experiment." And that is the way it remained.

## Chlorophyll and Plant Pigments

Willstätter's magnificent investigations on chlorophyll were partly carried out in Zürich. It was obvious at that time that the green pigment of the plants not only satisfied man's aesthetic feelings but acted as a photosensitizer in the light-induced reduction of carbon dioxide to carbohydrates, quantitatively the most important organic systhesis on earth. There was nothing in this field on which Willstätter was able to build. The extraordinary sensitivity of the leaf green had led to the most contradictory statements. Willstätter, using refined methods of work-up, was able to isolate from more than 200 plant species one and the same chlorophyll, a mixture of the components *a* and *b* in constant ratio.

Chlorophyll *a*—$C_{55}H_{72}N_4O_5Mg$

Chlorophyll *b*—$C_{55}H_{70}N_4O_6Mg$

A complication in the work-up procedure is worth recounting. The transfer from the test tube to the isolation on a pilot plant scale had been a bit hasty. The Merck Company at Darmstadt extracted huge amounts of spinach in copper kettles with organic solvents. Unfortunately, all of the chlorophyll obtained turned out to be the copper complex.

Willstätter recognized chlorophyll as a magnesium complex from which the metal could be removed by acids. Chlorophyll turned out to be a dicarboxylic acid esterified with methanol and a new unsaturated alcohol phytol. On treatment of plant material with ethanol, the enzyme chlorophyllase catalyzed a trans-esterification of phytol by ethanol. In the autumn of 1906 Willstätter crystallized ethylchlorophyllide. His biography describes the scene where he poured the pure crystals, sparkling like jewels, on to a plate at the dinner table, letting his young wife share in his pride and delight. In 1907, Willstätter published a paper describing the acid and alkaline degradation of chlorophyll, a paper which he later considered the highlight of his scientific career.

**Degradation with acid and alkali**

Phäophytin a $C_{32}H_{32}N_4O(COOCH_3)$ $(COOC_{20}H_{39})$ $\xrightarrow{OH^\ominus}$ Chlorin e $C_{31}H_{33}N_4(COOH)_3$

Chlorophyll a $C_{32}H_{30}N_4OMg(COOCH_3)$ $(COOC_{20}H_{39})$ $\xrightarrow{H^\oplus}$ Phäophorbid a $C_{32}H_{32}N_4O(COOCH_3)$ $(COOH)$

Chlorophyllin a $C_{32}H_{30}N_4OMg(COOH)_2$ Äthyl-chlorophyllid a $C_{32}H_{30}N_4OMg(COOCH_3)$ $(COOC_2H_5)$

Rhodophyllin $C_{30}H_{30}N_4Mg(COOH)_2$ $\xrightarrow{soda lime}$ Pyrroätiophyllin $C_{30}H_{32}N_4Mg$

Willstätter learned that the oxygen content of chlorophyll is not involved in the binding of the magnesium. Rhodophyllin, the product of a several-step alkaline degradation, gave on decarboxylation with soda-lime an oxygen-free pyrro-etiophyllin which was still a magnesium complex. He suggested a chelation with the pyrrole nuclei. He knew already of the close relation between leaf green and the red hemoglobin, and he degraded hemin in a similar way to the oxygen-free mother substance etioporphyrin.

Willstätter concluded his investigations on chlorophyll in 1913 with a book "Untersuchungen über Chlorophyll," in collaboration with Arthur Stoll (Fig. 2), who served for many years as president of the International Union of Pure and Applied Chemistry. Chlo-

rophyll still had not given away the secret of its structure. Shortly before, Küster had proposed a structure for hemin, based perhaps mainly on intuition, which afterwards proved to be correct. Willstätter himself preferred a tetrapyrrylethylene structure.

Many scientists have asked why Willstätter, one of the most famous chemists of his time, dropped his work on chlorophyll. The difficulties of isolation had been overcome, and the field was open for chemical investigation. Did he tire of the problem which he had been studying for so many years? Did he consider the spade work complete and the rest of the task as a mopping-up operation to be left to others? I suppose that Willstätter in 1913 was so filled with new problems and plans that he simply had to abandon some old ones. Free from envy, he later appreciated and admired Hans Fischer's brilliant structural elucidation and partial syntheses of chlorophyll.

**Figure 2. Arthur Stoll.**

On the other hand, the process of *photosynthesis* in the green leaf commanded Willstätter's keen interest. Extensive investigations dealt with the constancy of the photosynthetic coefficient (absorbed $CO_2/O_2$ set free), the chlorophyll content during photosynthesis, the system chlorophyll and carbon dioxide, the dark (Blackman) reaction of assimilation, and the ratio between chlorophyll content and photosynthetic activity. In 1917, Willstätter published his experiences in book form. Here again foundations were laid for others to come. His search for the intermediates of photosynthesis had not yet been successful. The time and the methods were not ripe for an attack on this problem.

In 1910 the Kaiser Wilhelm Institutes were founded in Germany—free and independent institutes where outstanding scientists, free of all teaching obligations, dedicated themselves to self-chosen problems. In 1911, Willstätter accepted a call as director of the Kaiser Wilhelm Institute of Chemistry, and in 1912 moved to the new building at Berlin-Dahlem. A true friendship soon bound him to his institute neighbor Fritz Haber, the discoverer of important catalytic and electrochemical processes. At the opening of Willstätter's institute, Adolf von Harnack made a classic understatement: "Well-equipped laboratories are essential prerequisites for the progress of chemistry.

Indeed, science is capricious and its progress does not always follow the prefixed river-bed, but often goes its own way. Nevertheless, a well-equipped laboratory saves a great deal of energy."

The larger technical facilities of the institute and the prospects of continuing an investigation on the red and blue pigments of flowers without interruption had attracted Willstätter to Berlin. The crystallization of the blue dye of the bachelor's button or cornflower was a success of his last year at Zürich. Starting material had been dried bachelor's buttons ordered from the Merck Company. In Berlin Willstätter not only brought fresh plants into the laboratory but he also cultivated the various flowers. In the summer after Willstätter's arrival the institute was surrounded by gorgeous fields of blossoming flowers: Double bachelor's buttons, scarlet dahlias, large-petaled asters, red sage, violet pansies, and bronze-colored chrysanthemums.

The double purplish cornflowers contained up to 14% of their dry weight of the dye cyanin, a glycoside split by acids into 2 moles of glucose and the aglycon cyanidin. The blue sodium salt of cyanidin was dissolved in acids with a color change to red. Willstätter's surprise is not hard to visualize; such a behavior points to a basic function in an nitrogen-free dye! In the red solution he recognized an oxonium salt derived from a hydroxychromane. Was it not a breath-taking discovery when Willstätter, on harvesting his flower fields in the fall, found the same *cyanidin* as coloring matter in the red rose, certain dahlias, the red poppy, and somewhat later in the colors of cherries, plums, cranberries, and elderberries? Nature's grandiose palette of red and blue hues and shades had been reduced to a few closely related structural types, of which cyanidin is the most widespread. Willstätter found that subtle variations in $pH$ were mainly responsible for the multitude of shades in the flower garden. The proportions of the red oxonium salt, the violet phenol, and the blue phenoxide anion change with the hydrogen ion concentration.

Chromophore of the colouring matter of roses, corn flowers, dahlias, poppies, cherries and cranberries

Cyanidin

Synthesis of pelargonidin

*( R. Willstätter and L. Zechmeister, 1914 )*

Two years later the outbreak of the first world war brought this investigation to a close. In August, 1914, all co-workers were drafted. The crop of flowers was carried in large baskets to the military hospitals. Shortly before, Zechmeister, now professor at the California Institute of Technology, had completed the synthesis of pelargonidin. Willstätter never resumed this work, which was masterfully continued and completed after the war by Sir Robert Robinson.

The Swedish Academy awarded Willstätter the Nobel prize of 1915 for his research on plant pigments. The diploma was trimmed with ornaments of green leaves, blue bachelor's buttons, and scarlet geraniums.

A small piece of applied military research is connected with Willstätter's name. At the outbreak of chemical warfare there were no protective or defensive measures on either side. Perhaps it is not well known that the gas-mask is an invention of Fritz Haber and Richard Willstätter. More precisely, Willstätter's contribution was the construction of a cartridge containing mainly charcoal and hexamethylenetetramine which absorbed chlorine and phosgene from the incoming air. Not only were the German gas-masks equipped with such filters, but the Allied Forces analyzed captured gas-masks and soon hexamethylenetetramine was found in every filter.

In 1915 Willstätter received honoring calls to chairs in Göttingen, Vienna, and Munich. A cordial letter from his old teacher Baeyer strengthened him in his resolution to return to Munich where the foundation of his scientific career had been laid. The Bavarian Minister had promised to begin with the urgently needed enlargement of the laboratory despite wartime conditions. The building of a new lecture hall seating 600 people was to replace Liebig's old auditorium, but it was not completed until 1920.

### Enzyme Chemistry

It was an admirable venture that Willstätter, despite the lack of co-workers and the terrible wartime conditions, should attack the biggest and toughest problem: the nature of enzymes and their mode of action. In 1911 he had begun investigating peroxidase and catalase, two enzymes that destroy hydrogen peroxide. The isolation work which was started in the Zürich laboratory was now resumed on a broad basis. Soon similar investigations were started on carbohydrases, proteinases, and lipases.

The enrichment of enzymes by adsorption techniques can be traced back to Willstätter. The difficulties in obtaining reproducible activities of adsorbants stimulated fundamental studies on metal hydroxides and hydrogels. These were courageous forays into inorganic fields. Free silicic acid supposedly should not exist; the text books maintained that instead, hydrosols of silicon dioxide are obtained. Willstätter proved the transient existence of the monomeric ortho acid, $H_4SiO_4$, which is capable of permeating plant membranes and seems to be responsible for the silicification of wood.

The results of ten years' hard work were collected in a book in 1928. The "Untersuchungen über Enzyme" was published jointly by Willstätter and his excellent collaborators Wolfgang Grassmann, Heinrich Kraut, Richard Kuhn, and Ernst Waldschmidt-Leitz. No fewer than 43 additional names are listed as co-workers. A later generation tended to criticize repeatedly the outcome of the enzyme work as generally unsatisfactory. It is true that the rather lengthy enzyme adsorption methods did not become standard methods of the biochemical laboratory. Nevertheless, the first successful separations of carbohydrases and peptidases were made possible in this way. Willstätter enriched horse-radish peroxidase by a factor of 12,000 and the invertase of yeast 3500-fold. He did not have the good fortune to obtain a crystalline enzyme. In retrospect, Willstätter's selection of enzymes was not an auspicious one. Invertase from yeast, for example, so far has defied all attempts at crystallization.

Enzyme chemistry owes to Willstätter a significant impetus. He inaugurated *in vitro* reduction by fermenting yeast as a laboratory technique. The reduction of chloral and bromal yielded the corresponding carbinols. The tribromoethanol known under the trade mark "Avertin" came into wide usage as a rectal anaesthetic. A renowned English physician considered the drug as being "one of the most beneficial aids to relieve human suffering we know of at the present time."

Dark clouds overshadowed Willstätter's time in Munich. Perhaps I have been paying more attention so far to his work than to his personal fate. After 5 years of happy marriage, his young wife died in 1906. He never married again. He gave his son and his daughter a careful education. In 1915 he lost his son as a consequence of a serious illness.

Let us go back further into the past: Willstätter's youth, spent at Karlsruhe and Nuremberg, was somewhat overshadowed by his Jewish origin. A. v. Baeyer recommended christening to the young lecturer as a means of avoiding obstacles in his academic career. Christening at that time removed the barriers erected by society. A. v. Baeyer, himself of Jewish origin on his mother's side and distantly related to Heinrich Heine, advocated the principle of assimilation. Willstätter's pride refused such an action. Not at all an orthodox Jew, he preferred like many other scientists to be free from religious and confessional ties.

## Early Retirement

In the summer of 1924 the Munich faculty had to look for a successor of the famous crystallographer and mineralogist Paul Groth. Groth himself proposed passionately Viktor M. Goldschmidt in Oslo, the founder of modern geochemistry. Goldschmidt was a Jew. At the instigation of some members the Faculty refused consent, giving way to the pressure of the street, as it were. That very same day Willstätter tendered his resignation. Demonstrations of sympathy from the students, the faculty, the university, and the ministry of education did not change the tragic decision of the 53-year-old Willstätter. His final official action in the faculty was the suggestion and appointment of the highly esteemed Heinrich Wieland as his successor (Fig. 3).

After his self-imposed retirement in September of 1925, Willstätter never set foot into the institute again. He declined brilliant offers from domestic and foreign universities, including three in the United States. Wieland installed a special laboratory for Willstätter's co-workers, who were thus enabled to finish their doctoral or habilitation theses. Until 1938 Margarete Rohdewald continued her investigations on the metabolism of sugar in muscle. Daily she reported the newest

results to Willstätter, who retained his residence in Munich.

Willstätter's foresight of things to come proved to be correct. He was not born a fighter to stem the rising tide of intolerance in political life. He retired and maintained his contacts with good friends. Hardly had Hitler seized power when discrimination against the Jews found expression in vicious pogroms. The dreadful aspects of these persecutions are well known. The German universities were forced to dismiss Jewish professors. In 1936, Carl Bosch, Director of the Badische Anilin-und Sodafabrik, warned Hitler of the set-backs in chemistry and physics as a consequence of these dismissals. The fanatic's answer: "Then we have to get along without chemistry and physics in the next 100 years."

Figure 3. Heinrich Wieland.

In 1938 Willstätter saw his hope vanish of spending his remaining years in his home in Munich. After a month-long martyrdom he succeeded, with the help of his true friend Arthur Stoll, in obtaining an emigration visa for Switzerland. Only a small part of his belongings and art treasures could be saved. The great old man spent the last three years of his life in Muralto near Locarno. From his home, Villa Eremitaggio, he enjoyed the wonderful view of the Lago Maggiore. Here he found time to rest and write his autobiographical sketches. On the 3rd of August, 1942, he died of cardiac failure.

During the war and Nazi regime, the German chemists were allowed neither to hold memorial lectures nor to publish obituaries for Richard Willstätter. In 1956, a worthy tombstone and memorial was erected, not in his homeland but in the country of his last refuge. A black marble stone at Muralto tells of a rich and well-filled life. Besides the symbols of wisdom and some alchemical instruments, leaves, fruits, grapes, and a fermentation vat remind us of his research.

Willstätter's biography "Aus meinem Leben" was edited by Arthur Stoll and published by the Verlag Chemie. In an epilogue added by Stoll, the mere enumeration of the honors and awards bestowed upon the great scientist requires the space of three pages. Let me conclude the lecture with Willstätter's words on the occasion of the Award of the Willard-Gibbs Medal in Chicago in 1933: "Our experiments are not carried out to decide whether we are right, but to gain new knowledge. It is for knowledge's sake that we plow and sow."

# GEORG LUNGE (1839–1923)[1]

## E. BERL

Carnegie Institute of Technology, Pittsburgh, Pennsylvania

GEORG LUNGE was born in Breslau, Upper Silesia, September 15, 1839. He was the son of a merchant. He studied under the famous botanist and founder of bacteriology, Ferdinand Cohn (1828–1898) who did fundamental work on protoplasm.[2]

Lunge got his doctor's degree from the University of Breslau in 1859, when he was not quite twenty, with a dissertation on alcoholic fermentation—just when the famous discussion between Liebig (1803–1870) and Pasteur (1822–1895) concerning fermentation and catalysis began to develop. Lunge then went to Heidelberg and studied under Bunsen (1811–1899), in the same year that the spectral analysis was developed by Kirchhoff (1824–1887) and Bunsen. It may be of interest to cite the letter which Bunsen wrote on November 15, 1859, to Roscoe (1833–1915), describing one of the most wonderful discoveries and progresses ever made by man.

"Actually Kirchhoff and I are occupied with a mutual investigation which does not let us sleep. Kirchhoff has made a wonderful, totally unexpected discovery. He has found the cause of the dark lines in the spectrum of the sun and has reproduced the same artificially in the spectrum of the sun and in the spectrum of flames without lines, coinciding their position with the identical lines of Fraunhofer (1787–1826). Now the way is given to investigate the material composition of the sun and the fixed stars with the same exactitude as we can determine sulfur, chlorine, and so forth, by our reagents.

"On the earth all these substances can be distinguished and found with the same exactitude as on the sun so that, for instance, I can detect a content of lithium in 20 g. of sea water.

"For the detection of certain substances this method is preferred to all other known methods. If you have a mixture of Li, K, Na, Ba, Sr, Ca, then you need only to bring 1 mg. of it in our apparatus to read all those substances directly by telescope by simple observation. Some of these reactions are wonderfully sharp. For instance, one can detect 0.005 mg. of Li with the greatest ease. I have found this material in nearly all potashes."

The Latin inscription on the grave of Fraunhofer—"He brought us nearer the stars"—could be used with the same, or perhaps greater, right for Bunsen and Kirchhoff.

From Heidelberg Lunge published a paper on the composition of the gases in the dark cone of nonluminous gas flames (Bunsen burner flames). This first publication of Lunge became important when Smithells split the flame of the Bunsen burner in two parts and when, forty-five years later, Haber (1868–1934) carried out his very important work concerning the water-gas equilibrium of the Bunsen flame.

The next year, in 1860, Lunge, the twenty-one-year-old doctor of philosophy, became a chemist in a German fertilizer plant. He made experiments on the production of white paper from straw. In 1862 he established his own plant for the production of potassium ferrocyanide, sal ammoniac, lead salts, tartaric acid, and

GEORG LUNGE

so forth. This plant did not operate according to Lunge's wishes. Therefore, he decided to go to England.

At this time England was the country where applied chemistry was most advanced, especially inorganic chemistry. The cradle of modern chemistry was in France where, at the end of the eighteenth and the beginning of the nineteenth centuries, many great scientists, like Lavoisier (1743–1794), Dulong (1785–1838), and Dumas (1800–1884), carried out their important work. It is known that in 1822 Liebig went to Paris to study under Thénard (1777–1859), the discoverer of hydrogen peroxide, and under Gay-Lussac (1778–1850). The development of the German scientific chemistry and chemical industry was greatly influenced by this transplantation of the new French chemistry to Germany.

[1] Presented before the Division of History of Chemistry at the ninety-eighth meeting of the A. C. S., Boston, Mass., September 12, 1939.

[2] At the beginning of a semester Cohn used to say, "The plant body is composed of carbon, oxygen, hydrogen, and nitrogen" and, writing the chemical symbols of these elements on the blackboard, his name, COHN, appeared.

The very important British textile industry was responsible for the development of the British chemical industry. Large quantities of sodium carbonate, caustic sodium hydroxide, soap, and bleaching materials had to be produced. In the first sixty years of the last century sodium carbonate was produced exclusively by the Leblanc (1742–1806) soda process. Our present chemical industry would not have been developed to

FRITZ RASCHIG

the present stage without the teaching and experiences gained by the development of the Leblanc process. The utilization of all compounds entering into the Leblanc process is ideal. The basic materials of the Leblanc process were sodium chloride, sulfuric acid, limestone, and coke.

P. A. BOLLEY

The sulfuric acid industry has its own most important history. On Clement's (1779–1841) and Desormes' (1777–1862) observations (1806), Berzelius (1779–1848) based his conception of catalysis (1835). The

Gay-Lussac tower was invented in 1827 and used for the first time in 1842. Many sulfuric acid producers did not use the Gay-Lussac tower at this time and afterwards. John Glover (1817–1902) introduced the Glover tower in 1859. It was improved in 1864 when towers were built of about the same construction as today. Lunge saw this tower first in 1865 and gave it its name. In the following years, as usual when new, surprising things are invented, a discussion took place concerning the advantages and disadvantages of the Glover tower. Today one cannot believe that this great advance was resisted. There is no doubt that Lunge's publications on the merits of the Glover tower are responsible for the rather quick acceptance of this important amelioration. It may be of interest to note

KARL BOSCH

that Clemens Winkler (1838–1904) in 1867 also proposed to denitrate nitrosylsulfuric acid from the Gay-Lussac tower acid by hot sulfur dioxide, not knowing that this process had already been used by Glover and others for several years. He had to add water. Glover's proposition to use water in the form of diluted sulfuric acid certainly presents a great progress over Winkler. The sulfuric acid was used mostly for the production of sodium sulfate, superphosphate, and of nitric acid.

In these years when soda was produced in several places in England, especially in Newcastle-on-Tyne and other places near Liverpool, enormous amounts of hydrochloric acid escaped without being recovered. They caused the destruction of all vegetation. Lord Derby's Act of 1863 demanded a nearly complete recovery (more than ninety-five per cent.) of this harmful substance. This Act became very important because now the British industry was forced to convert the recovered hydrochloric acid into chlorine, chlorates, and into bleaching powder necessary for the bleaching of the British textiles. This was done first with manganesedioxide whose recovery with the Weldon (1832–1885) process (1866) was of great importance. In 1867 Deacon (1822–1876) invented his catalytical process for the conversion of hydrochloric acid into chlorine This is one of the first, modern, heterogeneous catalytic processes introduced in the chemical industry.

During Lunge's stay in England new and important changes in the production of soda had taken place. In 1861 Ernest Solvay (1839–1922), then an employee

J. B. A. DUMAS

of the Brussels Gas Works, tried to find some use for ammonia which was produced as a by-product of the production of illuminating gas. At this time practically no application was known for large quantities of ammonia. Its use as a fertilizer (ammonium sulfate or ammonium nitrate) and as a material for the production of nitric acid and urea became important afterward. Solvay, with the help of money lent by his family and by friends, built his first plant in Couillet, near Charleroi, Belgium, in 1863. He based his process on the reaction $NaCl + NH_4HCO_3 = NaHCO_3 + NH_4Cl$. Enormous difficulties had to be overcome. In 1872 Solvay gave a license for England to Ludwig Mond (1839–1909) who, with a Swiss companion, founded the company, Brunner, Mond and Company, now I. C. I. This company also had tremendous difficulties and, soon after the start, was on the verge of bankruptcy. Solvay and his brother, Alfred, who, as a business man, had the same genius as Ernest Solvay as a chemical engineer, developed the Solvay process so that fifty years afterward not one single Leblanc soda plant existed in the world. For the writer it is an unforgettable episode when, in 1910, he made the personal acquaintance of Ernest Solvay. Solvay told him that if he had known that great men like Dyar, Hemming, Schlösing (1824–1885), and Bolley (1812–1870) had tried unsuccessfully to use this reaction between am-

JOHN GLOVER

monium bicarbonate and sodium chloride, he would not have dared, as a young, inexperienced engineer without capital, to enter this field. It is very well known that both industrialists, Ernest Solvay and Ludwig Mond, died extremely rich men. Toward the end of his life Solvay seemed to be rather disappointed. He gave great sums to many research institutions, especially to the University of Brussels, hoping that the puzzle of life could be explained. We know very well that the progress in this field is extremely slow; that money alone cannot contribute very much for the development of this most important problem of mankind.

As long as Lunge was in England the progress of the Solvay soda process was rather slow so that in 1876, when he left England, the competition with the Leblanc process was not yet serious. At this time about eight per cent. of the total soda production was made with the ammonia process. But soon afterward the price for one ton of sodium carbonate went down from fifty-six dollars (gold) to twenty-two dollars. Finally, the Leblanc process, in spite of its perfect utilization of all components of

LUDWIG MOND

the raw materials, could not resist. On the other hand, very often the Solvay process wastes practically all chlorine of the sodium chloride. In the Leblanc process one has to handle solid substances. In the ammonia soda process, solutions and gases have to be transported, and

H. DEACON

HENRY DEACON

only at the end of the operation solid sodium bicarbonate results. Furthermore, the Leblanc soda process needs much more fuel, power, and labor than the

Solvay process. These are the reasons why the Leblanc process could not compete with the Solvay process.

This was the situation during Lunge's stay in England. On the Continent at this time, the chemical industry was not developed in the same way as the British industry was. The French chemical industrialists did not use the really wonderful teachings of the French scientists at the end of the eighteenth century and the first forty years of the nineteenth century. The German chemical industry really only started in the sixties of the nineteenth century.[3] A. W. Hofmann (1818–1892) had just returned to Berlin (1865) from London where he and his seventeen-year-old assistant, Perkin (1838–1907), laid the foundation for the industry of the artificial dyes (1856).

Lunge's first position in England was in a plant where coal-tar products were made. In 1867 he published his first book on coal tar and ammonia which up

GEORG LUNGE

to 1912 was published in five editions in German and in English. In 1865, first as chemist, then as superintendent, he came into a newly founded, rather small soda plant in South Shields, near Newcastle-on-Tyne. Here he was in direct contact with that part of the chemical industry to which he devoted practically his whole future life. This was the acid and alkali industry. Very soon he founded the Newcastle Chemical Society which afterward was converted into the Society of Chemical Industry. He developed his soda plant and found time to publish articles on many different subjects so that his name became well known in the chemical industry and in the academic world. Reading his publications today, one is surprised at how broad Lunge's interest was, and how well informed he became on different subjects.

Lunge studied all of the advances which were made in the field of his activity with the greatest care. He

[3] The Badische Anilin u. Sodafabrik was founded May, 1865; the Farbenfabriken vorm. Bayer and Company, 1863.

defended every improvement with great vigor, and is certainly responsible for quick advances in different industries.

There must have been a desire on Lunge's part to return to the academic world, in spite of his interest and success in technical matters. In 1875 at the Polytechnical School (now Technical University) in Zurich, the position of a professor of technical chemistry became vacant. In this position were Bolley, the editor of the first handbook on chemical technical analysis, and after him, Emil Kopp (1817–1875) who excelled in the field of dyestuffs. At this time the Polytechnical School was governed by an extremely capable, former lawyer, Karl Kappeler (1816–1888).[4] Kappeler, after Emil Kopp's death, first asked Heinrich Caro (1834–1910), the leading chemist in the dyestuff field of the rather small German Badische Anilin und Soda Fabrik at this time, if he would accept this position. Caro was then occupied with very many extremely important problems in the field of organic dyestuffs. He declined the offer but suggested that Kappeler should get in touch with Lunge. Both men met in Köln, and Lunge decided to accept Kappeler's offer. He went to Zurich in 1876 and filled a position there for thirty-two years, and brought world fame to the Polytechnical School of Zurich. At this time and later this school was really one of the first technical schools in the world.[5]

There is no doubt that Lunge was one of the most excellent teachers of his time. The progress in the field of chemical engineering and chemical technology can be traced back to Lunge's activity as a teacher. The writer attended some of his classes, and he remembers very well the deep impression he got from Lunge's lectures, thirty-five years ago. Most of his teachings were based on his own experience, and the student was taught this field of chemical technology in a really ideal way.[6] At the beginning of his Zurich activity, Lunge had to cover not only the field of inorganic technology and fuels, but also the field of organic technology, especially the field of artificial dyestuffs, natural and artificial fiber goods, bleaching, and dyeing.

In 1886, with Victor Meyer, he built a chemistry building in Zurich which, at the time of its construction, certainly was the most perfect of its kind.[7] In it

[4] At a dinner in honor of Victor Meyer (1848–1897), Kappeler gave the following definition of chemistry, "Chemistry is a terrible science, costs a lot of money, and stinks horribly."

[5] Zeuner, Reuleaux, Clausius, Semper, Bolley, Kopp, V. Meyer, Escher, v. d. Linth, Kullmann, Nägeli, Fiedler, and many other great scientists taught there. Several of them knew well their position in the learned world. One used to say, "There are only two famous representatives in my profession—the other is already dead."

[6] He spoke, for example, of the blast furnace process and the vain efforts to convert all carbon monoxide into carbon dioxide by increasing the size of the blast furnace stoves. In former times the escaping gases were burned and one of these stoves on the coast of Scotland seemed like a lighthouse and was the cause of several shipwrecks.

[7] Fifty years ago Lunge built there one of the first air conditioning installations by cooling warm air with cold water. The greatest difference in temperature in this building, summer and winter, was 5°C.

very important contributions to science and industry were and are made. Great scientists like Heumann (1851–1894), Gnehm (1852–1923), Treadwell (1857–1918), Hantzsch (1857–1935), E. Bamberger (1857–1932), Willstätter (1872–), Staudinger 1881–), Wiegner (1883–1936), Ruzicka (1887–), and others worked and taught there. The center of gravity of Lunge's teaching activity was in the laboratory. He saw every student in his fifth and sixth semesters every day. Accompanied by his assistant, he discussed with the student his particular problem, gave the necessary instruction, and in this way educated a large number of excellent men in the field of technical analysis. At the end of this laboratory course, the student very often began his activity in research work. With the help of graduate students, Lunge solved many important problems in his later years. His experimental work during the first twenty years of his scientific activity at Zurich was made practically without the help of collaborators.

R. C. BÖTTGER

A great part of his scientific activity in Zurich was devoted to the study of the sulfuric acid lead chamber process. It is greatly to Lunge's credit that he clarified many of the complicated questions. His last scientific work with the writer during the years 1904–1907 was devoted to this problem.

Fritz Raschig (1863–1928), certainly one of the best-informed men in the field of the chemistry of sulfur-nitrogen compounds, in 1887–8 developed a very interesting theory of the lead chamber process which was objected to by Lunge. Raschig afterward entered the service of Badische Anilin und Sodafabrik, Ludwigshafen (now I. G.). After a few years he left the I. G. and founded his own company which did extremely successful work. Raschig made many very valuable inventions, especially in the field of synthetic phenol, phenol derivatives, and phenol-formaldehyde compounds. He invented a very important process for the production of hydrazine. His Raschig rings are well known all over the world. He developed an

K. F. KUHLMANN

interesting, continuous process for the distillation of complicated mixtures like coal tar. After having done such excellent work in the field of applied chemistry, in 1904 Raschig returned again to his theoretical views which he had developed more than twenty-five years before.

The discussion with Raschig which followed afterward (1904–1907) was of great importance for the development of the lead chamber process. From this discussion sprang up a new development which is known as the intensified production process of sulfuric acid. Opl in Czechoslovakia was the first to make use

M. P. E. BERTHELOT

of Lunge's and the writer's experiments whereby nitrosylsulfuric acid in a somewhat labilized state did convert per one mol many thousand mols of $SO_2$ and oxygen into sulfuric acid. Unfortunately, during this discussion with Raschig, the personal element entered in and excited Lunge so much that in 1907 he resigned his professorship and retired to private life. The study of the theory of the lead chamber process was later taken up by the writer and his collaborators. It was shown that the theory developed with Lunge was right, and that, based on this theory, by the use of increased pressure, the output per unit of time and unit of volume could be increased ten thousand times compared with the output in older systems. When Raschig died in 1928, the writer paid him the last honor. Raschig's collaborator, Prahl, told him then that the late, great scientist and industrialist had convinced himself that some of his former views were wrong He had decided to publish this, but, unfortunately, Death took his pen from his hand. After his death, Prahl did it in his name.

Besides extensive and intensive work in the field of sulfuric acid, lead chamber and contact process, Lunge did work in the field of coal tar. His researches on cellulose nitrates (Chr. F. Schönbein, R. C. Böttger) are important. Here he cleared up many wrong views and created the basis of the modern production of these cellulose esters. He determined the density of the most important acids, alkalies, and salt solutions. This work is just as important today as it was fifty years ago. Further work was done in the field of water-gas production and gas producers.

Other research work concerning the Deacon-Hurter process for the production of chlorine from hydrochloric acid and oxygen has thrown important light on this very interesting catalytic process. Connected with this work were his important studies on the constitution and formation of bleaching powder.

RENÉ BOHN

Lunge did important work for the elimination of yellow phosphorus in the match industry. The yellow phosphorus caused a terrible disease among the workmen, the so-called phosphorus necrosis.

Besides this research work, Lunge made several important inventions. Before the oleum contact process was worked out, he introduced an ingenious process (1882) to produce sulfuric acid monohydrate by freezing concentrated ninety-four to ninety-seven per cent. sulfuric acid and separating the frozen monohydrate formed from the weaker mother liquid (containing ninety-two per cent. sulfuric acid).

A very important invention was his reaction tower (1886) known under the name of the Lunge-Rohrmann plate reaction tower. This tower, used formerly on a rather large scale in the chemical industry, increased the production of sulfuric acid in the lead chamber process considerably. This reaction tower was used also in other industries. It is the forerunner of the packed towers which, filled with rings or saddles, have obtained widest use in industry.

Lunge's process to form nitric acid and alkali by heating sodium nitrate with iron oxide did not become

A. F. HORSTMANN

important from a technical standpoint, in spite of the interesting, underlying reaction. At that time materials could not be found which would stand the action of alkali and acid at the same time. It may be that this process today, with our improved construction materials, could be carried out in an industrial way. He contributed important progress based on the analysis of silicates, finding the differences in the reactivity of colloidal and crystallized silicic acid with weak and strong alkali. This work is important for the knowledge of fire-proof clay.

Another field of Lunge's activity was the invention and the improvement of many laboratory methods. We owe to him the introduction of methyl orange (1878) as an indicator and the study of the action of other indicators. This work was done in connection with the use of filtered drinking water from the Lake of Zurich. Typhoid epidemics which caused many

ALFRED WERNER

deaths by the use of unfiltered water disappeared when, through careful filtration, all dangerous bacteria were removed.

His publications on standard solutions and on standard titrimetric substances are of greatest importance. Lunge's method for the analysis of pyrites is used with slight modifications all over the world. His gas analysis methods, especially the development of his nitrometer (1878) and gas volumeter (1890–1892) are of the greatest importance for technical analysis. The nitrometer method was first described by Crum (1847). Lunge's modification, by using the mercury not only as a reducing agent but also as confining liquid, is the reason for the broad application of this method. His gas volumeter, whereby the reduction of a gas volume to 0°C. and 760 mm. pressure is made mechanically, is based also on a very ingenious idea. Lunge introduced other gas volumetric methods, for instance, the determination of hydrogen peroxide by hypochlorites. The determination of the strength of permanganate solutions with hydroperoxide and, vice versa, the introduction of sodium carbonate as a standard titrimetric substance, and other methods have found much use in technical chemical laboratories.

We cannot overestimate the importance of this part of Lunge's experimental work. Before his time the recipe of the foreman ruled in the older chemical technic. Through Lunge's work, this was replaced by a

D. M. KILIANI

strong bridge of scientific certainty. Now it became possible to get an insight into the complicated reactions of the chemical industry, and to reproduce them without failures and setbacks.

Lunge was an extremely fertile writer of technical publications and very valuable books. His work is known all over the world. Altogether he published six hundred seventy-five publications, among them eighty-six books and pamphlets. He had the wonderful talent to write with the greatest ease. During forty-five years he worked sixteen hours a day. His book on coal tar and ammonia (five editions) has been mentioned. His books on soda manufacture, and especially his book on sulfuric acid, are fundamental. This handbook of the soda industry was first published in 1879. The fourth and last edition was published in 1916. He translated this handbook himself from German into English. It has also been translated into French by Naville.

Lunge published three editions of a comprehensive work on "Technical Methods of Chemical Analysis." The first two editions of this book were published by F. R. Böckmann. The writer had the privilege of publishing the sixth edition with Lunge, and the seventh and eighth editions after Lunge's death. These "Technical Methods of Chemical Analysis" were published first in two volumes. Lunge increased the number of volumes to three and, with the writer, the number was increased to four, and finally to five volumes. The "Pocket Handbook for the Inorganic Chemical Industry" was edited in 1893 by Lunge in connection with the association of the German soda producers. The fourth, fifth, and sixth editions also were published

by Lunge and the writer, and the seventh edition by the writer alone after Lunge's death. It was translated also into English and French.

These books are of great importance for the chemical industry. Lunge, who had the broadest experience in the field of technical chemical analysis, laid down all his experiences in these books. Furthermore, those parts for which he was not a specialist were written by the best specialists.

Lunge was the kindest of men. Misfortunes he had in his own family did not harden his heart. He did all that was in his power to bring his students into positions and to improve their situation. For many years the English, Swiss, and German industries got many of their best men in the field of technical chemistry from

P. T. HÉROULT

Lunge's laboratory. René Bohn (1862–1922) and Robert E. Schmidt (1864–1938), certainly the greatest chemists of their time in the field of alizarin dyestuffs, especially indanthren dyestuffs, were former students and assistants of Lunge. Alfred Werner (1866–1919), the "great inorganic Kekulé," and Nobel prize winner (1913), also Lunge's pupil, always had the greatest admiration for Lunge who was responsible for his advanced studies under Berthelot (1827–1907) in Paris. After having discovered the asymmetry of nitrogen in 1890, Werner became assistant to Lunge. After one semester of this activity, Lunge told Werner, "You are fired as my assistant. I cannot use your services any more because you

ALWIN MITTASCH

are much too good for this minor position. I know that your father is a man of little means. With his and my help it may be possible for you to study one year in Paris." In this one year the theory of inorganic compounds ripened in Werner's head. It is not widely known that, in preparing his notes for his lectures, he dreamed his theory which afterward made him famous. Within one week, working day and night, Werner worked out and wrote down the theory of inorganic compounds which was published in 1892. This fundamental publication contains all the elements of his future scientific work which he carried out until 1915 when he became ill. Alfred Werner died in 1919. Without Lunge's help he would probably have had to spend much more energy to reach this highest peak of any scientific activity.

The writer of these lines also owes much gratitude to Lunge. During the years of their collaboration, from 1904 until his death in January, 1923, Lunge was like a father to him.

When Lunge entered the chemical industry, this industry was based mostly on the production of lead chamber sulfuric acid, sodium carbonate according to the Leblanc process, and the caustification of sodium carbonate with lime. At the end of his life, of which he had given more than sixty years to research, the contact sulfuric acid assumed a very important place. The Leblanc soda industry was superseded by the Solvay process. The caustification alkali hydroxide was partly replaced by the mightily developing electrolytic industry. Chlorine which was formerly produced by the Weldon and Deacon process is now produced by the electrolytic process. Organic chemistry celebrated its great triumphs. Willstätter (1872–), Lunge's colleague in the Technical University of Zurich, did his fundamental research work on chlorophyl, the assimilation of carbonic acid and water in the plant and on enzymes. The organic dyestuff industry got a tremendous development, also the pharmaceutical industry, and the explosives industry. Alfred Nobel (1833–1896), who made his most important first inventions when Lunge entered the field, left the world with the most powerful explosives for war and for civilian purposes.

The rayon industry, based on Count Chardonnet's (1839–1924) and Cross' (1855–1935) inventions, developed to a most important industry. Progresses in the production of pig iron, steel [(Bessemer, 1813–1892),

(P. Martin, 1824–1915), (Thomas, 1850–1885)], and special steels (B. Strauss, 1880–) and alloys were made. The industry of aluminum [(Wöhler, 1800–1883), (Bunsen, 1811–1899), (Hall, 1863–1914), (Heroult, 1863–1914), (Kiliani, 1858–1895)], magnesium, and light alloys was developed.

The physical chemistry was created by van't Hoff (1852–1911), Arrhenius (1859–1927), W. Ostwald, Horstmann (1842–1929), and many others. The most important industrial consequences of this science were drawn by Lunge's distant relative, Fritz Haber. The formation of ammonia from its elements by the high pressure synthesis of Haber and Bosch (1872–), its combustion to nitric oxides and their conversion to nitric acid [(Kuhlmann, 1803–1881), (W. Ostwald, 1853–1932), (Mittasch, 1869–), (Bosch)], the hydrogenation of coal by Bergius (1884–) the first steps to produce liquid hydrocarbons, alcohols, acids, and so forth, by the hydrogenation of carbon monoxide (Mittasch), were made before Lunge died. These sixty years of his life covered the greatest progress in the field of industrial chemistry in which he, through his own work as a chemical engineer and as a research man, contributed immensely.

Lunge was forced to retire in 1907 because his health was impaired by arteriosclerosis. Unfortunately, after his retirement, his memory suffered greatly. After a life which lasted eighty-three years and three months, Death took him away, honored and loved by many hundreds of his former pupils.

Lunge's personality cannot be better characterized than with these words which Fritz Haber, then president of the German Chemical Society, spoke after Lunge's death:

"His example is a reminder that science not only serves its own systematic progress, but it has to help men so that they find better conditions of life. In the realm of scientific abstraction there are independent kingdoms of thought and experiment, and ruler is he whose glory outlasts the centuries. The masters of thought and experiment are not the only kings in science. He is also a king who, through knowledge and work, through teaching and research in the field of applied science, guides the spirits of the contemporaries, and who in scientific work conquers provinces in which previously only the craft undertook expeditions. Such was the kingdom of Georg Lunge."

# KARL ZIEGLER

RALPH E. OESPER
University of Cincinnati, Cincinnati, Ohio

CHEMICAL RESEARCH is rapidly being revitalized in war-torn Germany. There is shortage of chemicals, glassware, and equipment; recent foreign books and periodicals are seldom available; heat, water and current, etc., are often interrupted, but the old-time energetic spirit is bravely meeting and overcoming these handicaps. The German chemical journals are beginning to appear again when the paper supply permits, and new books are likewise coming on the market. One of the leaders in this postwar revival is the well-known organic chemist, Karl Ziegler.

Born November 26, 1898, at Helsa near Cassel, he studied at Marburg under K. von Auwers. After receiving the doctorate in 1920 he stayed on as assistant and *privat dozent*. In 1925 he transferred to the University of Frankfort a. M. and then (1926) to the University of Heidelberg, where he headed the organic section. In 1936 Ziegler visited a number of American universities and was guest lecturer at Chicago for several weeks. On his return to Germany he was called to head the chemistry department at Halle. He filled this post

(Concluded on page 284)

# CARL AUER von WELSBACH

**FRITZ LIEBEN**

University of Vienna, Vienna, Austria

*(Translated by Ralph E. Oesper, University of Cincinnati)*

WILHELM OSTWALD, who made a special study of the characteristic features of eminent scientists, distinguished between two types of research personalities: the classicists and the romanticists. The former work independently and place more stress on the content than the form of presentation; also they usually are not inclined to teaching, particularly not large groups of students. In contrast, the romantic type works more expansively and tries to awaken the interest of many in his achievements. Moreover, he is usually talented in speaking and writing; he attracts students readily and tends to develop them into collaborators. The members of both categories, however, regard research as an end in itself. They are not primarily interested in practical applications of their findings or in the monetary rewards that may result. However, there is a third class of research men: the inventors. They have the gift of recognizing the desires and needs of the great mass of people before the latter themselves know what they want and require, and by fulfilling these desires they become benefactors of mankind. Carl Freiherr von Welsbach was a fine example of this type of gifted discoverer.

The Auer family hailed from Wels in Upper Austria. Carl Auer's father, Alois Auer (1813–69) was uncommonly gifted. He began as apprentice printer and on his own initiative studied English, French, Italian, and pedagogy. He brilliantly passed an examination at the University of Vienna and then became a language teacher in Wels and Linz. His memoir on the establishment of a great "polygraphic" government institute brought to him directly the post of director of the Court and State Printing Office in Vienna (1841). Under his direction, this establishment acquired an international reputation. The Vienna press had the richest collection of types in the world. At the 1851 London Industrial Exhibition the Vienna establishment was awarded all five of the highest honors.

Carl Auer, the youngest of four children, was born in Vienna in the old buildings of the Court and State Printing Office on September 1, 1858. His mother (born 1831) came from a business family in Wels. The boy was educated at a Gymnasium and then at a Realschule in Vienna where he passed the final examination in 1887. He lost his father at 11, and the mother had to see to the education and bringing up of the children. Throughout his life Auer was closely attached to his mother, who was taken from him in 1910.

## STUDIED UNDER LIEBEN AND BUNSEN

Even as a young boy, Auer was attracted to chemistry, and he made it his chief subject as soon as he entered the University of Vienna. His professor was Adolf Lieben (1836–1914). Robert Wilhelm Bunsen (1811–99), with whom Lieben had studied and taken his doctorate in 1855–56 at Heidelberg, was recognized as one of the leading European chemists and teachers. Auer went to Heidelberg in 1880 and stayed four semesters, receiving the doctorate in 1882. As a student he showed the tenacious diligence, which so often characterizes those who have a special aptitude for science, and he studiously avoided the distractions of student life. Bunsen seemingly was impressed by the reserved Austrian student and recognized that the young man was endowed with exceptional experimental skill and observational powers. Bunsen's instruction became the foundation on which Auer built his life's work. He always held the great teacher and investigator in high and grateful regard. After Bunsen's death he acquired his library.

## RESEARCH ON RARE EARTHS

It is said that Auer's interest in the problem of the rare earths was awakened in Heidelberg—an area which he was destined to advance mightily, even though many eminent chemists had previously been active in this field.

Full of zeal and new ideas, Auer returned to Vienna and re-entered Lieben's laboratory. First of all he took time out to fulfill his military obligations. His first scientific study (1883) was presented before the Vienna Academy of Sciences. It dealt with "the earths of gadolinite from Ytterby." It described an improvement of the separation procedure by means of the basic nitrates introduced by Bunsen. He precipitated 10% of the earths as oxalates, ignited them to oxides, which he then added to the solution of the nitrates, thus producing basic nitrates. In this way the ytterbia and erbia earths, for example, were separated into groups which could then be further divided by fractional recrystallization.

As is well known, Bunsen, along with Kirchhoff, had made spectrum analysis a scientific tool. Here also Auer at this time made notable improvements in the apparatus for producing spark spectra. It was thus made possible to follow much more closely the separation of the rare earth metals. In 1885 Auer was able to announce his first really great achievement, namely, the separation of didymium, the twin of lanthanum, into two new elements which he named neodymium and praseodymium. There had been numerous previous indications that didymium actually represented a mixture of elements, but Auer was the first to carry out an impeccable separation. He introduced the fractional crystallization of the ammonium double nitrates as a separation method, using concentrated nitric acid solution at first and later going over to neutral solution. Auer is the only Austrian chemist to have discovered a chemical element.

## THE WELSBACH MANTLE

Auer's researches now advanced steadily. With intuitive perception, he always sensed the most interesting of the many problems that presented themselves to him. At this time he invariably worked alone. While still under Bunsen he had noted the remarkable light-emitting powers of the rare earth oxides when they are inserted into the flame of a Bunsen burner. Thomas Drummond was probably the first (1826) to have employed glowing metal oxides for the production of light when he heated quicklime pastilles in the oxy-hydrogen flame. Later zirconium oxide was used. Auer preferred the Bunsen burner to the blast lamp and stressed that the position of the oxide in the flame is an important factor. To this end he invented the famous Auer stocking (or Welsbach mantle) made of cotton thread (later cotton batiste) and soaked in a solution of the earth metal salts.[1] After the organic matter was burned off, a fairly substantial skeleton of the metal oxides was left. This constituted the source of the world-famous Auer (or Welsbach) light.

Auer had on hand a considerable quantity of pure lanthanum salts derived from the didymium splitting. However, the lanthanum oxides produced in the incandescent mantle, though giving higher luminescence, did not last long. A combination with zirconium oxide was better. At night there now came from the window of Auer's study on the second floor of the laboratory building a light so bright that it aroused the wonder of the passersby. This new incandescent mantle suspended in the Bunsen flame was christened actinophore by its inventor. At that time (1886) he tried to interest the public in his invention by inviting the press to witness demonstrations of his "incandescent light" or "incandescent gas light" and he also gave a lecture on it before the Austrian trade union in Vienna.

Public interest was soon at a high pitch. Companies and syndicates were organized in Austria, Germany, and England and large-scale production was soon started. Auer started a factory near Vienna in 1887; its function was the preparation of the rare earth salts and of the impregnating or "lighting fluid." This factory was supervised by Ludwig Haitinger, who from his 15th year had been an assistant in Lieben's laboratory, and who had been instructed by Auer with regard to his inventions and objectives.

Auer unceasingly continued efforts to improve his incandescent light. A second patent proposed the addition of the oxide of thorium (an element discovered by Berzelius in 1828). The mixture was to consist of 30% $ThO_2$, 30% $ZrO_2$, 40% $La_2O_3$. However, this combination was not completely satisfactory; in particular, unexplained variations in the luminosity proved annoying. The initial promising public interest had died down in the meantime and business fell off to the point

Carl Auer von Welsbach (1858-1929)

that the factory had to close (1889). Nevertheless, about 50,000 Auer burners had already been installed in Austro-Hungary.

But Auer was not a man to be discouraged by such reverses. It is true that the impulse for the subsequent fundamental advance came from Haitinger, who had returned to Lieben's laboratory. The study of the publications by Crookes and Lecoq de Boisbaudran had led him to see the analogy to the action of small admixtures on the luminescence of metal oxides in the cathode tube and the Bunsen flame, respectively. Haitinger was then able to secure, with mixtures of alumina and a little chromium oxide, a brightness about three times as great as that yielded by the lanthanum-zirconium oxide mixture. But because of the volatility of these oxides, the $Al_2O_3$-$Cr_2O_3$ mixtures did not have sufficient stability. Auer and Haitinger then returned to trials with thorium oxide, which was obtained as a byproduct of the Carolina gold washing; this operation had already served to provide the raw material for obtaining lanthanum oxide. Monazite sand, from Brazil, was the source for all the subsequent experiments. The purification process for the thorium oxide proved of decisive influence, and for this Auer employed the crystallization as thorium ammonium nitrate. It was now possible to determine precisely the role of the admixed material in decreasing or favoring the light intensity, and also to prove that certain impurities distinctly shortened the life of the incandescent mantle. But the decisive finding of these experiments was that the intensity of the light was tremendously heightened by adding cerium oxide. The thorium-cerium incandescent body gave an optimal brightness and the Auer (Welsbach) burner was now prepared to start its triumphal march across the world.

In 1892 Vienna began to light its streets with gas lamps and Auer mantles. By 1893 Berlin had 100,000 of the new burners in operation and Paris was using 150,000. By the time of Auer's death (1929) about five billion incandescent mantles had been produced which consumed about 200 billion cubic meters of gas. Haitinger returned to the Auer factory in Vienna in 1892 and introduced there the principles of large-scale production after Auer had worked out the processing of monazite sand as raw material (decomposition with sulfuric acid,

---

[1] In 1898 the Deutsche Gasglühlicht A. G. substituted China grass (ramie) fibers, and later, also in Germany, artificial silk was used for Welsbach mantles. The oxides were then fixed in the fibers with ammonia or organic bases.

etc.). This manufacture now progressed despite vicious attacks and troublesome legal conflicts. Auer's mantles were the first that were really usable. The earlier attempts of other inventors had yielded products that did not give enough light or were too fragile or too expensive. There is not space to relate how the Auer burner enabled the gas-lighting industry to survive for a comparatively long time in competition with the growing use of electricity. The prolonged patent litigation likewise cannot be discussed here.

## INCANDESCENT OXIDE FILAMENTS FOR ELECTRIC LIGHTS

Auer's other researches adhered to his motto: "Plus lucis" (more light), which appears on the Auer crest. First of all he tried to adapt the great light emissivity of the thorium oxide-cerium oxide mixture to electric lighting. The mixture was applied to platinum wires and when the current was passed a brilliant light resulted. The wire melted and the metal oxides continued to glow in wonderful fashion. Unfortunately, when the current was switched off the light went out and could not be revived by a further application of the current.[2] Auer then tried a metal with a higher melting point than platinum, namely osmium. Because of its brittleness, he was forced again to invent a special process, which was the earliest usable method for preparing metal filament lamps. In one process osmium tetroxide was precipitated hot on platinum or the platinum wire was passed through a slurry containing osmium; the platinum was then vaporized by intense heating. In the second process osmium was deposited hot on carbon threads or fibers, or the osmium was made into a paste with collodion or a sugar solution, the mass then extruded, and the collodion denitrified and burned away. This is only a partial account of what Auer described in his patents. The osmium incandescent bulb was subsequently further developed especially by the Auer Gesellchaft, a German company. The advantage of the osmium incandescent bulb as contrasted with the carbon bulb is shown by the fact that the latter requires 3.5 watts per candle power as opposed to 1.5 watts for the osmium bulb. Admittedly, Auer missed using tungsten and tantalum for metal filament lighting bulbs, but his method of shaping difficultly fusible metals remained the preferred process.

Around 1900 the Austrian authorities requested Auer to take over the direction of the iron works at Treibach in Carinthia. He set up there a large chemical research laboratory from which he then developed the Treibach chemical works. First of all, the earlier findings regarding praseodymium and neodymium were confirmed and their respective atomic weights were determined (140.57 and 144.54; the modern values are 140.92 and 144.27). Also a part of the operational procedure for manufacturing osmium bulbs was developed in the Treibach laboratory in collaboration with Anton Lederer.

## THE AUER LIGHTER

From among the many researches conducted during this period, only one will be mentioned, namely, the utilization of the considerable quantities of cerium sulfate accumulated from the working-up of the monazite

[2] Inspired by Auer's mantle, Walter Nernst also used mixtures of rare earths in his electrical incandescent lamp.

sand. Twenty years earlier, in Bunsen's laboratory, Auer had seen the sparking of cerium metal when scratched or drawn over a rough surface. Since the pure metal was too costly to utilize this characteristic for ignition purposes, a mixture of the cerite earths was subjected to fusion electrolysis with an iron cathode. It was found that the sparking ability of the resulting cerium-iron is dependent on the iron content of the alloy. The optimum is at 30% iron. Many other alloys of cerium with various metals were prepared but none was as good as this "cerium steel" for igniting gases and vapors of volatile liquids. The Auer lighter became almost as famous as the incandescent mantle. The production of cerium-iron reached approximately 100,000 kilograms annually by 1930; it served to prepare 500 million flints which could be used for 500 billion ignitions, and replaced six billion boxes of matches.

## IDENTIFICATION OF OTHER RARE EARTHS

From this time on, all of Auer's researches were carried on in his laboratory at Schloss Welsbach, after he had turned over the direction of the Treibach chemical works to Dr. Fattinger. Auer now turned his attention again to the yttrium earths. After isolating the erbium-ytterbium group, the latter was further separated by fractional crystallization of the ammonium double oxalates in excess ammonium oxalate solution. Erbium (discovered by Mosander in 1843) and thulium (discovered by Soret and by Cleve in 1878–79) were thus separated out, and in the course of the operations an alteration was observed in the relative intensity of the spark spectrum of the ytterbium. By further fractionation Auer, in 1905, came to the undoubted conclusion that ytterbium must consist of two elements. A preliminary announcement (1905) and a paper in the *Lieben Festschrift* (1906) on the employment of the spark spectrum for testing the homogeneity of elements were followed by a detailed account (1907) in which the two newly discovered elements with atomic weights 172.90 (now 173.04) and 174.23 (now 174.99) were given the names "aldebaranium" and cassiopeium."

Georges Urbain had made the same separation, though somewhat later than Auer, but the French chemist published earlier. He suggested the names "neo-ytterbium" and "lutetium," which were accepted by the International Atomic Weight Commission. However, the German atomic weight commission assured Auer's priority; the main constituent of Marignac's "ytterbium" (about 90%) was continued to be called ytterbium, and the second constituent, following Auer's suggestion, was given the name cassiopeium (though the name lutetium continued in use by some). The study of the spectra of his thulium fractions occupied Auer until his death. His last paper (1926) dealt with the element 61 (the present promethium) which he could not find in monazite sand.

Auer's life work, a chain of discoveries and inventions, included others of interest. For example, in his factory at Vienna he had the first ten tons of the residues from the preparation of uranium salts from Joachimsthal in Bohemia worked up and the first considerable amounts of radium salts were prepared in this establishment. He also prepared the precious polonium, ionium, and actinium salts that are still in the possession of the Vienna Academy of Sciences. His researches on spectroscopy and his improvements of spectrum apparatus had a permanent effect. The standard studies of the Austrian scientists Exner and Haschek and of Eder and Valenta[3] were inspired by Auer's studies and greatly aided by his gifts of rare specimens of the highest purity. Among the permanent applications of the rare earths is their use in the coloring of glasses. For instance, praseodymium tints glass green-yellow, neodymium tints glass red-blue.

Auer married when he was quite mature and already at the height of his career. Three sons and a daughter resulted from this happy marriage. Numerous honors came to him from the state and scientific societies, including, of course, election to the Imperial Academy of Sciences in Vienna. He was made a baron in 1911; the title was hereditary. Accordingly, he is often referred to as Auer von Welsbach.

He was a man of the laboratory rather than of the pen. For the most part his papers are short. He gave few references to the literature since he was usually working in little explored territory. He preferred telegrams to letters, and at every festive occasion in the life of this writer's father (Adolf Lieben) Auer's telegram was invariably the first to arrive expressing his congratulations and his gratitude to his former teacher.

[3] Exner, F., and E. Haschek, "Die Spektren der Elemente bei normalen Druck," 2nd ed., 1911; Eder, J. M., and E. Valenta, "Atlas typischer Spektren," 1911.

He ordinarily worked alone; only on special occasions did he employ the help of a few well-tested associates. He had no talent for teaching. He loved the beauties of nature and was an ardent hunter and fisherman. Increasing deafness in his later years forced him to give up hunting; he then took up motoring.

On August 2, 1929, he suffered excruciating abdominal pains and knew that death was near. He made a final visit to his laboratory to bid farewell quietly and heroically to his beloved instruments and specimens, and then returned to bed. The end came on August 4, 1929. A useful life had come to its end, a life filled with merited brilliant successes, the fruits of hard work.

## ACKNOWLEDGMENT

The writer is indebted to Professor Bruhl of the University of Vienna for information regarding the Auer family and for the photograph.

## BIBLIOGRAPHY

D'Ans, J., "Carl Auer Freiherr von Welsbach," *Ber.*, **64A**, 59–97 (1931).

Sedlacek, F., "Blätter für Geschichte der Technik," **1934**, Heft 2. This contains much material on the history of incandescent bodies and carbon and metal filament bulbs.

Mayer, F. E., "Pioniere der Technik," **1945**, pp. 45–52.

Weeks, Mary E., "The Discovery of the Elements," Chemical Educ. Publ. Co., Easton, Pa., **1957**.

Kurzel-Runtscheiner, E., "Oesterreichische Naturforscher und Techniker" (published by the Austrian Academy of Sciences) **1951**, pp. 122–24.

---

## Karl Ziegler    *Continued from page 280*

with such distinction that in 1943 he was named to succeed Franz Fischer as director of the world-famous Kaiser Wilhelm Institut für Kohlenforschung at Mülheim (Ruhr).

Dr. Ziegler opened his scientific career with the synthesis of some new free radicals. The early conviction that purely preparative organic studies would never result in definite theoretical conclusions induced him to enter on a comprehensive series of studies of the reaction kinetics and energetics of labile polysubstituted ethanes (1929, 1930, 1933, 1942).

The work with free radicals led him to the organo compounds of the alkali metals. He discovered that ether scission opened a new method of preparing sodium and potassium alkyls; later (1930) he directly synthesized lithium alkyls and aryls from metallic lithium and halogenated hydrocarbons. This important discovery made the lithium compounds as readily available as the familiar Grignard reagents. Because of their greater activity, impressive developments in organic synthesis arose from the Ziegler organo-metallic compounds. He himself found new reactions in the heterocyclic field (1930) and he observed the addition of alkali alkyls to —C≡C—double bonds (1927). This latter observation initiated comprehensive studies of certain polymerization reactions, especially the formation of butadiene-sodium rubber (1929, 1934, 1939).

The alkali alkyls also opened a way to solving the problem of the synthesis of large ring compound from long aliphatic chains. The consequent combination of the "dilution principle" with the new ring closure reactions made possible the synthesis, in good yields, of many polymethylene ketones. An outstanding instance was the preparation of muscone, the odoriferous principle of animal musk. Ziegler, together with A. Lüttringhaus, and then the latter alone, used the new methods for preparing unusual (*m-*, *p-*, etc.) rings.

Cantharidine, the active principle of Spanish fly, was synthesized by Ziegler in 1942. An outgrowth of this work was the preparation by him and his student, G. Schenck, of the natural peroxide ascaridole from α-terpenes. Ziegler also found that *N*-bromo-succinimide is an excellent reagent for introducing a bromine atom into the allyl position of unsaturated compounds. This reagent has now found wide favor in preparative work.

Most of Ziegler's papers have appeared in the *Annalen der Chemie*. He is the author of various chapters in the Freudenberg "Stereochemie" (1933) and the "Handbuch der Katalyse" (1943). He is a member of the Academies at Halle and Munich. In 1938 he was awarded its Liebig Medal by the Verein Deutscher Chemiker, and since 1946 has been the president of the Gesellschaft Deutscher Chemiker.

# THE ROLE OF CHEMISTRY IN THE DEVELOP-
# MENT OF DYEING AND BLEACHING

**SIDNEY M. EDELSTEIN**

Dexter Chemical Corporation, New York, New York

## INTRODUCTION

Today, beautifully dyed and bleached fabrics are as much a matter of course as the water we drink or the food we eat. It is difficult for us to imagine that not so long ago, such display of color existed only in nature. Actually, only a few centuries ago, a bleached linen shirt or a dyed coat was worn only by the well-to-do. In more ancient times, dyed and bleached textiles were forbidden to all except royalty.

As to when, where, and how dyeing and bleaching first began, we can only hazard a guess. That these arts date back to the earliest times of which we have records is unquestioned. As to how dyeing and bleaching reached its present great development, however, need not be guessed. For its main path is recorded in the works of many chemists and of many men who followed the scientific way.

Our main purpose is to trace this development. But the accomplishments of the prescientific period also merit our attention, if only to appreciate better the accomplishments of science.

The ancients had only a comparatively few coloring principles and a limited number of mordants. Coloring principles giving compound colors were not known and such colors were dyed by superimposing one primary color an another. Blues were prepared from indigo, tyrian purple, woad or pastel dyed from a fermentation reduction bath. Reds were dyed with extracts of such insects as kermes or cochineal, or with the vegetable madder. These reds were all dyed on an alum mordant. Yellows were prepared from a number of vegetable extracts and were also dyed on alum.

The great cost for dyeing and bleaching in ancient times was not due to some special fee charged by the dyer for his secret knowledge. The high price for dyeing and bleaching was inherent in the high cost of the dyestuffs and in the long and laborious processes by which these colors and chemicals were applied. This may well be understood when we realize that it took from one to two years to prepare a well-bleached linen fabric and that several thousand shell fish were required to produce enough purple to dye a single garment.

The ancients could and did dye and bleach fabrics having good properties even by today's standards, but their art was completely empirical. The principles

[1] Presented before the Division of the History of Chemistry at the 112th meeting of the American Chemical Society in New York City, September, 1947.

Figure 1. A European Dyehouse, Circa 1700.

involved were not understood and in fact there was no desire to understand. The industry thus remained static for thousands of years.

## BLEACHING BEFORE 1756

In tracing back the history of bleaching to the earliest times, it is difficult to distinguish between bleaching proper, laundering, and preparation of the goods for dyeing. Nevertheless, at some distant period there arose a distinct art in the production of white fabrics. This art was probably first practiced by the same artisans who prepared dyed fabrics. It was not until comparatively recent times that bleaching as a distinct industry separate from dyeing came into existence.

From the earliest times, bleaching was a special art when applied only to fabrics made of linen and cotton. Silk and wool were usually dyed, but if desired in white it was only necessary to expose the fabrics of these materials to burning sulfur to obtain satisfactory results. With the cellulosic fibers, however, the problem was entirely different, as satisfactory whites could only be obtained by long and drastic treatment.

The system of bleaching used by the ancients was little changed during two thousand years. Different alkalies were introduced from time to time and every bleacher had his own special variation, but the process still consisted of alternate boiling of the goods, exposure to the sun, neutralizing in buttermilk or sour milk, rinsing and then repeating this whole process time after time until the goods were a satisfactory white. Improvements in the art were not only hindered by lack of the application of chemical knowledge but also by the various governments, which through ignorance, actually prohibited the use of certain beneficial materials such as lime in bleaching. The art of bleaching was actually more backward than the art of dyeing, for chemistry was not made use of in bleaching until almost a century after it had been successfully applied to dyeing. Once chemistry was called in, however, the progress made in 50 years was more revolutionary and important than that of the previous two thousand years.

## HOME AND THE FIRST APPLICATION OF CHEMISTRY TO BLEACHING

Dr. Francis Home of Edinburgh was the first to apply chemistry to the problems involved in bleaching. In 1756 he published what was probably the first book on bleaching and his researches paved the way for the revolutionary advances in the art which took place at the end of the 18th century. The book accomplished this by getting the bleachers interested in the chemistry of their process for the first time.

In the preface to this work, Home summed up his main thesis in these words: "I find the most skillfull bleachers understand the general theory of their art tolerably well; but being ignorant of the principles of chymistry, cannot make proper use of this theory, or apply their knowledge to the advancement of their art."

Home, by way of example, studied the bleaching industry in detail. He investigated the alkalies used, showed their method of action, and developed methods for their analysis. He showed that sulfuric acid could be used as a sour in place of stale milk, with better control of the process and a saving in time and money. Finally, he was the first to study in detail the types of water hardness and the causes, the effects of hard water on the bleaching process and chemical methods for the control of this hardness.

DISTRICT OF MASSACHUSETTS DISTRICT, TO WIT.

BE it remembered, That on the thirteenth day of November, in the twenty-third year of the Independence of the United States of America, ASA ELLIS, JUN. of the said district, hath deposited in this Office, the title of a Book, the right whereof he claims as Author, in the words following, to wit. "THE COUNTRY DYER's ASSISTANT, by ASA ELLIS, JUN."

In conformity to the Act of the Congress of the United States, entitled "An Act for the Encouragement of Learning, by securing the Copies of Maps, Charts, and Books, to the Authors and Proprietors of such Copies, during the time therein mentioned."

N. GOODALE, Clerk of the District of Massachusetts District.

A true Copy of Record.
Attest, N. GOODALE, Clerk.

Figure 2.  Registration of First American Book on Dyeing.

## THE CHEMICAL REVOLUTION IN BLEACHING

The death knell for the old process of bleaching, which depended on the action of sunlight, was sounded in 1774 when Scheele, discussing the properties of chlorine, which he had just discovered, wrote: "The bodies which I wished to expose to the action of this dephlogisticated aerial fluid were fixed in a glass tube which passed through the cork of the receiver. I observed (a) that the corks became yellow within the receiver, as from *aquafortis*, and the lute was likewise corroded during the distillation. (b) paper colored with lacmus became nearly white; all vegetable red, blue, and yellow flowers grew likewise white in a short time; the same thing happened to green vegetables. Meanwhile the water in the vessel was changed in a weak but pure muriatic acid. (c) The former colour of the flowers, or of the green vegetables, could not be recovered, either by alkalies or acid."

Scheele thus was aware of the bleaching properties of chlorine, but he made no attempt to put these properties to commercial use. It remained for Claude Louis Berthollet to tame this intractable element and to put it to commercial use.

Berthollet first used chlorine in the form of a water solution, as a bleaching agent for cotton and linen with satisfactory results as far as the fabrics were concerned, but the injurious effect of the gas given off led him later to use the chlorine in alkaline solution. Within a short time Berthollet's alkaline solution came into wide use under the name of "Eau de Javelle" and as "Eau de Berthollet."

The new method of bleaching was so much simpler and cheaper than the old that within a few years the bleach fields of Europe had disappeared. It is noteworthy that James Watt, having been present at some of Berthollet's experiments with the bleaching action of chlorine, immediately saw the commercial possibilities and shortly thereafter introduced the process in Great Britain.

Still further economies in the cost of chlorine bleaching were achieved in 1798 by Charles Tennant when he substituted milk of lime for caustic potash as the solvent for chlorine, and in 1799 when by passing chlorine

Figure 3. Thomas Cooper

over slaked lime he was able to supply active chlorine in the form of bleaching powder.

The new process of Berthollet and the improvements of Tennant came at a most fortunate time. The introduction of the power loom and power spinning was furnishing greatly increasing volumes of goods and this growing output called for a more rapid and economical

method of bleaching. Chemistry, through Berthollet, Watt, and Tennant, met this challenge.

Today the chemists and chemical engineers of the textile industry are still meeting the challenge for speedier and more economical methods of bleaching. The introduction of peroxides at economical prices and the development of high speed continuous bleaching equipment have made the whole process a matter of minutes instead of days. Certainly chemistry has an even more important role in what was formally the art, and now the science, of bleaching.

## DYEING BEFORE THE INTRODUCTION OF THE SCIENTIFIC METHOD

The history of dyeing followed very closely the same pattern as that of bleaching but its problems were much more complex.

Although alchemy had been founded and a great mass of chemical facts had been accumulated during the middle ages, little progress in dyeing was made which can be attributed to chemistry until the middle of the 17th century.

Nevertheless some progress was made in the art during this period and dyed fabrics became somewhat more available. This was due to three causes. First, the widespread production of certain chemical materials used as mordants; second, the discovery of the New World and the introduction of new and cheaper color substances such as cochineal and logwood; and finally, an occasional accidental discovery such as the production of a fast scarlet with tin and cochineal.

By the middle of the 17th century dyeing was in no position to progress further until the principles underlying the processes had been studied and test methods had been developed for evaluating the results of these dyeing processes. For the next two hundred years gradual improvements were made in dyeing—not by accident but as the result of study along these lines by the foremost chemists of Europe.

## THE ROYAL SOCIETY AND DYEING

The first application of this scientific method applied to dyeing was by the early members of the royal society—by that band of men who have so many firsts in the scientific field to their credit. On April 30, 1662, Sir William Petty, one of the earliest members, presented "An Apparatus to the History of the Common Practices of Dyeing" in compliance with the previous request of the society. While this short paper presented the facts as to the materials and methods used in the English Dye Houses, it begins and ends with that modern scientific spirit which asks how and why.

In this paper Petty gives the following concise statement of the state of dyeing at the beginning of this scientific period: "First all the materials (which of themselves do give colour) are either red, yellow or blew, so that out of them, and the primitive fundamental colour, white, all the great variety which we see in dyed stuffs doth arise. . . . Many of the said colouring materials will of themselves give no colouring at all unless cloth be first covered or incrusted with some other matter."

Petty gives the following list of materials used in dyeing at that time: Copperas and alder, bark, pomegranate pills, walnut rinds, galls and sumach for blacks, alum, argol, salt-peter, sal ammoniak, pot-ashes and stone lime; wine, aqua vitae, vinegar, lemon juice, nitric acid, honey and molasses, bran, flour, egg yolks, leaven, cummin-seed and senna. Of the coloring matters themselves Petty says, "Blews are woad, indigo and logwood: The Yellows are weld, wood-wax and fustick, as also turmeric now seldom used. The Reds are red-wood, brazil, mather, cochineal, safflowers, kermes-berries and sanders; the latter of which is seldom used and the kermes not often. Unto these arnotto and young fustick making orange colors may be added, as often used in these times."

Petty, after examining the various explanations for the use of alum gives the following theory of its action in the mordant process: "I conclude that the use of alum is to be a vinculum between the cloth and the color, alum being such a thing, whose particles and aculei dissolved with hot liquors will stick to the stuffs, and fetch themselves into their pores; and such also, as on which the particles of the dyeing drugs will also catch hold." This theory is exactly the same as the one we hold today.

Among the other illustrious members who did not hesitate to study the dyeing process were Boyle and Hook. The former's famous "Experiments and Considerations, Touching Colors" contain several studies directly related to the dyeing process, dyestuffs and colored textiles. But as Bancroft observed: "From this time it does not appear that anything considerable was done for nearly the space of a century by men of science in Great Britain towards improving the arts of dyeing and calico printing."

## THE FRENCH CHEMISTS AND DYEING

In France, however, at almost the same time, chemistry began to serve the art of dyeing and continued to do so for two centuries, with the result that the dyeing industry of France quickly became one of the world's outstanding industries. The entrance of chemistry into this field in France, however, came about not because of the particular interest of a group of scientists, but through the auspices of a government which saw the possibilities of finanical return to France if the dyeing industry was put on a sound basis by the help of science.

In 1671 in France, the great minister Colbert caused to be published "The General Instructions for Dyeing" which divided the dyers into two classes: "Dyers of the true colors" and "Dyers of the false," and specified the types of dyestuffs, mordants, and chemicals which each group might employ. In addition there were contained therein strict regulations governing almost every detail of the practice of the art.

The government soon realized that in order to carry out the regulations properly, an exact study of the ingredients used in the "true" and "false" dyes would be required, as well as experiments as to the comparative fastness to light, weather, and washing of all the various colors. Finally, if the regulations were to be carried out promptly, proof liquors to distinguish

Figure 4. Scheele Monument in Stockholm

quickly the "true" from the "false" dyes would also be required.

To carry out this work the government chose the illustrious Dufay, member of the Academy of Science. Dufay was the first of a long line of great chemists who were employed by the government of France during the following century to supervise and study the dyeing industry.

The work of Dufay more then two centuries ago in many ways parallels work done by some of our modern color chemists on light and wash fastness. Dufay made hundreds of tests on the fastness of the various colors on wool and developed dyed fabrics which could be used as standards of comparison. In addition, he developed a series of simple testing solutions which by their reaction on a particular dyed fabric would distinguish the type of dyestuff used and whether or not it was properly applied.

Finally, Dufay was one of the first who held a true conception of the affinity existing between the coloring substances and the fiber of the dyed stuffs, and he noted the difference in dye affinity between wool, cotton, and silk.

Dufay was succeeded by Hellot, who published an excellent practical treatise on the art of dyeing wool and woolen cloths and assisted in the improvement of this art in France. Nevertheless, Hellot adopted an erroneous hypothesis in explaining the facts encountered in the dyeing of wool. He reasoned that in every dyeing process potassium sulfate was formed and that the whole art of dyeing consisted in first dilating the pores of the substance to be dyed, allowing the coloring matter to penetrate within the fiber, and then fastening the color atoms within the pores of the fibers with the small particles of potassium sulfate. According to Hellot, alum was useful in dyeing only because he supposed it to furnish the required potassium sulfate.

On the death of Hellot his assistant Macquer, the author of the "Chemical Dictionary" and the outstanding French chemist at the time, succeeded to the position of Commissioner of the Council for Dyeing.

Figure 5. Berthollet

Macquer endeavored to lay down the true principles of the art of dyeing and published a work on the dyeing of silk based on these principles. He developed processes for dyeing silk with Prussian blue and a method for obtaining on silk a scarlet with the same brilliance as that heretofore obtained on wool by means of cochineal.

Berthollet, the next in succession as Commissioner for Dyeing, has contributed so much to bleaching that his contributions to dyeing appear to be somewhat overshadowed. Nevertheless, Berthollet's "Elements of the Art of Dyeing," was for a long period the outstanding scientific work on this subject. In addition to this work he gave a scientific basis for most of the processes used in dyeing at that time. His researches on the nature and action of alum, the sulfates of iron, copper, and zinc, the alkalies, cochineal, indigo, and the action of the sun's rays on colors are just a few of his works related to dyeing. Perhaps of even more importance was the fact that the devotion of such an eminent chemist as Berthollet to the study of dyeing over a period of years gave an impetus to chemists in countries other then France to devote their science and abilities to improvements in the important art of dyeing.

Chaptal, Chevreul, and Dumas continued in the tradition of the earlier French chemists and each contributed his portion to the advancement of the color art.

## THE WORK OF BANCROFT

As mentioned above, there was little scientific activity in England in the field of dyeing for a century after that of Petty, Boyle, and Hook. In the fourth quarter of the 18th century, however, several English chemists, perhaps inspired by the work of the French chemists, began a series of researches in the field of dyes and dyeing which in certain instances were of outstanding importance. Edward Bancroft was perhaps the outstanding among these English chemists and he occupied a unique position in that practically all of his life was devoted to the study and scientific improvement of dyeing. His "Experimental Researches Concerning the Philosophy of Permanent Colors" was probably the outstanding authority on the chemistry of dyestuffs, mordants, and the dyeing process for fifty years. Bancroft's introduction of quercitron, the powdered bark of the black oak, for dyeing yellows, was an outstanding scientific commercial contribution.

## EARLY AMERICAN WORK IN DYEING

In the United States, little in the way of scientific research on dyeing or coloring materials was carried out before 1900. Nevertheless, several early American writers on this subject predicated their works on scientific principles and all insisted on the importance of chemistry in the proper carrying out of the dyeing art.

The first American work on dyeing was a small volume published in 1798 in Brookfield, Massachusetts, entitled "The Country Dyers Assistant." Little is known about the author, Asa Ellis, but that he was thoroughly influenced by the work of the French chemists is evident by his plea in the introduction to his book for the government of this country to follow that of France in promoting the dyeing art, and by his statement that, "Too many dyers of this country have precluded themselves from improvement. Confining themselves to incorrect recipes, they have neglected experiments and other general means of information." Ellis's little volume was eminently practical and contained the results of his experiments on a number of native coloring matters which had not heretofore been described.

The next American work, while apparently popular as it passed through two editions, may be dismissed from our discussion with the words of Thomas Cooper: "That of Elijah Bemiss is marked by such a total ignorance of chemical principles and some of the recipes are so strange, the work is not of equal merit with those which have preceded it."

The irrepressible Thomas Cooper may also be listed among the early American chemists who insisted on the improvement of dyeing. His large work entitled "A Practical Treatise on Dyeing and Calicoe Printing," published in 1815 was, in the words of a contemporary reviewer, "one of the greatest benefits conferred upon the useful arts of this country and an extensive prospect of improvement for every dyer."

Cooper's ideas on the importance of chemistry in the improvement of dyeing are summed up in his own words: "The art of dyeing is yet in its infancy. No one but a good chemist, who is at the same time a good dyer, could form any judgment of the very many unascertained points that yet remain in this art. I have felt this in almost every page of the work. It is in dyeing as in all other branches of knowledge, a man must know much before he is aware of how ignorant he is. The only cure for the evil is a general introduction of chemical knowledge, which bears upon the prnciples of almost every art and trade that subserves the comfort or convenience of common life."

## PERKIN AND THE CHEMICAL REVOLUTION IN DYEING

The year 1856 marked the beginning of the great revolutionary period in the dyeing art through chemistry. In fact it marked the beginning of a great revolution in chemistry in itself. For in that year Perkin discovered mauve, the first coal tar color.

The details of this great discovery are known to every young science student. The perseverance of 18-year-old Perkin in pushing through the commercial adoption of this color and its commercial production within a year despite the discouragement offered by his teacher, Hoffman, and the dyers and printers, has served as an inspiration to all chemists.

The introduction of mauve and the other synthetic dyestuffs completely changed the art of dyeing. The processes were simplified and scientific recipes furnished by color manufacturers were substituted for the old-time empirical formulas. Where before, the dyes were complex unstandardized mixtures, derived from natural products and subject to all the variations which climate, soil, and the human element could cause, they now became definite chemical substances, which could be tested, analyzed, and applied by standard methods.

After Perkin had removed the obstacles in the path of practical application and had shown the way for the commercial production of aniline, benzol, and anthracene, it became comparatively easy to introduce other coal tar colors. Color after color was rapidly discovered and introduced to an eager dyeing industry. Alizarin and finally indigo were synthesized and the synthetic products replaced madder and natural indigo. A new industry was born which completely changed within a short time the political and commercial pattern of the world. The production of dyestuffs became a matter which depended now on chemical knowledge and ingenuity rather than on particular circumstances of climate, soil, and cheap labor.

On the occasion of the celebration of the golden jubilee in New York of Perkin's discovery, the discoverer remarked: "The wonderful growth of this industry has also, as a matter of course, created not only directly but indirectly an immense amount of employment for men of all classes, especially for the working classes, and although America has not become the manufacturing center for the production of these dyes, no doubt many thousands of Americans are engaged in the application."

Today America has become the leader in the synthetic dye industry. Many thousand different dyestuffs are being made in this country and the dyeing industry of America has become a definite branch of applied chemistry. Dyeing today is less an art and more a science which is presided over by thousands of trained chemists. The future of dyeing remains completely in the hands of chemistry.

## LITERATURE CITED

MATTHEWS, J. MERRITT, "Applications of Dyestuffs," New York, 1920.

BERTHOLLET, C. L. AND A. B., "Elements of the Art of Dyeing." Translated by ANDREW URE, London, 1824.

BANCROFT, EDWARD, "Experimental Researches Concerning the Philosophy of Permanent Colors," London, 1813.

STILLMAN, JOHN M., "The Story of Early Chemistry," New York, 1924.

THOMSON, THOMAS, "The History of Chemistry," London, 1830–31.

SPRAT, THOMAS, "The History of the Royal Society of London," 1667.

ORNSTEIN, MARTHA, "The Role of Scientific Societies in the Seventeenth Century," Chicago, 1920.

HIGGINS, S. H., "A History of Bleaching," London, 1924.

HOME, FRANCIS, "Experiments on Bleaching," Edinburgh, 1756.

SCHEELE, CHARLES-WILLIAM, "The Chemical Essays." Translated from the "Transactions of the Academy of Sciences at Stockholm," London, 1780.

MEYER, ERNEST VON, "History of Inventions and Discoveries." Translated by GEORGE McGOWAN, London, 1898.

BECKMANN, JOHN, "A History of Inventions and Discoveries." Translated by WILLIAM JOHNSTON, London, 1817.

"Instruction Generale Pour La Teinture Des Laines," Paris, 1671.

"Le Teinturer Parfait," Leyden, 1708.

"The Whole Art of Dyeing," London, 1795.

"The Art of Dyeing Wool, Silk and Cotton," London, 1789.

ELLIS, ASA, JR., "The Country Dyer's Assistant," Brookfield, Massachusetts, 1798.

BEMISS, ELIJAH, "The Dyer's Companion," New York, 1815.

COOPER, THOMAS, "A Practical Treatise on Dyeing and Callicoe Printing," Philadelphia, 1815.

ARMSTRONG, EVA V., "Thomas Cooper as an Itinerant Chemist," J. CHEM EDUC," 14, p. 153–158.

PERKIN, SIR W. H., "Jubilee of the Discovery of Mauve and of the Foundation of the Coal-Tar Colour Industry," London, 1906.

HARROW, BENJAMIN, "Eminent Chemists of Our Time," New York, 1927.

————————●————————

# indexes

## Authors

Bartow, V., 34
Beck, A., 191
Benfey, O. T., 144, 236
Berl, E., 273
Brown, H. C., 229
Bykov, G. V., 257

Campaigne, E., 253

deMilt, C., 37, 222

Edelstein, S. M., 285
Eidinoff, M. L., 205
Elving, P. J., 104

Ferguson, E. G., 85, 93
Fitzgerel, R. K., 147
French, S. J., 4

Harteck, P., 119
Hein, G. E., 41
Hiebert, E. N., 237
Hudson, C. S., 262
Huisgen, R., 267

Ihde, A. J., 80, 247

Kamen, M. D., 213
Kauffman, G. B., 185, 191
Kohman, E. F., 36
Kohn, M., 151
Kritchevsky, D., 143

Lavrakas, V., 202
Leicester, H. M., 47, 245

Lieben, F., 281
Lindauer, M. W., 124
Lockemann, G., 78

Moreau, Henri, 49

Nyholm, R. S., 181

Oesper, R. E., 66, 77, 84, 92, 97, 244, 280

Partington, J. R., 1
Pearson, T. H., 80
Prandtl, W., 98

Quam, G. N., 158
Quam, M. B., 158

Siegfried, Robert, 178
Silverman, A., 138

Taft, R., 196
Taylor, W. H., 152

Van Klooster, H. S., 18, 23, 31, 46
Verhoeck, F. H., 147

Walden, P., 11
Wall, F. E., 110
Wallman, J. C., 209
Woolsey, G., 131

Zuman, P., 104

## Names

Abegg, R., 35
Abel, F. E., 40
Abelson, P., 213, 217
Achard, F. C., 96
Adams, E. Q., 167
Adams, R., 35
Aebersold, P. C., 216
Afzelius, J., 35
Albertus Magnus, 124
Aldini, G., 36
Alexander II, 48
Allison, F., 206
Alter, D., 82
Alvarez, L. W., 207
Amagat, E. H., 132
Amende, 255
Ampère, A. M., 40
Anderson, T., 40
Andrews, L. W., 28–30
Andrews, T., 132
Ångström, A. J., 83
Anschütz, R., 37–40, 234, 236, 237, 239, 241, 243, 248–49
Antropoff, A. von, 167
Apjohn, 40
Aristotle, 114
Armstrong, E. V., 29, 47
Armstrong, H. E., 160, 253
Arndt, F., 253–56

Arrhenius, S., 113, 129, 186
Aston, F. W., 203, 206
Audrieth, L. F., 35
Auer von Welsbach, C., 156, 281–84
Auwers, K. von, 250, 255, 280
Avogadro, A., 40, 131, 147, 153, 186, 231

Babcock, S. M., 28–30
Babicka, 105
Babo, H. L. J. von, 37, 40
Baeyer, A. von, 33–35, 40, 111, 241, 244, 251, 253, 267, 271, 272
Bahr, J. F., 40
Bailar, J., 35
Bailey, E. H. S., 197
Baker, T. R., 28
Bakir, N., 255
Balard, A. J., 37, 227
Bamberger, E., 269, 277
Bancroft, E., 288, 289
Bancroft, W. D., 113, 197, 200
Baraboshkin, N. N., 194
Barker, H. A., 220
Bartow, V., 34, 35
Bassett, H., 163
Battershall, J. P., 28

Bauer, E., 134, 160
Baumé, A., 88
Baumhauer, H., 169
Baxter, H., 92
Bayen, P., 5–8
Bayley, T., 166
Beal, G. D., 35
Beattie, J. A., 136
Beaumont, E. de, 18
Béchamp, A., 39, 40
Beck, A., 191
Becker, 40
Becker, H., 203
Beckmann, E. O., 250
Becquerel, A. E., 82
Beddoes, T., 88
Beilstein, F. K., 33, 40, 241, 248
Beketoff, N. N., 37
Bemiss, E., 289
Benedetti-Pichler, A. A., 210
Benfey, O. T., 229, 237
Benoit, J. R., 57, 63
Bergius, F., 280
Bergman, T., 2–3, 80–96, 124, 130
Berl, E., 273, 277, 279–80
Berlin, 40
Bernard, C., 243

Bertele, G. A., 100
Berthelot, M., 1, 44, 112, 126–28, 235, 277, 279
Berthollet, C. L., 34–35, 88, 91, 125–30, 194, 242
Berzelius, J. J., 14, 16, 22, 23, 25, 34–35, 38–40, 41, 44, 90, 91, 96, 98, 114, 126, 145–146, 147, 186, 223–25, 231, 237, 274, 282, 286, 289
Bessemer, H., 280
Bethe, H., 214
Beudant, F. S., 223
Bibra, E. von, 40
Biltz, 160
Biot, J. B., 93, 227
Bischoff, C. A., 40
Bjerrum, N., 185, 190, 193
Black, J., 67
Bleakney, W., 206
Bleekrode, L., 198
Blokh, M. A., 47
Blomstrand, C. W., 40, 185–90
Böckmann, F. R., 279
Bodenstein, M., 97, 119, 122–23
Boeckmann, 40
Bogert, M. T., 35, 113
Bohm, J., 106

# Subjects